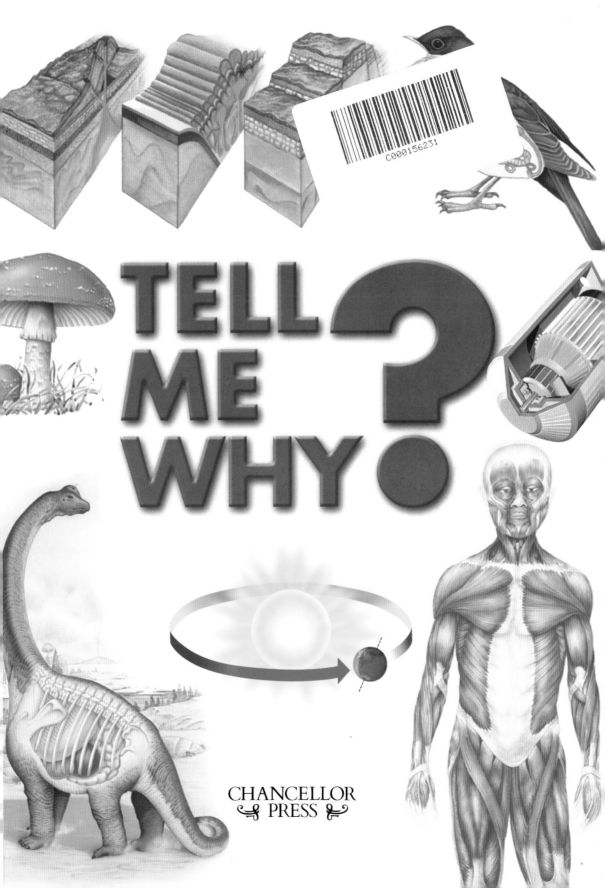

TELL ME WHY?

CHANCELLOR
PRESS

First published in 2001 by Chancellor Press,
an imprint of Octopus Publishing Group Ltd

Reprinted 2003 (twice), 2004 (three times), 2005 (three times),
2006 (three times), 2007 (twice), 2008, 2009 (twice)

New edition published in 2010 by Chancellor Press,
an imprint of Octopus Publishing Group Ltd,
189 Shaftesbury Avenue,
London WC2H 8JY

Reprinted 2011 (twice), 2012, 2013

An Hachette UK Company
www.hachette.co.uk

ISBN: 978-0-753720-90-5

A CIP catalogue record for this book is available from the British Library

Produced by Omnipress, Eastbourne

Printed in China

CONTENTS

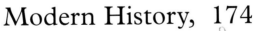

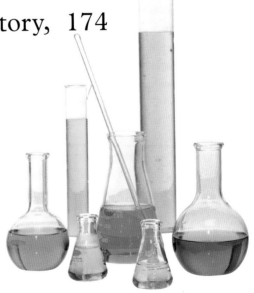

THE

HUMAN BODY

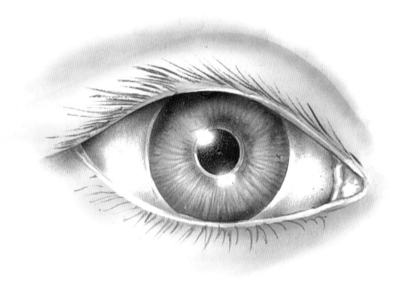

CONTENTS

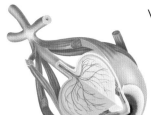

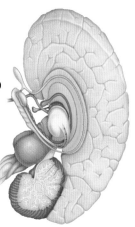

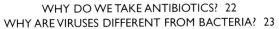

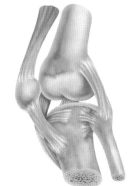

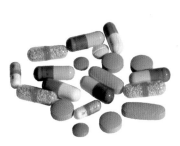

WHY IS OUR BLOOD RED?

The blood which flows through our body contains many different materials and cells. Each part of the blood has its own special job to do. The liquid part of our blood is called the plasma and makes up a little more than half the blood. It is light yellow in colour and thicker than water as many substances are dissolved in it. These substances are protein, antibodies that fight disease, fibrinogen that helps the blood to clot, carbohydrates, fats and salts, in addition to the blood cells themselves.

The red cells (also called red blood corpuscles) give the blood its colour. There are so many of them in the blood that it makes it all look red. There are about 35 trillion of these tiny, round, flat discs moving around in your body all at once.

As the young red cell grows and takes on adult form in the marrow, it loses its nucleus and builds up more and more haemoglobin. Haemoglobin is the red pigment, or colour. Red cells live only for about four months and then are broken up, mostly in the spleen. New red cells are always being formed to replace the cells that are worn out and destroyed.

vein

heart

A network of blood vessels

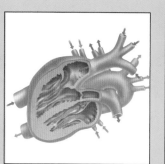

FACT FILE

Heart rate is the number of times that the heart actually contracts in a minute. You can measure this yourself by finding the pulse in your wrist, then gently holding your finger on it and counting the number of beats per minute.

WHY ARE ARTERIES DIFFERENT FROM VEINS?

There is no transportation system in any city that can compare in efficiency with the circulatory system of our body. If you can imagine two systems of pipes, one large and one small, both meeting at a central pumping station, you will have an idea of the circulatory system. The smaller pipes go from the heart to the lungs and back, while the larger ones go from the heart to the various other parts of the body.

These pipes are called arteries, veins and capillaries.

artery

Arteries are vessels in which blood is carried away from the heart. In veins, the blood is coming back to the heart. In general terms, arteries are carrying pure blood to various parts of the body, and the veins are bringing back blood loaded with waste products. The pumping station is of course the heart.

Arteries lie deep in the tissues, except at the wrist, over the instep, at the temple and along the sides of the neck. At any of these places the pulse can be felt, which gives the doctor an idea of the condition of the arteries. The blood in arteries is bright red in colour and moves through in spurts.

Veins lie closer to the surface of the skin, and the blood in them is much darker in colour and flows more evenly. Veins have valves at intervals all along their course.

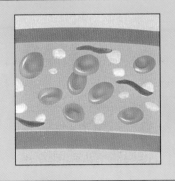

FACT FILE

Blood contains red and white blood cells that float inside a liquid called plasma. It also contains thousands of different substances needed by the body. Blood carries all these things round the body and also removes waste products.

WHY DO WE HAVE A SKELETON?

A skeleton is made up of a network of bones. Bones provide a framework that holds the whole body together.

Without a skeleton we would not be supported and would simply flop about like a rag doll. This would mean that we would not be able to move about.

The skeleton also gives protection to delicate organs in our bodies such as the brain, heart and lungs. It acts as a support to all the soft parts of the body.

The skeleton also provides a system of levers that the muscles can work on, enabling us to carry out all our movements.

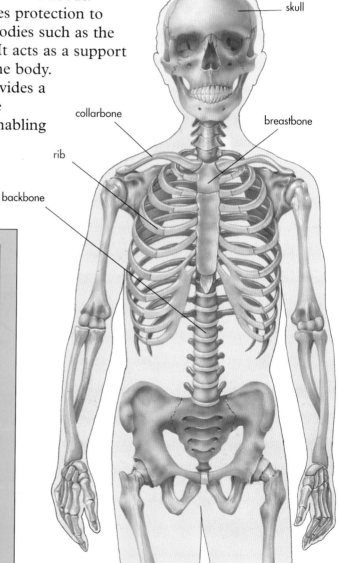

skull

collarbone

breastbone

rib

backbone

FACT FILE

At birth a baby has 300 bones, but 94 join together in early childhood. Your hand and wrist alone contain 27 bones.

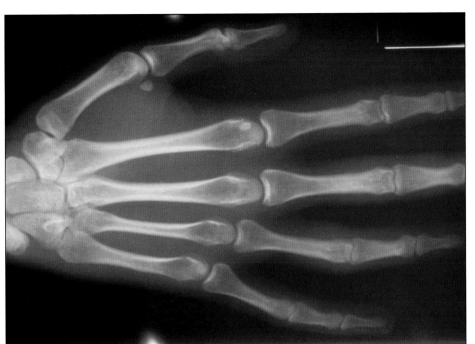

WHY DO PEOPLE HAVE X-RAYS TAKEN?

If we have an accident, often we go to hospital to have an X-ray taken of our body to see if we have any broken bones. The X-ray 'picture' is a shadowgraph or shadow picture. X-rays pass through the part of the body being X-rayed and cast shadows on the film. The film is coated with a sensitive emulsion on both sides. After it is exposed, it is developed like ordinary photographic film. The X-ray does not pass through bones and other objects so it casts denser shadows which show up as light areas on the film. This will show the doctor whether any bone has been broken or dislocated.

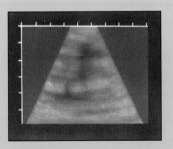

FACT FILE

Like X-rays, ultrasonic sound waves travel into the body and are bounced back by the organs inside. A screen can display the reflected sound as a picture. This is used to scan an unborn baby in the mother's womb.

WHY IS WATER GOOD FOR US?

Water is absolutely essential to every single form of life. Every living cell – plants and animals alike – depend on this substance.

More than half of the human body is made up of water. Much the same is true of other living things. Without water to drink, human beings would die in a very short time.

The reason every living thing needs a certain amount of water is because the cells, the basic units that make up living things, have water molecules in them. Without water these basic units would be very different and of no use to life as we know it.

In the course of a day, an adult human being takes in about two quarts of water as fluids, and one quart in what we call solid foods, such as fruit, vegetables, bread, and meat. These solid foods are not really dry, since they are thirty to ninety percent water.

Besides these three quarts that enter the body from outside, about ten quarts of water pass back and forth within the body between the various organ systems.

There are about five quarts of blood in the vessels of the body and three quarts of this is water. And this always remains unchanged. No matter how much water you drink you cannot dilute the blood.

FACT FILE

Our sense of thirst is controlled in the brain. When the body requires more water, we experience the sensation of thirst. Usually our mouth and throat become dry – a signal for us to drink more fluids.

WHY ARE CELLS IMPORTANT?

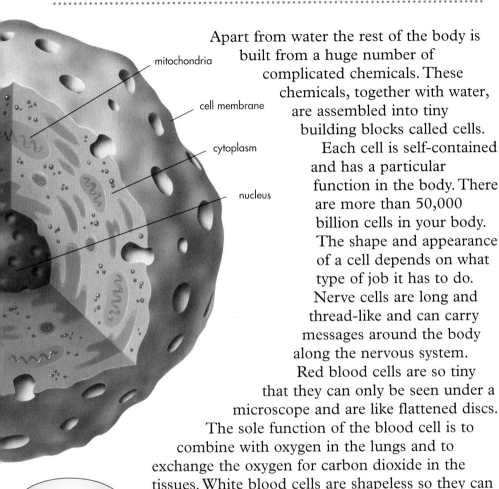

mitochondria

cell membrane

cytoplasm

nucleus

Apart from water the rest of the body is built from a huge number of complicated chemicals. These chemicals, together with water, are assembled into tiny building blocks called cells. Each cell is self-contained and has a particular function in the body. There are more than 50,000 billion cells in your body. The shape and appearance of a cell depends on what type of job it has to do. Nerve cells are long and thread-like and can carry messages around the body along the nervous system. Red blood cells are so tiny that they can only be seen under a microscope and are like flattened discs. The sole function of the blood cell is to combine with oxygen in the lungs and to exchange the oxygen for carbon dioxide in the tissues. White blood cells are shapeless so they can squeeze between other cells and attack invaders such as bacteria. Other cells control the production of essential substances called proteins.

Cross-section of an animal cell

FACT FILE

Metabolism is the term for all of the chemical activity that takes place inside the cells. Metabolism breaks down more complicated substances obtained from food. Our metabolic rate rises during vigorous exercise.

WHY DO PEOPLE GET ALLERGIES?

An allergy is any condition in which a person reacts in a hyper-sensitive or unusual manner to any substance or agent. The range of allergies is very broad and people may react to various foods, drugs, dusts, pollens, fabrics, plants, bacteria, animals, heat, sunlight and many other things.

Whenever a foreign material invades the tissues, the body reacts to fight against it. The body produces certain materials called antibodies which combine with the foreign material and render it harmless. But should it enter the body a second time, the antibodies are torn away from the body tissues to attack the substance. This causes a chemical substance called histamine to be released, which in turn produce the disorders which are symptoms of an allergy.

WHY DO SOME PEOPLE GET ASTHMA?

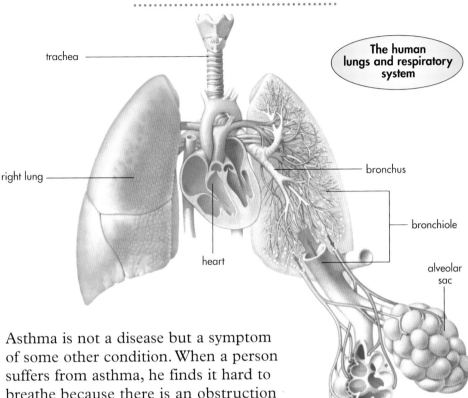

trachea

The human lungs and respiratory system

right lung

bronchus

bronchiole

heart

alveolar sac

Asthma is not a disease but a symptom of some other condition. When a person suffers from asthma, he finds it hard to breathe because there is an obstruction to the flow of air in and out of the lungs.

The cause may be an allergy, an emotional disturbance, or atmospheric conditions. If a person develops asthma before he is 30 years old, it is usually the result of an allergy. He may be sensitive to pollens, dust, animals, or certain foods or medicines.

Children, especially, tend to develop asthma from food allergies. These are often caused by eggs, milk, or wheat products. People who have asthma are often put on special diets to eliminate or minimise contact with these food products.

FACT FILE

People can develop allergies to many different foods. One of the most common is to dairy related products.

WHY DO WE OFTEN LOOK LIKE OUR PARENTS?

The characteristics of individual human beings are passed from one generation to the next in their chromosomes. Each of our parents gives us 23 chromosomes, making 46 in all. That means that we have two versions of each of our genes, but one is often dominant.

We see the effect of the dominant gene, but the other (recessive) gene is still there and can be passed on to our children.

Chromosomes are tiny threads that are present in all cells apart from the red blood cells. They contain all the information for an entire person to develop. There is a special pair that actually determine's a person's sex.

Short sections of a chromosome are called genes. Each gene carries the instructions for a specific characteristic, such as an eye colour. Many of these genes work with other genes, so it is not easy to say what effects they will have. Scientists are currently studying all the genes in a human cell, which will give them the complete blueprint for a human being.

FACT FILE

The gene for brown eyes is the dominant gene. Two brown eye genes give brown eyes, one brown gene and blue gene usually give brown eyes. Two blue eye genes give blue eyes.

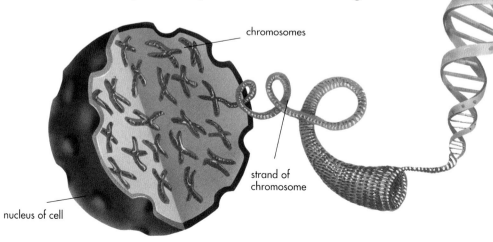

chromosomes

strand of chromosome

nucleus of cell

WHY DO WE HAVE CHROMOSOMES?

How a DNA molecule is formed

rings of pairs of amino acids

DNA strand looks like a twisted ladder

Every cell has a nucleus which is full of information coded in the form of a chemical called deoxyribonucleic acid (or DNA). The DNA is organized into groups called genes. Every chromosome contains thousands of genes, each with enough information for the production of one protein. This protein may have a small effect within the cell and on the appearance of the body. It may make all the difference between a person having brown or blue eyes, straight or curly hair, normal or albino skin.

At the moment the mother's egg is fertilized, the genes start issuing instructions for the moulding of a new human being. Every characteristic which we inherit from our parents is passed on to us through the coding of the genes within the chromosomes.

In rare cases, some people have 47 chromosomes. This occurs when people inherit Downs Syndrome, a genetic disorder.

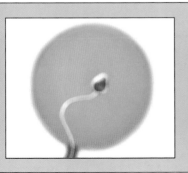

FACT FILE

A baby starts when two special cells meet – a sperm cell from a man's body and an egg cell from a woman's body. Joined inside the woman's body, these two cells grow into a whole new person.

WHY IS EXERCISE GOOD FOR US?

Regular exercise is important because it keeps bones, joints and muscles healthy. During any physical exertion, the rate at which the heart beats increases, as it pumps more oxygenated blood around the body. How quickly the heart rate returns to normal after exercise is one way to assess how fit someone is and how exercise is actually improving their fitness.

Once almost everyone did manual work of some kind. It was essential for survival. Human bodies were not designed for the inactive lives many of us now lead. That is why exercise is important for good health.

FACT FILE

Swimming is a very good form of exercise as it uses lots of muscles without causing strain.

WHY DO MUSCLES ACHE AFTER EXERCISE?

FACT FILE

It is important to stretch your muscles before and after exercise to distribute the lactic acid.

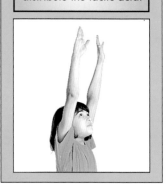

When you exercise your muscles contract and produce an acid known as lactic acid. This acid acts like a 'poison'. The effect of this lactic acid is to make you tired, by making muscles feel tired. If the acid is removed from a tired muscle, it stops feeling tired and can go right to work again.

So feeling tired after muscular exercise is really the result of a kind of internal 'poisoning' that goes on in the body. But the body needs this feeling of tiredness so that it will want to rest. During rest the joints of the body replace the supplies of lubricants they have used up.

WHY DO WE STOP GROWING?

The average baby is about one foot, eight inches long at birth. Over the next twenty years, man triples the length of the body he was born with and reaches an average height of about five feet, eight inches. But why doesn't he just keep on growing and growing?

In the body there is a system of glands called the endocrine glands which control our growth. The endocrine glands are: the thyroid in the neck, the pituitary attached to the brain, the thymus which is in the chest and the sex glands. The pituitary gland is the one that stimulates our bones to grow. If this works too hard our arms and legs would grow too long and our hands and feet too big. If the gland doesn't work hard enough, we would end up as midgets.

We continue to grow, but only slightly, after the age of 25, and we reach our maximum height at about the age of 35 or 40. After that, we shrink about half an inch every ten years. The reason for this is the drying-up of the cartilages in our joints and in the spinal column as we get older.

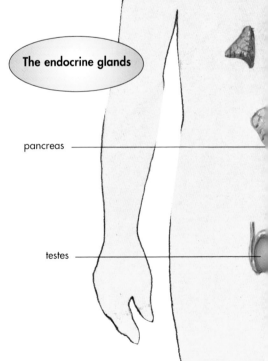

The endocrine glands

pancreas

testes

FACT FILE

Older people are no longer growing and so they are not as active as they used to be. For this reason they do not need to eat as much and quite often become thinner.

WHY DON'T WOMEN HAVE BEARDS?

We know that beautiful hair in a woman can be very attractive, but we must assume that hair on human beings formerly played a more practical role than it does now. When a baby is born he is covered with a fine down. This is soon replaced by the delicate hair which we notice in all children. Then comes the age of puberty, and this coat of fine hair is transformed into the final coat of hair which the person will have as an adult.

pituitary

thyroid

The development of this adult hair is regulated by the sex glands. The male sex hormone works in such a way that the beard and body hair are developed, while the growth of the hair on the head is inhibited, or slowed down in development.

The action of the female sex hormone is exactly the opposite! The growth of the hair on the head is developed, while the growth of the beard and body hair is inhibited, so women don't have beards because various glands and hormones in their bodies deliberately act to prevent this growth.

adrenals

FACT FILE

The custom of shaving was introduced to England by the Saxons. Barbers first appeared in Roman times in 300BC. Nowadays, there is a great variety of facial hair-styles from beards and moustaches to the clean-shaven effect.

FACT FILE

Vitamin C is an essential vitamin which helps to fight off infections and illnesses. This can be found naturally in oranges and other fruit and vegetables so it is very important that we include plenty of these in our everyday diet.

WHY DOES OUR TEMPERATURE RISE WHEN WE'RE ILL?

The first thing your doctor will do when you don't feel well is to take your temperature with a thermometer. He is trying to find out whether you have a 'fever'.

Your body has an average temperature of 98.6 degrees fahrenheit when it is healthy. Some diseases make this temperature rise and we call this higher temperature 'fever'.

Fever actually helps us fight off sickness. Fever makes the vital processes and organs in the body work faster. The body produces more hormones, enzymes and blood cells. The hormones and enzymes are useful chemicals in our body and when we are ill will have to work much harder. Our blood circulates faster, we breathe faster and so we get rid of wastes and poisons in our system. It is important however to get rid of the fever as quickly as possible as it destroys vital protein in your body.

The food we take in is fuel which the body burns up. In this process, about 2,500 calories are being used every day in the body.

WHY IS THE BODY WARM?

In order for the body to carry on its functions efficiently it needs energy. This energy is obtained through a process called combustion. The fuel for their combustion is the food that we take in. The result of combustion in the body is not, of course, a fire or enormous heat. It is a mild, exactly regulated warmth. There are substances in the body whose job it is to combine oxygen with the fuel in an orderly, controlled way.

The body maintains an average temperature regardless of what is going on outside. This is done by the centre in the brain known as the temperature centre, which really consists of three parts: a control centre which regulates the temperature of the blood, one that raises the temperature of the blood when it drops, and a third that cools the blood when the temperature is too high.

When we shiver it is the body's automatic reaction to the temperature of our blood dropping too low. Shivering actually produces heat!

WHY DO WE TAKE ANTIBIOTICS?

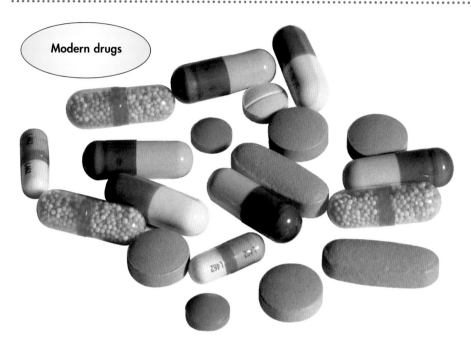

Modern drugs

Antibiotics are chemicals. When these chemicals are put into the body they kill or stop the growth of certain kinds of germs. In other words they help your body to fight off disease.

Many modern antibiotics are made from microbes, which are tiny living things. For example, bacteria and moulds are microbes. The microbes used in making antibiotics are chosen for their ability to produce chemicals that wage war on the microbes of disease. In simple terms this means that man is taking advantage of the struggle that goes on in nature among microbes.

Antibiotics are very effective at curing diseases and work in various ways. One antibiotic may act in different ways against different germs. It may kill the germs in one case and in another only weaken them and let the body's natural defences take over.

FACT FILE

Today a lot of people are turning to natural remedies rather than prescribed drugs. These are made from natural products like roots, plants, flowers and trees.

WHY ARE VIRUSES DIFFERENT FROM BACTERIA?

Both bacteria and viruses are the most important causes of disease. Bacteria are simple plant-like organisms that can divide very quickly. They cause many common infections such as boils and acne.

Viruses are very much smaller and technically they are not alive at all. They can take over the functioning of an infected cell and turn it into a factory producing millions more viruses. Viruses are responsible for many common diseases such as colds and influenza.

The diagram below shows us how a virus invades a cell: (1) they shed their outer layer (2) and take over the genetic material in the host cell in order to reproduce themselves (3). They begin to construct protein coats around the new viruses (4) and eventually burst out of the host cell (5) to leave it in an envelope (6) ready to infect new cells.

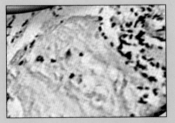

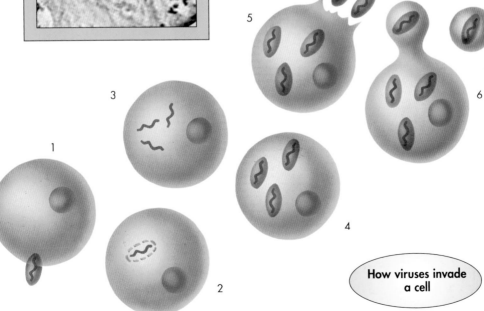

How viruses invade a cell

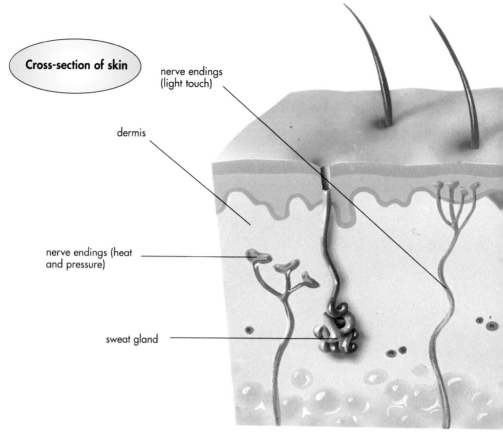

Cross-section of skin

nerve endings
(light touch)

dermis

nerve endings (heat
and pressure)

sweat gland

WHY DO WE HAVE SKIN?

Skin is a flexible, waterproof covering that protects us from the
outside world. It prevents harmful germs from entering the body.
Skin is your largest organ and it is sensitive to touch, temperature
and pain. Your skin tells you what is happening around your body,
so you can avoid injuring yourself. It also helps to prevent damage
from the Sun's harmful ultraviolet rays. Finally skin helps to
regulate body temperature by sweating and flushing to lose heat
when you get too hot.

FACT FILE

Over time, the appearance of skin changes: it
becomes more wrinkled and creased. As people
age, the collagen fibres in their skin weaken,
causing the skin to become looser.

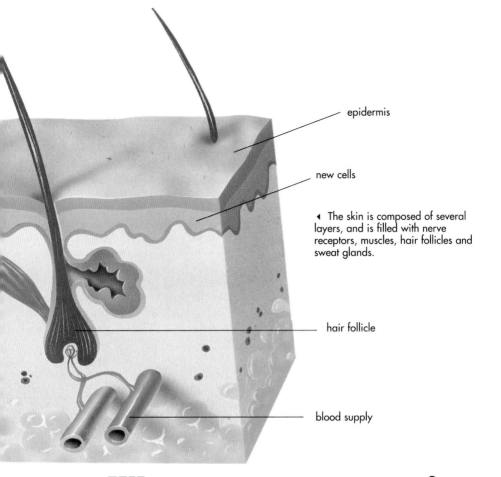

epidermis

new cells

◄ The skin is composed of several layers, and is filled with nerve receptors, muscles, hair follicles and sweat glands.

hair follicle

blood supply

WHY DO WE PERSPIRE?

FACT FILE

Perspiration is the body's own way of cooling down quickly. When a liquid evaporates it takes heat from wherever it is located.

Perspiration is one of the ways we keep our body at a nice normal temperature, around 98.6 degrees fahrenheit. When we become too hot the vessels in the skin are opened so that the extra heat can radiate away and also to help our perspiration to evaporate. Perspiration is like a shower which washes the body out from within. The fluid flows out through millions of tiny openings in the skin in the form of microscopic drops. These drops evaporate quickly and cool the body when necessary.

25

WHY DO WE DREAM?

All our dreams have something to do with our emotions, fears, longings, wishes, needs and memories. But something on the 'outside' may influence what we dream. If a person is hungry, tired, or cold, his dreams may well include these feelings. If the covers have slipped off your bed, you may dream you are on an iceberg. There are people called psychoanalysts who have made a special study of why people dream. They believe that dreams are expressions of wishes that didn't come true. In other words, a dream is a way of having your wish fulfilled. During sleep, according to this theory, our inhibitions are also asleep.

FACT FILE

Daydreaming is actually a form of dreaming, only it is done while we are awake. Night dreaming is done while we are asleep. That is the only difference between them, since both are done when the dreamer is so relaxed that he pays no attention to what goes on around him.

WHY DO WE AWAKEN FROM SLEEP?

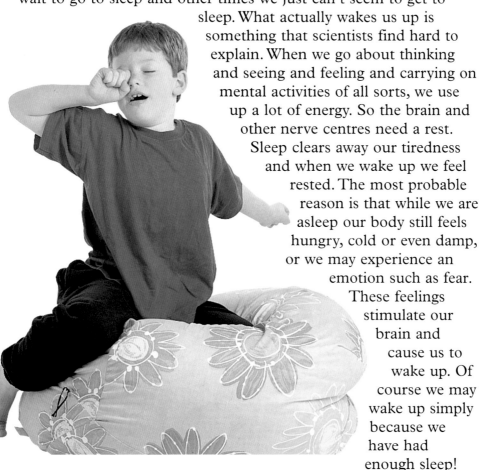

Everybody has strange experiences with sleep. Sometimes we can't wait to go to sleep and other times we just can't seem to get to sleep. What actually wakes us up is something that scientists find hard to explain. When we go about thinking and seeing and feeling and carrying on mental activities of all sorts, we use up a lot of energy. So the brain and other nerve centres need a rest. Sleep clears away our tiredness and when we wake up we feel rested. The most probable reason is that while we are asleep our body still feels hungry, cold or even damp, or we may experience an emotion such as fear. These feelings stimulate our brain and cause us to wake up. Of course we may wake up simply because we have had enough sleep!

FACT FILE

Even while the body sleeps, its nerve systems are active, continuously monitoring and adjusting the internal processes, and checking the outside world for danger. The heart never stops, but beats slower while at rest.

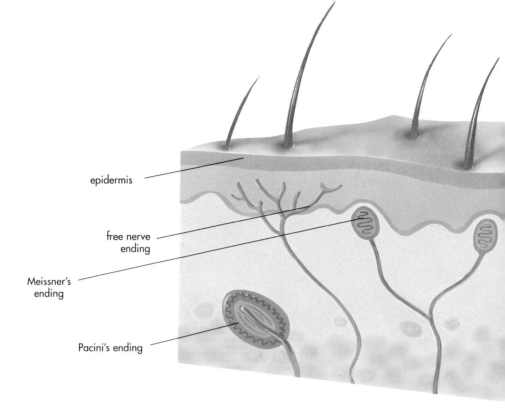

epidermis

free nerve ending

Meissner's ending

Pacini's ending

WHY IS TOUCH AN IMPORTANT SENSE?

Your skin is continuously passing huge amounts of information to your brain. It monitors touch, pain, temperature and other factors that tell the brain exactly how the body is being affected by its environment. Without this constant flow of information you would keep injuring yourself accidentally. You would be unable to sense whether something was very hot, very cold, very sharp and so on. In some rare diseases the skin senses are lost and these people have to be very careful so that they don't keep hurting themselves.

FACT FILE

Did you ever wonder why someone was called a 'touch typist'? This means that they are able to operate typewriter keys without actually looking at them.

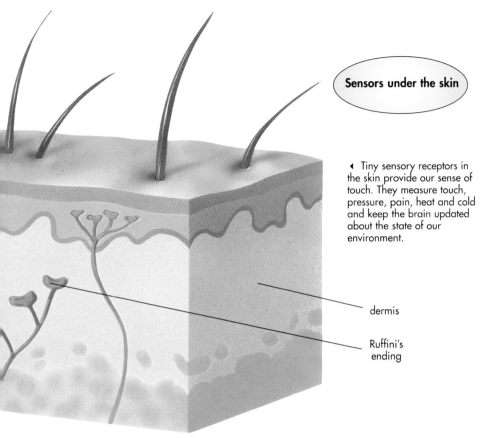

Sensors under the skin

◄ Tiny sensory receptors in the skin provide our sense of touch. They measure touch, pressure, pain, heat and cold and keep the brain updated about the state of our environment.

dermis

Ruffini's ending

WHY ARE SOME BODY PARTS MORE SENSITIVE THAN OTHERS?

FACT FILE

The hands are among the body's most sensitive parts. The fingertips are especially sensitive. On one hand there are millions of nerve-endings.

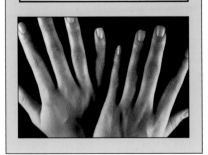

Sensations in the skin are measured by tiny receptors at the ends of nerve fibres. There are several different types of receptor. Each type can detect only one kind of sensation, such as pain, temperature, pressure, touch and so on. These receptors are grouped together according to the importance of their function. There are large numbers in the hands and lips, for example, where the sensation of touch is very important. Your back, however, is far less sensitive as there are fewer receptors in that area of your body.

29

WHY DO WE GET THIRSTY?

All of us have had the experience of being thirsty at times, but can you imagine how it would feel to be thirsty for days? If a human being has absolutely nothing to drink for five to six days, he will die. Feeling thirsty is simply our body's way of telling us to replenish its liquid supply.

The reason for this thirst is caused by a change in the salt content of our blood. There is a certain normal amount of salt and water in our blood. When this changes by having more salt in relation to water in our blood, thirst results.

There is a part of our brain called the 'thirst centre'. It responds to the amount of salt in our blood. When there is a change, it sends messages to the back of the throat. From there, messages go to the brain, and it is this combination of feelings that makes us say we are thirsty.

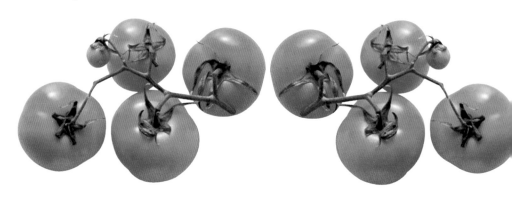

FACT FILE

Onions send out an irritating substance when we peel them. The onion has an oil containing sulphur which not only gives it its sharp odour, but it also irritates the eye. The eye reacts by blinking and producing tears to wash it away. That is why we cry when we peel onions.

WHY DO WE GET HUNGRY?

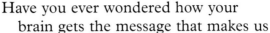

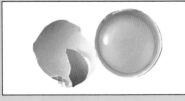

Have you ever wondered how your brain gets the message that makes us feel hungry? Hunger has nothing to do with an empty stomach, as most people believe.

Hunger begins when certain nutritive materials are missing in the blood. When the blood vessels lack these materials, a message is sent to a part of the brain that is called the 'hunger centre'. This hunger centre works like a brake on the stomach and the intestine. As long as the blood has sufficient food, the hunger centre slows up the action of the stomach and the intestine. When the food is missing from the blood, the hunger centre makes the stomach and intestine more active. That is why a hungry person often hears his stomach rumbling.

When we are hungry, our body doesn't crave any special kind of food it just wants nourishment. It depends on the individual how long we can actually live without food. A very calm person can live longer than an excitable one because the protein stored up in his body is used up more slowly.

FACT FILE

Eggs are an extremely good form of protein, which is vital for the building up and repair of muscles. Milk and dairy products are another good source of protein.

WHY ARE SOME PEOPLE LEFT-HANDED?

About four per cent of the population is left-handed. In the course of history many of the greatest geniuses have also been left-handed. Leonardo da Vinci and Michelangelo, the greatest sculptors of all times, were both left-handed.

The brain has a right half and a left half and these two do not function in the same way. It is believed that the left half of the brain is predominant over the right half.

As the left half of the brain predominates, the right half of the body is more skilled and better able to do things. We read, write, speak, and work with the left half of our brain. And this, of course, makes most of us right-handed too. But in the case of left-handed people, it works the other way around. The right half of the brain is predominant, and such a person works best with the left side of his body.

cerebrum

Cross-section of the human brain

hippocampus

pituitary gland

FACT FILE

Did you know that no two human beings have the same set of fingerprints? A fingerprint is the pattern formed by the ridges on the layers of skin at the tips of your fingers. If you press your finger on an ink pad and then onto a piece of paper, you should be able to see some of these patterns.

WHY CAN WE BALANCE ON TWO LEGS?

thalamus

Just being able to stand up or to walk is one of the most amazing tricks it is possible to learn. When you stand still you are performing a constant act of balancing. You change from one leg to the other, you use pressure on your joints, and your muscles tell your body to go this way and that way. Just to keep our balance as we stand still takes the work of about 300 muscles in our body. In walking, we not only use our balancing trick, but we also make use of two natural forces to help us. The first is air pressure. Our thigh bone fits into the socket of the hip joint so snugly that it forms a kind of vacuum. The air pressure on our legs helps keep it there securely. This air pressure also makes the leg hang from the body as if it had very little weight. The second natural force we use in walking is the pull of the Earth's gravity. When we raise our leg, the Earth pulls it down again.

brain stem

cerebellum

spinal cord

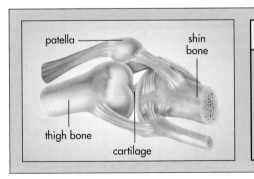

patella

shin bone

thigh bone

cartilage

FACT FILE

The knee joint, like your elbow, is a hinge joint. The end of one bone fits into a sort of hollow in the other. This kind of joint will only bend in one direction.

WHY DO WE NEED VITAMIN C?

The food we take into our bodies supplies us with many important substances such as proteins, fats, carbohydrates, water and mineral substances. But these alone are not enough. In order to maintain life we need other substances known as vitamins. Vitamin C can be found in citrus fruits and fresh vegetables. When there is a lack of vitamins in our body, diseases will occur. So what actually happens when there is a lack of this vitamin in the body? The blood vessels become fragile and bleed easily. Black-and-blue marks appear on the skin and near the eyes. The gums bleed easily. Our hormones and enzymes do not function well and our resistance to infection by bacteria is lowered.

Long before man knew about vitamins, it had been observed that when people couldn't get certain types of foods, diseases would develop. Sailors, for instance, who went on long trips and couldn't get fresh vegetables, would develop a disease called scurvy. In the seventeenth century British sailors were given lemons and limes to prevent this disease.

FACT FILE

Fruits contain energy and a wide range of essential vitamins and minerals. Vitamins are chemicals that we need to stay healthy. Some are stored in the body, others need to be eaten every day.

WHY ARE CARBOHYDRATES IMPORTANT?

Human beings need a certain amount of food each day to supply them with energy. Almost all foods can supply some energy, but carbohydrates give us the most. Carbohydrates include foods like bread, cereal, potatoes, rice, pasta.

Our bodies have other requirements as well. In order to make sure that we are taking in everything we need, we should eat a wide variety of foods, with the correct amounts of carbohydrates, fat and protein. A diet which fulfils these requirements is called a balanced diet.

These food groups serve different purposes: carbohydrates for energy, protein to build and repair cells and to keep our bones, muscles, blood and skin healthy.

FACT FILE

Bananas are a very good source of energy as the body absorbs them very quickly. Ripe bananas give off a gas that causes other fruit to ripen rapidly and then rot.

WHY DO SOME PEOPLE WEAR GLASSES?

If the eye is not exactly the right shape, or the lens cannot focus properly, you cannot form a clear image on the retina. In this case you may need to wear glasses to correct your vision. For a short-sighted person, distant object look blurred because the image forms in front of the retina. A short-sighted person can see nearby objects very clearly. For a long-sighted person, the image tries to form behind the retina, so it is blurred while the lens tries to focus on a nearby object. As people get older the lenses of their eyes grow harder and cannot change their shape to focus close up.

FACT FILE

Blinking is a very important function because it cleans and lubricates the surface of the eye. The cornea in particular is a sensitive area and must be protected from drying out and infection.

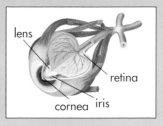

lens

retina

cornea iris

WHY DO WE SEE IN COLOUR?

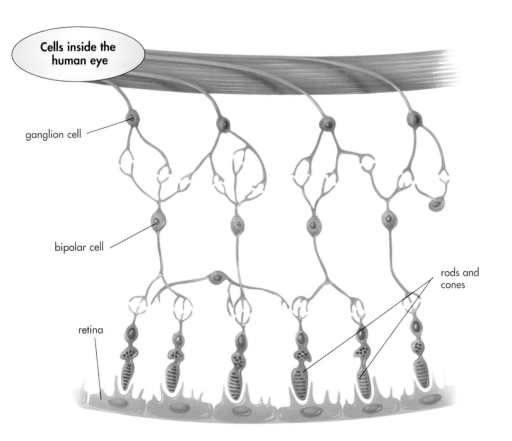

The retina of the eye is packed with a layer of tiny cells called rods and cones. These cells contain coloured substances that react when light falls on them, triggering a nerve impulse. Rods are slim cells that are responsible for black and white vision. Cone cells give us colour vision. They contain different light-sensitive substances that respond to either red, yellow-green or blue-violet light. Together with the black and white images produced from the rods, cone cells give you the coloured picture that you see. The cone cells only work in bright light which is why it is difficult to see colours in a dim light.

Cells inside the human eye

ganglion cell

bipolar cell

rods and cones

retina

THE NATURAL

WORLD

CONTENTS

WHY DO LIVING THINGS HAVE LATIN NAMES ?

Carl Linnaeus
(1707–1778)

Most plants and animals have popular names that can vary from place to place. So a name needed to be given that would be recognized everywhere. It was decided to use Latin for the scientific names, as it was the language used centuries ago by learned people. Carl Linnaeus was the man who established the modern scientific method for naming plants and animals.

Scientific names are in two parts. The first part is the generic name, which describes a group of related living things. The second name is the specific name, which applies only to that living thing. This specific name may describe the living thing, or it could include the name of the person who discovered it.

FACT FILE

The Latin name for a human is *Homo sapien,* meaning 'thinking man'. A fossil form of *Homo,* or man, is *Homo habillis* (tool-using man).

WHY IS CHARLES DARWIN REMEMBERED?

The English scientist Charles Darwin is remembered for his ideas about evolution after years of study and travelling on voyages of exploration. He discovered that many small islands had populations of unique creatures. Darwin was able to show how these creatures differed from their close relatives elsewhere. In the Galapagos Islands, for example, he found a unique range of animal life, due to their isolation from the mainland.

Charles Darwin
(1809–1882)

▾ The giant tortoise is just one of the animals that Charles Darwin discovered when he visited the Galapagos Islands.

FACT FILE

The giraffe is an example of how natural selection helps evolution. Their ancestors had longer than average necks so that they could reach more food.

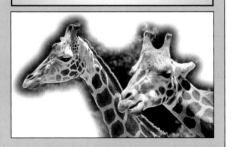

WHY DO TREES HAVE BARK?

The outer portion of a woody stem or root is called 'bark'. One of the main functions of bark is to protect the inner, more delicate structures. It not only keeps them from drying out, but it also guards against outside injuries of various sorts.

The process by which bark is formed may go on year after year. Some of the outer portions become dry and die. The dead, broken portions give the bark a rough appearance. Some of the dry pieces are shed or broken off as the twig grows larger and older.

Sometimes it is hard to tell how much of the stem should be called bark. In the palm tree, for example, there is no clear separation between bark and wood.

FACT FILE

The coconut is a large, hollow nut which grows on a palm tree. It contains a milky fluid which you can drink. The white lining is also edible and used in cooking. The coconut fibres on the outside of the shell are also used for making coconut matting and sacking.

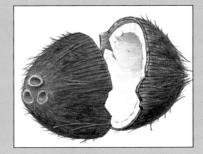

light energy
from the Sun

water is taken in
by the roots

WHY DO PLANTS HAVE ROOTS?

FACT FILE

Carrots are a good example of a plant having a taproot. It grows just one large root under the ground which absorbs all the moisture. This root is also edible.

A plant needs roots for two chief reasons: one as a means of anchoring itself to the ground, and secondly to absorb water and minerals from the soil. The roots of most plants grow in the soil. By elongating their tips, roots are always coming into contact with new portions of soil. Thousands of tiny hairs project from the surface of the young root which absorb the materials from the soil. Some plants have large bulbous roots called taproots. Grasses have fibrous root systems. Soil in which there are many fibrous roots is protected from erosion. Some tropical orchids that grow on trees have spongy roots.

WHY DO PLANTS PRODUCE SEEDS?

The seed of a plant contains an embryo from which a new plant will grow. It also contains a food store to nourish the embryo until it has developed roots and leaves. The seed is enclosed in a tough coat to protect it from drying out.

Many seeds are carried by the wind. Some, like the dandelion below, have fluffy 'umbrellas' which carry them for long distances. Others have wings that allow the seed to glide or spin around like a helicopter blade.

FACT FILE

The seed of the coco de mer can travel long distances by sea, until it is washed up onto shore. In the warm sand it sprouts and starts to grow into a new palm tree.

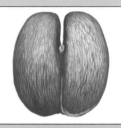

WHY DO TREES HAVE LEAVES?

Green plants and trees need leaves to help them manufacture food. Leaves of fruit trees, for example, make the food that helps to make the fruit. For example, peaches and maple sugar are sweet, so peach and maple tree leaves produce sugar. They do this by taking carbon dioxide from the air and water and nutrients from the soil. This process is called photosynthesis. Leaves contain many little green bodies called chloroplasts which act as the machine to produce the sugar. Sunshine is the power that runs these little machines.

FACT FILE

In the autumn many leaves change colour and drop from the tree. The reason for this is because the tree will not need to grow in the winter, so it conserves its energy by losing its leaves.

WHY ARE THERE SO MANY FLOWER SHAPES?

The reason that flowers come in so many different shapes and colours is to help ensure that they are fertilized. Flowers that rely on insects for pollination must make sure that the insect is carrying pollen from the same kind of plant. The shape of the flower ensures that only certain kinds of insect can pollinate it. Flat flowers, such as daisies and sunflowers, can be visited by hoverflies and some bees. Flowers that are formed into tubes only attract insects that have long tongues.

FACT FILE

Bees are attracted to the colour and scent of a flower. They feed on the nectar in the flower and gather pollen, which they store in sacs on their legs.

WHY ARE SOME FLOWERS VERY COLOURFUL?

FACT FILE

Did you know that the bat's long tongue is perfect for whisking out the nectar from a flower? Pollen is brushed onto the bat's fur as it moves from flower to flower.

A flower is the means by which a plant reproduces. It contains male or female organs or both together. Flowers usually have brightly coloured petals or sepals.

The reason that flowers are so brightly coloured and perfumed is to attract insects. Insects play a very important part in pollinating them.

Some plants also produce a sugary liquid called nectar which attracts the bees. As they fly from flower to flower they transfer the pollen to the stigma of the flower and fertilize it.

WHY ARE SPIDERS NOT INSECTS?

Spiders belong to the class of arachnids which also includes scorpions, ticks and mites. None of these are actually classed as insects. Unlike insects they have eight legs, eight eyes in most cases, no wings, and only two, not three parts to their bodies.

Spiders are found in practically every kind of climate. They can run on the ground, climb plants, run on water, and some even live in water.

The spider manufactures a silk, which it uses to spin its web, in certain glands found in the abdomen or belly. At the tip of the abdomen there are spinning organs which contain many tiny holes. The silk is forced through these tiny holes. When the silk comes out it is a liquid. As soon as it comes in contact with the air, it becomes solid. Spiders are meat-eaters, feeding on insects and other spiders which it traps in its web.

FACT FILE

The scorpion is related to the spider. A scorpion has four pairs of walking legs and a pair of strong pincers which it uses to grasp its prey. It also has a long, thin, jointed tail which ends in a curved, pointed stinger. This stinger is connected to poison glands.

WHY ARE SOME INSECTS BRIGHTLY COLOURED?

There are many different ways in which insects will try to protect themselves from their enemies. Some insects, such as wasps and ants, have powerful stings or are able to shower their attackers with poisonous fluid. The hoverfly does not sting, but its colouring is so like that of a wasp or bee that enemies are very wary of it. Other insects, such as stick insects, use camouflage. They look like the leaves and twigs among which they feed. The bright colouring on some insects warns its enemies that it may be poisonous.

FACT FILE

A ladybird is a very brightly coloured insect. The ladybird is a very useful insect in the garden as it will eat the aphids which eat your plants and flowers.

Frogspawn

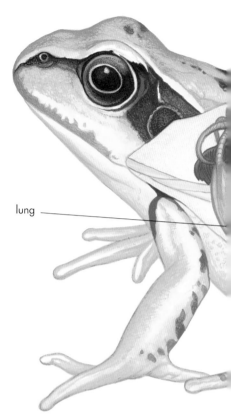

lung

▸ The internal organs of a frog are typical of vertebrate animals, although their lungs and heart are much simpler than those of mammals and birds.

WHY ARE SOME FROGS POISONOUS?

Not all frogs are poisonous but some have developed a venom that they can use should they come under attack from predators. The common toad contains a poison that it exudes through its skin if attacked. Dogs and cats commonly experience this poison, however they seldom suffer serious effects. It does teach them, however, to avoid these amphibians. Cane toads are very large toads which contain a drug capable of causing hallucinations if eaten. The skin of some frogs and toads contain poisons which are among the most powerful known to humans.

FACT FILE

The South American arrow frog is extremely poisonous. It advertises this danger by being very brightly coloured.

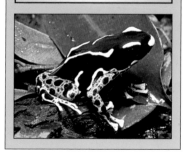

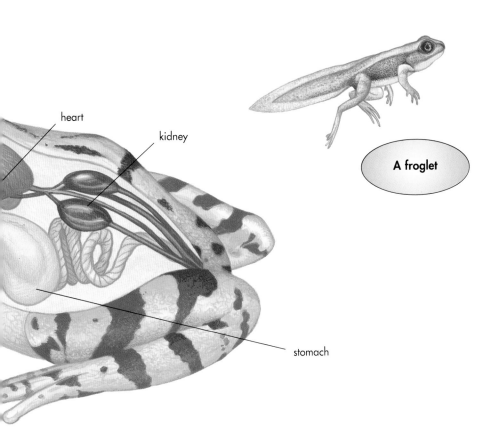

heart

kidney

stomach

A froglet

WHY DO FROGS VANISH IN WINTER?

FACT FILE

A frog's eyes are positioned on the top of its head so that it can see above the water's surface. In this way it can always be on the alert for predators.

Frogs vary considerably in shape, colour and size. Some little tree frogs, that live in the United States, are no more than one inch in length. Leopard frogs are about two to four inches long, while bullfrogs can reach eight inches and have legs that are ten inches long.

What do these frogs do in winter? In northern countries, when cold weather sets in, some frogs dive into a pond, bury themselves in the mud and stay there all winter. Ponds do not freeze solid, even when winters are very cold, so the frog does not freeze.

51

WHY DO SALMON GO UPSTREAM TO SPAWN?

Salmon have a natural instinct to return to the place they were born to lay their eggs (to spawn). This is a safe place, usually a quiet area of a river, where young salmon can grow. The adult salmon stop feeding when they first reach fresh water, so they gradually become weaker and weaker. They often wear themselves out trying to reach the exact place they want to deposit their eggs. The young salmon remain in the river for a few months, then make the journey to the sea. They stay there for up to four years, then the cycle begins all over again.

FACT FILE

Adult frogs very often return to the pond in which they hatched to lay their spawn. Frog spawn hatches into larvae called tadpoles after about a week.

WHY CAN'T FISH SURVIVE OUTSIDE WATER?

Fish are specially adapted so that they can breathe under the water. They have special organs called gills. Gills are bars of tissue at each side of the fish's head. They carry masses of finger-like projections that contain tiny blood vessels. The fish gulp in water through their mouths and pass it out through the gills. The gills are rich in blood, and they extract oxygen from the water and pass it into the fish's blood.

In this way the gills have the same function as the lungs of air-breathing animals. But these gills would not work without the aid of water.

FACT FILE

Most of a fish's body is composed of powerful muscles and its internal organs are squeezed into a tiny area. The fins are used to propel and stabilize the fish in the water.

WHY DO BIRDS SING?

The song of birds is one of the loveliest sounds in nature. When birds sing they are actually communicating with one another. Of course, at times the sounds birds make are mere expressions of joy. But for the most part, the sounds are attempts at communication.

When wild birds migrate at night, they cry out. These cries may keep the birds together and help lost ones return to the flock. Birds don't learn how to sing, it is an inborn instinct with them. It doesn't mean that birds can't learn to sing. In fact, some birds can learn the songs of other birds. If a canary was brought up with a nightingale, it could give quite a good imitation of the nightingale's song. And we all know how a parrot can imitate the sounds that it hears.

FACT FILE

A mother hen makes sounds that warn her chicks of danger and causes them to crouch down motionless. Then she gives another call which collects them together.

WHY IS BIRDS' VISION SO GOOD?

Vision is the dominant sense of nearly all birds. In most, the eyes are placed so far to the side of the head that they have mainly monocular vision, meaning that each eye scans a separate area. This feature is shared by all hunted creatures who depend on vision to warn them of possible danger. Birds of prey and owls have eyes set more to the front of the head, offering a wider angle of binocular vision, which is vitally important for judging distance. Birds also have a third eyelid which moves sideways across the cornea and keeps it moist without interrupting their vision.

FACT FILE

Accuracy is crucial for a hunting bird like the eagle which relies on its keen eyesight, first to spot the prey and then to catch it. The eagle's eyes are therefore positioned sufficiently far forwards to give it binocular or three-dimensional vision.

WHY DOES THE PEACOCK RAISE HIS FEATHERS?

One of the most spectacular sights presented by any bird is that of the peacock displaying his tail feathers. In fact, in ancient times, both the Greeks and Romans considered the peacock to be a sacred bird. The male peacock's display of gorgeous plumage is for the sake of the female, the peahen, and for her alone. It is usually the male bird that has the brighter colours and the more flashy appearance. The most remarkable feature of the male peacock, of course, is the train, or the extension of his tail. A peacock is about 7 feet (210cm) long, of which the tail takes up about 3 feet (90cm). The tail is a medley of blue and green and gold. Here and there in the regular pattern are 'eyes' which change colour. The train is raised and held up by the stiff quills of the shorter, true tail.

The female peacock is slightly smaller and quieter in tone. She has no train and only a short crest of dull colour. Peacocks are generally kept for ornament and for the sake of their plumage.

FACT FILE

Ostrich eyes are nearly as big as tennis balls! Ostriches lay bigger eggs than any other bird – they are 24 times bigger than a chicken's egg. The shell is so strong that even if you stand on top of an ostrich egg, it will not break.

The male peacock

FACT FILE

The puffin's big, bright beak is hinged so that it can snap up fish and still keep a grip on those it has already caught.

WHY IS A MALE BIRD BRIGHTER THAN A FEMALE?

One reason the male bird has brighter colours than a female is that they help attract the female during the breeding season. This is usually the time when the male bird's colours are brightest of all. Even among birds, you see, there can be love at first sight!

The female's plumage is not so bright is so that they blend in better with their natural habitat. The reason being that she needs the most protection when she is sitting on the nest and hatching her eggs. Nature has given her duller colours to keep her better hidden from her enemies. It seems that birds with brighter colours spend most of their time in treetops, while birds with duller colours live mostly near or on the ground.

WHY DON'T SNAKES HAVE LEGS?

Just because snakes do not have legs now, does not mean they did not have them at sometime in their development. Some experts believe that the ancestors of snakes were certain kinds of burrowing lizards. In time, the legs disappeared altogether. Despite this snakes are able to move and get along very well indeed. One of the most helpful things for them in moving are the belly scales that cover the entire undersurface of most snakes. Snakes can move in different ways. The concertina method, which is used for climbing. Sidewinding, where a loop of the body is thrown to one side. The lateral undulatory movement, where the snake forms S-shaped curves, and also the rectilinear movement where it uses its scales.

FACT FILE

Lizards and snakes belong to the highest order of reptiles. The main difference between lizards and snakes is in the structure of the jaws. In snakes, both upper and lower jaws have movable halves with sharp teeth.

WHY ARE CROCODILES NOT THE SAME AS ALLIGATORS?

Both crocodiles and alligators spend most of their lives in swamps and rivers in warm climates, although they breathe air through nostrils on the top of their snouts. They close these nostrils when they dive below the water. Caymans and gavials are relatives of crocodiles and alligators.

The simple way of telling them apart is that crocodiles show the fourth tooth in their lower jaw when their mouths are closed. Alligators, on the other hand, do not. It is probably wise not to go near enough to a live crocodile to find out, however, as they have been known to attack humans.

FACT FILE

The Komodo dragon is a huge monitor lizard found living in Indonesia. This fearsome lizard is known to live for about 100 years. It can grow to a length of 3 metres.

An alligator

A crocodile

WHY DOES A GIRAFFE HAVE A LONG NECK?

FACT FILE

The elephant is also an unusual animal because of its very long trunk. It is an extension of the nose and upper lip and serves the elephant as hand, arm, nose and lips all at once.

Giraffes in the wild

The giraffe is the tallest of all living animals. The strange shape and build of the giraffe is perfectly suited to enable it to obtain its food. A giraffe only eats plants, so its great height enables it to reach the leaves on trees which grow in tropical lands where there is little grass.

A giraffe's tongue can be 18 inches (46cm) long and it uses it so skillfully that it can pick the smallest leaves off thorny plants without being pricked. It also has a long upper lip which helps it wrench off many leaves at a time.

If a giraffe wants to take a drink from the ground, it has to adopt a peculiar stance by spreading its legs far apart in order to be able to reach down.

WHY ARE RHINOS BECOMING ENDANGERED?

FACT FILE

The red wolf became extinct in the wild in 1980, but small numbers of captive specimens were bred. There are now around 200 in captivity.

Some animal species have become extinct because they are less successful than other species that gradually replace them. But this is not so in the case of the rhinoceros. Hunting is the reason for their reduced numbers. In fact poaching has reduced the numbers of black rhinos to around 2,500. Most survive today only in protected game parks. A rhino horn can grow as long as 62 inches (157cm).

61

WHY DOES A COW CHEW ITS CUD?

Many thousands of years ago, there were certain animals who couldn't protect themselves very well against their predators. In order to survive, these animals developed a special way of eating. They would snatch some food whenever they could, swallow it quickly without chewing, and run away to hide. When they were safe in their hiding place, they would chew the food at their leisure. Some present day animals, such as cows, still eat this way. It is called chewing the cud and the animals are called ruminants. This way of eating is possible because such animals have complicated stomachs with five compartments. Each of these compartments processes the food.

FACT FILE

Other examples of cud chewing animals are sheep, goats, camels, llamas, deer and antelopes. Camels find this form of eating very useful for long desert journeys.

WHY ARE BEARS DANGEROUS?

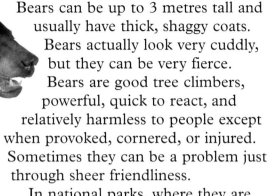

Bears can be up to 3 metres tall and usually have thick, shaggy coats. Bears actually look very cuddly, but they can be very fierce.

Bears are good tree climbers, powerful, quick to react, and relatively harmless to people except when provoked, cornered, or injured. Sometimes they can be a problem just through sheer friendliness.

In national parks, where they are familiar with human beings and come begging for food, visitors to the parks must keep to the protection of cars to avoid accidental injury from the bears' claws. Also with their big strong arms, bears could hug a person to death.

They are sometimes affectionately known as 'grizzly' bears. The reason for this is because the tips of their brown hairs are grey, or grizzled.

FACT FILE

Did you know that many bears have rotten teeth? This is because they love sweet foods. One of their favourite foods is honey which they steal from bees' nests high up in trees.

The American black bear

WHY IS THE LION CALLED 'KING OF THE BEASTS'?

Throughout history the lion has been considered the symbol of strength. In courts all over the world the lion was used on shields and crests and banners to indicate power. The lion's voice is a roar or a growl. The ancient Egyptians believed the lion was sacred, and during the time when Christ was born, lions lived in many parts of Europe. Today, the only places where lions are plentiful are in Africa.

FACT FILE

Lions and tigers are thought of as the greatest cats of the wild. Stripy tigers and lions never meet in the wild; lions are native to Africa, and stripy tigers are native to Asia.

WHY DO TIGERS HAVE DISTINCT COLOURING?

The tiger is one of the largest of the big cats. The base colour of the coat is fawn to red, becoming progressively darker the further southwards you go. The Balinese tiger is the darkest. The underparts of the tiger are white. The coat is overlaid with black to brownish-black transverse stripes and these contrasting colours provide a wonderful camouflage in its natural habitat.

FACT FILE

A leopard is another member of the big cat family which has a remarkable coat. Did you know that the name leopard is from the Latin word *leopardus* which means a 'spotted lion'?

WHY ARE SOME APES SO HUMANLIKE?

The great apes are the nearest living relative to man. There are four species of great ape: the orang-utan, chimpanzee, gorilla and the gibbon. Chimpanzees are particularly brainy and are one of the few animals to actually use tools. Apes generally walk on all fours but are able to stand and walk on two feet just like humans. Apes also have fingers and thumbs like a human hand, which makes them able to pick up and hold things as we do. The hair on an ape's head also turns grey with age as with humans. Baby gorillas, like human babies, learn to crawl at about ten weeks and walk at about eight months old.

FACT FILE

Apes like this gibbon give birth to helpless young that need looking after for a long time. Apes can look after their young for as long as five years.

WHY ARE MONKEYS DIFFERENT FROM OTHER PRIMATES?

All monkeys are primates. It is easy to tell them apart from the clever primates, people and apes, because they have tails. Their tails, which are generally long, can be used like an extra arm or leg to cling onto branches. A spider-monkey, from South America, can actually hang by its strong tail leaving both hands free for feeding. They live in family groups and spend much of their time in the trees. They are very careful to look around them before leaping from one tree to another as there could be danger close by. A large eagle may swoop from above or possibly a leopard could be lurking below so it is important not to lose their footing.

FACT FILE

Monkeys have a varied diet. They are not known for their fussy tastes and are omniverous by nature. They will eat a wide variety of food – from flowers, leaves and fruit to insects and small frogs.

WHY ARE RAIN FORESTS BEING CUT DOWN?

Tropical rainforests contain the most varied mixtures of animals and plants of any habitat on the Earth. They contain large and small predators and a bewildering variety of birds. All these animals are supported by huge numbers of trees that produce fruit to feed them and their prey all year round. Unfortunately though, man is destroying their natural habitat. Rainforests are being cut down at an alarming rate, nearly 90 per cent of rainforest have been destroyed. Both large commercial farming companies and individual farmers clear the forest to gain land to cultivate and graze animals. Secondly, trees have been felled to supply tropical hardwoods for furniture making and building.

FACT FILE

It is estimated that over two million different species of plant and animal thrive in the rainforests and many have been undiscovered by man. Their destruction is a serious threat to our planet.

WHY ARE MOST CORAL REEFS PROTECTED?

FACT FILE

A star fish is one of the many thousands of creatures that make their home among the coral reefs. The star fish moves around on thousands of tiny tube feet, or they can use them to grab their prey of shellfish.

Coral reefs are the marine equivalent of rainforests. They are homes to thousands of species of fish and invertebrates, all living in a complex balance which makes the reef system an extremely stable environment. That is until the intervention of man.

Marine biologists spend a lot of time studying the reef and valuable new discoveries are made all the time. There are a great number of threats to coral reefs. Work must be done quickly to protect them. Therefore the education of people throughout the world is necessary if coral reefs are to survive.

A kitten

WHY DO FLEAS LIVE ON CATS AND DOGS?

Fleas are parasites. A parasite is a plant or an animal that lives with or on another living organism. The flea lives on dogs and cats by sucking blood. The warmth of the body and thickness of a cat or dog's coat is an ideal place for a flea to live and breed. It has a small round head and mouth parts that are adapted to sucking. It has a tiny body, no wings, and three pairs of legs.

The flea is the champion jumper of all creatures. This tiny insect can jump 7 inches (17cm) in the air and sideways by 12 inches (30.5cm). For a man that would mean being able to jump 450 feet (137m) up and a long jump of 700 feet (213m)!

FACT FILE

Fleas don't just live on dogs and cats. They also infest rats, rabbits, squirrels, wild birds, and nearly all other warm-blooded animals.

WHY ARE SOME ANIMALS DOMESTICATED?

FACT FILE

One animal that is very popular with children to keep as a pet is the hamster. A hamster has an unusual way of storing food in pouches at either side of its head.

Dogs were probably the first animals to be domesticated, perhaps to help with hunting. By domesticating goats, cattle, sheep, pigs and poultry, humans have been able to ensure that food is always available. Horses, mules and camels have been used to carry people and goods over long distances. Pets provide companionship but can also be very useful. Sheepdogs help farmers to round up their flocks. Guide dogs for the blind and hearing dogs for the deaf help their owners to lead full lives. Animals are also used to guard property, perform rescues and carry messages.

The domesticated dog

SCIENCE AND

TECHNOLOGY

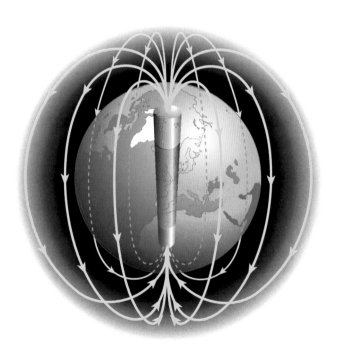

CONTENTS

WHY ARE ATOMS EVERYWHERE?

Atoms are the tiny particles that make up the whole universe. Enormous amounts of energy are locked inside atoms. Atoms are the tiniest particles into which a substance can be divided without changing into something else. Atoms actually consist almost entirely of open space, in which tiny particles orbit the central particle, or nucleus. The particles travel so fast that they seem to be solid.

Atoms are so minute that the smallest particle visible to the naked eye would contain about one million billion atoms. Despite their tiny size, atoms can be seen individually under very powerful electron microscopes.

Atoms linked to other atoms

FACT FILE

There are more than a hundred and nine different atoms. Atoms are so incredibly tiny – about 100,000 million atoms fit on this full stop.

atom.

WHY IS QUANTUM PHYSICS USED?

Quantum physics helps us to understand how energy is used or released by atoms. Negatively charged electrons circle about the positively charged nucleus of the atom. They stay in the same orbit until this is disturbed, and each orbit has its own lever of energy. If more energy is added when the atom is heated or when light shines on it, the electron jumps out to another orbit, absorbing the extra energy. Then when it drops back again to its original orbit, it releases this energy as heat or light. This tiny packet of energy is called a quantum. It is not possible to measure exactly where a subatomic particle is and how fast it is moving, because this will disturb the particle and change its characteristics.

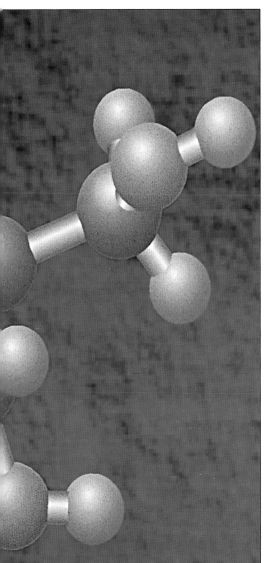

FACT FILE

An atom becomes linked to other atoms by electrical bonds, which work rather like chemical hooks. Some atoms only carry one of these hooks, while others may have many. Atoms with many hooks can build up with other atoms into complicated molecules or chemical compounds.

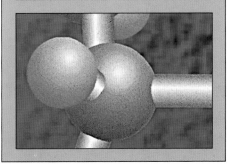

WHY ARE MICROSCOPES USED?

The word microscope is a combination of two Greek words, *mikros* or 'small' and *skopos* or 'watcher'. So this means that a microscope is a 'watcher of small' objects. It is an instrument that is used to see tiny things which are invisible to the naked eye.

Normally an object appears larger the closer it is brought to the human eye. But when it is nearer than 10 inches (25.5cm) it becomes blurred. It is said to be out of focus. Now if a simple convex lens is placed between the eye and the object, the object can be brought nearer than 10 inches (25.5cm) and still remain in focus. Today the microscope is important to man in almost every form of industry.

It was a Dutchman called Antonie van Leeuwenhoek (1632–1723) who discovered ground glass lenses which he used to examine the world about him. In the 1670s he made his first crude microscope with a tiny lens. This allowed him to be the first person to see microscopic life such as bacteria.

FACT FILE

Some microscopes are so powerful they can magnify the smallest objects many thousands of times. This plant cell would be invisible to the human eye without the use of magnification.

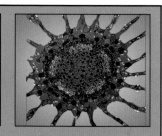

WHY IS PROTECTIVE CLOTHING WORN BY SCIENTISTS?

Two of the many things that scientists study are germs and bacteria that carry diseases. As many of these could be extremely dangerous if touched or sometimes just breathed in, it is essential for the scientist to wear protective clothing which would include masks, gloves, body and head protection.

Scientists sometimes have to handle radioactive material. Exposure to radioactive radiation can be fatal to any living organism. For this reason robots are used rather than human beings if at all possible. When people do need to handle such substances they wear protective clothing and carry a meter that records the amount of exposure to radiation they are receiving.

FACT FILE

This symbol on a container or buildings warns that there is some radioactive material inside.

neutral   acid   alkaline

WHY IS LITMUS PAPER USED IN CHEMISTRY?

Litmus paper is a quick way to test a liquid to see whether it is acid or alkaline.

Dyes called indicators show very quickly if a substance dissolved in water is acid or alkaline. One of these dyes is litmus. If a piece of paper impregnated with litmus is dipped into a solution, it immediately turns red if the solution is acid. If the solution is alkaline, the litmus turns blue.

A similar dye to litmus is present in some red vegetables, such as red cabbage and beetroot and this dye changes colour in the same way during cooking. If your tap water is hard, or alkaline, the vegetables will be coloured a deep purplish-blue.

FACT FILE

Bee stings are acidic. An acid is neutralized by an alkali, so as to reduce the painful effects of a bee sting. Soap is alkaline and will therefore help to lessen the effect of the sting if it is rubbed on the skin.

WHY ARE CRYSTALS FORMED?

Crystals are formed from dissolved substances, or when molten substances cool slowly. As the solutions evaporate or the melted materials cool, their atoms are forced closer together, producing a crystal. The crystal gradually grows as the process continues. Some crystals grow into complicated and beautiful shapes, which are often very brightly coloured.

Crystals are solid substances that have their atoms arranged in regular patterns. Most naturally occurring substances form crystals under the right conditions, although they are not always apparent.

FACT FILE

Snowflakes are made up of millions of ice crystals. If you were to look at them under a microscope each would appear to be a different pattern.

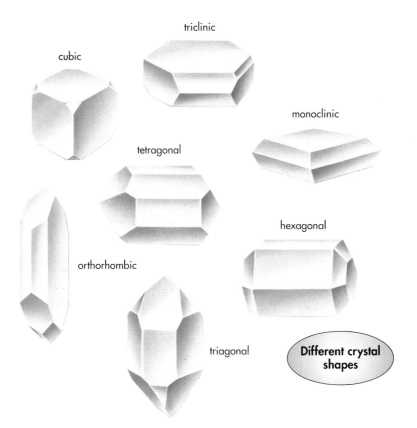

cubic

triclinic

monoclinic

tetragonal

hexagonal

orthorhombic

triagonal

Different crystal shapes

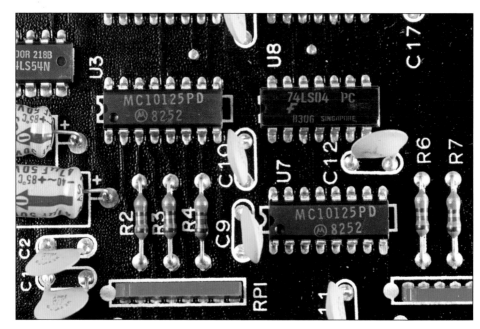

WHY DO WE USE CIRCUIT BOARDS?

Any modern electrical device requires a huge number of connections to join together all the small components needed for it to work effectively. At one time these connections were made by wires that had to be soldered together. The wires have now been replaced by the printed circuit board, which is effectively a picture of the wiring that works just as well.

The image is literally photographed onto a special board which is covered with a thin layer of copper. Chemicals are used to dissolve most of the copper leaving behind a thin film of metal bands to which all the components can be attached. Circuit boards are very light, compact and inexpensive to make.

FACT FILE

Appliances containing electronic circuits can perform very complicated tasks and even appear to think for themselves. A good example of this is a personal computer.

WHY DO WE SEE SO MANY PYLONS?

FACT FILE

In an electric light bulb an electrical current is passed through a very thin filament of metal. The filament becomes white hot and gives us light.

Electricity is used as a way of moving energy from place to place. It can take energy from burning coal in a power station into your home. Electricity is required for so many things in our homes and at our places of work that we need a way of getting the energy to travel. Giant masts called pylons have been erected all over the country which are connected by powerful electrical cables. Energy travels down these cables at about 250,000 kilometres a second, which is almost as fast as the speed of light.

WHY IS NUCLEAR POWER USED?

Inside a nuclear power station billions of uranium atoms are torn apart which create an enormous amount of energy. The energy is powerful enough to boil water, and steam from this hot water is used to generate electricity. Nuclear power holds out the promise of cheap and unlimited power, but with the technical difficulties and safety concerns their use is limited. The nuclear reactor at a power station is surrounded by thick concrete walls for safety.

FACT FILE

The atom bomb is such a powerful and dangerous weapon that it has only been used in anger twice. Even the testing of them has now been abandoned.

WHY ARE NUCLEAR REACTORS CONTINUALLY MONITORED?

People worry about nuclear power because when the energy is released from an atom, deadly rays, called radiation, can escape. Radiation is very harmful when it enters the body. When too much radiation passes through living cells, it may damage the cells or weaken the body's defences against disease. A typical nuclear power station produces about 20 bathfuls of dangerous waste each year. It is poured into steel tanks and are then buried in concrete.

FACT FILE

This is a nuclear reactor. Inside the reactor uranium or plutonium undergo a process called fission, which releases huge amounts of energy.

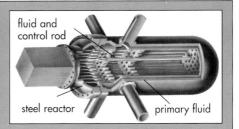

fluid and control rod

steel reactor   primary fluid

WHY ARE OPTIC FIBRES SO USEFUL?

An optical fibre is made of fine strands of glass, along which pulses of light can travel. Light travels much faster than electricity and it is therefore used in optical cables to carry communications for very long distances without electrical interference. The light travels along tiny glass fibres, usually packed into huge bundles capable of carrying many thousands of messages at the same time.

When you talk on the telephone your voice is turned into laser light signals and sent down very thin fibre glass tubes called optical fibres. Up to 150,000 different conversations can be sent down just one of these optical fibres.

Optic fibre is also used for ornate lighting. Light is reflected down thousands of tiny glass fibres as can be seen on some modern artificial Christmas trees.

FACT FILE

A great amount of communication these days is carried out via satellites. Radio, telephone and television messages are transmitted around the world with incredible speed. Such satellites orbit the Earth so that they appear to be in the same place all the time – even though the Earth is spinning round. This is possible because a satellite's orbit speed is matched with the Earth's rotational speed. These are known as geo-stationary orbits.

WHY ARE MEANS OF COMMUNICATION ALWAYS DEVELOPING?

light

glass fibre

Only a few hundred years ago, the fastest way a piece of news could travel was to be carried by a person on horseback. Messages sent overseas could only travel as fast as the fastest sailing ship. The breakthrough came with the invention of the electric telegraph and messages in Morse Code. The message was sent down a wire in bursts of electric current.

Today, however, images of written documents, sound recordings or television pictures can be flashed around the globe in less than a second by means of satellites and radio communications. Several satellites, in different orbits, are required to give coverage over the whole globe, and different satellites are used to reflect signals for different media, such as telephone messages and television pictures.

FACT FILE

Mobile phones work by using low-powered microwaves to send and receive messages to and from a base station. Otherwise known as a cellular phone, a mobile allows calls to be received and made wherever the caller happens to be.

WHY ARE WIND TURBINES USED AS A POWER SOURCE?

When oil, gas and coal run out, people will need other sources of energy to fuel their cars and light their houses. Concerns about pollution resulting from the production of electrical power have led to the development of wind turbines. Huge windmills situated on exposed and windy areas are a common sight in certain parts of the country.

Strong, steady winds can be put to work turning windmill blades. As the blades spin, they turn a shaft that generates electricity. These modern wind turbines come in several shapes. Large groups of them are called wind farms. The windmills of a wind farm can power generators to produce electricity for hundreds of homes.

FACT FILE

The principle of the windmill has been known since ancient times, but little is known of its use before the 12th century. They were used to pump water for livestock, household use, or for irrigation.

WHY ARE SOLAR PANELS ATTACHED TO ROOF TOPS?

There is always a constant search for new sources of energy. The Sun gives out vast amounts of energy, of which only a tiny fraction reaches the Earth. If we could use just a small part of this energy it would fulfil all the world's foreseeable needs for power. One way of

harnessing the Sun's power is by using solar panels. Today a number of houses generate some of their own power. Solar panels attached to rooftops absorb the Sun's energy which is later used to heat domestic water supplies. The first solar power station was built in 1969 at Odeillo in France. It uses solar power to generate energy and has many solar panels to collect as much energy from the Sun as possible. One day scientists hope to collect sunlight in space and beam it back to Earth.

FACT FILE

The Sun's rays heat water in a pipe system within the solar panels. Cold water enters the pipes and flows through the panel, heating up as it goes. Hot water is collected from the pipes and stored for future use.

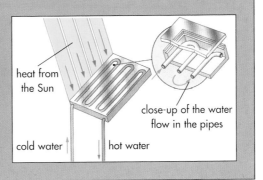

heat from the Sun

close-up of the water flow in the pipes

cold water   hot water

WHY DO SHIPS' NAVIGATORS RELY ON MICROWAVES?

Microwaves are a form of radiation. They can pass through things that would block ordinary radio waves, such as rain and fog. Microwaves can also be focused and sent in a narrow beam, making them very useful for transmitting radio messages over long distances.

Ships use these microwaves for navigation purposes. They have a radar screen which uses microwave radiation to detect distant objects. The microwaves usually scan round in a circle, and the echoes sent back produce an image on the screen.

A radar screen using microwaves

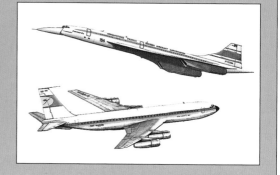

FACT FILE

Air traffic controllers use the same system for keeping track of aircraft to pinpoint exactly where they are. It is important to see that planes are kept safely apart and are guided correctly during take-off and landing.

WHY DOES LIGHTNING FLASH?

As the atmosphere heats and cools, it expands and contracts, causing changes in pressure and air movement. Water droplets inside clouds have a positive electrical charge at the top of the cloud and a negative charge at the bottom. When the negative charge comes near enough to an attracting positive charge on the Earth below or on another cloud, the electrical energy is released in a flash of light. There may also be a loud bang, called thunder, at the same time. This is caused by the air being heated to a tremendous temperature, and the explosive noise is when it expands suddenly. However, as light travels faster through the air than sound, we see the lightning flash before hearing the thunder.

WHY DO WE NEED OIL?

Fossil fuels, which include oil, coal and natural gas, were formed millions of years ago when prehistoric plants and animals died. Their decaying bodies were pressed under layers of rock and earth and became fossilized. Life as we know it today would not be possible without fossil fuels. Not only are they burned to supply heat and energy to our homes and industry, but by forming the fuel for power stations, they also supply most of the electricity we use. Also fossil fuels can be processed to produce many other useful materials, including plastics, dyes and bitumen.

Geologists know what kinds of rocks are likely to contain or cover oil deposits. When they find a likely area on land or at sea, test drilling is carried out to find out if there is any oil beneath the surface.

drill

FACT FILE

Helicopters are an oilrig's lifeline. They not only bring workers food and supplies but they can also airlift a person to hospital should they have an accident or be taken ill.

WHY DO OIL RIGS SOMETIMES CATCH FIRE?

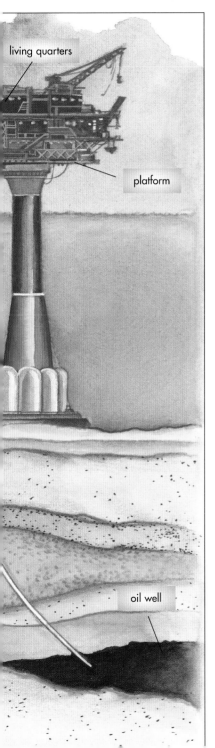

living quarters

platform

oil well

FACT FILE

The carbon and hydrogen in oil can be made to join up in different ways to make more than half a million things. One of these things is petrol which is the most common fuel used to power our cars.

Much of the world's oil is found buried beneath the seabed. Oil rigs are huge floating devices that are anchored to the seabed while wells are drilled into the oil-bearing rocks. These self-contained rigs contain all of the drilling machinery and a helicopter pad for receiving supplies.

When the oil is extracted from the rock it contains a large amount of gas which has to be burnt off at the surface. The gas gushing from an oil well can come out at great force and should this get ignited the resulting fire burns far too fiercely to be put out with water or normal fire extinguishers. Instead, firefighters use a special crane to position an explosive device in the flames. It may seem strange to fight a fire with an explosion, but when the explosion occurs, it takes the surrounding oxygen, temporarily depriving the fire and putting it out.

WHY IS STEEL AN IMPORTANT MATERIAL?

Iron has a lot of carbon in it which makes it crack very easily. If some carbon is removed, iron turns into super-strong steel. An enormous range of items can be made from steel, from tiny paperclips to huge girders forming the frames for skyscrapers. One very useful property of steel is that it can be recycled and used over and over again. Steel is the most important ingredient for making cars. Most screws, nails, nuts and bolts are made of steel and the huge cranes that make modern construction possible are built of steel. Also steel girders form the skeleton of new buildings.

FACT FILE

Stainless steel contains small amounts of nickel and chromium to make a metal that does not corrode. Many everyday things are made of stainless steel such as: cutlery, taps, sewing pins and needles and scissors.

WHY ARE BLAST FURNACES USED?

Iron is the most widely used of all metals. It is cheap and very strong, so it can be used to make the supports for huge buildings and bridges. Smelting is what is known as a reduction reaction. It is a method of extracting iron from iron ore. The process of smelting takes place in something called a blast furnace, as pictured above. The blast furnace gets its name from the hot air that is blasted into it. This is where iron ore, limestone and coke (a form of carbon) are heated together while hot air is blasted into the furnace. The carbon in the coke reacts with the oxygen in the air to form carbon monoxide. This in turn takes oxygen from the iron ore, leaving behind iron mixed with a little carbon. The temperature inside the furnaces reaches 2000°C.

FACT FILE

Alloys of steel, in which steel is combined with other metals, can be very useful. Railway tracks are made of an alloy of steel and manganese.

WHY ARE THE WRIGHT BROTHERS REMEMBERED?

People had been flying in small airships, but there was a race on to make the first successful aeroplane. The Wright Brothers were the first people to invent a practical aeroplane that could be flown under full control. Their first flight took place in 1903 at Kitty Hawk in the United States.

The Wright biplane looked like a huge box kite, with a home-made engine that drove two propellers by means of chains. It was however a practical and successful aircraft as it flew and it was controllable, unlike an earlier steam-powered aeroplane flown in 1890 by Clément Adler in France.

FACT FILE

Frank Whittle designed the first true jet engine between 1928 and 1930, but it was not used to fly a jet aircraft until 1941. A German engineer, Hans von Ohain, began work on a similar jet engine in 1936. His engine had flown a Heinkel aircraft by the year 1939.

WHY IS HELICOPTER FLIGHT NOT A MODERN DISCOVERY?

FACT FILE

The hovercraft is an ingenious machine that rides on a cushion of air. It looks like a flat-bottomed ship and is powered by huge propellers.

Leonardo da Vinci (1452–1519) drew his plans for a helicopter hundreds of years before people were first able to fly. Helicopters are lifted into the air by their large rotating propellers or rotors. These work like narrow wings, generating lift as they spin rapidly through the air. It climbs by increasing the angle of the rotor blades. It moves forward by increasing the angle of the blade moving back on every rotation so that it pushes against the air.

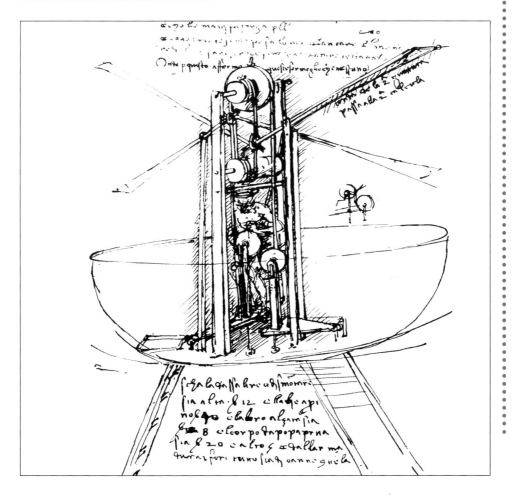

WHY ARE SUNDIALS USED?

The sun was man's first clock. Long ago men guessed at the time of day by watching the Sun as it moved across the sky. Then men noticed that the shadow changed length and moved during the day. They found they could tell the time more accurately by watching shadows than by looking at the Sun. From this it was an easy step to inventing the sundial. The first sundials were probably just poles stuck into the ground, with stones placed around the pole to mark the position of the shadow. Sundials have been in use for many centuries and are still in use today

FACT FILE

After the invention of sundials, other means of telling the time indoors were developed, such as hourglasses and burning candles. The invention of clocks allowed far more accurate timekeeping.

A sundial

WHY DO WE NEED TO MEASURE TIME?

People have always organized their lives by the passing of time. The earliest hunters had to hunt during the hours of daylight. When farming had developed, it was important for farmers to understand the seasons in order to plant their crops at the right time.

Long ago, people realized that the movement of the Sun allowed them to recognize the time of day.

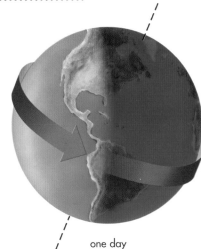

one day

They also realized that the movement of the Moon was regular and could be used to give measurements of roughly one month. Modern life is governed much more by time, and we now depend on highly accurate clocks to measure every second of the day.

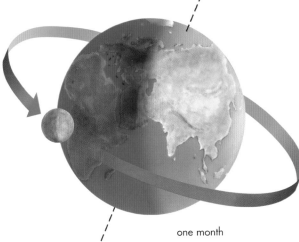

one month

FACT FILE

Modern timepieces are often digital. Such clocks contain electronic circuits which receive digital signals. The clocks receive the signals in binary code which it can understand.

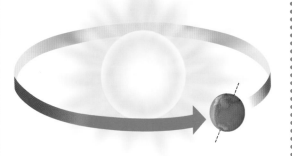

one year

WHY DO BOATS HAVE SAILS?

Nearly three-quarters of the Earth's surface is covered by water, most of it in the seas and oceans. For thousands of years people have been finding ways to cross this water. At first they built rafts, and boats with oars, but around 2900 BC, the Egyptians began to use sails. From then on, sailing ships ruled the seas until a century ago. Today, big ships have engines, but small sailing ships are used for sport, fishing and local trade.

Of course sailing ships are reliant on the wind to power them. Sailors are unable to change the direction of the wind, but they can change the direction of their sailing boats by steering a zigzag course, called tacking.

FACT FILE

Yacht racing is a very popular sport these days. In yacht racing it is very often the efficiency with which a boat tacks, compared with its competitors, that makes it a winner.

WHY DO CARS HAVE ENGINES?

The very first vehicle able to run on the open road was powered by steam. However, it was not until the development of the internal combustion engine in the second half of the nineteenth century that motor transport began to be successful.
Internal combustion engines are usually fuelled by petrol or diesel. This fuel is burnt (or combusted) within metal cylinders. The burning fuel causes a piston to move up and down inside each cylinder. It is this upward and downward movement that is translated into a turning movement by the crankshaft, causing the axles and wheels to turn and the car to move forward. The engine also powers an alternator which generates electrical current. This current is stored in the battery and is used for the car's lights, windscreen wipers, radio and other features such as electric windows.

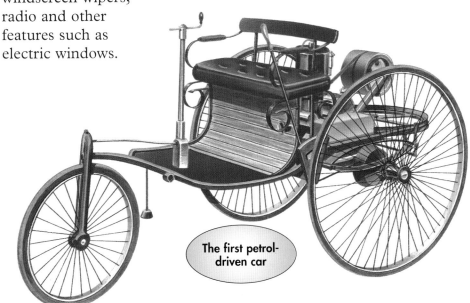

The first petrol-driven car

FACT FILE

Most petrol engines are quite noisy and give off harmful fumes. Quieter and cleaner electric cars are now being designed. However their batteries need continually recharging so they are only used for short distances.

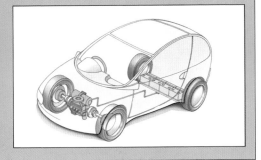

WHY IS FIRE SO HOT?

The answer to this question is really in the fire itself. Fire is a chemical reaction that occurs very quickly and gives off heat and light. The most common is the chemical action between oxygen and a fuel. If heat and light are given off, you have a fire. To make a fire, three things are necessary. The first is a fuel, the second is oxygen and the third thing is heat. Paper or wood that is simply exposed to air does not catch fire. When the fuel becomes hot enough, oxygen can begin to combine freely with it and then it will burst into flames. Every fuel has its own particular temperature at which it begins to burn. This temperature is called the kindling temperature or flash point of the fuel. When something catches fire, it is very important to bring the flames under control as soon as possible. This is especially true when a building catches fire.

FACT FILE

Firefighters need to wear protective clothing that does not conduct heat easily and therefore will not catch fire easily. Fireproof clothing often has a shiny surface, because this helps to reflect the radiated heat away from the body.

WHY CAN WAX BE BOTH NATURAL AND SYNTHETIC?

Wax can be obtained from many fruits, vegetables and plants. Waxes are also produced by animals and are found in minerals and petroleum. There are also synthetic, or man-made waxes. We acquire wax from many different sources.

Carnauba wax is obtained from the leaves of the carnauba palm tree of Brazil. It is a brown wax used in records, floor dressings and candles. Bayberry wax, from the berries of the shrub, is also used for making candles. Worker bees secrete wax that they use in making their honeycombs. This is used in making cosmetics, church candles, polishes, crayons and artificial flowers. Wool wax from wool-bearing animals is called lanolin and it used in some ointments, cosmetics and soaps.

More than 90 per cent of all commercial wax used today is petroleum wax. It has a wide variety of uses because it is odourless, tasteless and chemically inactive.

FACT FILE

Inside a hive, the bees store their honey in a network of wax which is called a honeycomb. Each one is made up of thousands of little six-sided cells. The bees feed on the honey during the cold winter months.

WHY IS ARCHIMEDES REMEMBERED?

Archimedes was a Greek mathematician who lived between about 287 and 212 BC. Archimedes believed in making experiments to prove that his theories worked. He made practical inventions such as the Archimedean screw which is still used today to lift water for irrigation. He also worked out the laws which govern the use of levers and pulleys.

Perhaps the most famous thing he is remembered for is when he jumped out of his bath and ran naked through the streets shouting 'Eureka!' which means 'I've found it!' in English. Whether this story is true or not, he did find that an object displaces its own weight of water when floating or submerged.

FACT FILE

Luigi Galvani (1737–1798) was an Italian scientist. He accidentally noticed that severed frogs' legs twitched when the nerve was touched with a pair of metal scissors during a thunderstorm.

The Archimedian Screw

WHY IS EINSTEIN REMEMBERED?

Albert Einstein (1879–1955) was a physicist who was born in Germany. He developed the theory of relativity, which led to the famous equation $E = mc^2$ (which very few people actually understand). Einstein's work is the basis for most of the modern theories about nature, history and the structure of the Universe. He laid down the rules that govern objects moving close to the speed of light, and explained why travel at this sort of speed could distort time itself. His work also proved invaluable in the development of the atomic bomb. He is remembered as one of the greatest scientists of our time.

FACT FILE

Benjamin Franklin (1706–1790) was an American with many talents. He was a printer, scientist and politician who played an important part in founding the United States. He developed lightning rods to protect buildings from storms.

WHY MUST THE PYRAMID BUILDERS HAVE BEEN GOOD MATHEMATICIANS?

FACT FILE

Mathematical formulae must have been used in the building of pyramids. An example is the Pythagoras Theorem below, a formula for calculating one side of a right-angled triangle, if the other two sides are known.

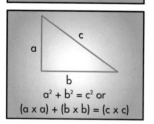

$a^2 + b^2 = c^2$ or
$(a \times a) + (b \times b) = (c \times c)$

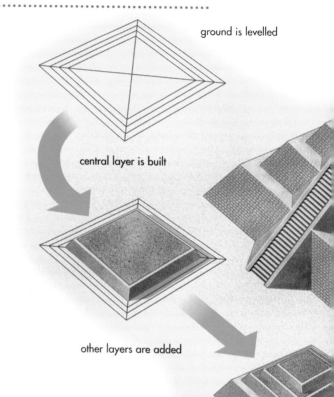

ground is levelled

central layer is built

other layers are added

The Egyptians were building massive pyramids almost 5,000 years ago. We are still not sure how they achieved this without the mechanical lifting and cutting equipment that we have today, but the answer must be that they used huge numbers of slaves to shape and haul the enormous stones with which they were built. Recently, scientists have calculated that as many as 10,000 slaves were probably needed to work on one of these structures.

The shape of a pyramid, which is a three-dimensional figure with flat faces, is called a polyhedron. These huge structures were very carefully designed and constructed. It is clear that the builders must have had a very good knowledge of mathematics to be able to build and measure these vast pyramids with such accuracy.

WHY DO WE NEED NUMBERS?

The building of pyramids

finished pyramid

the layers are built up

Numbers are used to describe the amount of things. We can express numbers in words, by hand gestures or in writing, using symbols or numerals. When we talk about a number we use words (five) rather than the number (5), but when we write we use both words and numerals. Numbers can describe how many objects there are, or their position among lots of objects, for example, 1st or 5th.

Other types of numbers describe how many units of something there are, for example how many kilograms (weight) or metres (length). Numbers are just a convenient way of describing ideas.

FACT FILE				
Roman numerals are still used today for certain purposes. They appear on watch and clock faces and when numbers have a certain importance, such as in the title of a monarch.	I	1	VIII	8
	II	2	IX	9
	III	3	X	10
	IV	4	XX	20
	V	5	L	50
	VI	6	C	100
	VII	7	M	1000

EARTH

AND SPACE

CONTENTS

WHY IS THERE NO LIFE ON OTHER PLANETS?

Planet of Jupiter

We are not completely sure that there is no form of life on any of the other planets and that is one of the things that space exploration is trying to find out.

But we do know that for life to exist, certain conditions must be present. All living things require certain things like light, water, food, oxygen and the right temperature.

But do all these conditions necessary for life exist on any other planet? It does not seem that way, judging by what we know so far about conditions on the other planets.

Venus is more like Earth than any other planet, but the surface is approximately 800°F. Life as we know it could not exist there.

Planets like Jupiter and Saturn are covered by very thick layers of clouds made up of gases that are poisonous to us. Each planet seems to have some conditions that either make life impossible or do not have the conditions necessary for life.

FACT FILE

Mars is a planet that is covered by a stony desert that contains lots of iron oxide. This makes it appear to be a rusty-red colour. The water and oxygen this planet once had are now locked in the rusty iron deposits.

WHY IS GRAVITY ON EARTH NOT THE SAME IN SPACE?

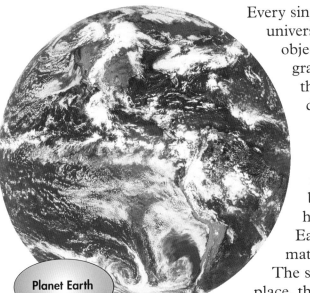

Planet Earth

Every single object in the universe pulls on every other object. This is called gravitation, or gravity. But the strength of that pull depends on two things. Firstly let's take a human being on Earth. The Earth has more matter than the human being, so its gravity pulls him to the Earth. But the Earth behaves as if all its matter were at its centre. The strength of gravity at any place, therefore, depends on the distance from the Earth's centre.

The strength of gravity is far greater at the seashore than at the top of a mountain. Supposing a human being goes some distance up into the air away from the Earth, the pull of the Earth's gravity will be even weaker.

When people go out into space, they are away from the Earth's gravitational field. There is no pull at all. They are in a condition of weightlessness. And this is why, in rockets and space capsules, weightless astronauts and objects float about in the air.

FACT FILE

Although it might seem that gravity carries food and drink down our throats, astronauts are able to eat and drink perfectly well in zero gravity. This is because it is the muscular contractions of the gullet that actually transport food and drink into the stomach.

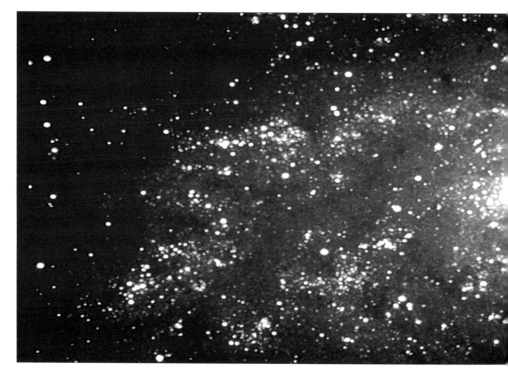

WHY DO STARS TWINKLE?

Most stars burn steadily and if we could see them from space they would not actually be twinkling at all.

As the light from a star passes through the Earth's atmosphere, it is bent by changes in the air temperature. This makes the light appear to flicker. Because of this effect observatories for studying the stars are situated on mountain-tops. The reason for this is because the higher up you go, the air becomes thinner and it is less likely to cause the twinkling effect.

FACT FILE

Sometimes a giant star explodes and is blown to pieces. This is called a supernova. A supernova explosion sometimes results in a pulsar. A pulsar is a rapidly spinning star that gives off pulses of radio waves.

WHY ARE GALAXIES DIFFERENT SHAPES?

A galaxy is an enormous group of stars which is held together by the force of gravity. Our own galaxy is called the Milky Way and this is in the shape of a spiral. There are possibly as many as 100 billion galaxies in the universe. Many of them are grouped together in clusters with huge areas of space between them and consequently form many irregular shapes.

FACT FILE

The Milky Way is a huge disc-shaped collection of billion of stars and interstellar debris. Most of these stars cannot be seen with the naked eye but their combined light produces a huge milky-looking path across the night sky.

WHY DO WE NEED SPACE STATIONS?

Space stations are usually made up of several modules that are sent into orbit one at a time, and then assembled once in space. Space stations allow the crew to work in space for long periods of time in conditions of zero gravity. While conditions in space capsules and the space shuttle are cramped, space stations are adapted for longer stays in space. Rockets or the space shuttle bring supplies of air and food to the space station and often a replacement crew.

Some space stations, such as the Russian Mir, stayed up for many years and their crews remained in space for months at a time.

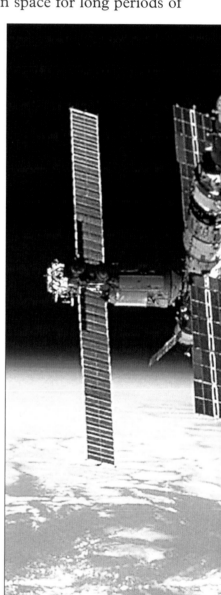

FACT FILE

If you blow up a balloon and let it go without tying a knot in the neck, the air will rush out very quickly. When the air goes out one way it pushes the balloon the other way – just like a rocket!

WHY ARE SPACE PROBES IMPORTANT IN SPACE EXPLORATION?

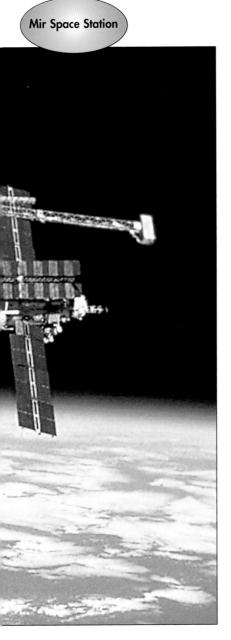

Mir Space Station

Space probes are small packages of instruments that are launched from the Earth to explore planets. Probes have landed small instrument capsules on Mars and Venus. They take photographs or test the atmosphere of a planet. Some probes use the gravity of other planets to extend their voyages. They pass close by a planet, using its gravity to swing around it and be hurled off towards another planet. Using this very technique the Voyager 2 space probe was able to visit Jupiter, Saturn, Uranus and Neptune. Probes do not have their own rocket power apart from tiny thrusters for steering.

WHY DO ASTRONAUTS NEED TO WEAR SPACESUITS?

A spacesuit is all that stands between an astronaut on a space walk and the emptiness of space. It must supply all his or her needs. There is no breathable atmosphere in space so a spacesuit supplies oxygen to the astronaut.

Within the helmet, headphones and a microphone enable the astronaut to communicate with crew members and mission control. All the joins in the spacesuit must be absolutely airtight. Inside the suit is pressurized like a deep-sea diver's suit. The visor and outer layer of the suit must be tough enough not to be torn or cracked by tiny meteorites that may bounce off the astronaut. A specially treated dark visor protects the astronaut's eyes from the glare of the Sun, while lights can illuminate dark areas.

FACT FILE

As well as supplying air to breathe, space suits have to remove moisture breathed out by the astronaut, so the clear face-place of the suit is not misted up by the cold of space.

WHY DO WE LAUNCH SATELLITES INTO SPACE?

Space satellites have revolutionized communication, making possible everyday developments such as mobile phones and television. Satellites receive signals beamed at them from the Earth and send them on to other places. They are also used in defence communications for checking on the movement of military forces. Satellites can also survey the surface of the Earth, predict weather changes and track hurricanes.

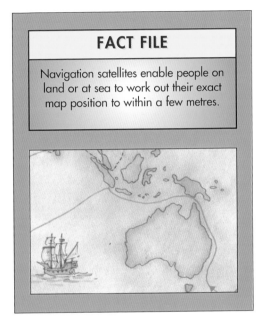

FACT FILE

Navigation satellites enable people on land or at sea to work out their exact map position to within a few metres.

WHY DOES THE MOON SHINE?

There is no mystery at all as to why the Moon shines. The Moon is a satellite of the Earth. That means it is a small body that revolves around it, just as the Earth revolves around the Sun.

The only reason we can see the Moon from Earth, or that it appears to 'shine', is because light from the Sun strikes its surface and is reflected to us. Strangely enough we can only see one side of the Moon from the Earth. This is because the Moon rotates on its axis in the same length of time it takes for it to make its journey around the Earth.

Since the Moon has no atmosphere, or air, the light from the Sun causes rather interesting effects. For about fourteen days, the surface of the Moon is heated by the direct rays of the Sun to a temperature above that of boiling water. The other half of the lunar month, it is exposed to the cold of a long, dark night.

FACT FILE

Eclipses happen for a brief period when the Moon, Earth and Sun are in line. A lunar eclipse happens when the Earth lies between the Moon and the Sun, blocking off the light to the Moon, so that the Moon seems to vanish.

new moon

first quarter

full moon

WHY DOES THE MOON FOLLOW US WHEN WE DRIVE?

The Moon doesn't look as if it is very far away, but its distance from the Earth is about 239,000 miles. It is this great distance that explains why the Moon seems to follow us when we drive in a car and look up at it.

To begin with, our feeling that this is happening is just that, only a feeling, a psychological reaction. When we speed along a road, we notice that everything moves past us. Trees, houses, fences, the road – they all fly past us in the opposite direction. But when we look at the Moon we naturally expect it also to be flying past us, or at least to be moving backwards as we speed ahead. When this doesn't happen, we have the sensation that it is following us. In fact we could go along a straight path for miles and the angle at which we would see the Moon would basically be the same.

The Moon

FACT FILE

The ebbing and flowing of tides are made by the Sun and Moon pulling on the oceans. When the Sun, Earth and Moon are in a line, there are large spring tides.

WHY ARE ASTEROIDS LIKE SMALL PLANETS?

Asteroids are smaller than any of the planets and only a few have a diameter of over 30 kilometres. Asteroids are small rocky or icy bodies that orbit the Sun. They are sometimes called minor planets. Most asteroids are found in an orbit between Mars and Jupiter, and more than 7,000 of them have been identified.

The term asteroid is usually applied to objects that are larger than 1.6 kilometres in diameter. One asteroid, called Ida, has a tiny moon all of its own. This is the smallest known satellite in the Solar System. Asteroids were probably formed at the same time as the planets.

FACT FILE

Many asteroids have struck the Earth already, and many scientists believe that such an impact resulted in the extinction of the dinosaurs about 65 million years ago.

WHY DO METEORS SOMETIMES CRASH INTO THE EARTH?

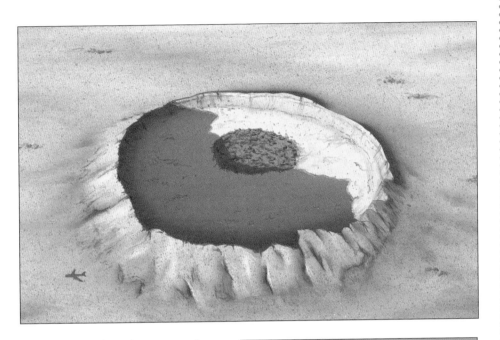

If a lump of rock or metal burns up before it reaches the ground, it is called a meteor or a shooting star. A large meteor that does not burn up as it plunges through the Earth's atmosphere is called a meteorite. It travels so fast it shatters into pieces as it hits the ground. It causes huge shock waves as it lands. The impact crater in the picture above is to be found at Wolf Creek, Australia, and was caused by a huge meteorite or small asteroid. The amount of energy released would be equivalent to hundreds of nuclear weapons.

FACT FILE

The asteroid belt lies between the orbits of Mars and Jupiter.
It is thought that this may be the shattered remains of a planet that has been destroyed by Jupiter's enormous gravity.

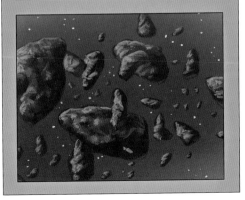

WHY DO NEBULAE EXIST?

Without nebulae stars would not exist in our skies. A nebula is a huge cloud of gas and material that appears to be solid. However, it is mostly composed of dust and gas, slowly condensing into stars.

Stars come into existence in the vast clouds of dust and gas that move through space. A star begins to form when a large number of gas particles whirl together within such a cloud. The whirling particles attract more particles, and as the group of particles slowly gets larger and larger, its gravitational pull gets stronger. The particles form a giant ball of gas.

As the ball grows larger, the particles press down on those below them and pressure builds up inside the ball. Finally the pressure becomes strong enough to raise the temperature of the gases, and the gases begin to glow. When the pressure and temperature inside the ball get very high, nuclear reactions begin to take place and form a star.

FACT FILE

A black hole is not really a hole but a very tightly-packed object. It is solid and does not reflect any light, so it looks like a hole!

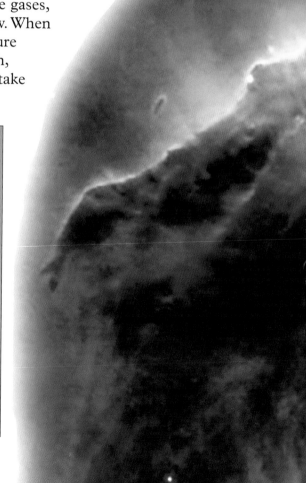

WHY DO STARS DIE?

Stars are huge balls of burning gas that are scattered throughout the Universe. They burn for millions of years, giving off both light and heat. Stars die when they eventually use up all their fuel and burn out. This process may take millions of years.

Towards the end of its life a star starts to run out of hydrogen to power its nuclear fusion. It starts to cool, becoming a red giant. The red giant swells, and the pressure at its centre becomes so great that the star begins to absorb energy instead of emitting it. In a matter of seconds the star collapses, then explodes into a supernova. This is a huge explosion of light and energy that can be seen right across the galaxy.

FACT FILE

In the night sky, all stars appear to be the same size. In fact, they are all different sizes. Some are much bigger than the Sun; others are much smaller than the Earth. The most common stars are the same size as the Sun.

A Nebula

WHY DO WE HAVE NIGHT AND DAY?

As the Earth spins on its axis, the Sun always shines on one side giving us daylight. On the shaded side it is night time. As the Earth continues to turn, the shaded side moves into the Sun's light, and the sunlit side turns away from the light. It takes 24 hours for the Earth to make one complete turn on its axis and our clocks are based on this principle.

In the 1940s people discovered that the Earth speeds up and slows down a little as it spins. We have now developed atomic clocks that can measure time exactly.

FACT FILE

The Earth's axis is an imaginary line through the centre of the Earth. This is what the Earth spins around. You can think of the axis as being a stick pushed through the middle of an orange.

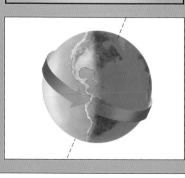

WHY DO WE HAVE SEASONS?

We have seasons because the Earth is tilted on its axis. As the Earth moves round the Sun, the hemisphere tilted towards the Sun receives more sunlight, and this is summer time. The days are longer and the weather is warmer because of the extra amount of sunlight. The hemisphere tilted away from the Sun receives less sunshine, has shorter days and is cooler. This is winter time. The area near to the Equator is always exposed to the Sun's rays, so it is warm all the year round. This means that there is little difference between the seasons.

FACT FILE

Coloured sunsets happen when light is scattered by dust and water particles in the air, as the Sun sets. The farther the light has to pass through the air, the more likely it is to be scattered causing the red colouration.

WHY IS THE SKY BLUE?

As the Sun's light passes through the atmosphere, its rays are scattered by tiny particles of pollen, soot and dust to be found there. As blue light is scattered most, the sky appears blue. At sunset and sunrise, sunlight has further to travel to reach us. Only red light can be seen because the blue light has been absorbed by the atmosphere.

FACT FILE

The amount of rain which falls is known as precipitation. This diagram shows the average annual precipitation level of the continents of the world

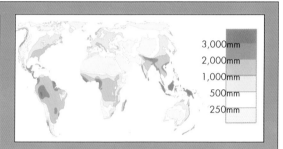

3,000mm
2,000mm
1,000mm
500mm
250mm

WHY DON'T ALL CLOUDS PRODUCE RAIN?

A cloud is just an accumulation of mist. There is always water vapour in the air but during the summer there is more because the temperature is higher. It takes only a slight drop in temperature to make water vapour condense in air full of moisture. So when saturated warm air rises to an altitude where the temperature is lower, condensation takes place and we have a cloud. The droplets of water in a cloud have weight, so gravity gradually pulls them down and they sink lower and lower. As most of them fall, they reach a warmer layer of air, and this warmer air causes them to evaporate. So here we have clouds that don't produce rain.

But suppose the air beneath a cloud is not warmer, but very moist air. Naturally, the droplets won't evaporate. Instead, the droplets will get bigger and bigger as more and more condensation takes place. Pretty soon each droplet has become a drop and it continues falling downward and we have rain.

FACT FILE

Rainbows occur in the sky when drops of rain in the air act as prisms to split the light into the seven colours of the spectrum. This usually happens just after a fall of rain.

WHY DO VOLCANOES ERUPT?

At about two miles below the surface of the Earth the temperature is high enough to boil water. If it were possible to dig down 30 miles, the temperature would be about 2,200 degrees fahrenheit. This is hot enough even to melt rocks. At the centre of the Earth scientists believe that the temperature could be as high as 10,000 degrees fahrenheit.

When rock melts, it expands and needs more space. When the pressure is greater than the roof of rock above it, it bursts out causing an eruption. When the volcano erupts it throws out hot, gaseous liquid called lava or solid particles that look like cinders and ash. The material piles up around the opening and a cone-shaped mound is formed.

FACT FILE

A *dormant* volcano is one that is actually 'sleeping'. A dormant volcano might erupt in the future. An *extinct* volcano, on the other hand, will not become active again.

WHY ARE VOLCANIC BOMBS DANGEROUS?

A major volcanic eruption can send boulders flying high into the air. These boulders, called volcanic bombs, can be very large. Most of the material thrown of the erupting volcano is ash, which forms a huge cloud. Steam and sulphurous gases are also released and these can be extremely dangerous to bystanders.

On August 24, in the year AD 79, Mount Vesuvius, a volcano in Italy, violently erupted. The lava, stones, and ashes thrown up by the volcano completely buried two nearby towns.

FACT FILE

Krakatau, Indonesia was a volcanic island which had been dormant for over two centuries. In 1883, a huge volcanic eruption occurred, destroying two-thirds of the island.

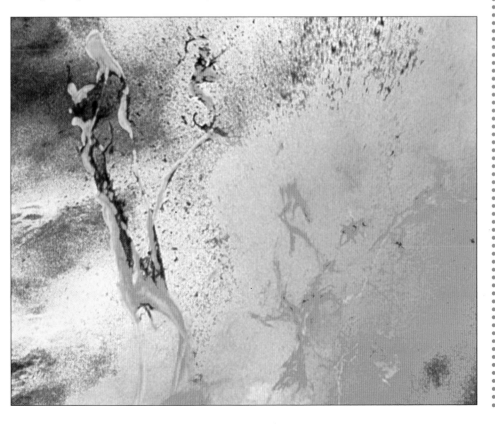

WHY IS THE PACIFIC PLATE ALWAYS MOVING?

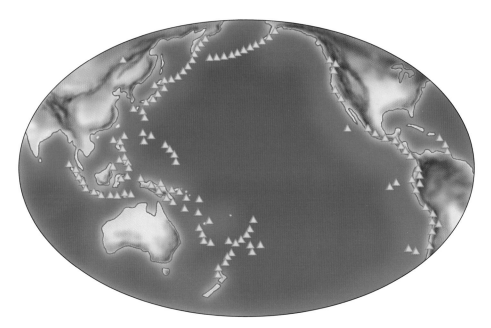

The Earth's crust is not one unbroken piece. It is made up of many pieces that fit together like a giant jigsaw puzzle. These pieces, called plates, ride on soft, partly melted rock moving underneath them. The pieces push against each other with spectacular effects. Earthquakes split the Earth's crust, volcanoes are formed, new land is made, and huge mountain ranges are pushed skywards.

The plates are never still, they are always moving. In one year alone they can move about 2.5 centimetres, about as much as your fingernails grow in the same amount of time.

FACT FILE

When water seeps into the ground and reaches hot rock, it boils violently. This produces steam which can shoot the water out of cracks, causing a geyser. Geysers can be very spectacular and some shoot water as high as 500 metres into the air.

WHY IS GERARDUS MERCATOR REMEMBERED?

FACT FILE

A map must be as easy to read as possible, which means that symbols and colours can often give more information than words. A key explains what the symbols and colours mean.

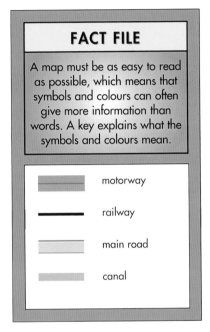

motorway

railway

main road

canal

Gerhard Kremer (1512–94) was called Gerardus Mercator, meaning merchant, because he made maps for merchants travelling from country to country. In 1569 he made a world map using a projection that has come to be known as Mercator's projection.

It is not possible to draw the curved surface of the globe accurately on a flat sheet of paper. He showed how to convert the rounded shape of the world into a cylindrical shape, which could be unrolled to make a flat map. However, this can distort the size of countries in the far north and south. But by dividing the Earth into 'orange peel' segments it gave a truer image of the size of the countries.

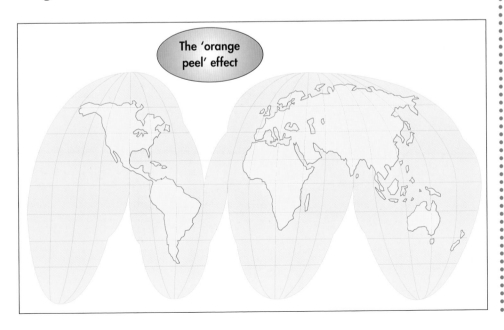

The 'orange peel' effect

WHY IS THE OCEAN SALTY?

Every now and then we come across a fact about our Earth which mystifies us and for which no answer has yet been found. Such a fact is the existence of salt in the oceans. The answer is we simply don't know how the salt got into the ocean. We do know that salt is water-soluble and so passes into the oceans with rain water. The salt of the Earth's surface is constantly being dissolved and is passing into the ocean.

If all the oceans were to dry up, enough salt would be left to build a wall 180 miles high and a mile thick. Such a wall would reach once around the world at the equator. The common salt which we all use is produced from sea water or the water of salt lakes, from salt springs, and from deposits of rock salt. The concentration of salt in sea water ranges from about three per cent to three-and-one-half per cent. The Dead Sea which covers an area of about 340 square miles, contains about 11,600,000,000 tons of salt.

FACT FILE

The Earth has five oceans. These are the Pacific, Atlantic, Indian, Arctic and Antarctic. In addition, there are several substantial seas such as the Mediterranean and the Black Sea.

WHY WERE THE FIRST EXPLORERS SO PIONEERING?

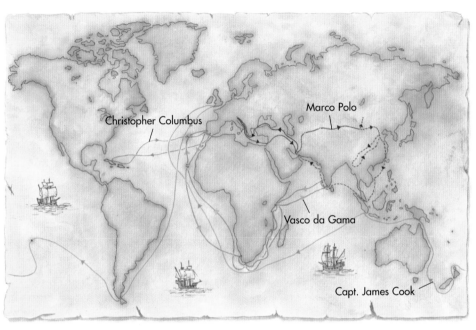

Christopher Columbus

Marco Polo

Vasco da Gama

Capt. James Cook

FACT FILE

In 1492 Christopher Columbus set out to find a new route to India and the Far East, in order to open up trading links for Spain. He arrived at the Bahamas, off the American coast, where he mistakenly called the native people 'Indians'.

About 50,000 years ago, the first explorers sailed from Southeast Asia to colonize Australia and New Guinea, which were joined together at that time. Later on, people crossed from Siberia into Alaska, passing over a land bridge that has since disappeared.

Marco Polo began his voyage to China in 1271. He reached his destination but parts of his journey (shown above with a dotted line) are in doubt. Christopher Columbus discovered Cuba and Haiti in 1492. In 1497 Vasco da Gama set out to find a sea route to India by sailing around the southern tip of Africa. Captain James Cook made three voyages to the South Seas. During his first voyage he discovered Australia.

WHY IS THERE FOG OVER WATER?

Fog, dew and clouds are all related. In order for fog to form, the moisture must leave the air and condense. this means it must be cooled in some way, because cooler air cannot hold as much moisture as warm air. When the air is cooled below a certain point, called the dew or saturation point, then fog starts to form.
One of the conditions in which fog forms is when a mass of warm air passes over a cold area of water. Or it could be the opposite, with cold air passing over warm water. The currents of warm and cold air mix gently and you get those familiar fogs which seem to hang in mid-air over a body of water.

FACT FILE

Tiny water droplets condensing from moist air cause both mist and fog. Mist is not as dense as fog. It commonly occurs on calm, clear nights when heat rises. This forms a thin layer of mist close to the ground.

WHY IS SNOW WHITE?

Snow is actually frozen water, and as we know ice has no colour, why then is the snow white? The reason is that each snowflake is made up of a large number of ice crystals. These crystals have many surfaces. It is the reflection of light from all of these surfaces that makes snow look white.

Snow forms when water vapour in the atmosphere freezes. As the vapour freezes, clear transparent crystals are formed. The currents that are in the air makes these crystals go up and down in the atmosphere.

FACT FILE

The Inuit people live in the icy lands of the Arctic North. They were self-sufficient and lived a life on the move, hunting and fishing to survive. They built homes, called igloos, out of solid snow.

WHY DO WE STILL HAVE GLACIERS TODAY?

The great ice mass that began the Ice Age in North America has been called 'a continental glacier'. It was possibly about 15,000 feet thick in its centre. This great glacier probably formed and then melted away at least four times during the Ice Age. The Ice Age or glacial period that took place in other parts of the world still has not had a chance to melt away. For example, the big island of Greenland is still covered with a continental glacier, except for a narrow fringe around its edge. So the reason we still have glaciers in certain parts of the world is that they have not had a chance to melt away since the Ice Age.

FACT FILE

There are more than 1,200 glaciers in the Alps of Europe. Glaciers are also found in the Pyrenees, Carpathian and Caucasus Mountains of Europe and in southern Asia. In southern Alaska there are tens of thousnads of such glaciers, some from 25 to 50 miles long.

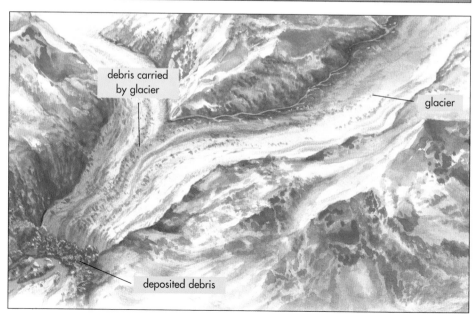

debris carried by glacier

glacier

deposited debris

WHY DO WATERFALLS EXIST?

When a stream or river plunges over a wall of rock called a cliff or a precipice, we have a waterfall. If the waterfall is of great size, it is called a cataract.

Where the rock wall is steeply slanted rather than vertical, the rushing water is called a cascade. Sometimes in a cascade, the water descends in a whole series of steep slopes.

Niagara Falls is an example of how an overhanging rock ledge can create a waterfall.

In some cases ancient glaciers cut deep into mountain valleys, leaving the sides as steep cliffs and precipices from which the waterfalls plunge down.

FACT FILE

Angel Falls in Venezuela, South America is the highest waterfall in the world. Niagara Falls and Victoria Falls have a greater volume of water, but the actual height of any fall is greatest at Angel Falls.

WHY ARE RAINFORESTS IN DANGER?

Rainforests are tropical evergreen forests. The climate is warm and moist all year round and offers an extraordinarily wide range of habitats for living things.

Rainforests are being cut down at an alarming rate for two main reasons. Both large commercial farming companies and individual families clear the forest to gain land to cultivate and graze animals. The rainforest soil, though, is not really suitable for agriculture.

Another reason the forests have been felled is to supply tropical hardwoods for furniture-making and buildings. Woods such as mahogany have been highly prized in wealthy countries for hundreds of years.

FACT FILE

Many areas of tropical rainforest are burned. The result after one or two years is useless, infertile land that is prone to flash floods. Rainwater strips away the topsoil, dumping it into rivers.

WHY IS TOO MUCH WATER BAD FOR FARM LAND?

Erosion is one of the most powerful ways in which the Earth's surface is being altered. Moving ice and flowing water wear away the surface and cut out valleys. Along the coast, tides and wave action wears away exposed cliffs, and currents carry away sand mud to be deposited elsewhere. Floodwater rapidly washes away fertile soil which can cause the loss of much fertile land. The bare ground becomes eroded because there is little vegetation to slow the run-off of rainwater.

FACT FILE

Low-level land becomes flooded very easily. It often takes months for the land to recover from flooding.

WHY IS MACHINERY IMPORTANT ON LARGE FARMS?

Machinery has made it possible for the work of a dozen farm workers to be done twice as quickly as by one worker. There are fewer people working on the land in developed countries than ever before.

Machinery also has a large effect on the environment as well, as hedges and ditches are removed to allow larger machines to work the enormous fields. Crops have also been bred for the machine age too. They need to ripen together, not over a period of time, so that machinery can harvest them in one operation.

There are still many parts of the world where traditional farming methods are used, but the use of machinery is increasing year by year.

FACT FILE

Arable farming is the growing and harvesting of crops, particularly where the ground is ploughed between harvests. Arable farming is of enormous importance to the world's population, since most of us rely on grains or vegetables for our staple foods.

WHY DOES TERRACING HELP FARMERS?

The terracing system of farming is particularly important where people have to grow their food on steep, erosion prone slopes. This agricultural system has been in use for three thousand years in hillside regions of Mexico.

Terracing slows the rate of intense rainfall runoff which often comes in bursts, thereby minimizing erosion while still conserving water. After rainfall the terraces enabled captured water to slowly percolate into the fields, making for an efficient irrigation system.

FACT FILE

Rice is the main food for over half the world's population. Bali is famed for its unique rice terraces carved into the hillside and the mountain slopes.

ANCIENT

HISTORY

CONTENTS

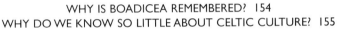

WHY DID THE FIRST HUMANS LOOK MORE LIKE APES?

Scientists believe that humans and apes had a common ancestor. About 10 million years ago, some apes left the trees to walk on the open plains. They had large brains, and used their fingers to pick up food. About 4 million years ago, the human-like ape *Australopithecus* (southern ape) lived in Africa. It probably used sticks or stones as tools, in the same way that chimpanzees do. It walked upright, had long limbs, and its body was covered with hair. The first human species was *Homo habilis* (handy man), who lived in East Africa 2 million years ago. By 1.5 million years ago, the more advanced *Homo erectus* (upright man) had appeared, and by 500,000 years ago Homo erectus had learned to make fire. They communicated in some form of language, and worked together gathering plants and hunting animals for food.

◄ Modern man

Neanderthal man ►

Upright man

FACT FILE

Neanderthals were the first humans to bury their dead. Archaeologists have found evidence of Neanderthal burial ceremonies. The remains of tools and meat have been found in the graves, showing that the dead were buried with care.

WHY WAS THE STONE AGE SO-CALLED?

The Stone Age was named because stone was the most important material used by the first tool-makers. These early stone-crafting techniques show surprising skill. Axes and scrapers were made from flint. Spear heads were shaped from deer antlers. The hand axe was probably the most important early Stone Age tool.

Stone Age people hunted with bows, spears and flint axes. On the American grasslands, groups of hunters drove to extinction large grazing animals such as mastodons and giant bison. The humans' intelligence, weapons and teamwork made up for their comparative lack of strength and speed.

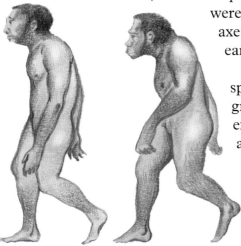

Handy man

Southern ape

FACT FILE

People discovered how to make fire by using a simple wooden stick called a fire drill. The drill was turned quickly over a piece of dry wood until it produced enough heat to start the fire.

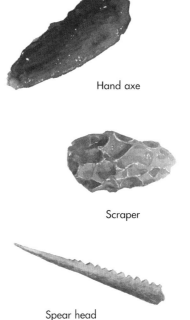

Hand axe

Scraper

Spear head

WHY DID THE ABORIGINES BELIEVE IN 'DREAM TIME'?

The Aborigines probably reached Australia overland. They lived by gathering food and hunting. Along the coast they fished with nets, basket traps and spears. In the bush they used fire to drive animals into traps and made poisons from leaves and roots to drug fish in pools. They wore no clothes and rubbed animal fats onto their bodies to protect themselves from the cold.

Aboriginal rock artists looked 'beneath the skin' to show a person's bones or organs. Paintings of people and animals are found at sites linked in Aboriginal belief to the Dream Time. This is the time when the spirits were supposed to have created the world.

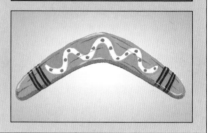

FACT FILE

The Aborigines used ritual boomerangs in magical dances, decorated with secret symbols. They were also used for hunting purposes and for war.

WHY DID CAVE PAINTERS PAINT?

Many thousands of years ago people painted pictures of bulls, horses and antelopes on the walls of their caves. We will never be sure why they actually did this – perhaps it was to make magic and bring people luck in their hunting. Another theory was that it may have been part of their religion.

Cave artists used natural paints which were made from coloured earth and plant extracts. These paints have often been hidden from view for thousands of years. Viewed by the flickering light of burning torches, as they would have been when first painted, the animals almost seem to come to life.

FACT FILE

Woolly mammoths were found painted on the walls of caves. As well as being an important source of meat, woolly mammoths provided skins for clothing and shelter. Their tusks were also carved into tools and ornaments.

WHY WERE THE PEOPLE OF MESOPOTAMIA CALLED SUMERIANS?

About 7,000 years ago, farmers began to move into an area of land between the Tigris and the Euphrates rivers. This fertile land was called Mesopotamia, in what is now called Iraq. In the south of Mesopotamia was the land known as Sumer. The Sumerians, as they became known, were a very inventive race. They developed the first form of writing and recording numbers.

The Sumerians drew pictures on soft clay with a pointed reed. The pictures were drawn downwards in lines, from the right-hand side. Later, they started to write across the tablet from left to right. The reed tip became wedge shaped, as did the marks it made.

FACT FILE

Reed houses were built using reeds cut down from the marshes around the Tigris and Euphrates rivers. The Sumerians also made canoes from these reeds.

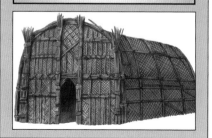

WHY IS THE INVENTION OF THE WHEEL CREDITED TO MESOPOTAMIA?

FACT FILE

The wheel was first used by the Sumerians in making pottery in about 3500 BC. Around 300 years later this invention was adapted for a startling new use – that of transportation.

The Sumerians were also credited for the revolutionary invention of the wheel and the plough. They grew bumper crops of cereals, which they traded for items they needed: wood, building stone or metals. Wheeled carts and their skills in writing helped them develop long-distance trade.

The first wheels were made of planks of solid wood held together with crosspieces. They were clumsy and heavy at the beginning. In time, lighter wheels were made; these had many spokes. The first ploughs were also made of wood with the blade made from bronze.

147

WHY WERE ATHENS AND SPARTA RIVAL STATES?

The Greeks defeating the Persians at the battle of Salamis

FACT FILE

Broken pieces of pottery were used for letter-writing in the Greek world. Clay fragments are still found today, with business notes written on them.

Athens was a rich and cultured state. Among its citizens were astronomers, mathematicians, thinkers, writers and artists. Although this was a society with slaves, the rulers had vision, and its government was the first real democracy.

Athens had the best navy in Greece while Sparta had the best army. Sparta's economy, like that of Athens, was based on slave workers but there was no democracy. Sport was encouraged, and girls as well as boys were expected to be fit and athletic. Sparta was run like an army camp, in which everyone was expected to obey. Boys as young as seven were taken from home and trained to be soldiers.

WHY WAS TRADE IMPORTANT TO THE GREEKS?

FACT FILE

Much of what we know about how the Greeks lived comes from pictures on vases.

Towns in Greece were a centre for government, religion and trade. In the marketplace farmers sold produce such as cheese, wheat, meat, eggs, sheepskins and olive oil. Fast-food sellers did a brisk lunchtime trade in sausages and pancakes. In the dusty lanes around the marketplace, skilled craftworkers carried on their businesses. They included sandal-makers, potters, tanners (who prepared animal skins), armourers, blacksmiths and jewellers. Wherever they settled, Greek farmers relied on three main crops: grapes, olives and grain. Most colonies were near the sea and fishermen sold freshly caught fish in the markets.

A Greek country house

WHY IS THE HISTORY OF AGAMEMNON'S MASK UNCLEAR?

The Myceneans were warlike people who lived in Greece, possibly from around 1900 BC. By 1600 BC they were trading in the Aegean, and after the fall of Crete they became the major power in the region. The Mycenean rulers lived in hilltop citadels overlooking cities protected by thick stone walls.

The mask of Agamemnon

The city of Mycenae was at the heart of their civilization. People entered Mycenae through the Lion Gate, a great stone gateway from which a path led straight to the royal palace. Graves of the ruling family, filled with treasure and personal possessions for the afterlife were found near the gate in AD 1876.

Weakened by interstate warfare, the Mycenean cities were destroyed and lost. During an excavation of the graves at Mycenae in the late 1800s, the so-called 'mask of Agamemnon' was uncovered. It is unclear of the origin of this mask because so much of the cities and their history were destroyed, but it is believed to be the mask of an earlier king.

FACT FILE

The Myceans had forms of writing which they used in business and government. They wrote on clay tablets and possibly also in ink on papyrus, like the Egyptians.

WHY WERE GODS SO IMPORTANT TO THE ANCIENT GREEKS?

The ancient Greeks believed in many different gods. The most important of these were a family of supernatural beings who lived on Mount Olympus and watched over humanity. Certain gods looked after the harvest; others cared for wild animals, the sea, war and so on. The Romans took over many of these Greek gods and gave them Latin names.

They believed the gods could and did interfere in human affairs, bringing success or disaster. King of the gods was Zeus, whom the Romans called Jupiter.

The Minoans, from the island of Crete in the Mediterranean Sea, favoured goddesses in their worship, including the snake goddess who protected the home.

The snake goddess

FACT FILE

According to legend, King Minos kept a half-human, half-bull called the Minotaur in his palace at Knossos.

WHY WAS THE MEGALITHIC ERA SO-CALLED?

More than 5,000 years ago Europeans were building spectacular stone monuments. Many of these are still standing today, as mysterious relics of a long-gone society.

These enormous stones are called megaliths (which literally means 'big stones'). Some were set up on their own, others in groups or in circles. Some megaliths marked the burial place of an important ruler, while others seem to have had a religious meaning.

Tall single stones (menhirs), stone slab-tombs (dolmens) and the remains of large circles of stones and wooden posts (henges) are still standing today.

Stonehenge is an example of remainders from the Megalithic era.

Stonehenge

FACT FILE

Rock tombs, slab tombs (such as this dolmen) and stone circles and temples lie scattered across Europe. Many have been discovered on the island of Malta.

WHY WAS STONEHENGE BUILT?

When we try to learn of the accomplishments of ancient man, we usually have to search or dig for evidence. But there is a case where all the evidence has been left standing in a huge structure, and we still cannot figure out what it is, what it was used for, and exactly who built it! This is Stonehenge. It is a complicated structure on the outside of which is a circular ditch, with an entrance gap.

Stonehenge was built in stages between 1800 and 1400 BC. During the second stage of building, blue stones from the Preseli mountains in Wales were hauled onto the site in an astonishing feat of organization and transport.

Local stones were added in the third stage and were up to 10 metres long and weighed 50 tonnes.

The Stonehenge builders had only stone or bronze tools to work with. They had no machines and yet they tackled huge digging works. They buried their chieftains, with treasures and food for the next world, beneath mounds of earth they called barrows.

WHY IS BOADICEA REMEMBERED?

Boadicea (Boudicca) was the queen of the Iceni, a tribe of Celts living in eastern England. Her husband was a governor, who worked with the Romans. After his death the Romans tried to take control. Boadicea led a rebellion, which sacked the towns of Colchester and London, until the Roman armies marched against her. The Romans defeated the Iceni and their Celtic allies. She is renowned for fighting from a chariot, and the Romans had to develop special tactics to combat these fast-moving warriors. Boadicea ended her own life by taking poison to avoid being captured.

FACT FILE

Celtic poetry - 'STORM AT SEA'
Tempest on the plain of Lir
Bursts its barriers far and near
And upon the rising tide
Wind and noisy winter ride
Winter throws a shining spear.

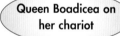

Queen Boadicea on her chariot

WHY DO WE KNOW SO LITTLE ABOUT CELTIC CULTURE?

The Celts came from central Europe, although their previous origins are unclear. Around 500 BC, perhaps to escape wars with their Germanic neighbours, they began to move westwards. Groups of people settled in what are now Spain, France, Britain and Ireland. Celts were warlike and their arrival usually led to fighting.

The Celts were artistic people. They loved stories and music, and they made beautiful jewellery and metalwork decorated with abstract designs and animal shapes.

They had no written language, passing on their legends of gods and heroes in stories around the fire. Most of what we know of the Celts today comes from the writings of their enemies, such as the Romans. The Celts themselves left a legacy of art and legend, and language: Welsh, Breton, Cornish, Irish and Scottish Gaelic are all Celtic languages.

FACT FILE

The Celts often constructed their settlements on hilltops which could be easily defended. They are identified by circular defensive ditches that still survive in former Celtic areas.

An example of Celtic art

WHY IS CONFUCIUS REMEMBERED?

Confucius

Confucius was an ancient Chinese philosopher who taught the need for moral responsibility and virtue. His teachings did not make much impact during his lifetime, but they later became the central part of Chinese moral and religious thinking.

Confucius probably lived from 551 to 479 BC, in the time of the Zhou dynasty. The Zhou was the longest-lasting group of Chinese rulers, who governed the country from 1122 to 256 BC. Confucianism was probably the most important feature in Chinese life until the appearance of Communism in the 20th century. Confucianism resembles a religion, but instead of worshipping gods it is a guide to morality and good government.

Although Confucius lived thousands of years ago, his influence in everyday life is still strong in China today.

FACT FILE

The oldest printed book known is the Diamond Sutta, a Buddhist scroll made from sheets of paper printed with woodblocks. It was made in China in AD 868.

WHY ARE THE TERRACOTTA WARRIORS FAMOUS?

In China the powerful Qin dynasty came to power in the 3rd century BC. They swiftly conquered their neighbours to make a large empire covering most of modern China. The Qin emperor Shi Huangdi standardized weights and measures and introduced a single form of currency. He is best remembered for his construction of the Great Wall of China which stretches for 2,250 km across the north of China.

When the emperor died a huge tomb was built to hold his body. It was filled with a guardian army of thousands of life-sized terracotta (or pottery) warriors. Each figure was individually modelled. The figures were placed in three pits inside the large complex surrounding the emperor's tomb.

FACT FILE

The Chinese so much admired the swift horses of the central Asian steppes that they made bronze statuettes of 'flying horses'.

157

WHY IS THE SPHINX SUCH A MYSTERY?

Religion played an important part in Egyptian life. The Egyptians believed in many gods and goddesses. Gods looked after every aspect of life. Every town and city had its own god, too. Temples were dedicated to a particular god or a dead pharaoh. Pyramids are the oldest stone structures in the world. They were built as tombs, to keep the body of the dead king safe for eternity and perhaps to ease his passage to the heavens. The Great Sphinx is a mysterious rock sculpture with a human head on the body of a lion. This was built near the pyramids, outside modern Cairo, but the exact reason is unknown. Historians believe it is older than the pyramids themselves.

FACT FILE

The sun god Ra was often portrayed simply as a sun disk. He appeared in other forms too, including a cat, a bird and a lion.

The Great Sphinx

WHY DID THE EGYPTIANS MAKE MUMMIES?

Tutankhamun

TELL ME WHY : ANCIENT HISTORY

FACT FILE

Osiris, god of the dead, was often shown as a mummy on a throne, wearing the crown of Upper Egypt.

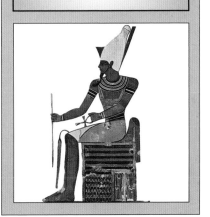

The Egyptians believed in an afterlife to which human souls journeyed after death. They thought it important that the bodies of the dead should be preserved for life in the next world, and so they developed techniques for making 'mummies'.

The dead person's organs were removed and the body was embalmed and dried, using salts and chemicals, and then wrapped in linen bandages. It was then placed inside a coffin. Even animals such as cats and monkeys were sometimes mummified. Many thousands of mummies must have been made, but only about 1,000 survive today.

Tutankhamun (pictured above) became king of Egypt at the age of nine and died when he was about 18. His tomb is one of more than 60 royal tombs around the Valley of the Kings. Its four rooms contained more than 5,000 objects which included ostrich feathers, model ships, a throne and a gold death mask.

WHY DOES JERICHO HAVE A PLACE IN JEWISH HISTORY?

The Bible records that Abraham had two sons, Ishmael (the ancestor of the Arabs) and Isaac. Isaac had two sons, Esau and Jacob, and Jacob (also called Israel) had 12 sons. These sons became the heads of the Twelve Tribes, the Israelites of the Bible.

The Israelites became wealthy and powerful people. Perhaps they are remembered best for their conquering of the city of Jericho. At God's command the walls of Jericho tumbled down at the sound of the Israelite army shouting and banging their drums.

FACT FILE

Solomon was the son of David, an Israelite king who ruled from 1010 to 970 BC. David defeated the Philistines and enlarged the kingdom, making Jerusalem its capital city. Soloman was responsible for building the sacred Temple in Jerusalem.

WHY IS THE DOME OF THE ROCK CELEBRATED BY TWO RELIGIONS?

The Dome of the Rock which stands in Jerusalem is worshipped by both the Jews and also the Muslims as a holy shrine.

Firstly the Jews believe that the Dome of the Rock is built over the rock on which Abraham, on God's orders, prepared to sacrifice his son to Isaac.

Secondly, the Muslims believe that Muhammad rose to heaven from the very same rock.

FACT FILE

Moses, the leader of the Hebrew people, receives the two tablets from God. The stone tablets bear the Ten Commandments, as described in the Old Testament. They became the basis for Jewish law.

WHY DID THE ASSYRIAN EMPIRE BECOME THE PERSIAN EMPIRE?

Persia grew from the rubble of the defeated Assyrian empire. In 612 BC Nineveh, the Assyrian capital, fell. This left Babylon and Media to wrestle over the remains of the empire. In 550 BC the Persian king Cyrus defeated the Medes and made himself ruler of a new empire. It was known as the Achaemenid Empire. The Persians were good fighters with cavalry and iron weapons, and their military energy proved too strong for their neighbours.

FACT FILE

Ten thousand soldiers called the Immortals formed the core of the Persian army. Each spearman or archer was instantly replaced if killed or became sick.

The ruins of Persepolis (below), the capital of the Persian Empire, lie near the modern city of Shiraz, in southwest Iran. Part of the ruined palace of Darius I is still standing.

Darius I

WHY WAS PERSIA A WELL-ORGANIZED EMPIRE?

Darius I ruled Persia from 521 to 486 BC. He was a very able administrator. He organized the empire into provinces, each governed by a satrap. A satrap was like a king, but not as powerful as the emperor himself whose word was final. He encouraged trade through the use of coins and new canals. Darius and his son, Xerxes, tried to bring Greece within their empire, but failed. However Persia stayed rich and powerful until 331 BC, when it was conquered by Alexander the Great.

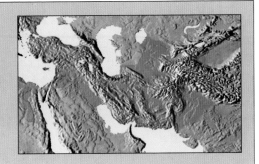

FACT FILE

The Persian Empire stretched from North Africa as far as the Caucasus Mountains in the north, and the borders of India in the east.

WHY WAS THE ROMAN ARMY SO SUCCESSFUL?

The 'tortoise' formation

The Roman army invented a method of warfare that persisted for 2,000 years. Its troops were rigorously trained and exercised and divided into small detachments under the control of officers. Roman soldiers wore effective armour, and developed tactics that allowed them to fight successfully against almost any enemy. They were particularly good at defence. They used to close ranks and protect themselves with large shields, which deflected arrows and spears, until they reached close quarters and could use their own weapons. The group of soldiers shown above was called the 'tortoise' formation and it proved to be impregnable against their Celtic foes.

FACT FILE

Emperor Trajan built a monument 30 metres high to the Roman army. This section shows Roman legionaires, who were builders as well as fighters, constructing a fort.

WHY DID THE ROMANS BREAK DOWN MOST OF THEIR EMPIRE?

FACT FILE

Hadrian's Wall was built across from the east to the west coasts in an attempt to keep the northern tribes out of the occupied areas.

It soon became evident that the Roman Empire was far too big to survive in its original form. A huge civil service and army were needed to maintain the empire, and these became extremely expensive. Also there were numerous rebellions in different parts of the empire, mostly headed by army commanders with designs on becoming emperor. Eventually, in AD 284, Emperor Diocletian broke the Roman Empire into smaller self-governing units, each with its own army. The whole empire was split into two sections: Eastern and Western. Eventually the Roman Empire was weakened to such an extent that it was successfully attacked and overrun by invading barbarians.

Part of Hadrian's Wall

The Sermon on the Mount

WHY DID THE ROMANS PERSECUTE CHRISTIANS?

The teachings of Jesus were spread widely by His followers after His death. At first, the Christians were ignored by the Romans, especially as they did not join in the Jewish rebellion against Roman rule in AD 66. However, the early Christians began to travel around the Roman Empire, and when they reached Rome they began to recruit new followers. The Roman authorities became concerned that this new religion would threaten the established order.

The Romans did not object to the new religion itself, but they did object to the fact that it denied the emperor's divinity. The new religion appealed to the poor and to the slaves, and its popularity was seen as a threat to Roman society.

FACT FILE

The symbol of a fish was used by the early Christians in Rome as a secret symbol to identify themselves to other Christians. The symbol was simple and quick to draw. It was not likely to be noticed by the Romans.

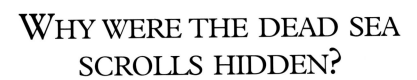

WHY WERE THE DEAD SEA SCROLLS HIDDEN?

The Dead Sea Scrolls are religious writings that were first discovered in 1947, hidden in caves near the Dead Sea. The dry atmosphere of the caves had the effect of preserving the scrolls. About 800 scrolls have been found, mostly in a place called Qumbran in Israel. They date from between 150 BC and AD 68, and they include all of the books of the Old Testament, or Hebrew Bible, except for Esther.

Scholars believe that the scrolls were concealed by members of a religious sect called the Essenes, who lived in the isolated community. They hid the scrolls to keep them safe during political unrest in the area, where they remained hidden for hundreds of years.

FACT FILE

The Dead Sea scrolls are ancient documents written on leather and copper.

The museum in Jerusalem which holds the Dead Sea Scrolls

WHY WAS ATTILA THE HUN SO FEARED?

Attila the Hun

Attila was the ruler of the Hun kingdom, in what is now called Hungary. The Huns began to expand beyond this area, conquering surrounding countries until they controlled a region from the Rhine to the Caspian Sea, extending all the way to the Baltic. The Huns were among the fiercest of the many barbarian tribes who eventually destroyed the power of the Roman Empire. Attila, who is still renowned for his cruelty and the ferocity of his troops, led the Huns from their homeland and almost conquered Europe. He forced the Eastern Roman Empire to pay him a fee in exchange for not attacking them. He also demanded to marry the sister of the emperor of the Western Empire, with half the empire as a dowry, a request which was refused and caused bloodshed.

FACT FILE

A Roman coin stamped with the head of the Emperor Hadrian. During his reign, he personally visited nearly every province in the Roman Empire.

WHY DO ISLAMIC BELIEVERS FOLLOW THE KORAN?

The Koran is the holy book of the Islamic religion. It contains the words of Allah as revealed to Mohammed by the archangel Gabriel in a series of visions. The Koran is a series of verses describing the ways in which Muslims should conduct their lives. It specifies daily prayers, and emphasizes the need for brotherly love and charity between Muslims. Although Muslims do not worship Mohammed, they show him the greatest respect. They believe that the Koran is the word of Allah and was not composed by Mohammed.

FACT FILE

Mecca is the sacred city of the Islamic world. The city is closed to all non-believers and each year millions of Muslims visit in a pilgrimage. The Kaaba is a cubical building in Mecca.

The Holy Koran

WHY WAS FUJIWARA JAPAN A STRONG EMPIRE?

Prince Shotoku ruled Japan from AD 593 to 622, strongly encouraged by Chinese ways. Shotoku believed that the Japanese emperor should be all-powerful, like the ruler of China. In AD 858, however, the emperor lost control to a strong noble family called the Fujiwaras. The Fujiwaras had built up their power in the countryside, where they owned huge estates. Other nobles too had built up small 'empires' of their own.

The Fujiwaras gradually won control of the emperors, and of government, by marrying their daughters into the imperial family. The Fujiwaras held onto power in Japan for 300 years. During this time the great estates grew bigger and stronger, until the lords ruling them were almost like kings.

The Court of the
Fujiwaras

FACT FILE

A paper-maker at work, spreading wet pulp over a mesh frame. The invention of paper was announced by the director of the Chinese imperial workshops in AD 105. The Chinese began to use paper money under Sung rule.

WHY DID ANCIENT CHINA HAVE SUCH ADVANCED CIVILIZATION?

Chinese cities were a wonder to foreign visitors. Chang'an had more than one million citizens, yet its cleanliness was startling. There were public baths, and hot water was sold in the streets for washing. Toilet facilities in houses were fairly basic, emptying into cesspits, but waste was collected in carts every evening and taken away. The Chinese habit of using toilet paper came as another surprise to visitors.

The Chinese were fascinated by machines. They invented the wheelbarrow for carrying loads, and even fitted barrows with sails to make pushing easier. They used waterwheels to mill rice and drive hammers to beat metal into shape. They knew about the magnetic compass, and their ships had stern rudders. Chinese soldiers had the best crossbows in the world, and smoke and fire weapons.

171

WHY WERE VIKING LONGSHIPS CRUCIAL TO THEIR RAIDS?

A Viking longship

At a time when sailors dared not venture far from the coasts, the Vikings boldly sailed out, far across the Atlantic in their small open longships. The Viking longships were fast and very strong. They had a long slender hull with a single mast and sail and were very adept at crossing the oceans.

During the 8th century the Viking people began to leave their homes in Scandinavia and explore Europe in search of treasure and places to settle. The Viking invaders are remembered as ruthless raiders and their routes took them throughout Europe and beyond.

FACT FILE

Both Viking men and women dressed in hard-wearing clothing made from linen or woollen cloth. They wore shoes made from leather.

172

WHY WAS VIKING CULTURE COMPARATIVELY CIVILIZED?

FACT FILE

Decorative brooches such as this were used by both Viking men and women to hold their outer garments (cloaks and tunics) in place.

Viking towns such as Kaupang in Norway and Hedeby in Denmark flourished on deals in furs, reindeer antlers and walrus ivory. These materials were exchanged for weapons, jewels and pottery.

Viking home life was based on farming and fishing. Several generations (including uncles and cousins) often shared one single-roomed house made of wood, stone or turf with a roof thatched with straw. A good sword was highly valued and would be passed down from father to son.

A Viking town

MODERN

HISTORY

CONTENTS

WHY WAS THE TURKISH LEADER OSMAN SUCCESSFUL?

In about 1300, a Turkish leader called Osman ruled a small kingdom in Anatolia (modern Turkey). His family name in Arabic was 'Othman', and is better known to us today as Ottoman.

Osman and his descendants were to build up one of the most important and long-lasting empires in world history. The Ottoman Turks started to take over parts of the weak Byzantine Empire. The new empire was a strong Muslim answer to the power of Christian Europe in the west.

In 1346 a Byzantine leader hired some Ottomon troops to fight for him, but this turned out to be a big mistake. It allowed the Ottomans to cross into Europe, therefore increasing their empire.

FACT FILE

An intricately carved doorway marks the entrance to an Ottoman mosque.

WHY WAS TIMUR LANG NOTORIOUS?

FACT FILE

When Timur seized the city of Isfahan in 1387, he ordered his men to execute all 7,000 citizens and pile their heads in huge mounds outside the city walls.

Timur Lang (or Timur the Lame), who claimed to be a descendant of Genghis Khan was a ruthless leader. When the Ottomans tried to expand their empire eastwards there was a nasty shock in store for them. Timur had already conquered Persia and ravaged much of central Asia, including Russia and India, before the Ottomans attacked.

Timur fell on the Turks like a hurricane, ransacking their chief city in Anatolia, wiping out their army and capturing their leader. Then he began to loot their empire and break it up. That might have been the end of the Ottoman story, but in 1405 Timur died and the last of the Mongol kingdoms fell apart.

St Peter's Church in Rome

WHY DID THE RENAISSANCE TAKE PLACE?

The Renaissance began in Italy. Rome, the capital city, had been one of the main centres of the classical world. It was full of magnificent old buildings and other objects that inspired the 'rebirth' of culture.

Money was an important reason why the Renaissance started in Italy. The Italian city-states were home to many wealthy families, who were eager to pay for new paintings, sculpture and architecture. Many of the great artists who were available to do the work lived in Italy. They made this one of the most stunningly creative periods in history.

Head of Leda by Leonardo da Vinci

WHY WERE SO MANY ARTISTS LIBERATED IN THE RENAISSANCE ERA?

For the first time since the classical period, artists felt free to show the beauty of the human body. They were helped by two things – the old Greek ideas of proportion and perspective, and the new research on how the body worked. A nude sculpture such as Michelangelo's *David* shows a deep knowledge of the action of muscles, sinews and bones.

A painting of Lorenzo de Medici

Almost all medieval art had depicted religious subjects. Renaissance artists began to paint other things, such as landscapes and scenes of gods and goddesses from mythology. They also painted portraits – of their patrons and of themselves – which expressed human emotions more openly than ever before.

WHY WERE DA VINCI'S IDEAS AHEAD OF HIS TIME?

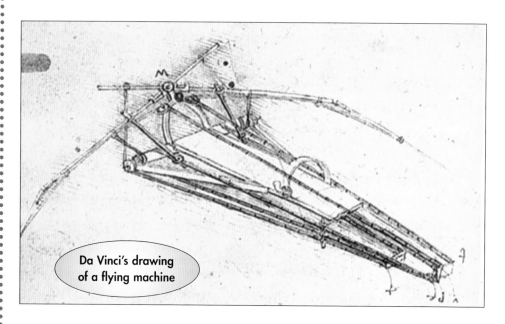

Da Vinci's drawing of a flying machine

During the Renaissance period scientists and inventors were making important discoveries. They were asking questions which would change our view of the Earth – and the Heavens – forever. Of course not all the inventions actually worked. The great artist and engineer Leonardo da Vinci was determined to find a way of making people fly like birds.

Throughout his life Leonardo da Vinci drew many designs for flying machines. Among these was a kind of parachute and a helicopter with spinning blades. His grandest idea was for an aircraft with flapping wings, which he dreamed up in about 1503. He organized a test flight but according to legend the machine crashed. The first successful aircraft did not actually fly for another 400 years so he was certainly well ahead of his time.

FACT FILE

Galileo Galilei was both an astronomer and a physicist. His observations about the heavens helped to confirm the ideas of Copernicus.

WHY IS COPERNICUS REMEMBERED?

FACT FILE

Galileo's telescopes were more powerful than any that had been used before. He was the first person to study the night sky through a telescope.

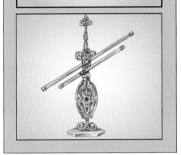

Nicolaus Copernicus was a Polish astronomer. Pictured below is his view of the Universe. He proposed that it was the Sun – not the Earth – which was at the centre of the Universe. The Earth and the other planets simply revolved around it.

His idea was proved correct in the 1620s when the Italian Galileo Galilei used an early telescope to observe the planet Jupiter. He could clearly see that there were other moons in orbit round Jupiter. Here were bodies which were not moving round the Earth. This meant one thing: that the Earth was not the centre of the Universe.

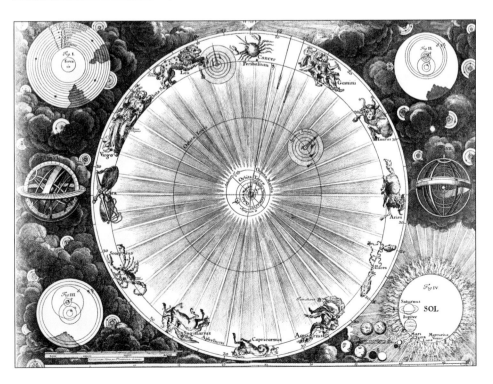

Luther at Wittenberg Castle

WHY DID THE REFORMATION TAKE PLACE?

Martin Luther was a Catholic monk from Germany. In 1510 he visited Rome, the home of the Catholic church, and was deeply shocked. He saw the Pope and his household living in great luxury, and realised the church was bloated with wealth and power. Luther nailed his list of 95 arguments against the church's sale of indulgences to the door of Wittenberg Castle in 1517. His ideas quickly spread across northern Europe. He begged the nobles of Germany to help him reform the old religion. This alarmed the Pope, who sent an order declaring that Luther was a heretic.

FACT FILE

During the Reformation the Bible became available for all to read, thanks to the new printing technology. Also for the first time it was translated from Latin into local languages.

WHY DID KING HENRY VIII DEFY THE POPE?

As Martin Luther's ideas spread, reformers, who became known as Protestants, emerged throughout Europe. A theological debate followed that eventually erupted into religious warfare that was to last for well over a century.

In England, Henry VIII initially defended the Catholic church. However, the lengths to which Henry VIII went to get a male heir shocked Europe. In 1509, he married Catherine of Aragon, but when all her sons died in infancy, Henry wanted the marriage declared invalid. The Pope refused this request. As a consequence Henry cut all ties between England and the Catholic Church in Rome and declared himself Supreme Head of the Church of England.

Henry VIII

FACT FILE

Excommunicated by the Pope, Henry gave himself unrestricted power and set about consolidating the spiritual independence of England from Rome. In 1536, Henry VIII ordered that monasteries such as Tintern Abbey be 'dissolved', or closed down and ransacked.

WHY DID THE SPANISH ARMADA SET OUT TO ATTACK?

Philip of Spain had once hoped to return to England to Catholicism by marrying Queen Elizabeth. She refused him, so he decided to change England's religion by force. In 1588, Philip assembled a fleet of 130 ships and sent them to pick up solders from the Netherlands and invade England. The great Spanish 'Armada' sailed across the English Channel, but never reached its goal. The remnants of the Armada struggled into Spanish ports during autumn 1588.

The defeat of the Armada did not end the war with Spain – it dragged on for another sixteen years.

FACT FILE

Mary Queen of Scots was not a good ruler. In 1568 she was forced to flee Scotland and find refuge in England, throwing herself on the mercy of Elizabeth I.

WHY WAS THE REIGN OF ELIZABETH I SUCCESSFUL?

Despite a traumatic early life – her mother was executed when she was only three and her half-sister Mary had her imprisoned during her brief reign – Elizabeth displayed strength of purpose and prudence as Queen. Strong-willed like her father Henry VIII, but unlike him was fair and grateful to devoted servants, picking advisers who proved able and loyal. In 1559 she pushed through laws which confirmed England as a Protestant nation, with priests ordered to use the new English Prayer Book. Elizabeth ended her reign as one of the best-loved and most successful of all English rulers. Her country was stronger and more peaceful than it had ever been.

FACT FILE

Elizabeth's signature on the death warrant of Mary Stuart. Elizabeth hesitated for days before signing it. She knew that Mary's death would give her Catholic enemies an excuse to attack her.

WHY DID THE THIRTY YEARS' WAR TAKE PLACE?

The struggle between Catholics and Protestants in Europe lasted for more than a century. It was made up of a series of great 'wars of religion', which involved countries as far apart as the Netherlands, Spain, Sweden, France and England. The last and biggest of these religious wars began where the Reformation itself had begun – in the bickering states of Germany. This messy conflict became known as the Thirty Years' War.

The war started in a dramatic way. Protestants in Bohemia were angry with their new king, Ferdinand. He wanted to restore Bohemia to the Catholic faith so he closed Protestant schools and ordered Protestant churches in Prague be pulled down. The Protestants banded together and threw some Catholic officials from an upstairs window in Prague Castle. This incident sparked off a civil war in Bohemia.

Defenestration of Prague

FACT FILE

This matchlock musket gun is a typical weapon used by infantry soldiers during the Thirty Years' War.

WHY WAS THE PALACE OF VERSAILLES BUILT?

FACT FILE

The master Dutch painter Rembrandt van Rijn was at work during the period of the Thirty Years' War. He produced a great number of works of art, including around 600 paintings and about 100 self-portraits.

In the 17th century, Louis XIV of France was famous for his power and wealth. He was the most important monarch in Europe. The palace that was built for him at Versailles, outside Paris, became the model for palaces throughout the continent.

It took forty-seven years to build and was renowned for its extreme grandeur. Great crystal chandeliers hung from the ceilings, their candlelight reflected in gilded mirrors. Fine tapestries and paintings decorated the walls. There is an emblem of the Sun on the main gate of the palace. It portrays Louis as the 'Sun King'.

WHY DID A FARMING REVOLUTION TAKE PLACE?

In 1700 more than 90 percent of Europe's population lived in the countryside. Most were peasants working on the land. They grew their own food, using tools and farming methods which had changed very little since medieval times. By 1800 the number of people in Europe soared from 120 million to over 180 million. Farmers needed to find ways to grow much bigger quantities of crops so that there was enough food to feed many more people.

FACT FILE

As a result of improved breeding techniques, farmers were able to produce sheep which gave better wool. They also had short legs and barrel-like bodies for more meat.

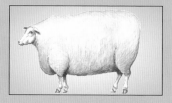

turnips

barley

clover

WHY DID THE PRACTICE OF CROP ROTATION PROVE SUCCESSFUL?

The medieval system of growing crops was wasteful. By about 1650, Dutch farmers had developed a more efficient way of 'rotating' their crops. Instead of leaving a field fallow, they made it fertile more quickly by spreading manure or growing clover and grasses to improve the soil.

In the 1730s, farmers such as Charles Townshend of England, began using a four-part system of planting crops in rotation. In this system wheat was grown in the first year and turnips in the second. Sheep or cattle ate the turnips, providing valuable manure. Barley was sown in the third year, then grass or clover. This method was widely adopted and became known as the 'four-course crop rotation system'.

Four-course crop rotation

wheat

FACT FILE

Since farming began, farmers had scattered seed by hand. Jethro Tull's seed drill put the seed directly into the soil in neat rows.

WHY DID MACHINES AND FACTORIES TAKE OVER PRODUCTION?

Ironworks at Coalbrookdale

During the 1700s the whole world was speeding up, populations were growing, and these extra people needed more food, more homes and more jobs.

At the same time, industry was expanding at an amazing rate, thanks to the development of new machines, new methods of making things and new sources of power. The result was a dramatic change in the way people lived and worked. Machines in factories created millions of new jobs, so many people began to leave the countryside to work in towns. We call this change the Industrial Revolution.

FACT FILE

Whitney's cotton gin machine was a simple way of cleaning raw cotton. It brushed out the seeds from the cotton fibres.

WHY WERE DAVY LAMPS USED?

During the time of the Industrial Revolution, coal became increasingly important as the fuel for ovens and forges. Coal mines were dug deeper as demand grew, leading to greater dangers of floods, collapse and gas explosions. Inventions such as Newcomen's steam pump (to remove water) and Davy's safety lamp eased these problems.

Davy's safety lamp warned miners of gas leaks underground. Inventions such as this only encouraged coal miners to go into farther and more dangerous depths.

Abraham Darby's discovery that coal could be turned into coke led to the production of coke-smelted iron. The improved iron could be used to make everything from ploughs and bridges to steam engines and drilling machines.

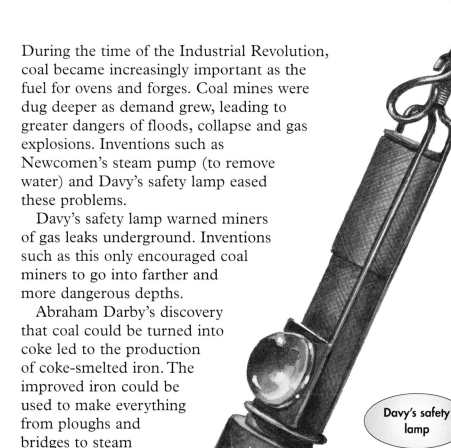

Davy's safety lamp

FACT FILE

Benjamin Franklin was an American statesman as well as a scientist. Franklin proved that lightning and electricity are the same thing by flying a kite in a storm. He was struck by lightning and was lucky to survive.

WHY DID THE AMERICAN REVOLUTION TAKE PLACE?

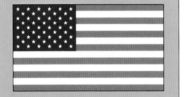

The Seven Years' War saw the end of French power in North America. By 1763 more than two million British colonists were living there. These people now wanted to be able to govern themselves.

Britain, however, had different ideas about her colonies, because they were an important market for trade. A large British army and naval fleet was still stationed to protect North America. The British government was concerned about who was going to pay for these forces. The answer was the colonists themselves – through new and increased taxes.

American victory at Saratoga in 1777.

WHY DID THE BOSTON TEA PARTY TAKE PLACE?

The British government imposed several new taxes, on things as different as official paper and molasses. The Americans had never been taxed before, and protested loudly. Some of the taxes were removed, but import duties on luxury goods such as tea were increased. The Americans had no-one to put their case democratically to the parliament in London, so they decided to take direct action for themselves.

In 1773, a band of colonists seized three British ships in Boston harbour, Massachusetts and dumped their cargo of tea overboard. This became known as the 'Boston Tea Party'. It enraged the British government, who sent troops to put Massachusetts under military rule.

FACT FILE

In 1775 George Washington was elected as commander-in-chief of the colonists' army. To many Americans at that time, he became a leading symbol of their fight for independence.

WHY DID NAPOLEON TAKE FRANCE TO WAR?

After years of political dispute and unrest, the French people welcomed Napoleon as their new leader in 1799. Not only was Napoleon a brilliant general, he also proved himself to be a skilful administrator.

Although Europe was at peace briefly in 1802, Napoleon, after abandoning attempts to increase French influence in North America, turned his attention to expanding his empire in Europe. To raise money, he sold a huge area of land in North America, called Louisiana, to the Americans. In 1803, France and Britain went to war again.

FACT FILE

Napoleon is considered to be a great military genius, and one of the greatest commanders in history. Yet he was also described as an 'enemy and disturber of the peace of the world'.

Napoleon wanted to land an army in Britain, so he needed to control the seas. But in 1805, a British fleet under Lord Nelson defeated the combined French and Spanish fleets at the battle of Trafalgar. This defeat ended Napoleon's hopes of invading Britain.

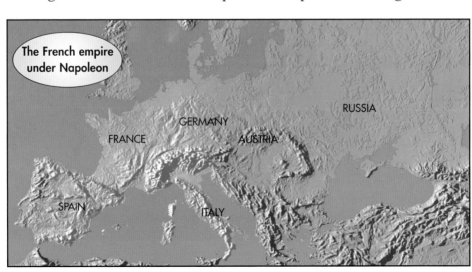

The French empire under Napoleon

RUSSIA

GERMANY

FRANCE

AUSTRIA

SPAIN

ITALY

The battle of Waterloo

WHY WAS THE BATTLE OF WATERLOO A SIGNIFICANT LOSS TO THE FRENCH?

By 1812, Napoleon had created a French empire that covered almost the whole of Europe. However, after a disastrous campaign in Russia Napoleon's empire began to crumble. In April 1814, Napoleon was forced to abdicate. He went into exile in Elba, an island off the coast of Italy, only to return with fresh troops the following year to make another bid for power. The combined armies of Britain, Austria, Prussia and Russia defeated Napoleon's army at the battle of Waterloo in 1815. It was to be Napoleon's last battle. The French had more soldiers and better artillery but they were still soundly beaten. He was sent into exile on the island of St Helena, where he died in 1821.

FACT FILE

Napoleon's distinctive hat. Napoleon was a great military strategist, who seemed instinctively to know the best time to attack during a battle.

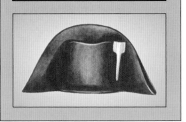

195

WHY DID GARIBALDI UNIFY ITALY?

The Treaty of Paris that brought the Crimean War to an end did little to bring stability to Europe. The leader of Sardinia-Piedmont, Count Cavour, used the meetings at Paris to demand unification for Italy. At that time, Italy was made up of many separate states, most controlled by Austria. The movement for independence, known as the Risorgimento, started in the 1820s and 1830s. In 1858, Sardinia-Piedmont allied itself with France and drove out the Austrians from much of northern Italy. The successful revolt by Guiseppe Garibaldi and his 'red shirts' led eventually to the unification of all of Italy. Italy was declared a kingdom under King Victor-Emmanuel II in 1861. Rome was captured and made the capital of a unified Italy in 1871.

FACT FILE

Paris in 1848. People took to the streets to demand a new republic as well as votes for all males. Government soldiers shot and killed some of the rioters.

WHY IS FLORENCE NIGHTINGALE REMEMBERED?

Florence Nightingale was an English nurse who single-handedly revolutionized nursing practices, sanitation in hospitals and public health in the 19th century.

When war broke out in the Crimea, Nightingale volunteered for duty, leaving with 38 nurses in her charge. She organized the barracks hospital after the Battle of Inkerman, and by introducing discipline and hygiene to hospitals she managed to reduce the death toll. When she returned to England in 1856, she was rewarded with a fund of £50,000 for training nurses.

FACT FILE

Florence Nightingale was known as the 'Lady with the Lamp' because of the light she carried at night. She would walk through the hospital corridors, checking on her patients.

WHY DID THE FAMINE IN IRELAND BEGIN?

At the beginning of the 1800s, the population of Ireland stood at about five million. In the first 40 years of the century the population increased to about eight million. Many people lived in extreme poverty. In 1845 a fungus affected the vital potato crop in southern England, which soon spread to Ireland. With the failure of the potato crop, people began to die in their thousands either from hunger or disease.

The famine came to an end after 1849 when the potato crop only partially failed. By then the population of Ireland had been reduced to just over six million by famine and emigration.

FACT FILE

When Ireland's potato crop failed, people dug up their crops only to find them rotting in the ground. Others picked what looked like sound potatoes, but they simply went rotten later on.

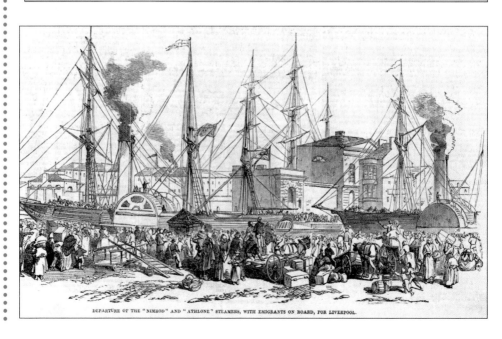

DEPARTURE OF THE "NIMROD" AND "ATHLONE" STEAMERS, WITH EMIGRANTS ON BOARD, FOR LIVERPOOL.

WHY DID GLADSTONE NOT HELP THE IRISH?

The British prime minister, Sir Robert Peel, organized relief for the poorest people of Ireland during the famine. This enabled them to be able to buy cheap corn imported from the United States. It helped to prevent many people from starving to death. But it was a different story when Peel resigned.

William Gladstone was the dominant figure in Britain's Liberal Party from 1868 to 1894. He was actually prime minister four times during the reign of Queen Victoria. His belief was that Ireland should run their own affairs, and was a strong supporter of Home Rule.

Supporters of Home Rule wanted a separate parliament to deal with Irish affairs in Dublin.

FACT FILE

Irish politician Charles Parnell addresses an audience in support of Home Rule. He became leader of the Home Rule Party in the British parliament, and fought tirelessly for his beliefs. Parnell was even imprisoned by the British for a time.

WHY DID THE SUFFRAGETTE MOVEMENT TAKE PLACE?

During war time women were brought in to fill the jobs of those men that had gone to fight in the war. The poster (shown here on the right) emphasized the important role women had to play. In 1893, New Zealand became the first country in the world to allow women to vote in national elections. Australia followed suit in 1903, and Finland in 1906. In other parts of the world, however, women were engaged in a bitter and often violent battle for the right to vote.

In Britain, Emmeline Pankhurst founded the Women's Social and Political Union in 1903. The WSPU believed in actions rather than words, and many of its members, known as suffragettes, were arrested and imprisoned. One suffragette called Emily Davison was killed when she threw herself beneath the king's horse at a race.

FACT FILE

In Britain, the suffragette campaigners often went on hunger strike when imprisoned for their actions. The authorities did not want the suffragettes to die – and arouse public sympathy – so they fed the women by force.

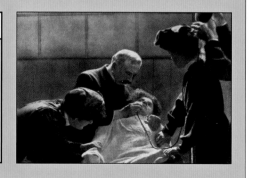

Emmeline Pankhurst being arrested

WHY DID WWI AID THE PLIGHT OF EQUAL RIGHTS FOR WOMEN?

FACT FILE

The suffragettes engaged in many different forms of protest, from interrupting public meetings by shouting slogans to chaining themselves to railings outside the residence of the British prime minister.

World War I was a turning-point in many countries for the women's movement. During the war, women had filled the places of the men who had gone off to fight, working in industries such as munitions factories, on farms as labourers, and in the mines. After the end of the war, equal voting rights were introduced in Canada (1918), Austria, Czechoslovakia, Germany and Poland (1919), and in 1920 in Hungary and the USA. The right to vote was extended to all women over the age of 21 in 1928. Emmeline Pankhurst, founder of the WSPU, died a month after British women gained equal voting rights.

WHY DID WAR BREAK OUT IN 1914?

FACT FILE

A World War I gas mask. After the Germans used poisonous gas for the first time in April 1915, masks became an essential part of every soldier's kit.

As the 19th century drew to a close, rivalry increased between the different nations of Europe.

In June 1914, the heir to the Austro-Hungarian throne, Archduke Franz Ferdinand, and his wife Sophie made a tour of Bosnia. As they drove through the streets of Sarajevo, a Serbian assassin shot them both dead. In retaliation, Austria-Hungary, backed by Germany, declared war on Serbia. Soon all the major European powers were drawn into the conflict. Russia, backed by France, supported Serbia. Then Germany invaded neutral Belgium and attacked France, drawing Britain into the conflict.

WHY DID THE USA ENTER THE WAR IN 1917?

From the start of the Great War, the name by which World War I was first known, British warships blockaded German ports. In this way Britain's navy prevented supplies from reaching Germany, causing severe shortages of food and other goods. The Germans retaliated with their submarines, called U-boats. After 1915, U-boats attacked both warships and merchant shipping carrying supplies to Britain. In May 1915, a German torpedo hit a British passenger ship called the *Lusitania*. The ship was carrying nearly 2,000 passengers, including many Americans. The sinking of the Lusitania was one of the factors that eventually drew the United States into the war.

FACT FILE

Poppies were in flower on many of the French battlefields of World War I. Today, artificial poppies are sold in Europe and the USA to raise money for war veterans.

WHY DID THE BATTLE OF BRITAIN TAKE PLACE?

The evacuation from Dunkerque

In March 1939, the German leader Adolf Hitler threatened to invade Poland. Both Great Britain and France gave guarantees to help Poland if it was attacked. So when Hitler invaded Poland on September 1, 1939 Britain and France were forced to declare war on Germany. The majority of the British army was saved in 1940 by a desperate evacuation from the French port of Dunkerque.

The Battle of Britain began in July 1940 between the German airforce, the Luftwaffe, and Britain's Royal Air Force (RAF). Nightly air raids that took place in the autumn and winter of 1940–1941 are known as the Blitz. However, by May 1941 the RAF had gained the upper hand, and Hitler gave up the attempt to bomb Britain into submission – although air raids continued throughout the war.

FACT FILE

The Battle of Britain was the world's first major air battle. The British fighter planes were able to shoot down many of the long-range German bomber aircraft, shown here.

WHY WERE THE D-DAY LANDINGS A TURNING POINT IN THE WAR?

FACT FILE

Charles de Gaulle was leader of the French troops, known as the Free French, who had escaped occupied France. After the war he became one of France's most powerful presidents ever.

In June 1944, Allied leaders decided that it was time to attack Germany itself. Under the overall command of US General Eisenhower, Allied troops landed in Normandy and advanced across France. Meanwhile, Soviet troops moved across eastern Europe.

On the morning of 6 June, 1944, thousands of Allied troops went ashore along the coast of Normandy in northern France in what became known as the D-Day landings.

D-Day landings

The Damascus Gate

WHY WAS ISRAEL CREATED?

At the end of World War II, the demands for a Jewish state in Palestine grew. In 1947, the United Nations took over responsibility for Palestine, dividing it into an Arab state and a Jewish state. The Jews agreed to this plan, but the Arabs did not. The state of Israel came into being on May 14, 1948. It was immediately attacked by Arab armies from Egypt, Syria, Lebanon, Iraq and Transjordan (Jordan) – known collectively as the Arab League. By 1949, Israel had defeated the Arab League and added land to its own territory.

FACT FILE

Civil war broke out between Christians and Muslims in the Lebanon in 1975. Fighting caused extensive damage in Beirut.

WHY WAS THE
COLD WAR STARTED?

After World War II, the United States and the USSR (Union of Soviet Socialist Republics) emerged as the two main powers in the world – known as 'superpowers'. Although they had fought together to defeat Nazi Germany, differences between the two superpowers soon led to the start of the 'Cold War'.

The Cold War was a political war between the USSR and its communist allies, and the USA and other non-communist countries. It did not involve fighting, although there was a threat of military action on several occasions.

FACT FILE

In 1945 the three Allied leaders – Winston Churchill, Franklin D. Roosevelt and Joseph Stalin – met at Yalta to discuss the problems facing postwar Europe.

The Berlin airlift

HOLLYWOOD:
THE NEW GENERATION
James Cameron-Wilson

HOLLYWOOD:
THE NEW GENERATION
The Hottest Young Stars in Hollywood

James Cameron-Wilson
B.T. Batsford Ltd London

© James Cameron Wilson 1997

First published 1997

All rights reserved. No part of this publication may be
reproduced in any form or by any means without permission from the Publisher.

Printed in Spain for the publishers
B.T. Batsford Ltd
583 Fulham Road
London
SW6 5BY

ISBN 0 7134 8119 6

A CIP catalogue record for this book is available from
the British Library.

DEDICATION

To Nigel Mulock, my closest friend for thirty-five years – thank you for being there.

ACKNOWLEDGEMENTS

I would like to thank the following for their assistance in the preparation of this book. My endless gratitude must go to Virginia Palmer and Nigel Mulock for supplying me with so much useful material. Also, my thanks to the stars (particularly Sandra Bullock) who talked to me, enabling me to gain a greater perspective on my subject. But most of all, I must thank my mother for furnishing me with office space, and my wife, Frances, for suffering my extensive leaves of absence.

Rosanna Arquette in *After Hours* – a better actress than the press made out

Introduction

Sorry, you won't find chapters here on Humphrey Bogart, Marilyn Monroe or James Dean, nor indeed entries on Kevin Costner, Bruce Willis or Tom Hanks. These stars have, I feel, been exhaustively chronicled elsewhere.

The aim and intent of this book is to focus a comprehensive spotlight on those luminaries who make up the next generation. Taking 1955 as an arbitrary cut-off date (albeit the year of my birth), I have rounded up everybody from Jim Carrey via Michelle Pfeiffer to the decidedly upwardly-mobile Claire Danes, all of whom were born after that year. The sole exception to the rule (and rules were invented to be broken) is the inclusion of Patrick Swayze. Not only does he *look* as if he was born after 1955 (he was actually born in 1952), but he has appeared in many films in the Brat Pack canon, such as *Red Dawn*, *Youngblood* and, most notably, *The Outsiders*. Thus he is this tome's honorary member – a sort of grandfather of the Brat Pack.

Other stars have been omitted because their careers seem to belong elsewhere. Even though Melanie Griffith was born in 1957, her very first leading man was Gene Hackman, in *Night Moves*, in 1975, followed by Paul Newman, in *The Drowning Pool* a year later. Since then, her co-stars have included such hardy veterans as Harrison Ford, Michael Douglas, Nick Nolte and her frequent ex-husband, Don Johnson.

Also, TV stars are, for the most part, excluded. Thus you won't find David Duchovny nor Pamela Anderson – the former because he has yet to prove himself as a viable leading man on the big screen, the latter because *Barb Wire* sucked. On the other hand, George Clooney is included as he has already exercised his grip on the medium with such titles as *From Dusk Till Dawn*, *One Fine Day*, *The Peacemaker* and *Batman and Robin*. Narrow escapes also includ-

ed Marisa Tomei (whose career failed to take off after *My Cousin Vinny*), Antonio Banderas (whose Hollywood films have not fulfilled the promise of his Spanish output) and Steve Buscemi (still very much a character actor, in spite of wonderful turns in *Living in Oblivion* and *Fargo*). Others on my shortlist who didn't *quite* squeeze their way onto the register include Cameron Diaz, Linda Fiorentino, Cuba Gooding Jr, Jada Pinkett, Campbell Scott and future megastar Renee Zellweger. My apologies.

Moreover, this book has dropped a number of stars included in my 1994 tome, *Young Hollywood*. Due to considerations of space, it seemed redundant to retain entries on the likes of Rebecca DeMornay, Steve Guttenberg, Daryl Hannah, Mary Elizabeth Mastrantonio, Kelly McGillis and Lou Diamond Phillips, all of whose careers have gained little momentum in the last three years.

However, I *have* expanded and updated existing chapters detailing the lives and careers of those stars still very much in the public eye, in some cases substantially. (cf. Tom Cruise, Brad Pitt, Johnny Depp). Furthermore, I have slipped in a number of intriguing personal details that I failed to unearth the first time round – such as Demi Moore's blind left eye, Rob Lowe's deafness, Eddie Murphy's compulsive hand-washing and the ten-year sentence doled out to Keanu Reeves' father for drug offences. All this and more you will find in the following pages: gossip, personal defects, salaries, box-office performance, critiques and as-complete-as-damn-it filmographies.

Personally, I am fascinated by the lives and careers of the actors of my generation (and the next), by the political ups and downs, the unexpected flops and successes, and the money that these icons make. While I reserve considerable admiration for the stars of

yesteryear – Lillian Gish, Buster Keaton, Cary Grant and Grace Kelly are favourites – I wasn't there at the time, and so don't feel qualified to trace their careers in quite the same depth.

And so to the matter of ground rules. Unless otherwise specified, the dates which precede the films in the filmographies indicate the year of their American release, while titles are also American. However, it should be borne in mind that some films are subjected to several name changes in their transition from country to country and then on to video and TV. Where a title has been altered for its UK release, I have listed this in brackets, and the same applies to any alternative titles – all in an effort to save researchers the embarrassment of confusing one film for two or even three (you would be surprised how many reference books list alternative titles as two separate works). The filmographies themselves are as complete as they can be, and include all cinema, TV and video titles – however brief the entrant's appearance may be in them.

Due to the public interest in stars' birth dates, I have included as many as I could find in the entries, but in spite of the tireless help of learned colleagues (in particular David Quinlan and his Web-surfing associates), I have been unable to excavate every single birthday (Claire Danes and Matthew McConaughey still elude me).

Still, I think there is enough material here to fascinate, beguile and educate those with an interest in the faces that light up the lives of so many. And with the growing amount of ephemera dedicated to them – the calendars, posters, postcards and fanzines – I trust this book will be a welcome and useful companion.

James Cameron-Wilson

A

PATRICIA ARQUETTE

Five feet two and pretty as an Alpine meadow, Patricia Arquette displayed a considerable range in a very short career. She showed a winning aptitude for comedy and, for the most part, was equally adept at drama, playing a teenage mother in the acclaimed TV movie *Daddy* and a young woman plagued by horrific dreams in *A Nightmare On Elm Street 3 – Dream Warriors*. For a while she was known as the younger sister of Rosanna Arquette (which she is), but the only thing they seemed to have in common was beauty and talent. 'If there were a similarity between us,' Patricia says, 'I would accept it gladly. But we have totally different personalities.' She admits that she was wary of following in her famous sister's footsteps: 'When I told Rosanna I wanted to be an actress, I was really afraid about it because she was doing so well. I was going through a really insecure time in my life, but she said, "Look, I really believe in you. I know you can do it."'

And she did.

The latest bud from a theatrical dynasty that was appearing in vaude-ville four generations ago, Patricia was born on 8 April 1968, the middle child of five. She admits: 'I never exactly trained as a little kid, but we did do all these little shows ...' She made her professional debut in a children's version of Paul Sill's Story Theater, and did voice-overs and radio commercials on America's East Coast. Then, in 1974, she moved with her family to Los Angeles. During her early teens, she worked as a model in Portugal, France and Italy, and later trained with the famous drama coach Milton Katselas.

She returned to Europe as an actress, playing 'Zero' in the film *Pretty Smart*, a routine sex-in-high school malarkey, set in an all-girls academy on a Greek island. There, she graduated high school herself, and returned to the USA to star in *A Nightmare On Elm Street 3 – Dream Warriors*. She played Kristen Parker, a girl suffering from a sleep disorder who battles Freddie Krueger through a series of stunning

We all have to start somewhere: Patricia Arquette cradles Heather Langenkamp in her arms in **A Nightmare on Elm Street 3: Dream Warriors**

special effects. Most famously, it was young Patricia who was swallowed by Krueger in a legendary, jaw-dropping sequence. She was offered *Nightmare 4*, but declined, explaining: 'I was very honoured, but I didn't want to get stuck doing horror for the rest of my life.'

Meanwhile, she won glowing reviews (*The Los Angeles Times* called her 'superb') in the TV movie *Daddy*, in which she played a teenage girl encumbered with a child that nobody wanted her to have (including boyfriend Dermot Mulroney). Ironically, a year later she was pregnant herself and, barely out of her teens, she gave birth to Enzo, a son she named after a character in *The Godfather*. But, in contrast to the conclusion in *Daddy*, she went on to rear the child by herself. She says: 'On the one hand I was really happy, but on the other I was very afraid and scared. I was given a part in *Last Exit to Brooklyn*, but it was a very dark and violent film and I did-n't want to take that into me when I was pregnant, because I absorb so much when I work. I just couldn't do it.' Later, she revealed: 'I'm so glad I'm young having a kid. My body bounced back. And I have the energy.'

In 1988 her 'life-long dream' came true when she was cast in Sam Shepard's film *Far North*. 'I had an English teacher who made us read *Curse of the Starving Class*,' she explained, 'and I was totally blown away. I took out all of Sam's plays and read each one and was completely taken by his writing.' Unfortunately, *Far*

North – in which she played Jilly, the rebellious and highly-sexed teenage niece of Jessica Lange – was a stagy, mannered piece that only came alight when Arquette was on screen.

She was also the best thing in *Prayer of the Roller Boys*, a confused futuristic yarn with only occasional glimpses of comic invention, in which she played a sexy undercover cop. She then went up for the role of Dorothy, the pregnant girlfriend of Viggo Mortensen, in Sean Penn's *The Indian Runner*. Penn explains: 'I was exhausted, but I had finally found someone who could play Dorothy well, and I just did not want to see another actress.' But Arquette

As Alabama, the heroine of Tony Scott's lyrical, hard-hitting **True Romance**

*With Ben Stiller and child in David O. Russell's hilarious **Flirting With Disaster**, the funniest film of Patricia's career*

was already booked for an audition, so Penn was forced to go through the paces. 'She was Dorothy,' he marvelled. 'We all knew the minute she came into the room. It was that simple.'

On TV, she was directed by Diane Keaton in a CBS Schoolbreak Special called *The Girl With the Crazy Brother*, which led to the TV movie *Wildflower*, also directed by Keaton. In *Wildflower*, she played Alice Guthrie, a teenage epileptic, and was simply sensational. Liam Neeson caught the movie and was stunned: 'For the first time in ten years I saw a performance by an actress that made me think, "Oh my God."' When he heard that Arquette was to be in the film version of Edith Wharton's ironic novella *Ethan Frome*, he agreed to join her. 'Liam had just seen *Wildflower* and was writing me a note,' the actress recalled, 'and it all came together.' She played Mattie Silver, the spirited young woman who brings brief light into the drab existence of the disfigured Ethan (Neeson). The film, directed by John Madden, was a loving, beautifully crafted version of the novel, although some critics found it a trifle stiff.

Meanwhile, she was excellent as a dignified lesbian in the charming comedy *Inside Monkey Zetterland*, also starring Martha Plimpton and Rupert Everett, and then, in *Trouble Bound*, played a Mafia princess who falls in with an ex-con on the run from the Mob (Michael Madsen). Next, she was running from the Mafia again in Tony Scott's *True Romance*, this time hitched to Christian Slater and a suitcase full of stolen contraband. From the director of

Top Gun and *Beverly Hills Cop II*, and with a hot, hot script from Quentin Tarantino, *True Romance* was every bit as exciting as it promised it to be. Patricia received $500,000 for her part and got to top-bill the likes of Dennis Hopper, Gary Oldman (as a Rastafarian!), Brad Pitt, Val Kilmer and Christopher Walken. Yet while the film made the top ten list of several critics, it failed to generate much excitement at the box-office.

Nevertheless, she reportedly pocketed a cool million for the central role in *Beyond Rangoon*, after Meg Ryan had unceremoniously baled out. However, while the film was highly-charged and enthralling to look at, it was, at times, surprisingly slipshod – a particular disappointment as John Boorman (director of *Deliverance* and *Hope and Glory*) was at the helm. Furthermore, as the grieving wife and mother who finds herself caught up in the life-and-death struggle of Burma in 1988, Arquette was way out of her depth.

Still, *Beyond Rangoon* was light years superior to the Hutterite farce *Holy Matrimony*, surely the most embarrassing movie of 1994. There was also *The Gold Cup*, with Forest Whitaker and Martin Landau, and the troubled *Infinity*, with Matthew Broderick, who also directed. Arquette played the first wife of real-life physicist Richard Feynman (Broderick) but, with a perfectly misjudged performance, almost single-handedly destroyed the movie. However, she recovered her dignity with David O. Russell's simply hilarious *Flirting With Disaster*, once again revealing that her real forte was come-

dy. She played the wife of entomologist Ben Stiller, and was delightful as a sex-starved slob, eating in bed, sniffing her armpits and fellating her husband as he holds their baby.

Then, in April 1995, she married Nicolas Cage, revealing that they were made for each other: 'We stay at home and talk a lot. Laugh a lot. Jump on the bed. Bark at each other.'

Next, she was a gangster's moll and *femme fatale* in David Lynch's characteristically bizarre *Lost Highway*, starred opposite Ewan McGregor and Nick Nolte in the thriller *Nightwatch*, and headed the cast of Roland Joffé's *Goodbye Lover*.

FILMOGRAPHY

1987: *Pretty Smart; A Nightmare On Elm Street 3 – Dream Warriors; Daddy* (TV). 1988: *Time Out; Far North*. 1991: *Dillinger* (TV); *Prayer of the Rollerboys; The Indian Runner; Wildflower* (TV). 1992: *Inside Monkey Zetterland*. 1993: *Ethan Frome; Trouble Bound; True Romance; Betrayed By Love* (TV). 1994: *Holy Matrimony; Ed Wood; The Gold Cup; Beyond Rangoon*. 1995: *Infinity*. 1996: *Flirting With Disaster; Joseph Conrad's The Secret Agent; Lost Highway*. 1997: *Nightwatch; Goodbye Lover*.

ROSANNA ARQUETTE

Rosanna Arquette suffered from the celebrity syndrome. Her films were seldom as well known as she was, but still fame followed her like an obedient puppy. In 1983 she had a song named after her (Toto's No. 2 hit *Rosanna*), two years later she top-billed in *Desperately Seeking Susan*, whose unknown co-star – Madonna – turned the comedy into a sensational cult, and then she moved in with rock star Peter Gabriel, formerly of Genesis. When she posed naked for Playboy, Gabriel reportedly threw a fit and terminated their relationship. Instantaneously, the media scrambled for crumbs of scandal.

The tabloids regaled their readers with stories of the actress's unorthodox upbringing, her flower power childhood, the rallies she attended (with 'Stop the war' painted across her infant chest), her drug addiction at 13, her cohabitation with a man at 15, her marriage at 17 ...

But Rosanna Arquette was a better actress than her press would have us

Rosanna as Roberta in Susan Seidelman's charmingly idiosyncratic **Desperately Seeking Susan**

the ages of 11 and 13 she lived in 'this spiritual brotherhood – an actor's and musician's commune. And I was going to school in this town in Virginia where it was like the Civil War was still going on. Most of my friends were black, so I was always writing B-L-A-C-K P-O-W-E-R on my hands and flashing the rednecks.'

At 14, she moved to New Jersey on her own and attended South Orange Junior High, where she first became interested in drama. She rejoined her family in Chicago a year later and then, with her parents' blessing, hitchhiked to San Francisco, where she studied acting for a year. Winning a part in a play in Los Angeles, she was spotted by a casting director who recommended her to an agent. This in turn led to a number of small parts on television, including a role in NBC's *Shirley*, in which she played Shirley Jones' daughter Debra. On the big screen, she had a walk-on in *More American Graffiti* and then landed a good role opposite Bette Davis in the well-received TV film *The Dark Secret of Harvest Home*, a Gothic tale set in New England. She then appeared in the awful *Gorp*, with fellow unknown Dennis Quaid, and played a topless hitchhiker in Blake Edwards' showbiz spoof *S.O.B.*

But it wasn't until NBC's scorching TV movie *The Executioner's Song* that critics woke up. Rosanna played Nicole

believe. It was just that her timing was bad. From the start she was typecast. 'I played every pregnant teenage runaway hooker addict that was ever on the planet,' she recalls. Then, when she broke that mould, 'I did *Desperately Seeking Susan*, *After Hours* and *Nobody's Fool* and they all came out within a year of each other. Those are the films that stuck in people's minds – but I'm an actor, not a little ingenue chickie,' she insists.

And, to her credit, Rosanna Arquette was attracting the attention of some top-level directors: not least Martin Scorsese, Lawrence Kasdan and John Sayles. Sayles, who directed her in his 1960s high school romance *Baby, It's You*, ventured: 'When I cast Rosanna, I knew she was the only person who could play the innocent in the first half of the movie and bring out the emotional depth for the second part.' Mike Hodges, who guided her performance as a travelling clairvoyant in *Black Rainbow*, volunteered: 'Rosanna played the toughness any entertainer on the road would have, but she was extra wonderful because a little-girl-lost emerged above my original intentions.'

But soon her career was to stumble. Her leading role in John Milius's *Flight of the Intruder* was hacked back to a romantic subplot in order to accommodate her male co-stars (Danny

Glover, Willem Dafoe and Brad Johnson). Then, when she landed the lead in *Radio Flyer*, Columbia Pictures' $30 million sci-fi fantasy, the film was shut down after two weeks of shooting. First-time director David Mickey Evans (who had written the script) was replaced by Richard Donner, Donner taking it upon himself to recast the movie, supplanting Arquette in favour of Lorraine Bracco.

The actress's next two movies – *The Linguini Incident*, with David Bowie, and *Father & Sons*, with Jeff Goldblum – were both bombs.

Rosanna Arquette was born into theatrical tradition. Her great-grandfather was an actor, as was her grandfather, Cliff Arquette, who became immortalised on American radio and television as the beloved bumpkin Charles Weaver (on *Dave and Charley*, *The Charles Weaver Show*, etc). Rosanna's father, Lewis Arquette, is an actor-producer, and her mother, Mardi, a poet and playwright. Even three of her four siblings have gone into acting, namely sometime drag queen Alexis (*Last Exit to Brooklyn*), David (TV's *The Outsiders*) and Patricia (*True Romance*, *Nightwatch*).

Rosanna herself was born on 10 August 1959 in Manhattan, and made her theatrical debut aged eight in *Story Theater*, directed by her father. Between

Rosanna as the mixed up, alluring Marcy in Martin Scorsese's unpredictable comedy **After Hours**

Baker, the girlfriend of convicted killer Gary Gilmore (Tommy Lee Jones), who famously pleaded for his own death sentence. The film was a compelling portrayal of real-life crime, scripted by Norman Mailer from his own bestseller, and was released theatrically in Europe.

This led to another star-making performance in the TV movie *Johnny Belinda*, with Quaid and Richard Thomas, and then the lead in John Sayles' *Baby, It's You*, co-starring Vincent Spano as Rosanna's 'Sheik'. *Baby, It's You* was a sensitive, credible tale of a schoolgirl exploring her centre of gravity through sex and amateur dramatics and, turning in an affecting, naturalistic performance devoid of mannerisms, Arquette has seldom been better since. More TV films followed, and a tedious vehicle for Christopher Reeve, *The Aviator*, in which the actress was at her annoying worst as the latter's reluctant passenger. Then, thankfully, came

*As the talented fake medium Martha Travis in Mike Hodges' **Black Rainbow***

Desperately Seeking Susan.

Rosanna played Roberta, an inept, bored housewife, ignored by her husband and reduced to following the personal ads in the paper for entertainment. Gradually, she becomes intrigued by a recurring entry headed 'DESPERATELY SEEKING SUSAN' and follows it up incognito. Soon, she finds herself trailing Susan (Madonna) on a shopping spree, buys Susan's jacket

from a second-hand clothes shop and then becomes mistaken for her after Roberta loses her memory. It transpires that Susan was one in-demand dame and everybody is after her – now unwittingly impersonated by Roberta.

Farce is one of the most difficult forms of comedy to pull off on film, but director Susan Seidelman had the good sense to inject it with a decent shot of realism, making this a credible, hilarious ride. Rosanna was never better as the housewife with dreams above her station, transformed by fate at its most bizarre. Madonna was better than anybody expected, but it was still Rosanna Arquette who carried the film.

And so the next bout of typecasting set in. She played another New York kook in Scorsese's *After Hours*, leading a hapless Griffin Dunne into a night of chaos, but left the picture all too soon. For Lawrence Kasdan's starry western *Silverado* she spent five months in preparation, only to find her part virtually discarded in the editing room. She played a gangster's moll in Hal Ashby's *8 Million Ways To Die*, but the film was so bad it didn't even get a release in Britain – even with Jeff Bridges top-billed. *Nobody's Fool*, a bizarre romantic comedy, saw her as an eccentric looking for Mr Right (Eric Roberts), but the film was a flop; as was the omnibus turkey *Amazon Woman on the Moon*.

Luc Besson's *The Big Blue*, a magical, unusual aquatic epic, had all the potential to be a hit, but was too off-beat for most tastes (and Rosanna was in a particularly irritating mood). She was much better as the clairvoyant in Mike Hodges' *Black Rainbow*, a serious, intriguing examination of the paranormal which fell apart when it turned into a routine thriller. The role was actually suggested to the actress by Scorsese, who had just directed her in his 'Life Lessons' segment from *New York Stories*, an unsuccessful trio of short films depicting life in the Big Apple.

There were more TV movies and a couple of box-office stiffs: the Australian romantic comedy-fantasy *Wendy Cracked a Walnut* (and laid an egg), and *The Linguini Incident*, another oddball comedy about eccentric New Yorkers.

More recently, she played the female interest in *Nowhere To Run*, a timeworn, action-packed vehicle for Jean-Claude Van Damme. Oddly, Rosanna shed her clothes (twice) for the under-written role of a widow and mother who seduces Van Damme on her farm. For many years Rosanna had protested against nudity in films, explaining: 'I don't like the way it feels. I'm not going to do that again. Fuck that!' She disrobed again in *The Wrong Man*.

At the end of 1993 the actress married for a third time (she was previously wed to the composer James Newton Howard), in this instance to the restaurateur Johnny Sidel. And then, briefly, her career picked up. She was terrific in *Pulp Fiction*, as the foul-mouthed wife of Eric Stoltz, sporting a Fred Flintstone T-shirt and rings in her nose, eyebrows and lip (and, as we discover, more intimate places as well). She was then at the centre of a storm of controversy over her role in David Cronenberg's *Crash*, playing a nymphomaniac in callipers who gets it on with James Spader. Although her role was a relatively small one (as it was in *Pulp Fiction*), the part was one nobody could forget in a hurry.

FILMOGRAPHY

1977: *Having Babies II* (TV). 1978: *Zuma Beach* (TV); *The Dark Secret of Harvest Home* (TV). 1979: *More American Graffiti*. 1980: *Gorp*. 1981: *S.O.B.*; *A Long Way Home* (TV); *The Wall* (TV). 1982: *The Executioner's Song* (TV; UK: theatrical); *Johnny Belinda* (TV). 1983: *Baby, It's You*; *Off the Wall*; *One Cooks, the Other Doesn't* (TV). 1984: *The Parade* (TV); *The Aviator*. 1985: *Survival Guides* (TV); *Desperately Seeking Susan*; *After Hours*; *Silverado*. 1986: *8 Million Ways To Die*; *Nobody's Fool*; *Amazon Women On the Moon*. 1988: *The Big Blue*; *Promised a Miracle* (TV). 1989: *New York Stories* (episode: 'Life Lessons'); *Black Rainbow*. 1990: *Wendy Cracked a Walnut*; *Sweet Revenge* (TV); *Separation* (TV). 1991: *Flight of the Intruder*; *Son of the Morning Star* (TV). 1992: *The Linguini Incident*; *Father & Sons*; *In the Deep Woods* (TV). 1993: *Nowhere To Run*; *The Wrong Man*. 1994: *Pulp Fiction*; *La Cité de la Peur*: *Une Comédie Familiale* (aka *Fear City: A Family-Style Comedy*); *Nowhere to Hide* (TV); *Search and Destroy*. 1996: *Gone Fishin'*; *Crash*. 1997: *Do Me a Favor*; *Hell's Kitchen*. 1998: *Hope Floats*.

B

KEVIN BACON

The features are unmistakable. The famous upturned nose, the impish smile, the small, demonic eyes and those wicked, wicked dimples. If Kevin Bacon was to try Shakespeare, he would be typecast as Puck. Or Caliban.

And yet, in a medium obsessed with killing, Bacon avoided psycho typecasting. At least, until *Criminal Law*, his 18th picture. But then, he was originally approached to be the good guy. When Gary Oldman was signed up for the lead, Bacon jumped at the chance of playing the serial killer Oldman defends and then brings to justice. But of course Bacon's character is meant to look innocent – at first. Then, two years later, the actor went on to win some of the best notices of his career as the homosexual prison inmate in *JFK*.

More often than not, Kevin Bacon was the clean-cut good guy. Hell, on a few occasions he even got to play the romantic lead. But Bacon is a better actor than that, and has displayed a remarkable range, both in the types of films he has appeared in and the roles

he has played. He also has a roguish sense of humour, admitting: 'I judge whether or not I can be in line with someone's sense of humour based on whether or not they enjoyed *This is Spinal Tap*. I've seen it no less than 20 times.'

The son of an architect father and a mother involved in child education, Kevin Bacon was born on 8 July 1958, in Philadelphia. At an early age he started taking drama lessons with a church group, and later became the youngest member of the Manning Street Actor's Theater. 'From the moment I started drama,' he says, 'I knew that I wanted to be an actor. It was just something I knew I had to do.'

With the endorsement of his parents, he moved to New York at the age of 17 and spent a year with the Circle in the Square Theater. He then appeared in a number of off-Broadway productions and did time in TV appearing in the daytime soap *Search For Tomorrow* (which had previously boasted Robert De Niro, Jill Clayburgh and Kevin Kline in its ranks) and *The Guiding Light*, as the runaway T.J.

In 1978 he made his film debut as Chip Diller in the phenomenally successful, anarchic comedy *National Lampoon's Animal House*, a film which

blessed a number of its cast members' futures (newcomers John Belushi, Tom Hulce, Karen Allen, Peter Riegert, et al.). He had a small part as a young husband in *Starting Over*, with Burt Reynolds and Jill Clayburgh, and had a bigger role in the well-received TV movie *The Gift*, starring Glenn Ford.

In the original *Friday the 13th* he played Jack, an unhappy camper who is summarily butchered immediately after making love (he was the guy who got an arrow through the throat). The film was another enormous success, spawning seven frightful sequels which, thankfully, Bacon had nothing to do with. Instead, he segued into a much better ensemble piece, *Diner*, which was to set new standards for cinema aimed at and about young people. Bacon had the flashiest role, as Fenwick, an immature, ghoulish alcoholic who opens the film by staging his own death in a car wreck. Written and directed by Barry Levinson, *Diner* also starred Steve Guttenberg, Daniel Stern, Mickey Rourke and Ellen Barkin; it was a critical triumph.

After that, Bacon played a teenage hustler in *Forty Deuce*, based on the off-Broadway play by Alan Bowne (in which the actor had starred). This was followed by the so-so TV movie *The*

Kevin as the deviant serial killer Martin Thiel (with Gary Oldman in the background) in **Criminal Law**

The star and his wife: Kevin Bacon and Kyra Sedgwick pose on the set of **Pyrates**

Demon Murder Case and then a three-part omnibus production, *Enormous Changes at the Last Minute*, also featuring Ellen Barkin and co-scripted by John Sayles.

Then came the biggie: *Footloose*. Kevin Bacon was at his most appealing as 'Ren', the city boy who turns up at a small Midwestern town to discover that dancing has been outlawed. Rather good at moving his feet, Ren objects to this Terpsichorean censorship and strives to set matters straight. After putting his foot in it, he dances up a storm and even wins the affections of the stern preacher's daughter (Lori Singer). The director Herbert Ross, who started out as a dancer and choreographer, brought an enormous zing to the proceedings and helped the film to a healthy box-office run.

With this commercial success under his belt, Kevin Bacon saw his career nosedive. He was a star, but his films didn't measure up. He tamed the wilderness in *White Water Summer*, and played a bicycle messenger boy in *Quicksilver*, neither of which gained a theatrical release in Britain. There was also a mediocre, stagy TV movie, *Lemon Sky*, which, although it left the critics cold, did introduce him to the actress Kyra Sedgwick, whom he married a year later, in 1988.

Next, he took a cameo in John Hughes' *Planes, Trains and Automobiles* (in which he stole a taxi from Steve Martin), and he then accepted a supporting role in the whimsical *End of the Line*, produced by and co-starring Mary Steenburgen. He was at his charismatic best as the young husband burdened by domesticity in Hughes' *She's Having a Baby* (Elizabeth McGovern was having it), but the film went nowhere. *Criminal Law* did little better, but was a good-looking, atmospheric attempt at *film noir*, with Bacon the serial killer gleefully tormenting his own lawyer (Gary Oldman).

He had the lead in *The Big Picture*, a winning, occasionally hilarious spoof on Hollywood, pre-empting *The Player* by three years. Bacon was Nick Chapman, a scrupulous film student who believes in black-and-white, simple camera moves and heterosexual relationships. In an industry devoted to the quick buck, Chapman is eventually forced to contemplate a movie called, um, *Beach Nuts*. A stalwart supporting cast included Martin Short (superb as Chapman's agent), Jennifer Jason Leigh, Roddy McDowall, Elliott Gould and John Cleese.

An even better picture turned up in the form of *Tremors*, a hugely entertaining comic-thriller with Bacon and Fred Ward as a pair of tough, wiry handymen encountering giant worms in the Nevada desert. Again, Bacon was top-billed, and he made an engaging leading man, complete with a no-bull, off-kilter sense of humour.

He was offered the starring role in *Flatliners*, but instead opted for the straighter part of the idealistic David Labraccio, who initially resists the idea of experimenting with death in order to sample after-life experiences. Kiefer Sutherland took the part Bacon rejected, Julia Roberts and William Baldwin also starred, and the film was a hit.

His next one, *He Said, She Said*, a romantic comedy with Elizabeth Perkins, wasn't. Neither was *Queen's Logic*, a 'reunion' picture in the tradition of *The Big Chill*, which also starred John Malkovich, Joe Mantegna and Jamie Lee Curtis. Next came *JFK*, Oliver Stone's much-publicized conspiracy thriller, with Kevin Costner top-billed as a crusading DA sifting through the red herrings surrounding Kennedy's assassination. Although Bacon only had a small role, he got better notices than Costner.

In *Pyrates*, he and Kyra Sedgwick played a sexually active couple who caused fires whenever they made love. Although occasionally amusing, this bizarre sex comedy strived *too* hard to be original and failed to catch on. Then it was back to the ensemble ranks to play a hard-edged navy lawyer in *A Few Good Men*. With a cast that included Tom Cruise, Jack Nicholson and Demi Moore, Bacon had to struggle to make an impression, but succeeded in holding his own in the courtroom. In fact, he was one of the best things in the film.

He then journeyed to Africa to play a basketball coach in *The Air Up There*, a slight if amiable comedy, and starred opposite Meryl Streep in Curtis Hanson's gripping *The River Wild*, playing a charismatic killer (for which he won a Golden Globe nomination). He was superb as a wronged prisoner in *Murder In the First* (receiving some of the best reviews of his career), and followed it with a stellar turn as astronaut Jack Swigert in the mammoth hit *Apollo 13*. He also registered strong reviews as the sadistic reform school guard in *Sleepers*, another hit, but found true fame emerging from a most unexpected direction.

From who knows where, a bizarre game filtered out of Hollywood called 'Six Degrees of Kevin Bacon'. Obviously inspired by the play and film by John Guare (*Six Degrees of Separation*), the sport was easy enough

Victim of injustice: Bacon in possibly the best performance of his career, in **Murder in the First**

*As Nokes, the sadistic homosexual prison guard in Barry Levinson's **Sleepers***

to play. One simply had to think of anybody in the movie business and then link them to Kevin Bacon within six moves. A must at dinner parties on both sides of the Atlantic, the diversion only failed to appeal to those who had no idea who Kevin Bacon was.

Then, in 1996, the genuine article made his directorial debut with *Losing Chase*, an intriguing drama in which a mother's help (Kyra Sedgwick) has a profound effect on a woman (Helen Mirren) going through a mid-life crisis. Bacon exhibited an intelligent grasp on his material, ably assisted by an evocative score from his brother, Michael. He then teamed up with Brad Renfro and Armin Mueller-Stahl for the Cleveland-set drama *Telling Lies in America*.

FILMOGRAPHY

1978: *National Lampoon's Animal House*. 1979: *Starting Over; The Gift* (TV). 1980: *Friday the 13th; Hero At Large*. 1981: *Only When I Laugh* (UK: *It Hurts Only When I Laugh*). 1982: *Diner; Forty Deuce*. 1983: *The Demon Murder Case* (TV); *Enormous Changes at the Last Minute*. 1984: *Footloose*. 1986: *Quicksilver*. 1987: *White Water Summer* (a.k.a. *Rites of Summer*) (filmed in 1985); *Lemon Sky* (TV); *Planes, Trains and Automobiles; End of the Line*. 1988: *She's Having a Baby*. 1989: *Criminal Law* (filmed in 1987); *The Big Picture*. 1990: *Tremors; Flatliners*. 1991: *He Said, She Said; Queen's Logic; JFK*. 1992: *Pyrates; A Few Good Men*. 1994: *The Air Up There; The River Wild*. 1995: *Murder In the First; Apollo 13; Balto* (voice only). 1996: *Losing Chase* (directed only); *Sleepers*. 1997: *Picture Perfect; Telling Lies in America*. 1998: *Wild Things*.

ALEC BALDWIN

Alec Baldwin is an exceptionally talented actor with charisma to spare. He's also as good-looking as they get, six feet tall, with a strong jaw-line and pale-blue, fluorescent eyes that female journalists are prone to swoon over. He's been described as a ladies' man, and has been involved with Michelle Pfeiffer, Ally Sheedy and Cynthia Gibb. He was also engaged, briefly, to Janine Turner in 1983. He's had his bad press, too, thanks largely to a high-profile liaison with Kim Basinger, but more often than not he has shown an integrity rare in a burgeoning film star. Once, he turned down a $1 million offer from a Japanese tobacco company to promote their product. With typical candour, he explained: 'I could make a fortune if I wanted to. But doing a piece of acting is like making love to somebody. I say to myself, "Can I get it up for this? Can I make love to this every day?"'

Baldwin is also courageous enough to express his political (or otherwise) views in public, and pulls no punches. He's unafraid to take a supporting role if the film merits it (*Glengarry Glen Ross* did), and if a big movie conflicts with a previous commitment, he has been known to jettison the better offer. And even before he was a star, the cream of Hollywood came begging for his services. 'He is so eminently gifted,' offered Jonathan Demme, who cast Baldwin as Mafia hitman Frank

'Cucumber' DeMarco in *Married to the Mob*. 'We were very fortunate to get Alec to play a relatively small part, one that required tremendous presence.'

'I'd call him a working-class Cary Grant,' added Oliver Stone, who directed the actor in *Talk Radio*. 'I thought he did us a big favour, because he was getting hot then, and it was a small budget movie in which he took a supporting role. But he approached it as an actor wanting to be part of a team, not a star.'

'Some people you will find are very good actors, and some have that indefinable screen charisma,' continued James Foley, director of *Glengarry Glen Ross*. 'But Alec Baldwin is one of those rare people who have both. That's what makes him a movie star.'

Baldwin himself has said: 'If I have one stupid, childish thing I wish for, I'd like to win a Tony award. That would really, really make me happy.' Ironically, when he was cast as Jack Ryan in the $42.5 million movie *Patriot Games* (with a series of lucrative sequels attached), Baldwin jumped boat. *Games* was running behind schedule, and the actor had promised his services to the play *A Streetcar Named Desire* on Broadway, so he turned down the biggest star-making part of his career and was replaced by Harrison Ford. Still, Baldwin got rave reviews for his role as Kowalski in *Streetcar* and, on 4 May 1992, he was nominated for a Tony – alongside Alan Alda, Brian Bedford and Judd Hirsch. A month

*Alec Baldwin in an early role, as the bible-thumping Jimmy Swaggert in **Great Balls of Fire!***

Alec Baldwin as CIA analyst Jack Ryan in the box-office smash
The Hunt For Red October

Hollywood took note.

His big-screen debut came with the male lead in *Forever, Lulu*, a picture he describes as, 'one of the worst films ever committed to celluloid'. He then played Kevin Bacon's smarmy best friend in *She's Having a Baby* and Michelle Pfeiffer's husband in *Married to the Mob* – after Ray Liotta turned the role down. He was a friendly ghost in Tim Burton's hit *Beetlejuice*, a talk show producer in *Talk Radio*, and Melanie Griffith's cheating boyfriend in *Working Girl*. He was superb as the exuberant evangelist Jimmy Swaggart in *Great Balls of Fire!*, and was even better as the amoral ex-con in *Miami Blues*, produced by Jonathan Demme. Next, he landed the role of Jack Ryan (turned down by Harrison Ford) in *The Hunt For Red October*, and made a dynamic, hugely appealing hero. The film grossed $200 million worldwide, and Baldwin was declared the biggest new male star of 1990.

But then things went badly wrong. After he dropped out of Philip Kaufman's prestigious *Henry and June* – due, he contends, to 'exhaustion' – he lost the showy role of Vincent Mancini in Francis Ford Coppola's *The Godfather Part III* (Andy Garcia got it). Some even say he dropped the first film to get the second. He was, however, looking forward to playing the David Janssen part in the $30 million film version of TV's *The Fugitive*, for director Walter Hill. But this, too, failed to materialize, and was put on hold due to script difficulties. Two years later, Harrison Ford walked off with the part.

Baldwin took a cameo in Woody Allen's *Alice* (playing another ghost) and then landed the title role in Disney's *The Marrying Man*, with Kim Basinger. The on-set troubles on the latter are now part of Hollywood legend. Basinger and Baldwin, playing on-again, off-again lovers, fell for each other hard, and apparently declared war on Disney in the process. Basinger reportedly fired cameraman Ian Baker and forced the film's writer – Neil Simon, no less – off the set. Baldwin admitted, 'It was a terrible, terrible experience,' and the film turned out to be both a critical and box-office disaster. However, Baldwin and Basinger proved their love was for real when

later, the prize was presented to Judd Hirsch for his performance in *Conversations With My Father*, and a week after that *Patriot Games* opened across the USA to gross a staggering $25 million in seven days. Baldwin's own movie that year, *Prelude to a Kiss*, only made $19 million in its entire run. Still, the critics loved it.

He was born Alexander Rae Baldwin III on 3 April 1958, the second eldest of six children. Three of his younger brothers have gone on to successful acting careers of their own, namely William (*Backdraft, Sliver*), Daniel (*Harley Davidson and the Marlboro Man, Knight Moves*) and Stephen (*The Usual Suspects, Fled*). Alec, or 'Xander' as his family knew him, grew up in Massapequa, on Long Island, New York, where his father taught riflery at the local high school. Xander dreamed of a career in public service, but enjoyed acting in school productions. He figured maybe acting could lead him to bigger things.

For three years he studied political science at George Washington University but became disillusioned

with electoral politics and, following the break-up of a two-year relationship, he moved to New York University and studied drama under Lee Strasberg. He was yet to finish his course when he landed the role of the odious Billy Allison Aldrich in the daytime TV soap *The Doctors*, a role he essayed for two-and-a-half years. 'I thought, "I'll do this for a while, make some money, be able to pay for a year or two of law school, and then get out of this business."' I don't think so.

Instead, Baldwin followed the advice of his agent, moved to Los Angeles and got another TV series, *Cutter To Houston*. Baldwin played internist Dr Hal Wexler, one of three physicians working at a Texas community hospital (the other two were Jim Metzler and Shelley Hack). There was another soap, *Knot's Landing*, but enough was enough, and Baldwin fled to New York in 1986 after his character, a disturbed evangelist, was killed off. He made his stage debut in a Broadway revival of Joe Orton's *Loot*, and won a Theater World Award for best performance by a newcomer.

Alec Baldwin with the love of his life, Kim Basinger, in Disney's troubled **The Marrying Man**

they tied the knot on 19 August 1993, at a private ceremony on the beach at East Hampton, Long Island.

Next came the romantic fantasy *Prelude to a Kiss* (a flop), with Baldwin repeating his stage role to fine effect, and then a powerhouse cameo in *Glengarry Glen Ross*, James Foley's potent adaptation of David Mamet's Pulitzer Prize-winning play. Baldwin played a ruthless company spokesman and delivered his hard-hitting dialogue with gusto (sample: '*Fuck you*. That's my name. You know why, mister? Cause you drove a Hyundai to get here tonight, I drove an $80,000 BMW. *That's* my name.'). He then joined Nicole Kidman in Harold Becker's corkscrew thriller *Malice*, bringing all his smarmy charm to bear as Jed Hill, a brilliant, smooth-talking trauma surgeon who moves to a quiet Massachusetts town (just as a series of brutal rapes terrorize the community). The film ploughed familiar territory, but did so with aplomb, helped not a little by Baldwin's unsettling, ambiguous performance.

He teamed up with Kim again in the remake of the 1972 Steve McQueen-Ali MacGraw thriller *The Getaway*, repeating the husband-and-wife formula to little effect. While Baldwin attempted to smoulder, he looked like he had a severe case of the sulks, whereas the film itself suffered from that prevalent affliction of who-

givesashit? And although the action sequences were well handled (by director Roger Donaldson), the frank sexual activity between Kim and Alec unsettled many viewers.

The actor's career continued to splutter with the abysmal *The Shadow* (in which he played millionaire playboy-cum-crime fighter Lamont Cranston), based on the radio serial; the glossy, unconvincing thriller *The Juror* (as a debonair sadist who torments Demi Moore); and the melodramatic, hackneyed *Heaven's Prisoners* (as a bayou cop with a drinking problem). He then took a supporting role in Al Pacino's hugely entertaining documentary, *Looking For Richard*, playing both himself and Clarence in Shakespeare's *King Richard III*, confessing to the camera: 'I'm getting forty dollars a day and all the donuts you can eat.'

Meanwhile, he found himself in trouble with the law when he struck a paparazzi photographer who had attempted to snap a picture of his newborn daughter, Ireland Eliesse. Sued for assault, he faced a potential six months in prison but, thankfully, was cleared of all charges by a merciful jury. He also had an ally in Whoopi Goldberg, who, as host of the 68th Oscar ceremony, broke off from her spiel about ribbons for causes to blare: 'There is someone who deserves a ribbon ... Alec Baldwin, Bravo Baby!'

He and Whoopi were shooting Rob Reiner's *Ghosts of Mississippi* at the time, the true story of a crusading assistant DA (Baldwin) who takes up the 25-year-old cause of the widow of a slain civil rights activist. Whoopi was the widow, and was very good indeed, but Baldwin failed to bring anything but a superficial gloss to his character, not helped by an under-nourished script.

He then joined Anthony Hopkins and Elle Macpherson in the action-thriller *Bookworm*, from a screenplay by David Mamet.

FILMOGRAPHY

1984: *Sweet Revenge* (TV). 1985: *Love on the Run* (TV). 1986: *Forever, Lulu*. 1987: *She's Having a Baby; The Alamo: 13 Days to Glory* (TV). 1988: *Married to the Mob; Beetlejuice; Talk Radio; Working Girl*. 1989: *Great Balls of Fire!* 1990: *Miami Blues; The Hunt For Red October; Alice*. 1991: *The*

Tough guy: Baldwin in sultry mood in Walter Hill's **The Getaway**

Marrying Man (UK: *Too Hot To Handle*). 1992: *Prelude to a Kiss; Glengarry Glen Ross*. 1993: *Malice*. 1994: *The Getaway; The Shadow*. 1995: *The Juror; A Streetcar Named Desire* (TV); *Two Bits* (narrated only). 1996: *Heaven's Prisoners; Looking For Richard; Ghosts of Mississippi* (a.k.a. *Ghosts From the Past*). 1997: *Bookworm*. 1998: *Simon*.

Bayou blues: Baldwin battling the bottle in **Heaven's Prisoner's**

STEPHEN BALDWIN

If Alec Baldwin is the tough guy and William Baldwin the romantic, then Stephen Baldwin is the fool. More often than not cast as a smart alec, the youngest Baldwin made up in energy what he lacked in sheer good looks. And, unlike William, he was not afraid to take on anything that came along. Consequently, by the late 1990s, he was one of the most visible faces around.

Stephen Baldwin made his breakthrough in acting in the surprisingly frank campus sex comedy *Threesome*, in which he played a sex maniac on amphetamines. Commercially, he made his mark in *The Usual Suspects*, as the devil-may-care thief Michael McManus. Then, by the time he teamed up with Laurence Fishburne in the comedy-action-thriller *Fled*, he was making a million dollars a movie.

Born on 12 May 1966, on Long Island, New York, the youngest of the six Baldwin progeny (Beth, Alec, Daniel, William, Jane, in descending order), Stephen had a lot to live up to. 'We've always got along,' he notes, 'but now we live far apart from each other, we appreciate each other more. When we were at home, yeah, we competed, athletically. We beat each other up. And, being the youngest, I got squashed all the time – but I held my own and learned quickly how to resort to guerrilla tactics.'

In his late teens Stephen enrolled at the American Academy of Dramatic Arts and co-starred opposite Daryl Hannah in *Out of America* off-Broadway, his stage debut. Then, when he was just 20 years old, he encountered a Brazilian beauty called Kennya – on a bus in New York. 'There she was, an angel glowing,' he marvels, somewhat poetically. 'And there I was. I wouldn't say a devil, but well on the way. It was love at first sight. I was going to see my manager, and told him I'd just met the girl I was going to marry.' Alec Baldwin was best man, and the couple moved to an adobe residence in Arizona, where they resolved to bring up their daughter, Alaia, far from the corrupting influences of Hollywood.

In the mean time, Stephen landed a starring role opposite Jason Patric in *The Beast*, as a Russian – Golikov –

*Three's a riot: Stephen Baldwin (right) with Lara Flynn Boyle and Josh Charles in **Threesome***

stranded in the Afghan desert, and then won the part of Buffalo Bill Cody in ABC TV's western series *The Young Riders*. The series was a success and, at the age of 23, Baldwin was experiencing his first morsel of fame.

He followed this with small roles in *Last Exit to Brooklyn* and *Born on the Fourth of July*, and a starring one in *Crossing the Bridge*, a nostalgic comedy-drama set in 1975 in Detroit in which three friends attempt to smuggle hashish into the USA. The film wasn't up to much, but it did showcase Baldwin in a telling performance as the more reserved member of the trio of adventurers. In the all-star *Posse* he was 'Little J', a strutting cowboy in a largely Afro-American cast; he played a yokel involved with Patsy Kensit *and* Jennifer

Rubin in the schlocky erotic melodrama *Bitter Harvest*, and joined Luke Perry in *8 Seconds*, John G. Avildsen's so-so biography of rodeo star Lane Frost. He had little to do as the nefarious brother of Gabriel Byrne in the heartfelt Steve Martin vehicle *A Simple Twist of Fate* (updated by Martin from George Eliot's *Silas Marner*), and then there was *Threesome*, the story of three students – Baldwin, Josh Charles and Lara Flynn Boyle – who find themselves thrown together due to a clerical error. As different as chalk, cheese and chilli con carne, the trio of misfits eventually warm to each other and engage in a startling *ménage à trois*. However, once the film lost its ability to shock it somewhat ran out of steam, although Baldwin's depiction of unbri-

*Tough guy: Stephen B. mates out a bit of old testosterone in **Fall Time** (with Jonah Blechman and David Arquette)*

Another culprit? Stephen Baldwin with Kevin Pollak in **The Usual Suspects**

dled lust was quite unforgettable.

He then had a cameo in *Mrs Parker and the Vicious Circle* (as a swain of Jennifer Jason Leigh's Dorothy Parker), before starring in a quirky little thriller called *Fall Time*, in which he played a psychotic bank robber who is mistakenly abducted by two high school graduates as part of a practical joke. Needless to say, the joke backfires to tragic ends as Baldwin breaks free and tortures his kidnappers. Attempting a cross between *Blood Simple* and *Reservoir Dogs*, the film lacked the calibre of both, but was engrossing while it lasted.

Much, much better was *The Usual Suspects*, in which Baldwin teamed up with Gabriel Byrne, Kevin Pollak, Kevin Spacey and Benicio Del Toro as a quintet of crooks who are summarily rounded up for a crime they didn't commit. Many have offered various interpretations of the film's elaborate narrative twists, but whatever one's take, *The Usual Suspects* is a stylish, chilling thriller of rare pedigree. Baldwin in particular cut a dashing figure as the bearded, hot-blooded McManus, although it was Spacey who walked off with an Oscar for best supporting actor, as did Christopher McQuarrie for his highly-inventive screenplay.

Then Baldwin joined Emily Lloyd in the barely noticed *Under the Hula Moon*, an engagingly offbeat comedy, and next starred in the equally obscure *Dead Weekend*, the story of a female alien who needs sex to flourish. *Bio-Dome* followed, an unbearable farce with MTV jock Pauly Shore, which

Baldwin described as 'like *Dumb and Dumber* – a very broad comedy about two silly guys who drive by the biosphere and mistake it for a mall opening'. The reviews were not kind.

Critics were no more generous to *Crimetime*, a silly thriller in which Baldwin played an American actor in England who takes on the role of a real-life serial killer in a crime re-enactment TV show. Pete Postlethwaite co-starred as the genuine article and, by all accounts, the actors virtually came to blows on the troubled set. In *Fled*, Baldwin looked much more comfortable playing a computer hacker who infiltrates the account of a multi-national corporation, transferring $25

On the run: Stephen B. as computer hacker Luke Dodge in the fast-moving **Fled**

million into his own coffers. In prison for his deeds, he escapes into the Georgia countryside with a disgruntled Laurence Fishburne handcuffed to his wrist, resulting in no end of derivative and improbable high jinks. Again the critics sharpened their scalpels, but *Fled* never pretended to be anything more than an excursion of good old-fashioned action pumped with testosterone. Besides, Baldwin and Fishburne made the most bewitching double-act since Bob Hoskins and Jessica Rabbit.

Next, Baldwin teamed up with Gabrielle Anwar and Tom Conti in the thriller *Crush Depth*.

FILMOGRAPHY

1988: *The Beast*. 1989: *Last Exit to Brooklyn; Born on the Fourth of July*. 1992: *Crossing the Bridge*. 1993: *Posse; Bitter Harvest*. 1994: *8 Seconds; A Simple Twist of Fate; Threesome; Mrs Parker and the Vicious Circle; Fall Time*. 1995: *The Usual Suspects; Under the Hula Moon; Dead Weekend*. 1996: *Bio-Dome; Crimetime; Fled*. 1997: *Crush Depth*. 1998: *One Tough Cop; The Object of My Affection; Frogs for Snakes*.

WILLIAM BALDWIN

The Baldwin brothers came in all shapes and sizes. Alec, the eldest, was the handsome one, a could-be Cary Grant. Daniel was stockier, tougher-looking, and played bad guys and aggressive cops. The youngest, Stephen, was the mischievous baby of the family, always ready with a wicked grin and a prank. And then there was William – or Billy – lanky, 6'4", sensitive, more beautiful than his brothers, in a love-me-or-step-on-me sort of way. While the twentysomething generation was swooning over the antics of Alec Baldwin in *The Hunt For Red October*, teenage girls were revving up their pulses for Billy in *Flatliners, Backdraft* and *Three of Hearts*.

Ironically, Billy got his first break playing a killer in the TV movie *The Preppie Murder*, based on the true case of ladies' man Robert Chambers. Co-star Tuesday Knight was impressed by the actor's ability to immerse himself in the role. 'His eyes go so blank,' she explained. 'Yet in other scenes he shows a vulnerable, gentle side like Chambers must have had. Even though you know he's a murderer, you can see why girls

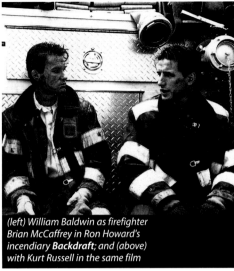

like him.'

Veteran actor Danny Aiello, who played the policeman interrogating Chambers, had a major emotional scene with Baldwin. 'It was one of the greatest scenes I've ever been involved in,' Aiello says. 'Billy had a very tough role. He had to stay flat the entire time before he finally broke down and cried ... He's wonderful. I never had so much pleasure working with a kid.'

William Baldwin was born on 21 February 1963 in Massapequa, Long Island, New York, the fourth child (of six) to high school coach Alexander Rae Baldwin Jr. Billy's mother, Carol, recalled: 'Their father gave the kids enormous drive. He instilled in them the feeling that they could do anything. All the children set goals for themselves.'

Billy's goal was law school, and he graduated from the State University of New York with a degree in political science. However, inspired by his brother's success in showbusiness, he abandoned law and tried drama himself, signing up with the renowned Ford model agency to pay for acting class. From TV commercials (in partic-

ular his endorsement of Levi's 501 jeans), he landed the role of a Vietnam soldier in Oliver Stone's *Born on the Fourth of July* (interestingly, both Stephen and Daniel Baldwin had roles in the same movie). This led to the starring role in *The Preppie Murder*, for which he won excellent reviews as the smarmy, ruthless Chambers, luring Jennifer Levin (Lara Flynn Boyle) to her death in Central Park.

In Mike Figgis's *Internal Affairs*, he played corrupt cop Richard Gere's emotionally unhinged and ultimately ill-fated partner, and then teamed up with Kiefer Sutherland, Julia Roberts and Kevin Bacon as one of five medical students experimenting with death in Joel Schumacher's MTV thriller *Flatliners*. Baldwin played Joe Hurley, a somewhat smarmy ladies' man whose past sexual conquests literally come back to haunt him. The film was a hit, and Baldwin was instantly in demand.

He was offered the part of the young hitchhiker who seduces Geena Davis in *Thelma and Louise*, and accepted it, then landed the key role in Ron Howard's big-budget, all-star *Backdraft*. He walked off *Thelma and Louise* (and

was replaced by an unknown Brad Pitt) and joined Kurt Russell, Scott Glenn, Jennifer Jason Leigh, Rebecca De Mornay, Donald Sutherland and Robert De Niro for *Backdraft*, playing the son of a heroic Chicago firefighter who cannot accept his father's death. Russell was his big brother, determined to teach him a few life lessons. In spite of the spectacular cast, it was the firefighting scenes that stole the acting honours, although the film's $76 million box-office gross in the USA hardly damaged any careers.

Indeed, Baldwin landed top-billing in his next picture, *Three of Hearts*, in which he played male escort Joe Casella, who claims that he can win 'any woman – any time – any place – guaranteed'. However, when he is used as a prop in the tug-of-hearts between lesbians Kelly Lynch and Sherilyn Fenn, he is pitched into a romantic whirlwind. Long in pre-production, the film was originally destined as a vehicle for Robert Downey Jr, but it was hard to imagine any actor making Casella quite so arrogant or appealing as Baldwin. Then he won the male lead in the erotic thriller *Sliver*, opposite Sharon Stone, described by director Phillip Noyce as 'the *Rear Window* of the 1990s'. In order to secure the part over a roster of potential leading men, Baldwin had to screen test with Ms Stone to establish their sexual chemistry. And he emerged triumphant.

However, billowing in the slipstream of *Basic Instinct*, the film was a box-office disappointment. Stone

*With Sharon Stone in **Sliver***

played a New York book editor who moves into a Manhattan apartment block that is the scene of a series of murders. Baldwin was on particularly predatory form, engaging in some steamy sex with La Stone, and on one occasion daring her to remove her knickers in the middle of an up-market restaurant.

In the quirky and frequently delightful romantic comedy *A Pyromaniac's Love Story*, he played Garet Lumpke, a hot-blooded Romeo with a gammy leg who burns down a bakery in a fit of romantic jealousy. Yet in spite of its many pleasures – and an engaging cast – this loopy entertainment failed to lure the audience that had so will-

*Tough guy: William B. as stubborn cop Max Kirkpatrick in **Fair Game***

ingly embraced the similar *Moonstruck*. He then tried on the mantle of maverick cop for the Joel Silver actioner *Fair Game* (a remake of *Cobra*, which starred Sylvester Stallone), teamed with Cindy Crawford in her film debut. As it happens, Warner Brothers had so little faith in this perfectly serviceable entertainment that they refused to show it to critics. True, there was scant thermodynamics between Baldwin and Crawford, but the film moved at the rate of knots and boasted some spectacular stunts.

He then played a rakish serial killer in the black comedy *Curdled*, based on a short that had inspired the final passages of *Pulp Fiction*. As a tribute to this fact, Quentin Tarantino served as executive producer, but the film went nowhere.

FILMOGRAPHY

1989: Born on the Fourth of July; The Preppie Murder (TV). 1990: Internal Affairs; Flatliners. 1991: Backdraft. 1993: Three of Hearts; Sliver. 1995: A Pyromaniac's Love Story; Fair Game. 1996: Curdled. 1998: Virus.

DREW BARRYMORE

Many scenes from the highest-grossing film of its time, *E.T. The Extra-Terrestrial*, stand out in the memory. But one of the most poignant and unforgettable must be the one in which little Gertie, her hair in pigtails, presents E.T. with a pot of flowers and then kisses him on the nose. As screen kisses go, it is one of the most indelible.

At the time, Drew Barrymore was only seven years old, the youngest in the cast. It was inconceivable then, back in 1982, that *E.T.* (described as the best film Disney never made) would become the biggest money-maker of all time, and that a decade later the most famous member of its cast would be the kid sister.

Drew Barrymore's fame rests on a number of factors. She is the youngest member of one of Hollywood's most prestigious acting dynasties. Her grandfather is the legendary actor, matinee idol and writer John Barrymore; her great-aunt the Oscar-winning actress Ethel Barrymore, and her great-uncle the Oscar-winning actor Lionel Barrymore. Even her father, the actor-turned-poet John Jr., courted some

fame, although his drug busts and failed marriages earned the lion's share of public attention.

Drew herself became a tabloid favourite when she took to drinking at nine, became a cocaine addict at 12, and entered rehab at 13 – all of which she chronicled in her 1989 book, *Little Girl Lost*.

She is also one of the few child actresses who has managed to make a successful transition to adult star, winning special kudos for her role as a psychotic nympho in the 1992 *Poison Ivy*. While *Playboy* singled out her 'emphatic screen presence', *Rolling Stone* raved: 'as the teen fatale of this low-budget, high-style find, Drew Barrymore kicks her *E.T.* image over the rainbow. Now little Gertie rivals Sharon Stone in indulging basic instincts ... Barrymore nails every carnal, comic and vulnerable shading in her role; she's a knockout.'

Drew herself is a little more philosophical. Although in 1992 she admitted, 'Everybody's all over me,' she was quick to add, 'but I know that next month the hype might not be there.'

Born Andrew Blyth Barrymore on 22 February 1975, in Los Angeles, the actress made her professional debut at 11 months, doing a dog food commercial. Eighteen months after that she appeared in the TV movie *Suddenly, Love*, with Cindy Williams and Joan Bennett, played William Hurt's daughter, Margaret, in *Altered States*, and did another TV movie, *Bogie*, a poor biog of Humphrey Bogart. Then came *E.T.*

When Drew was cast as Henry Thomas's cute kid sister (who screams the house down on encountering the alien, then dresses him in drag), her formidable lineage was unknown to Spielberg. However, she had enough professional confidence that the director allowed her to 'let me do what I wanted ... as long as I knew my lines'.

In *Irreconcilable Differences* she played Ryan O'Neal and Shelley Long's daughter, Casey, who sues her insufferable parents for divorce; and she landed the title role in *Firestarter*, as a 'pyrokinetic' nine-year-old on the run. In the latter she was supported by no less than George C. Scott, Martin Sheen, Art Carney and Louise Fletcher.

Stephen King, on whose novel *Firestarter* was based, was so impressed with the little actress that (with a little

*It started with a hiss: child star and pyromaniac Drew Barrymore in **Firestarter**, from the Stephen King bestseller*

encouragement from Dino De Laurentiis), he wrote *Cat's Eye* specially for her. This was the story of a little girl whose cat protects her from a menacing troll hiding in her bedroom wall. Two other segments based on Stephen King short stories completed the movie, with the likes of James Woods and Robert Hays filling out an impressive cast.

Drugs, booze and rehab followed, and the little child star with the heart-breaking gaze vanished.

Four years later, aged 14, Drew Barrymore returned with a vengeance. In *Far From Home* she played her first sexy adolescent, Joleen Cross, who is struggling to put away childish things while fighting off an insane killer in a trailer park. The film tried to be more than just another slasher movie, bringing in themes of father–daughter bonding (Matt Frewer, who top-billed, played her old man), but it was hardly par for the course.

She fared better, in a supporting role, in Alan J. Pakula's classy, semi-autobiographical *See You In the Morning*, the story of musical families. Psychiatrist Jeff Bridges has two children by model Farrah Fawcett, and falls for photographer Alice Krige, who has three kids of her own. Barrymore played the eldest, Cathy, and improvised her scenes with Krige. Particularly memorable is the episode in which mother and daughter lie in bed talking. Looking at her child's blossoming form, Krige remarks wistfully, 'How I

longed to be big-breasted.' To which Barrymore answers smartly, 'It's no fun, believe me.'

Neither *Far From Home* nor *See You In the Morning* did well at the box-office, and Ms Barrymore threw herself into a flurry of work – before her options could run out. She burned up the screen in *Poison Ivy* (French-kissing co-star Sara Gilbert, coming on to her best friend's father, making love on the bonnet of a Mercedes) and won the reviews of her career. If 1992 didn't give her any commercial breaks, it was her most visible year since *E.T.* phoned home.

Besides the widely-publicized release of *Poison Ivy*, she had a cameo in the road movie *Motorama*; played a victimized eyewitness in *Sketch Artist*, with Jeff Fahey; was haunted by her own malevolent spirit in *Doppelganger*; was nominated for a Golden Globe as a man-eating killer in *Guncrazy* (a teenage version of *Bonnie and Clyde*), and played the actress tenant of a prostitute in the TV movie *2000 Malibu Road*. She also starred in *Ectopia*, with her then-boyfriend Balthazar Getty, and played the title role in the timid TV movie *Beyond Control: The Amy Fisher Story*, based on journalists' accounts and court records of the notorious case surrounding the 17-year-old would-be murderess.

On a personal note, she was spotted dating Billy Idol in January 1994, then married the British club owner Jeremy Thomas two months later, even chang-

ing her name to Drew Thomas. By June the marriage was over. She also caused a furore when she bared her breasts on TV's *The David Letterman Show*, danced topless in a ritzy night-club and posed completely naked for *Playboy*, a stunt which she described as 'an amazing and daring adventure'.

But, while she continued to compete for the title of busiest actress in Hollywood, she *was* honing her craft. She was terrific as a wild and unpredictable runaway in the touching, funny *Boys On the Side*, a female road movie that teamed her with Whoopi Goldberg and Mary-Louise Parker. She was also startlingly good in *Mad Love*, as another runaway, this time a wayward, unstable spirit in love with Chris O'Donnell (although the film itself smacked of MTV opportunity). And in Woody Allen's *Everyone Says I Love You* she played a Manhattan socialite with a propensity for swallowing engagement rings. 'Getting hired to work on a Woody Allen film is the biggest compliment you can get,' she allowed, 'because he is showing that he trusts you and believes you have the ability to be prepared and deliver the performance that he wants.' She even got to sing a solo number ('I'm a Dreamer, Aren't We All?'), although her voice was dubbed by Olivia Hayman. She then landed a genuine hit, playing a

*Posing seductively as Amy Fisher in **Beyond Control - The Amy Fisher Story***

*Drew, as Sugar, escorts Jim Carrey to the ball in **Batman Forever***

high school student lured into a series of deadly games by an anonymous caller in Wes Craven's wicked horror spoof *Scream*.

Romantically, she has been involved with Eric Erlandson, guitarist for Courtney Love's anarchic grunge act, Hole.

FILMOGRAPHY

1978: *Suddenly, Love* (TV). 1980: *Altered States*; *Bogie* (TV). 1982: *E.T. – The Extraterrestrial*. 1984: *Irreconcilable Differences*; *Firestarter*. 1985: *Cat's Eye*. 1986: *Babes in Toyland* (TV). 1987: *Conspiracy of Love* (TV). 1989: *15 and Getting Straight* (TV); *Far From Home*; *See You in the Morning*; *No Place To Hide*; *Tipperary*; *Baby Doll Blues*. 1992: *Poison Ivy*; *Motorama*; *Sketch Artist*; *Doppelganger*; *Guncrazy*; *Waxwork II: Lost in Time*; *2000 Malibu Road* (TV); *Ectopia*. 1993: *Beyond Control: The Amy Fisher Story* (TV); *Bad Girls*; *Wayne's World 2* (cameo). 1994: *Inside the Goldmine*; *Boys on the Side*; *Mad Love*. 1995: *Batman Forever*. 1996: *Wishful Thinking*; *Everyone Says I Love You*; *Scream*. 1997: *Independence*; *Home Fries*; *Frigid and Impotent*. 1998: *The Wedding Singer*; *Cinderella*.

ANNETTE BENING

Annette Bening's rise to stardom was so swift that no one saw her coming. From virtual obscurity, she played Dan Aykroyd's wife in a John Hughes movie, took the female lead in a Milos Forman epic, worked opposite Meryl Streep in *Postcards from the Edge*, won an Oscar nomination, played leading lady to Robert De Niro and Harrison Ford, bagged the coveted role of Catwoman

in *Batman Returns* and then snared Hollywood's most famous and unattainable bachelor, Warren Beatty, giving birth to his daughter and leading him to the altar. And all this in the space of three years.

Born in Topeka, Kansas, on 29 May 1958, Annette was the daughter of an insurance salesman, and the youngest of four children. In the 1960s the Benings moved west, and Annette grew up in San Diego, where her passion for acting developed. For a short time she studied at the San Francisco State University (earning a bachelor's degree in theatre arts), and then spent five years at San Francisco's American Conservatory Theater. It was there that she met her husband, Steven White, who was then directing her in a production of *Romeo and Juliet*.

To further her career in theatre and film, Mr and Mrs White moved to New York in 1986. There, Annette landed a bit part in *Miami Vice*, did a TV commercial for Arrid deodorant (which was never aired), and appeared in a pilot for the sitcom *It Had To Be You*, with Tim Matheson (which went on without her). Her luck changed when she was cast in her first play, Tina Howe's *Coastal Disturbances*, as Holly Dancer, a photographer burned by romance. The play transferred to

Broadway, and for her performance Annette was nominated for a Tony and won the Clarence Derwent Award.

When the run of *Coastal Disturbances* ended, the actress was offered the part of Dan Aykroyd's sexually frustrated wife in *The Great Outdoors*, written and produced by John Hughes. Unfortunately, the comedy was both predictable and overly familiar, borrowing plot elements from such earlier Hughes pictures as *National Lampoon's Vacation* and *Planes, Trains and Automobiles*.

The TV movie *Hostage* was better, in which she portrayed Carol Burnett's bitter daughter, shortly before Burnett is held hostage by an escaped con (played by Burnett's real-life daughter, Carrie Hamilton) who ultimately replaces her in her mother's affections. Bening then auditioned for the role of Madame de Tourvel in Stephen Frears' *Dangerous Liaisons*. At the same time, Milos Forman was casting *Valmont*, his version of the Choderlos De Laclos story of sexual corruption in 18th-century France. Michelle Pfeiffer won the part in Stephen Frears' production, but Frears was impressed enough with Annette that he wanted her to play the courtesan whose naked derrière is used as a writing desk by John Malkovich. Tough luck. Forman cast Annette in

*Annette Bening as the conniving Marquise de Merteuil in Milos Forman's sumptuous **Valmont***

Trick or Treat? Annette Bening as con artist Myra Langtree in
Stephen Frears' **The Grifters**

the even bigger role of the Marquise de
Merteuil in *Valmont* (which Glenn
Close played in *Liaisons*). Of the two
versions, Forman's made more sense as
his characters were substantially
younger (and consequently more sympathetic), their games of cruel seduction attributed to the hot-headed con-
ceit of youth. Bening was nothing short
of superb, eschewing the mannered
nuances of evil that Glenn Close laid
on with a shovel. By refusing to under-
line her character's roguery, Bening's
performance was all the more credible
and chilling.

After this, she had an effective
cameo as Dennis Quaid's jilted lover in
Mike Nichols' *Postcards from the Edge*,
spilling the beans to an indignant
Meryl Streep. Catty, beautiful and short
on brain cells, Bening was a delight,
and the film went on to become a
resounding hit. Meanwhile, Stephen
Frears returned to her door, offering
her the role of the libidinous con artist
Myra Langtry in *The Grifters* (after
Geena Davis had turned it down). This
time the actress said yes, and acted her
co-stars – John Cusack and Anjelica
Huston – off the screen. The film was a
critical success, and earned Bening an
Oscar nomination and the best actress

award from the National Society of
Film Critics.

She was Robert De Niro's neglect-
ed wife in *Guilty By Suspicion*, an
absorbing, authentic account of the
Communist witch hunt in 1950s
Hollywood, and she then played
Harrison Ford's better half in Mike
Nichols' *Regarding Henry*. The latter was
unfairly knocked by the critics, as it
was a moving, thought-provoking look
at Henry (Ford), a hot-shot lawyer
who's reduced to an infantile state
when shot in the head. With his career
wiped out, Henry finds his better
instincts revitalized as he starts life
anew, with the fresh viewpoint of a
child. The film had plenty to say, and
did so with a maturity and insight that
went straight for the heart. Nichols,
considered by many in Hollywood to
be the consummate actor's director, was
bowled over by his leading lady. 'She's
got this unique combination of sexiness
and intelligence,' he ventured. 'It's what
you dream of: someone beautiful and
sexy who's also a character actor. We
were in the middle of shooting when I
saw *The Grifters*; and I was really
shocked, because it was someone I did-
n't know at all. I have no idea how she
does it.'

Her next leading man starred opposite her in real life, following his stormy
relationship with Madonna and the
tabloids. He was Warren Beatty, and he
cast her in his next picture, *Bugsy*,
which he also co-produced. A romanti-
cized look at Benjamin 'Bugsy' Siegel,
the prince of gangsters, the film concentrated on Bugsy's romance with
society hostess Virginia Hill (Bening), a
cookie as tough as Bugsy was ruthless.
Bening won equal billing to Beatty
above the title (a rare honour,
Madonna note), and held her own in a
very strong cast (Ben Kingsley, Joe
Mantegna, Harvey Keitel). Her brush-
off line to Beatty at the beginning of
the film became a classic of its kind, as
she belittled the gangster with a with-
ering 'Why don't you run outside and
jerk yourself a soda?' This time the critics approved, and the film stormed off
with no less than ten Oscar nominations (although it only won two).

Next, Bening was to play an
unmarried mother in the rural Irish
drama *The Playboys*, but changed her
mind at the last minute. The film's production company was not amused, and
sued the actress to the tune of $1 mil-
lion for breach of oral contract (Robin
Wright took over the part, and was
brilliant). Meanwhile, Ms Bening had
more important things to occupy her,
as she had won the most coveted role
of the year, beating Julia Roberts, Cher
and Michelle Pfeiffer to play
Catwoman in *Batman Returns*. Batman
himself, Michael Keaton, explained:
'Annette has this really great off-centre
quality, and I'd just seen her in *The
Grifters*. So when [director] Tim
[Burton] said to me, "We've got to
think about Catwoman," I mentioned
Annette and he said, "What a good
idea." No one else was discussed.'

Then the impossible happened: she
conceived Warren Beatty's child. For
the second time Michelle Pfeiffer took
a part Bening had hoped to make her
own and, again, Bening's replacement
turned out to be ideal. In both *The
Playboys* and *Batman Returns*, it's hard to
imagine that Annette Bening could
have been as effective, and yet she has
been so good in everything else.
Anyway, she gave birth to all 8 pounds
11 ounces of Kathlyn Beatty in January
1992, and married the child's father in
March.

Vegas Virginia: *Annette Bening as Bugsy Siegel's wilful mistress Virginia Hill*

Presidential material: Annette Bening in The American President

She joined Beatty again, professionally, in Glenn Gordon Caron's *Love Affair* (a re-make of the 1939 romantic comedy starring Irene Dunne and Charles Boyer, with a new script by Beatty and Robert Towne). However, the film wallowed in its own gloss, and besides a terrific cameo from Katharine Hepburn (as Beatty's aunt), the movie lacked spark. In fact, Warner Brothers were so dispirited by the project that they released it straight to video in Britain.

Following the birth of her second child, Ben, the actress returned to box-office favour in Rob Reiner's *The American President*, a beguiling fantasy in which she played a tough environmental lobbyist who loses her sang-froid when courted by the President of the United States (Michael Douglas). Rob Reiner, who had directed Kathy Bates to an Oscar in *Misery*, knew that the success of his film hung on the casting of the President's date. 'The character called for someone who could believably stand up to the President, who would be smart enough and strong enough to hold her own – even when she is a little thrown off by the fact that she might find herself alone in the Oval Office,' the director emphasized. 'The part also required someone attractive, who had sexuality, a sense of humour and intelligence. And, quite frankly, I couldn't think of any actress but Annette Bening who combined all of these things.' He was quite right, of course, his choice going on to land a Golden Globe nomination for best actress in a comedy.

The same year she called upon her experience at the Summer Shakespeare Festival and played Queen Elizabeth in Ian McKellen's stellar, brilliantly cinematic adaptation of *Richard III*. She then let her hair down as the cerebrally challenged ex-stripper wife of Vegas entrepreneur Jack Nicholson in Tim Burton's sci-fi B-movie spoof *Mars Attacks!*, and in January of '97 gave birth to Isabel Ira Ashley.

FILMOGRAPHY
1988: *The Great Outdoors; Hostage* (TV). 1989: *Valmont*. 1990: *Postcards from the Edge; The Grifters*. 1991: *Guilty By Suspicion; Regarding Henry; Bugsy*. 1994: *Love Affair*. 1995: *The American President; Richard III*. 1996: *Mars Attacks!*

Neil Simon, Broadway's favourite son, selected Matthew Broderick to play his alter ego in his autobiographical hits *Brighton Beach Memoirs* and *Biloxi Blues*. Sidney Lumet, who has directed the likes of Paul Newman, Dustin Hoffman and Al Pacino in his time, has called Broderick 'one of the two best young actors in the United States. There's just this profundity to his work that you rarely, if ever, see in actors that young. He's totally involved, and he's incapable of being a cliche.'

Matthew Broderick can also boast such enormous hits as *WarGames, Ferris Bueller's Day Off* and *Biloxi Blues* to his name, as well as such superb films as *Torch Song Trilogy* and *Glory*. At the age of 20, he was an award-winning stage actor and a movie star. Furthermore, he remained faithful to the theatre, developing a working relationship with the dramatist Horton Foote, and appearing in Foote's plays *On Valentine's Day* and *The Widow Claire*. But, in spite of two tragedies – his father's death in 1982 and a fatal car accident in 1987 – Broderick could not seem to shed his boyish, good-natured persona, and became branded the eternal teenager. Even when he tackled the bravest role of his career – Colonel Robert Gould Shaw in *Glory* – it was his older co-stars Denzel Washington and Morgan Freeman who rode off with the acting honours.

Matthew Broderick was born on 21 August 1962, in New York, the third child and only son of playwright/painter Patricia and actor James Broderick (*Five Easy Pieces, Dog Day Afternoon*). When he was eight years old, 'my father said he was doing a play that had two parts for kids,' Broderick recalls. 'The idea of actually going on the stage scared me so much that I started crying. I thought I didn't want to be an actor after that, and I didn't get back into it until high school.'

Even then, it took a whole year before he could summon up enough courage to audition for a minor role in *A Midsummer Night's Dream* at Manhattan's Walden School, an establishment famous for its theatre programme. Still, once started, he appeared in a total of ten plays in three years,

Matthew Broderick as he looked in 1988

prompting his drama coach to reveal: 'It was pretty clear to me that he had it. Matthew had an incredible ability to be natural, to be warm. He had this magnetism.'

Shortly after graduation, Broderick made his professional stage debut in Horton Foote's *On Valentine's Day*, starring his father, and then he won the young male lead in the film *No Small Affair*, to be directed by the formidable Martin Ritt, and co-starring Sally Field. The young actor was ecstatic, rehearsed his Oscar speech and then watched in horror as the film collapsed, due to – in the euphemism of the film industry – 'creative differences'.

With his self-confidence buffeted, Broderick failed to capitalize on a string of auditions and, in desperation, accepted a commercial for an anti-itch cream. There was a small part in a gay play at a minor, sleazy New York theatre, and Broderick's agent advised him against it, explaining: 'There's no money in it, and you'll be typecast as a gay for the rest of your life.' Still, it was work, and Broderick was in no position to be worried about typecasting. The play was Harvey Fierstein's *Torch Song Trilogy*, and Broderick played David, a troubled, streetwise teenager adopted by Arnold Beckoff, a drag queen played by Fierstein himself. *Newsweek* raved, 'Matthew Broderick gives one of the most original, witty and touching performances I've ever seen from a young actor,' while *The New York Times* praised him for his 'naturalness and spontaneity'. The play later transferred to a bigger theatre, did excellent business, and

Broderick won the Outer Critics' Circle and Village awards for his performance. He was on the way.

'Herbert Ross, the director, saw me in the show and asked me to come audition,' Broderick remembers. 'He was directing Neil Simon's play *Brighton Beach Memoirs* and his own movie, *Max Dugan Returns*. I read for both. Later, when I was putting on my coat to leave, the casting director said, "You had a good day." I said, "I got the movie, didn't I?" She said, "No, you got them both."'

In *Brighton Beach* he played the 15-year-old Eugene Morris Jerome, and won the Tony award for his performance, Broadway's highest honour. In *Max Dugan Returns*, also written by Simon, he starred alongside Marsha Mason, Jason Robards and Donald Sutherland. Immediately afterwards, he landed the starring role in *WarGames*, the highly entertaining story of a computer whiz-kid who thinks he's playing sophisticated video games when in fact he's locked into the government's Norad missile-defence system, prompting the onslaught of World War III. Broderick lent the film an added boost with his boyish zest and charm, and the movie went on to make a mint at the box-office.

Sadly, Matthew's father never lived long enough to witness his son's overnight celebrity. Aged 55, James Broderick died on 1 November 1982. Consequently, young Matthew failed to fully appreciate his new-found success. Even when he won the auditions for both *Max Dugan* and *Brighton Beach*, it

wasn't until his father's enthusiasm that he fully appreciated the significance of his triumph.

After *WarGames*, things slowed down a bit as the young actor agonized over future roles. Besides his stage work, he appeared in the film version of Horton Foote's *1918*, taking a fraction of his now considerable salary. He played Brother Vaughn, a restless Texas teenager – a supporting part he played in honour of his father, who had appeared in the original stage production. Next, he was engaging but miscast as a medieval thief in the romantic fantasy *Ladyhawke*, aiding and abetting the romance of Rutger Hauer and Michelle Pfeiffer; and then he starred in a TV edition of Athol Fugard's *Master Harold ... and the Boys*. There was a video version of *Cinderella*, with Jennifer Beals, and he then recreated his stage role (Brother Vaughn) in Horton Foote's *On Valentine's Day*, a prequel to *1918*. But it wasn't until *Ferris Bueller's Day Off*, written, produced and directed by John Hughes, that Matthew Broderick came into his own as a movie star.

Combining an impish charm with a rebellious, in-your-face bonhomie, Broderick was perfect as the resourceful, 17-year-old truant, even though he was now 24 himself. The film was an enormous hit at the box-office, and Broderick's grinning, cheeky mug was all over the media. Under the sly direction of Hughes, Broderick became a contemporary anti-hero for downtrodden teens and was launched into the popularity polls, just above Michael Douglas and Harrison Ford. *Ferris Bueller* also introduced him to Jennifer Grey, who played his sister Jeanie, and the couple became a couple – for three years.

Ironically, in his next film, a dud, he co-starred with his future girlfriend, Helen Hunt. This was the ambitious *Project X*, a well-researched tear-jerker for animal lovers and anti-nuke protesters. Broderick played a demoted airman, relegated to a top-secret military training programme to look after 'simian guinea pigs' – chimpanzees. Naturally, Broderick finds his loyalties divided between his professional duty and the call of his own heart. A sort of *Short Circuit* gone ape, but without the laughs, *Project X* was a noble, sober

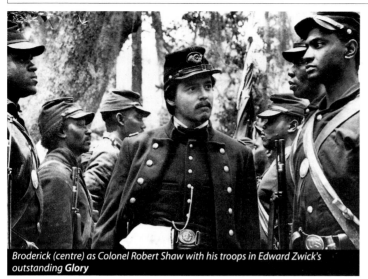

Broderick (centre) as Colonel Robert Shaw with his troops in Edward Zwick's outstanding **Glory**

effort, and for the most part avoided sentimentalizing its subject.

After that, he returned to the off-Broadway stage to star in Horton Foote's *The Widow Claire*, and then repeated his turn as Eugene Morris Jerome in the film version of *Biloxi Blues*, the second leg of Neil Simon's autobiographical trilogy. This time Eugene found himself in a steaming Mississippi boot camp, pitted against drill sergeant Christopher Walken and falling in love with Penelope Ann Miller. Superbly written by Simon and sensitively directed by Mike Nichols, the film further benefited from Matthew Broderick's endearing, funny performance as the gauche wit discovering the complexities of adult life. Unlike the screen adaptation of the first play, *Brighton Beach Memoirs* (in which the Simon/Broderick/Eugene role was played by Jonathan Silverman), *Biloxi Blues* was a resounding hit.

But the movie's success was tinged with tragedy. On 5 August 1987, following the film's completion, Broderick and Grey were holidaying in Ireland, just outside Enniskillen, when their rented BMW 316 collided with a Volvo, killing both occupants – 28-year-old Anna Gallagher and her 63-year-old mother, Margaret Dohetty. Broderick himself suffered several broken ribs, a fractured thigh, a collapsed lung, concussion and facial cuts, while Jennifer was let off with minor bruises. Today, Broderick admits that he may have been driving on the wrong side of the road, and faced a five-year prison

sentence for reckless driving. On 15 February 1988, the actor pleaded guilty in absentia to careless driving and was fined £100, prompting the headline 'FERRIS BUELLER'S LET OFF' in *The New York Post*. After the accident, the star spent a year in physiotherapy and underwent extensive psychotherapy. While he endured his first month in hospital, Jennifer Grey told the press: 'Matthew and I held hands and read together for hours. An accident like that means you never again take a single day for granted. I feel so lucky to be alive and to have Matthew beside me.' Nevertheless, their relationship failed to survive the trauma, and the couple separated in 1988.

Now older and wiser, Broderick found himself being more picky when it came to selecting roles. He was announced to star in *Chances Are*, with Cybill Shepherd, but the part went to Robert Downey Jr. He took a supporting role in the film version of *Torch Song Trilogy*, now playing Alan, the gay boyfriend of drag queen Arnold Beckoff, again essayed by Harvey Fierstein. The play lost none of its bite nor humour in its transfer to the screen, but the accolades were slapped squarely on Fierstein's shoulders.

Broderick's next three films also gave freer range to his co-stars, and not surprisingly so. In Sidney Lumet's limp crime comedy *Family Business*, Broderick was improbably cast as the son of Dustin Hoffman and grandson of Sean Connery (!), and the film was a box-office stiff. He was much better in

Glory, playing a character roughly his own age, the 25-year-old Colonel Robert Gould Shaw, who leads a regiment of Negro soldiers on a heroic charge on a Confederate stronghold in the American Civil War. Broderick was superb as the confused, obstinate Bostonian officer, but he was criticized for being too young for the role. Ironically, the actor was actually two years older than his real-life counterpart. However, it was Denzel Washington, as a rebellious slave who signs up with the 54th Regiment, who won an Oscar that year (for best supporting actor). Broderick then returned to more familiar terrain with *The Freshman*, as a film student pressed into the services of a Mafia don, played by Marlon Brando with an uncanny resemblance to Vito Corleone in *The Godfather. The Freshman* was an amiable enough caper, but it is Brando's cameo that people remember.

It was to be another two years before Broderick returned to cinema screens, and then he must have regretted it. In the unbelievably bad *Out on a Limb*, he played a city yuppie who drops a $140 million take-over bid to rescue his sister in a backwater town called Buzzsaw. The trade paper *Variety* was uncharacteristically charitable when, in September 1992, it described it as 'a moronic comedy' and 'the worst film of the year so far'.

Next, Broderick appeared with Max Von Sydow in Philip Borsos's *Cider House Rules*, and was then very good as a lovelorn gourmet cook in

Broderick with Marlon Brando in Andrew Bergman's **The Freshman**

Say owwww! Anthony Hopkins inspects Broderick's oral depths in Alan Parker's **The Road to Wellville** (Bridget Fonda looks on)

FILMOGRAPHY

1983: *Max Dugan Returns; WarGames*. 1984: *1918*. 1985: *Ladyhawke; Master Harold ... and the Boys* (TV); *Cinderella* (video). 1986: *On Valentine's Day; Ferris Bueller's Day Off*. 1987: *Project X*. 1988: *Biloxi Blues; Torch Song Trilogy*. 1989: *Family Business; Glory*. 1990: *The Freshman*. 1992: *Out on a Limb*. 1993: *The Cider House Rules; The Night We Never Met*. 1994: *The Lion King* (voice only); *Mrs Parker and the Vicious Circle; A Life In the Theater* (TV); *The Road to Wellville; Arabian Knight* (voice only). 1996: *Infinity* (also directed); *The Cable Guy*. 1997: *Addicted to Love*. 1998: *Godzilla*.

SANDRA BULLOCK

the ensemble New York comedy *The Night We Never Met*, co-starring Annabella Sciorra and Kevin Anderson. In the mean time, his romance with Helen Hunt had foundered, and he took up with the actress Sarah Jessica Parker (*LA Story, Honeymoon in Vegas*).

Interestingly, he found his biggest audience yet as the voice of the adult Simba in Walt Disney's phenomenally successful *The Lion King*, but he then slipped back into supporting roles for other stars. In Alan Rudolph's lugubrious *Mrs Parker and the Vicious Circle*, he was the womanizing reporter Charles MacArthur to Jennifer Jason Leigh's Dorothy Parker. In Alan Parker's beautifully crafted *The Road to Wellville* (a glorious hymn to the quackery of bowel connoisseur Dr John Harvey Kellogg, played by Anthony Hopkins), Broderick portrayed the hapless Will Lightbody, who, in Parker's words, is

'douched, scrubbed, fried, prodded and purged, his intestines "snipped out like a wart"'. And in *The Cable Guy* he was the hapless, emotionally constipated straight man to Jim Carrey.

He tried his hand at directing with the somewhat turgid *Infinity*, the story of the love life of the atomic physicist Richard Feynman (played by Broderick). The screenplay was written by his own mother, Patricia, a situation the actor-director summed up as: 'incredibly difficult. But even if she drove me crazy sometimes, I was thanking God she was there, because she's very smart and a good producer.' He then starred in the black romantic comedy *Addicted to Love*, playing a fastidious astronomer whose girlfriend (Kelly Preston) dumps him for Tcheky Karyo, thus activating a liaison of revenge with Karyo's ex, Meg Ryan.

She was the ultimate girl next door – if you're lucky enough to live next door to somebody as cute, ebullient and pretty as Sandra Bullock. And yet she was no film star, surely not. She hadn't the drop-dead beauty of a Michelle Pfeiffer, or the searing sex appeal of a Sharon Stone, or even the mammary endowments of a Pamela Anderson Lee. She was just friendly, good to spend time with; not a threat.

Bullock herself admits: 'I'm just the kid who happens to live next door. I am not like Doris Day, who was the perfect, perky girl next door. I'm just kinda there. It's like, "Oh. Yeah. Her."'

Her colleagues are more positive. Joel Schumacher, who directed her in *A Time to Kill*, observes: 'Sandra possesses the attribute I value over all else: she is a truly kind young woman. She is one of the most inclusive people I have ever met. There's always room at Sandra Bullock's table for everyone. The driver is treated better than the studio executive because she knows how hard people have to work. We're all living in a very mean-spirited world, and I seek out and admire people who can find gratitude, humility and kindness within their own success. Sandra is one of those people, and that's very, very, very rare.'

Bill Pullman, her co-star from *While You Were Sleeping*, adds his own record of commendation: 'She's not a depressed, dark person. She hasn't got some spot that's going to be rubbed raw. She's not hiding anything. She just has a great personality. I think she's really enjoying herself and it shows.'

Broderick (right) threatens Jim Carrey in **The Cable Guy**

*Sandra Bullock with Robert Duvall in **Wrestling Ernest Hemingway***

Irwin Winkler, who directed the actress in *The Net*, would agree: 'When she walked into my office for the first time, she was wearing overalls, the chunkiest shoes you ever saw, and a baseball cap turned backwards. Most actresses would wear the highest heels, shortest skirt, and lowest blouse to meet the director, but that's not the way she is.'

To put it succinctly, Denis Leary, Bullock's friend and co-star from *Demolition Man* and *Two If By Sea*, offers: 'If she has a skeleton in her closet, she probably put it there.'

Sandra Bullock was born on 26 July 1964 in Arlington, Virginia, the daughter of John Bullock, a contractor for the Pentagon and part-time voice coach, and a German opera singer, Helga. Fluent in German, Sandra spent her childhood traversing the Atlantic, staying with her aunt and grandmother in Nuremberg and studying English in the afternoons. At eight she made her professional debut appearing on stage with her mother.

In the USA, she attended Washington-Lee High School with her younger sister, Gesine (now her legal adviser), an institution that, three decades earlier, had produced Warren Beatty and Shirley MacLaine. There, Sandy was nominated 'Class Clown' and did all the things an all-American girl should: ballet, piano, gymnastics and, of course, cheerleading. 'I had every experience in the world growing up,' she affirms. 'Living in Europe, coming back to the States, going through

puberty and being alienated, trying to conform ... I was in the drama department at school for two years and then decided, well, "I'd like to be a cheerleader, because my boyfriend is a wrestler."' Former classmate Katrina Luedtke recalls: 'Sandy was a beautiful girl with a silly, giggly sense of humour – she just liked to have fun. She was warm and caring and was one of the most popular kids in school.'

In spite of her father's desire to see her graduate from Julliard in New York (his alma mater), Sandra opted to major in drama at East Carolina University – in order, she says, to avoid having 'to live up to anyone's expectations of

what I can and can't do'.

Failing to earn her degree by a matter of three credits, she moved to New York, waited tables, took acting classes and auditioned religiously. It wasn't long before she landed the lead in a minor off-Broadway production, *No Time Flat*, and earned her first glowing reviews. This led to a role in the mini-series *Lucky Chances*; eight minutes in the misconceived satire *A Fool and His Money* (as a public defender), her first film; the lead in the TV movie *The Bionic Showdown: The Six-Million Dollar Man and the Bionic Woman* (plus a $10,000 pay cheque); a small part in the TV movie *The Preppie Murder*, and the female lead in *Who Shot Patakango?* The latter was a small-budget, independent production set in Brooklyn in the 1950s, with Bullock cast as a sophisticated college girl who falls for a boy from the wrong side of the tracks (David Knight). A convincing, buoyant look at a bygone era, the film won upbeat notices but little exposure in cinemas.

Next, she played the Melanie Griffith part – Tess McGill – in NBC's short-lived small-screen adaptation of the hit comedy *Working Girl*, and she then starred opposite Craig Sheffer in the Roger Corman exploitationer *Fire on the Amazon*, in which she endured her first sex scene (covering her nipples with duct tape).

Bullock found a wider audience in

*Sandy takes over the wheel in **Speed** (with Keanu Reeves)*

Sandy and Matthew McConaughey in Joel Schumacher's *A Time to Kill*

the daft romantic comedy *Love Potion No. 9*, in which she and Tate Donovan played a biochemist and animal psychologist who volunteer to try a new love drug. The film was dismissed by critics, but at least it gave the actress a higher profile and introduced her to her first serious boyfriend – Tate Donovan.

She secured third-billing in the contemporary LA drama *When the Party's Over*, winning good notices as a spirited feminist painter who shares a house with Rae Dawn Chong and Elizabeth Berridge and hooks an eccentric performance artist (Fisher Stevens).

She had little to do in the American remake of the Dutch hit *The Vanishing* but, as Kiefer Sutherland's girlfriend, she was a key character in a major film. As the girl who vanished she was simply breathtaking, even when raking Kiefer over the coals. Peter Bogdanovich had to fight to get her to play the aspiring country singer LindaLu in *The Thing Called Love*, as studio executives wanted a bigger name. As it happens, Bullock rose to the occasion, going so far as to write her own song for the movie ('They were paying these talented songwriters all this money to do it, when it was supposed to be a metaphorically bad song,' she reasoned). As it happens, the film became something of a milestone, as it turned out to be River Phoenix's last completed picture before his death.

She was then enchanting as the waitress who played along with the romantic fantasies of old codger

Robert Duvall in *Wrestling Ernest Hemingway*. And then came *Demolition Man*. Budgeted at $70 million, *Demolition Man* was a big, muscular sci-fi movie starring Sylvester Stallone and Wesley Snipes and produced by 'the Selznick of Schlock', Joel Silver. Silver had hired Lori Petty – fresh from her success in *A League of Their Own* – to partner Stallone in the story of a maverick cop who's thawed out from his cryogenic prison in order to combat a master criminal of the future. Three days into shooting, Silver realized that the chemistry between Stallone and Petty wasn't working.

'I had seen Sandra in *The Vanishing*,' recalls the producer, 'and I was very impressed. She's sexy, she's articulate. You see the soul behind her eyes.' And so Petty was fired and Bullock hired. A carnival of spectacular stunts and special effects – spiced with politically incorrect satire – *Demolition Man* rose head-and-shoulders above the competition. Yet it was the witty repartee between Sly's hell-for-leather law enforcer and Bullock's culturally reserved cop that stuck in the memory. Spurning the former's offer of physical intimacy, Bullock snaps, 'Sex? Do you know what sex leads to?', to which Stallone retorts, 'Yeah. Kids. Smoking. Raiding the fridge.'

While not the commercial blockbuster that Silver had hoped for, *Demolition Man* racked up a respectable $58 million at the US box-office and over $150 million worldwide. Bullock was getting noticed.

For her next movie, the $25 million

Speed, she was to get $600,000 to play a feisty young thing who boards a bus in downtown Santa Monica only to have to take over the wheel when the driver is shot. The bus has been wired by a mad terrorist (Dennis Hopper) and is set to blow should the vehicle slow down to under 50 miles per hour. As the heroine, Bullock was deliriously attractive, confessing – as she takes over the controls of the fugitive bus – that she was once booked for speeding. A four-star action movie with knobs on, *Speed* went on to gross $320 million worldwide, and established Bullock as a bona fide star.

However, her new-found celebrity was tempered by the break-up of her four-year relationship with Tate Donovan. 'I adored Tate so much,' she revealed, with some reserve. 'It's like they say, there's one person in your life, and Tate and I are closer than any two people I've ever experienced in my life. There's nobody that means more to me, and I know for a fact that I mean the most to him, in that certain way. I can't explain why things worked out the way they did. We both know why it happened.'

When Demi Moore pulled out of *While You Were Sleeping*, Bullock jumped at the chance to play the humble transit teller who's mistaken for the fiancée of her dreamboat (Peter Gallagher), turning down the female lead in *Batman Forever* for the privilege. With her salary jacked up to $1.2 million, Bullock was now expected to carry a film on her own, which, naturally, she did with flying colours. While the romantic comedy failed to match the warm glow generated by *Ghost* or *Pretty Woman*, it was nice enough, and was distinguished by some fine playing from Bullock and co-star Bill Pullman. The public agreed, and *While You Were Sleeping* went on to generate an extremely healthy $81 million at the US box-office.

Next, she joined her old friend Denis Leary for another romantic comedy, albeit cursed with the impossible title of *Two If By Sea*. Co-scripted by Leary himself, the film was a largely charmless exercise, not helped by Leary's turn as a totally moronic loser. Not surprisingly, the movie bombed with critics and audiences alike.

The critics were not too kind to

*Love in Venice: Sandy pines for Chris O'Donnell in Richard Attenborough's In **Love and War***

The Net, either, in which the actress starred as Angela Bennett, a freelance computer analyst who inadvertently hacks into a nefarious security system with the ability to access any top-secret database in the world. Angela is duly punished for her blunder, resulting in her deletion from the collective computers of America. Suddenly she has no passport, driving licence, national security number or even her own name. A superbly engineered warning of the dangers of translating our lives into digital information, *The Net* worked as both human drama and Orwellian nightmare, but was dismissed for being silly and improbable. Nevertheless, the film made a tidy $50.7 million in the USA, more than making up for Bullock's $2 million salary.

The media's intrusion into the actress's private life continued, a sure sign of her position on the totem pole of success. Following her break-up with Donovan, Bullock was seen in the company of Don Padilla, who had worked as a camera grip on *The Net*. 'I met him on the set,' Bullock reveals, 'Heavy D was playing, and I was like, "OK, the boy's got rhythm; this is a good thing." We went out dancing in New York until four in the morning. He knows how much I love salsa, and the other day he said, "I think I'm gonna take up salsa so I can dance with you," and I thought, "Oh, many bonus points!"'

Meanwhile, Bullock's standing in the industry was reflected by the $6 million she was paid to add box-office muscle to the fourth screen incarnation of a John Grisham novel, *A Time to Kill*. Grisham himself had elected to choose a newcomer – Matthew McConaughey – for the central role of Jake Brigance, a Southern attorney who defends a black factory worker (Samuel L. Jackson) after the worker murders two white thugs for raping and beating his ten-year-old daughter. Every star from Val Kilmer to Woody Harrelson was mooted for the role, but Grisham stood his ground, forcing Warner Brothers to come up with an alternative name to add box-office ballast to their project. Bullock had relatively little to do (she played McConaughey's assistant and lover) but, as ever, was eminently watchable in a thriller that dealt with genuine issues – racism, murder and legal corruption – with a fresh and eloquent passion.

A Time to Kill went on to make a resounding $152.2 million worldwide, and Sandra Bullock's asking price edged up into eight figures. She was paid $10.2 million to star in Richard Attenborough's epic romance *In Love and War* – playing Agnes von Kurowsky, the older woman courted by a 19-year-old Ernest Hemingway (Chris O'Donnell) – and then $15.3 million for *Speed 2: Cruise Control*, making her the highest-paid actress of all time. In *In Love and War*, she was simply irresistible as the no-nonsense nurse who falls for the 'kid' against her better judgement, although O'Donnell failed to register the sexual danger that would have made the romance entirely credible. But, for Bullock, it was a departure: 'This was an opportunity to play a character who was incredibly modern for her time,' the actress illuminated. 'Until now, my roles have been contemporary women. Here was a chance to play a woman who was in a class of her own. She did it her way, got a lot of heat for it and was pretty impressive.'

In *Speed 2: Cruise COntrol* she moved on from Keanu Reeves to new boyfriend Jason Patric, and again found herself in the wrong place at the wrong time (in this instance, on a boat hijacked by a petulant Willem Dafoe). According to director Jan De Bont (who also made the first film), 'the [male] character in *Speed 2* wasn't necessarily specific to Keanu. It could have been any young, talented actor. The key was to find a person who has a chemistry with Sandra. I think this movie would be hard to imagine without *her*, though.'

Meanwhile, Sandra was reported to be very much the main squeeze of Matthew McConaughey, whom she cast in her first film as writer-director, a 40-minute short called *Making Sandwiches*, the story of a young couple in the sandwich trade. Of her new companion she volunteered: 'He's a great spirit. He's one of the best things to cross my path.'

She then signed up for another comedy, *Hope Floats*, for director Forest Whitaker.

FILMOGRAPHY

1988: *A Fool and His Money*. 1989: *The Bionic Showdown: The Six-Million Dollar Man and the Bionic Woman* (TV); *The Preppie Murder* (TV). 1990: *Who Shot Patakango?* (a.k.a. *Who Shot Pat?*); *Religion Inc.* (video). 1991: *Fire on the Amazon* (unreleased). 1992: *Love Potion No. 9*; *When the Party's Over*. 1993: *The Vanishing*; *The Thing Called Love*; *Wrestling Ernest Hemingway*; *Demolition Man*. 1994: *Me & the Mob*; *Speed*. 1995: *While You Were Sleeping*; *The Net*. 1996: *Two If By Sea* (a.k.a. *Stolen Hearts*). 1996: *A Time to Kill*; *Making Sandwiches* (40-minute short; also wrote and directed); *In Love and War*. 1997: *Speed 2: Cruise Control*; *The Prince of Egypt* (voice only). 1998: *Hope Floats*.

C

NICOLAS CAGE

Nicolas Cage in Alan Parker's Birdy

The same year that Ralph Macchio (born in 1961) was portraying the wide-eyed, teenage Daniel in *The Karate Kid Part II*, Nicolas Cage (born in 1964), was playing Kathleen Turner's middle-aged husband in *Peggy Sue Got Married*. Such is Cage's brawny, hairy and weathered physique that he has been able to play a wide range of characters – mostly older than himself. With his drooping eyes and unruly nose, he displays the appearance of a permanently offended bloodhound. He is the first to admit 'I don't think I really look like a romantic leading man', and he has capitalized on the fact. Richard Benjamin, who directed him in *Racing with the Moon*, suggests that he does have: 'movie looks. Look at Bogart. Look at Cagney. They weren't conventionally handsome either.'

Actually, there's nothing conventional about Nicolas Cage. 'He's a little *Addams Family*,' admits Joel Cohen, who directed the actor in *Raising Arizona*. 'He likes to promote that image, anyway. He's a strange guy.' Indeed, *The Los Angeles Times* once described him as 'the crown prince of the darker realms of absurdity'. Cage himself confides: 'I get turned on by craziness.' His problems with drugs and

alcohol have been no state secret, either. Neither have his one-night stands with loose-mouthed women.

And there's no pretence at movie star urbanity when you meet him. His hair disarranged with the finesse of a hurricane, he'll as likely be unshaven, half-dressed and resentful of the intrusion. Yet, broach the subject of acting, and he'll happily pass an afternoon with you. And *does* Nicolas Cage take his acting seriously. But more of that anon.

Born Nicolas Coppola on 7 January 1964, in Long Beach, California, the actor was the youngest of three sons. His father, August Coppola, taught comparative literature at California State University and went on to become dean of the School of Creative Arts at San Francisco State University; his mother, Joy Vogelsang, was an interpretive dancer and choreographer from New York. More famously, his uncle is the film director Francis Ford Coppola, his aunt the actress Talia Shire (Adrian Balboa in the *Rocky* films), and his cousin Sofia Coppola, who played Mary Corleone in *The Godfather Part III*.

Nic was 12 when his parents divorced and, after his mother was hospitalized for a nervous breakdown, he moved to San Francisco with his father. There are various theories surrounding his ambition to become an actor: one that he was inspired after seeing James Dean in *East of Eden*, another that he thought it was an easy way 'to get laid'. Anyhow, at 15 he enrolled in San Francisco's Young Conservatory, part of the American Conservatory Theater, where he appeared in a production of *Golden Boy*. He then moved on to the Beverly Hills High School, when, at 16, he won a small role as a surfer in the pilot TV movie *The Best of Times* – which he described as 'probably the worst TV show on the air'.

Encouraged by this propitious start, he dropped out of school in his senior year and immediately got a job in the cinema – selling popcorn. He played a larger part in the history of movies when he won his first role, as Bud, in the enormously popular *Fast Times at Ridgemont High*, playing Judge Reinhold's sidekick. He then auditioned for his uncle. 'I auditioned for him for the role of Dallas in *The*

Outsiders,' Cage recalls. 'I was there for nine hours. But I was so nervous, I didn't know what I was doing.' He says that to prepare for this ordeal he locked himself in his room for two weeks, downed a quantity of beer and contemplated a poster of Charles Bronson – hoping to become a hooligan through osmosis. Come the big day, Uncle Francis changed his mind and asked Nic to read for the role of 'Two-Bit' instead. 'I couldn't change gear and everything fell apart,' the actor complains. 'I was in hospital for a while after that and decided I didn't want to act anymore.' The role of Dallas went to Matt Dillon and Emilio Estevez got the part of 'Two-Bit'. Nicolas Coppola changed his name to Nicolas Cage.

However, his uncle persuaded him to take a part in *RumbleFish*, as 'Smokey', the hunk in the black cutaway T-shirt who steals Diane Lane from Matt Dillon. He then landed the lead in Martha Coolidge's surprising romantic comedy, *Valley Girl*, as the down-market slob who wins the heart of a preppy beauty (Deborah Foreman). It was a small film, but the critics warmed to it and it was a moderate success.

Cage as the passionate, one-handed baker Ronny Cammareri in Norman Jewison's Oscar-winning Moonstruck

Wild thing; Nicolas Cage at his absolute coolest in David Lynch's strange tribute to the Wizard of Oz: the Lynchian **Wild at Heart**

He played Sean Penn's best buddy in Richard Benjamin's tasteful, aesthetically composed *Racing with the Moon*, but the actor dismisses it in retrospect: 'I didn't think it was that good,' he insists. 'Richard Benjamin, who is really an actor, was too new at his craft. The film looked great because he spent more time on the technical aspects of it, rather than on the actors. Consequently, my character was terribly incomplete.' Others in the cast included Elizabeth McGovern and Nic's close friend from high school, Crispin Glover.

He was Richard Gere's hoodlum brother ('Mad Dog' Dwyer) in Francis Coppola's spectacular gangster/jazz epic *The Cotton Club*, a splendid film but a box-office flop; and then he segued into Alan Parker's *Birdy*. For this film, Nicolas Cage went hog wild in his preparation to play a disfigured Vietnam vet. Not only did he wear facial bandages on and *off* the set for a total of five weeks, but he had a tooth on either side of his jaw removed. 'It was my idea to have the teeth pulled and to wear the bandages,' he explains, as if to shift the blame from an invisible culprit. 'It gave me the right "feel". If you work honestly in one direction, you'll find that other directions are taken care of on their own. Because of the bandages my jaw always hurt, which in

turn made it difficult for me to eat, so I lost 15 pounds. My mental attitude to the part had helped me to alter physically.' Previewed at Cannes, *Birdy* prompted a 12-minute standing ovation and flew off with the Grand Prix Jury prize.

He then played real-life Canadian rowing champion Ned Hanlan in *The Boy in Blue*. This, too, required some preparation. The actor trained furiously on weights, rowed himself silly, and revealed: 'I couldn't begin to explain how painful it was.' He was due to star in the apocalyptic thriller *Miracle Mile*, and was already casting his co-stars when the picture was delayed. Instead, he played Kathleen Turner's loutish husband in Coppola's sweet time-travelling fantasy, *Peggy Sue Got Married*. His performance was wild and unpredictable; it also annoyed the heck out of Ms Turner, who reputedly wanted him fired. 'Can you blame her?' he proposes. 'I was basically working without regard for anyone in the movie, just doing whatever I wanted and hijacking the movie, for better or worse.' His own notices were not good, and he never worked with his uncle again.

He then hit on a golden streak that was to transform him overnight from underground punk to pretty well-known punk. The brothers Joel and Ethan Coen who, together, wrote, produced and directed the cult thriller *Blood Simple*, cast him as the dishevelled hero, H.I. (Herbert I. McDonnough), in their magical, hilarious and truly inspired comedy nightmare *Raising Arizona*. The story of an ill-matched

couple (Cage and Holly Hunter) who live in a trailer and dream of acquiring a baby any way they can, the film was one of the most original and best-honed comedies of the 1980s. But if *Raising Arizona* failed to gain the approval of the establishment, Norman Jewison's *Moonstruck* gained more than its fair share.

A heavily Italian-American comedy about a widow (Cher) caught between her affections for a sincere, overweight Danny Aiello and his one-handed, younger brother (Cage), *Moonstruck* was skillfully written, directed and acted, and won a handful of Oscars, including a best actress nod for Cher. Jewison admired Cage's total immersion into the role of the lovelorn, one-handed slob, even if, on this occasion, Cage kept his real limb intact. However, the actor's love-drenched outpourings to Cher were more than a little kindled by the break-up of his four-year relationship with the actress Jenny Wright (*Young Guns II*, *The Lawnmower Man*). 'I was kind of hoping that Jenny would be out there somewhere to hear my romantic pleading,' he admitted sheepishly.

Nic Cage was now an established leading man, but his choice of films was anything but orthodox. He accepted the part of a seedy literary agent who's convinced he's a vampire in *Vampire's Kiss*, a stylish psychological black comedy. Again, he took his quest for realism to unnatural lengths. He tried to persuade his director, the London-born Richard Bierman, to introduce a real bat (to no avail), and

As Ben Sanderson, the role that won Cage his Oscar

then switched the raw egg he had to eat for a live cockroach. 'I wanted there to be a moment of something so *real*,' he explains. 'When I saw the film with an audience, the reaction was so intense. All I had done was eat a cockroach.'

He then starred in an Italian war film, *Time to Kill*, and the poorly-received *Top Gun* clone *Fire Birds*, with Sean Young. *Wild at Heart* was all the rage at Cannes (it won the Palme d'Or), and became a must-see attraction for the seriously alternative. Cage was Sailor Ripley, a parole-jumping eccentric on the road with Laura Dern, with Mother (Diane Ladd) in hot pursuit. Directed by David Lynch with the self-indulgence of a disturbed teacher's pet, the film was an uneven mix of fantasy, gore and parody.

Even worse was Sam Pillsbury's erotic melodrama *Zandalee*, with Cage as a libidinous rogue who has to utter such dialogue as 'I want to shake you naked and eat you alive, Zandalee.' It wasn't a hit.

However, Andrew Bergman's *Honeymoon in Vegas* was. Cage was back in his *Raising Arizona* mode, playing a likeable goofball afraid to commit to marriage. However, when he loses his fiancée (Sarah Jessica Parker) to bigtime gambler James Caan in a poker game, he is transformed into a raving romantic. Harking back to the madcap comedies of the 1930s, *Honeymoon* displayed some charm, a good deal of slapstick and its fair share of belly laughs. It also won Cage a Golden Globe nomination for best actor in a comedy or musical.

He was then top-billed in the cowboy *noir* thriller *Red Rock West*, in which he played an honest Joe mistaken for a hitman – and who attempts to cash on the error (to his downfall). A deliciously offbeat tale, the film kept the audience guessing until the final reel, and even then was dishing out surprises. In the black comedy *Amos & Andrew* he was another blue-collar slob, this time an underdog who ends up in an exclusive island jail. And then he joined the all-star cast (Michael Biehn, James Coburn, Charlie Sheen, Peter Fonda, auntie Talia Shire) of *Deadfall*, directed by his older brother, Christopher Coppola – the story of two men caught up in a dangerous con game.

In Hugh Wilson's gentle love-hate comedy *Guarding Tess*, he played Doug Chesnic, a special agent who's landed with the task of babysitting former First Lady Shirley MacLaine. In *It Could Happen To You* he was New York cop Charlie Lang, a good-natured fellow who wins $4 million on the state lottery and shares it with waitress Bridget Fonda (to honour a promise). Based on a true incident, the film failed to evoke the magic of a *Sleepless in Seattle*, but it was sweet enough. Incidentally, Cage took the role after Billy Crystal bowed out. He made a terrific, bestial heavy in Barbet Schroeder's gritty and uncompromising *Kiss of Death* (a remake of the 1947 classic with Victor Mature), and he then segued into *Leaving Las Vegas*.

As Ben Sanderson, a failed Hollywood scriptwriter who decides to end his life via a drinking binge in Las Vegas, Cage gave another naked, excoriating performance. Based on the semi-autobiographical book by John O'Brien (who killed himself shortly after selling the movie rights), the film was an exploration of failure, redemption and love, for no sooner does Sanderson resign himself to his fate than he is transformed into a carefree, unusually open soul, his uncommon honesty attracting the interest of a battered prostitute (Elisabeth Shue). 'The script [by director Mike Figgis] astounded me,' Cage related. 'I was crying when I finished reading it. It is, more than anything, a story about unconditional love. It is definitely one of the coolest relationships I've ever read in a screenplay.'

At the time, Cage was breaking up with his own girlfriend, Kristen Zang, a predicament that stoked his performance: 'The split-up was a difficult one; it had been a tumultuous relationship. But it was also a sweet relationship. We just weren't right for each other. So there was a sadness when we had to split up and that sadness went into the movie, because the breakup came around that time. A lot of the time when I was saying "I love you" [on screen] I was just heartbroken.'

But there was a happy ending. In April 1995 he married the actress Patricia Arquette. 'I met her at Canter's, a deli, a long time ago – eight years

ago,' the actor revealed. 'I said, "I want to marry you." She said, "You're crazy," and she didn't believe me. But I was serious. We spoke six or seven times over eight years. But nothing happened until last year. I went back to Canter's and I ran into her again. This time there was a change. Maybe because we were back at the place where we had met. Two months later she called me and proposed.'

The same year, *Leaving Las Vegas* opened to ecstatic reviews. For his performance, Cage won the best actor award from the Los Angeles Film Critics, the National Board of Review, the National Society of Film Critics and the New York Film Critics' Circle. He also bagged the Golden Globe and, in March 1996, the Oscar. It got better.

Nicolas Cage on rare heroic form in the box-office smash **The Rock**

In his next film, *The Rock*, he played a nerdy chemical warfare expert who's roped into breaking *into* the Alcatraz fortress of the title in order to defuse a volatile hostage situation. While the movie flaunted such sure-fire commercial ingredients as scatter-gun pacing, buttock-clenching stunts, dynamic explosions and a spectacular car chase, the casting of real actors like Cage, Sean Connery and Ed Harris gave the film an edge. And the ploy paid off: *The Rock* grossed an astounding $329.4 million at the global box-office, making it Cage's biggest commercial success to date.

And now he was getting real money. Following another action-adventure, *Con Air* (the actor's co-star, Rachel Ticotin, noted: 'I see this movie as a modern-day western, and Nic Cage is John Wayne.'), he was paid $6 million to star in *Face Off* with John Travolta. He then teamed up with Meg Ryan in the drama *City of Angels*.

FILMOGRAPHY

1981: *The Best of Times* (TV). 1982: *Fast Times at Ridgemont High*. 1983: *RumbleFish; Valley Girl*. 1984: *Racing with the Moon; The Cotton Club; Birdy*. 1986: *The Boy in Blue; Peggy Sue Got Married*. 1987: *Raising Arizona; Moonstruck*. 1988: *Vampire's Kiss*. 1989: *Time to Kill* (a.k.a. *Short Cut/Tempo di Mecidere*). 1990: *Fire Birds* (UK: *Wings of the Apache*); *Wild at Heart*. 1991: *Zandalee*. 1992: *Honeymoon in Vegas*. 1993: *Red Rock West; Amos & Andrew; Deadfall*. 1994: *Guarding Tess; It Could Happen To You; Trapped in Paradise*. 1995: *Kiss of Death; Leaving Las Vegas*. 1996: *The Rock*. 1997: *Con Air; Face Off*. 1998: *City of Angels; Superman Reborn*.

JIM CARREY

Not Tom Cruise, Sylvester Stallone, Arnold Schwarzenegger – no other movie star arrived so fast and was paid so much in so little time as Jim Carrey.

On 4 February 1994, a film called *Ace Ventura: Pet Detective* opened at 1,750 screens across the USA. Starring a virtually unknown comic from Canada, the movie seemed an unlikely candidate to dispel the box-office blues of early 1994. As it happens, *Ace Ventura* went through the roof, knocking the competition into the gutter. Budgeted at a modest $15 million, the comedy grossed $74 million in the USA alone. Its star, Jim Carrey, had received just $350,000 for his services.

Carrey's next picture, *The Mask* – for which he was paid $450,000 – opened six months later and ended up with a $119.9 million American gross. Suddenly, the comic's bargaining power had grown biceps. He was due to star in *Dumb and Dumber* ('guess which part I play') for New Line Cinema, but the production company balked at the $1 million Carrey's manager was now asking. To be fair, New Line was a small company, and it fought hard to keep

Carrey's ballooning salary down by $200,000. Then the box-office tills starting ringing and, in an extraordinary turnaround, New Line shocked the industry by agreeing to pay Carrey $7 million. While mooted as a ploy to show other distributors that it was a serious player, New Line's 'gimmick' paid off handsomely: *Dumb and Dumber* went on to gross $127.2 million in the USA alone, making it Carrey's hottest ticket to date.

Then things got crazy. New Line offered Carrey another $7 million for *The Best Man*, and then another for a sequel to *The Mask*. Morgan Creek, who made *Ace Ventura*, threw $5 million at him for a sequel, and, for a supporting role, Warner Brothers coughed up $5 million for Carrey to play The Riddler in *Batman Forever*. 'The amount of money I'm getting is ridiculous,' the star remarked at the time. 'It's like looking at a Monopoly board. It's fun, and I have financial goals, but I've never lost sleep over money – even when I was struggling.'

Then, in June 1995, Columbia Pictures leaped between the covers of the *Guinness Book of Records* by offering Carrey $20 million to star in their black comedy *The Cable Guy*. The industry reeled: producers blanched, agents grinned and Sylvester Stallone rang his manager. With this kind of money flying around, stars could ask for the moon – and the talent *under* the title would have to tighten their belts. But maybe Columbia had a point.

Shortly afterwards, *Batman Forever* – fuelled by Carrey's turn as a demented Riddler – demolished box-office records, grossing a phenomenal $53.3 million in its opening weekend. Two months later, Universal Pictures signed Carrey up for another $20 million to star in *Liar, Liar*. By the end of 1995, *Batman Forever* had become the top-grossing movie of the year in the USA, while *Ace Ventura: When Nature Calls* had grossed $34.4 million more than the earlier film.

Of course, it's easy to get side-tracked by the fat paychecks and the box-office figures, a fascination that obscures a more significant aspect of the Jim Carrey spectacle – that he is a startling original. While constantly described as a modern-day Jerry Lewis, Carrey is in fact his own man, an elas-

*The film that turned the tide: Jim Carrey as **Ace Ventura: Pet Detective***

*Putting his heart into it: Carrey as Stanley Ipkiss rejuvenated, in **The Mask***

tic warhead, an arsenal of physical tics and double-takes. He says: 'I never wanted to do anything else. I looked at comedians on television, people like Dick Van Dyke, and I said to myself, "I want to be just like that." The physical stuff Van Dyke did was phenomenal.'

'Jim is an amazing athlete,' notes Chuck Russell, director of *The Mask*. 'What he does with his body reminds me of the old silent film star Harold Lloyd. The [special effects] guys from Industrial Light and Magic told me that we saved a million dollars in optical effects because of the things that Jim does for real. People will wonder where he stops and the morphing begins.'

Carrey's friend, Nicolas Cage, offered: 'Jim is like a human sponge, absorbing everything around him. He's very passionate about creative stimulant. He loves Salvador Dali and reads Joseph Campbell books on mythology. He paints and creates sculptures, so he's always feeding the beast within with creative input.' Even Jerry Lewis was magnanimous enough to concede: 'He is the most brilliant physical comedian to come along in decades.'

Jim was born on 17 January 1962 in Newmarket, Ontario (30 miles north of Toronto), the youngest of four children. His father, Percy, had been a sax player, but abandoned his vocation to become an accountant and then a janitor. At one point, following the birth of Carrey's older sister, he sold his sax to pay for the maternity fees. Carrey, who entertained his family with wicked sketches of their neighbours, was driven to succeed where his

father had failed. His mother, Kathleen, recalls: 'Jim was about five and he said, "When I grow up, I want to be a clown and make people laugh."'

But times were tough – so tough that Carrey was forced to drop out of school at 16: 'My parents didn't encourage me to drop out, but we were financially screwed. I was working eight hours a day in a factory after school and went from being top student to not understanding a word the teacher was saying.'

He practised his comic schtick in school, concluding each scholastic day with a 15-minute routine. Determined that his son should not repeat his own mistakes, Carrey Snr put him forward for a spot at the Toronto comedy club Yuk Yuk's. 'I got booed off stage,' Carrey recalls. 'I was dressed in a polyester suit that my mom told me would be a good idea. But it didn't go over so well.' It was to be two years before the shell-shocked would-be comic returned ('I have no idea what motivated me to try again.'), and this time he was a success. He polished his act on the Canadian comedy circuit, then, in 1982, he journeyed to LA to try his luck there.

After appearing at the Comedy Store and The Improvisation in LA, he worked the New York circuit and began 'opening' for Rodney Dangerfield, The Pointer Sisters, Sheena Easton, Pat Boone and Andy Williams. He was making $200,000 a year.

Meanwhile, his personal life was falling into place, too, marked by his relationship with the Country singer Linda Ronstadt ('Blue Bayou', 'It's So

Easy'). According to Jim's manager, David Holiff, 'Jim was 21, Linda was 37. He was living at her house in LA's Brentwood and he loved it. She had limos, famous friends, and Jim got his first taste of true fame.'

A year later he went into therapy, took acting lessons, then he was out of work for two years. Feeling limited as an impersonator (he mimicked everybody and everything from Clint Eastwood and Kevin Bacon to a cockroach and praying mantis), he turned to a new brand of comedy: his own brand.

In 1984 he landed the lead in the NBC TV sitcom *The Duck Factory*, playing Skip Tarkenton, employee of a cartoon studio. The show was short-lived, so the comic moved into movies, taking a small part in Richard Lester's disappointing *Finders Keepers*, starring opposite Lauren Hutton in the irredeemable *Once Bitten* (as a virginal victim) and playing Nicolas Cage's best friend, Walter, in *Peggy Sue Got Married*. In *The Dead Pool*, with Clint Eastwood and Liam Neeson, he was twelfth-billed (strangely, as James Carrey), and he then portrayed Wiploc, a mischievous, fur-covered alien, in *Earth Girls Are Easy*, with Geena Davis. In this film he bonded with co-star Damon Wayans, who was to become instrumental in Carrey's future rise to stardom. He was also featured in his own Showtime special, *Jim Carrey's Unnatural Acts*.

When Wayans suggested he join the cast of the innovative half-hour comedy series *In Living Color*, he cannot have foreseen the irony – that the

*Stupid is: Carrey gets **Dumb and Dumber***

As The Riddler (with Tommy Lee Jones) in Batman Forever

token white boy should become the show's most celebrated graduate. ,'It fuelled my desire to stand out,' Carrey reasons. 'Desperation drove me, made all these wild things come out.' It certainly got him noticed.

When the script for *Ace Ventura: Pet Detective* arrived on his doormat, 'everybody in town had already turned it down,' he remembers. 'And I didn't like it at all. I did like the idea of a pet detective, though, which was different.' Desperate to get their film made, the suits at Morgan Creek offered Carrey *carte blanche* to alter the material. Which he did. With a vengeance.

As it happens, *Ace Ventura* was yet another very silly, over-the-top American comedy featuring a mentally-challenged detective (albeit one modelling himself on Doctor Dolittle). We'd seen it all before, more famous

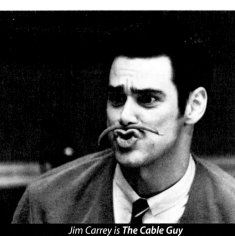

Jim Carrey is **The Cable Guy**

examples including Peter Sellers' Inspector Clouseau and Leslie Nielsen's Frank Drebin. But Carrey was different: his Ace Ventura was not as dumb as he behaved. He had some instinct for the game, and when he groaned, 'I'm *tired* of being right!', we had reason to believe him. 'What captures an audience is things that they have never seen done before,' the star argued. 'Until *Ace Ventura*, no actor had considered talking through his ass.' Besides, 'when the film was released everything else was so serious. You had *Schindler's List* and *Philadelphia*. People needed a laugh.' Nevertheless, the critics roundly dismissed Carrey's efforts, with the venerable double-act of Gene Siskel and Roger Ebert giving the film an unequivocal thumbs down. 'I'm afraid to get a good review from those guys,' Carrey counters. 'In fact, when the review came out, I said that we should use it in the ads: "Two thumbs down – worst movie ever made." How can you get a better endorsement?'

The reviews were better for *The Mask*, a perfect vehicle for the physical contortions of the comic, based on the *Dark Horse* comic series. Carrey played Stanley Ipkiss, a nerd who, when he dons an ancient Norse mask, is transformed into a cross between Kid Creole and the genie of the lamp. Following the singular antics of Ace Ventura, Carrey's new creation was like witnessing an atom bomb going nuclear. Besides the inevitable sequel (which has yet to be filmed), the movie also generated a cartoon TV series and

no end of merchandising tie-ins.

And then there was *Dumb and Dumber.* 'I was first attracted to the film,' Carrey says, 'because of its title. I read the script and liked the idea of working with someone and not carrying the whole film by myself.' Both Nicolas Cage and Gary Oldman were approached to play Carrey's sidekick, when Carrey settled on Jeff Daniels. 'Jeff is a quality actor,' Carrey reasoned, 'and at this point I want to work with people who can challenge me to do better.'

Stretching the premise of *Forrest Gump* to farcical extremes, the film pitted Carrey against the normally restrained Daniels. An unlikely double act, they played the Two Stooges on overdrive, guys saving up to open their own pet shop called 'I Got Worms'. Out of work and out of luck, the dweebs decide to return an attache case to its rightful owner – on the other side of the continent – and along the way get into (and out of) no end of trouble. Yet, as stupid as it sounds, the film does have the semblance of a reasonable story, and not all the laughs are reserved for the two stars. Even so, this was definitely Carrey's movie.

'Jim breaks the rules,' Daniels volunteered. 'They teach you in Hollywood that less is more, like Gary Cooper: do nothing. But Jim starts over the top and goes further. That was the challenge of working with him: he's so fast and furious, he's like a human tornado. I didn't know if I could hang with him. Ultimately, the art is not to get blown off the screen.'

While Carrey's career sky-rocketed, his personal life was winding down. Married for six years to the actress Melissa Jane Womer, the mother of his daughter, Jane Erin, Carrey's obsessive work schedule was taking its toll. 'It was really tough being married,' he ventured. 'I'm in love with my work, and it's hard not to be jealous of that. It's hard for anybody who's with me not to feel starved for affection when I'm making love to my ideas. I can see a real challenge in my life will be to settle myself down enough to be with someone. Maybe it's not meant to be for me. I don't have time for anything else right now but work and my daughter. Jane's my first priority.'

Despite this, in January 1995 Carrey

was talking wedding bells with Lauren Holly, his leading lady from *Dumb and Dumber*. Then, a month later, Melissa entered into legal negotiations to seek a major share of Carrey's fortune. In 1996, Carrey and Holly exchanged wedding vows.

In the interim, the star's career was taking no prisoners. His Riddler (a.k.a. Ed Nygma) in *Batman Forever* was another manifestation of prodigious excess, a worthy successor to such Caped Crusader adversaries as Jack Nicholson's The Joker and Danny DeVito's Penguin. As a scientific prodigy with the wherewithal to manipulate the nation's brain waves he was, well, pure Jim Carrey.

Ace Ventura: When Nature Calls had a terrific opening, but soon ran out of steam – in spite of a handful of inspired comic moments. Still, it's hard to forget the sequence when, trapped in a surveillance machine disguised as a rhinoceros, Carrey squeezes out of the rear, giving sightseers a unique insight into zoological obstetrics.

When *The Cable Guy* opened to mixed reviews and less than ballistic box-office returns, the press pounced like hyenas. It was as if Carrey's $20 million paycheck was some kind of divine reason for the film's 'failure'. Even the director, Ben Stiller, observed, nervously: 'Who wants to direct the first Jim Carrey movie that doesn't make $100 million?' As it happens, *The Cable Guy* was possibly Carrey's best movie to date, a daring, dark and inspired comedy that ripped the star's persona out of the comic-strip and plunged it squarely into something more classy. It is certainly the actor's most stylish and polished vehicle. Carrey played the eponymous electronics geek – Ernie 'Chip' Douglas – who attaches himself to one unfortunate customer (Matthew Broderick) and then bleeds him of his friendship. The reviews for *The Cable Guy* were certainly no worse than those for the original *Ace Ventura*, while the 'disappointing' box-office performance added up to $60.2 million in the USA – $7.5 million more than the much-ballyhooed *Four Weddings and a Funeral*. Furthermore, it grossed $102 million internationally. Some dud. However, Carrey was obviously past his 'best by' date, although such companies as

Morgan Creek and New Line had made a mint from the man, who was now cashing in his chips.

He next starred in Universal's *Liar Liar*, as a slick lawyer who's impelled to tell nothing but the truth for 24 hours. The film's director, Tom Shadyac, who previously steered Carrey through his paces in the original *Ace Ventura: Pet Detective*, promised that the star would be devoid of 'wild hairdos, wild wardrobe or missing teeth', adding that the movie would 'deliver Jim in a Steve Martin-ish, Tom Hanks-ish, Robin Williams-ish type role. He's a handsome, dynamic, charismatic lawyer.' Dynamic we can believe. The film grossed over $250m worldwide.

Then, in his first serious attempt to modify his image, Carrey took an $8 million salary cut to star in Peter Weir's drama *The Truman Show* – co-starring Dennis Hopper – the story of a man who's totally unaware that his life is actually a pseudo-TV drama.

FILMOGRAPHY

1984: *Finders Keepers*. 1985: *Once Bitten*. 1986: *Peggy Sue Got Married*. 1988: *The Dead Pool*. 1989: *High Strung* (unbilled); *Earth Girls Are Easy*; *Pink Cadillac*; *Mickey Spillane's Murder Takes All* (TV). 1992: *Doing Time On Maple Drive* (TV). 1989: *Ace Ventura: Pet Detective*; *The Mask*; *Dumb and Dumber*. 1995: *Batman Forever*; *Ace Ventura: When Nature Calls*. 1996: *The Cable Guy*. 1997: *Liar Liar*; *The Truman Show*.

GEORGE CLOONEY

After years functioning as fodder for lousy sitcoms and TV pilots, George Clooney had had enough. He'd served his time in B movies, he'd painted countless towns a tough shade of red and he'd enjoyed his fair share of women. It was time to grow up. If television was to be his medium, then he was going to tame it. 'It's not the kiss of death,' he reasoned. 'Most of them, starting with Eastwood, had television series. It's just finding the right one.'

The right one was *ER*, the molten-hot hospital drama in which Clooney carved his niche as the womanizing paediatrician Doug Ross. The series rocketed to the top of the American ratings, and the actor was suddenly courted by Hollywood. Fifteen months

As you know him: Clooney as Dr Doug Ross in TV's **ER**

after the show's debut on 19 September 1994, Clooney was signed to a $28 million, three-picture contract with Warner Brothers. He was to play Batman to Arnold Schwarzenegger's Mr Freeze in *Batman and Robin*, with a reported $10 million in the bank. Clooney was a movie star – and then some.

Chiselled from the same granite that fortified Rock Hudson and Bruce Willis – with a dash of Cary Grant thrown in for good measure – Clooney emanated eight-cylinder star power. Handsome, strong of jaw, commanding and yet velvet-voiced, he was a man's man that women swooned for. He could sink a beer with the guys, but also looked like he could cope in the kitchen – not to mention the bedroom. Thom Mathews, an old friend and acting crony, lent Clooney closet space during leaner years: 'George can say things that no one else can get away with,' he volunteered. 'What blew my mind was how he was able to get girls to go in that closet with him. I never understood how he did that.'

'It's his eyes,' reckons Nicole Kidman, Clooney's co-star from *The Peacemaker*. 'He can say so much without saying a word. You can't stop looking at him.'

*George Clooney makes a point in **From Dusk Till Dawn***

'He has a roguish charm coupled with a really remarkable comic ability,' offers Michael Chapman, director of *One Fine Day*. 'He's like watching Cary Grant. Men will like him because he's a respectable and viable advocate for their position. And women obviously love him.'

Yet Clooney himself modestly suggests that his appeal lies elsewhere. 'It's the show,' he says, referring to *ER*. 'If you were a mannequin on that show, they'd love the mannequin.' True, his co-stars Anthony Edwards, Noah Wyle and Eriq La Salle all went on to better things, but nobody else nailed down a $28 million movie contract.

George Clooney made his physical debut in Kentucky on 6 May 1961, the son of a former beauty queen, Nina, and talk show host Nick Clooney, 'the Johnny Carson of Cincinnati'. Obviously, showbusiness was in young George's blood. Besides his father, there were his aunts, the singers Betty and Rosemary Clooney, and Rosemary's husband, the Oscar-winning actor Jose Ferrer. In fact, it was Jose and Rosemary's son, Miguel Ferrer, who got George interested in acting.

Having said that, George Clooney had always been attracted to the limelight. When their father was in work, George and his older sister, Ada, used to help out on the show, arranging props, juggling cue cards and even appearing in the occasional skit. 'Ada hated it, but George was a natural,'

notes Nick Clooney. 'I remember asking him, when he was only five or six, what he wanted to do when he grew up. And his response was, "I want to be famous." We had no idea how serious he was.'

However, the notion of following in his father's footsteps was not on the cards. It was bad enough being dubbed 'the son of Nick Clooney'. As kids, 'people were always watching us,' he says. 'We'd move into a new neighbourhood and, just because of who my dad was, I'd have to get in fist fights to prove that I wasn't a wuss. And I was the worst at it. Everybody kicked my ass.'

At Northern Kentucky University, George studied broadcasting and drama, although his heart wasn't in it. There was too much partying to do. Then, at the age of 20, he visited Miguel and Jose Ferrer on the set of a low-budget movie about horce racing, *And They're Off*, and was given a small part. 'It was very seductive,' he says, 'with beautiful women paying attention to these guys, and this director saying, "You ought to be an actor, too," and me thinking, Well, yeah, I should be.' The film was never released, but George had been contaminated by the acting virus.

Hollywood was the next natural step, so Clooney took a series of jobs to pay for the fare: cutting tobacco, plugging insurance and selling women's shoes – even knocking off caricatures

at a local shopping centre. Once in California, he stayed with Aunt Rosemary for a while in Beverly Hills, but she was going through a difficult patch and asked him to leave.

Then, after a year of fruitless cattle calls, he landed a role in *Grizzly II – The Predator*, a minor feature with Charlie Sheen and Laura Dern, which was never released. However, he was spotted by a casting executive who signed him up for his first TV sitcom, in which he played a rookie medical technician. Believe it or not, the show was called *E/R* and was set in a Chicago emergency room. 'I played a dimwit,' he says with a smile, 'and I played him perfectly.' The sitcom was short-lived, but it led to another – the sixth season of NBC's *The Facts of Life*, in which Clooney portrayed a handyman called George Burnett. This, in turn, led to the starring role in the film *Return of the Killer Tomatoes*, in which he got to utter the immortal line, 'That was the bravest thing I've ever seen a vegetable do.' The movie was not a critical success, but it did lead to a sequel (without Clooney) called *Killer Tomatoes Strike Back*, and another sitcom for the actor, the much more visible *Roseanne*, in which he played Roseanne's factory boss, Booker Brooks, but he was only in it for one season.

Meanwhile, his private life was all over the place. After 20 days of dating Kelly Preston (who later became the wife of John Travolta), he bought a house for them to live in, but not long afterwards, in 1989, married a former girlfriend, the actress Talia Balsam. It was a spontaneous affair, starting with a wedding ceremony in Las Vegas and

Clooney with Michelle Pfeiffer in One Fine Day

ending three years later in relative amity – until the lawyers stepped in, that is, and charged Clooney $80,000 for their services. Later, he vowed: 'I'll never be married again, and I'll never have kids. From my point of view, the biggest part of why the marriage didn't work was my fault.'

After *Roseanne*, he played an undercover cop who moonlighted as a rock star in the series *Sunset Beat*, which was cancelled after one episode, and then starred opposite Dedee Pfeiffer (sister of Michelle) in a B movie called *Red Surf*.

The following year, 1991, he narrowly missed landing the role of J.D. in *Thelma & Louise* (the part went to Brad Pitt) and tried another sitcom, *Baby Talk*, a small-screen incarnation of *Look Who's Talking*. Following a row with the show's producer, Ed Weinberger, Clooney was fired. 'That was the low point,' he says now. 'That was literally the day I changed my life. I changed everything from that point on.' Be that as it may, he turned down a role in *Reservoir Dogs* ('he really blew that one,' offers director Quentin Tarantino), and opted for a leading role in a short-lived cop series called *Bodies of Evidence* (1992). A year later he played Detective Falconer in his first hit show since *Roseanne* – the popular *Sisters* – but his character had to be killed off when he landed *ER*.

There was also theatre work, notably the award-winning production of *Vicious* at the Steppenwolf Theater in Chicago, as well as turns in *South Pacific*, *Wrestlers* and *In My Father's House*. But with the soaring success of *ER* – and an Emmy nomination for best actor – Clooney was again eyeing the big screen. Apparently, Tarantino had forgiven him for his *Reservoir Dogs* blunder, and he was signed up to replace Robert Blake in *From Dusk Till Dawn*, a flashy cross between *Pulp Fiction* and *The Lost Boys*. Written by Tarantino two years before he got to direct *Reservoir Dogs*, the film – directed by Robert Rodriguez – received a mixed reception. However, Clooney's turn as a ruthless killer was a revelation. The movie earned $10.2 million in its opening weekend in the USA, and Clooney was away. The bidding had started.

Due to play the superhero Britt Reid in Universal's film version of *The Green Hornet*, Clooney was lured away with an offer of $3 million to star in *The Peacemaker*, a Cold War drama about a nuclear threat on the black market. This was the first project from Steven Spielberg's newly-formed DreamWorks enterprise (Spielberg's Amblin Entertainment having produced *ER*).

The following year, 1996, he partnered Michelle Pfeiffer in the romantic comedy *One Fine Day* (for which he was paid another $3 milion), playing an arrogant newspaper columnist who is forced to juggle babysitting duty while trying to save his career. In spite of being four years younger than Pfeiffer, Clooney exhibited such an air of lived-in authority that nobody noticed the age difference. Furthermore, he showed that he was as comfortable acting opposite kids as he was vampires (which he battled heroically in *From Dusk Till Dawn*). In fact, Clooney inhabited the part so completely that it was hard to imagine either Tom Cruise or Kevin Costner in the role, both of whom were previously offered it.

Then, when Val Kilmer – who had played the Caped Crusader in *Batman Forever* – double-booked himself as *The Saint*, Clooney was signed on in his place. Yet whereas Kilmer had 'only' pocketed $2 million to play Batman, Clooney was offered five times as much. In addition, the actor received a Golden Globe nomination for his work on *ER*, and found a new love interest, Celine Balitran, a French law student he had met in Paris. Michelle Pfeiffer, whose sister Dedee once dated Clooney, figures it's only a matter of time before he settles for fatherhood. 'He has a real love-hate relationship with children,' she notes. 'But once he gets started, he'll have ten.'

FILMOGRAPHY

1982: *And They're Off* (unreleased). 1983: *Grizzly II – The Predator* (unreleased). 1986: *Combat High*. 1987: *Return to Horror High*. 1988: *Return of the Killer Tomatoes*. 1990: *Sunset Beat* (TV); *Red Surf*. 1993: *Unbecoming Age*; *Without Warning: Terror in the Towers* (TV). 1995: *From Dusk Till Dawn*. 1996: *One Fine Day*. 1997: *The Peacemaker*; *Batman and Robin*; *Full Tilt Boogie*. 1998: *Out of Sight*; *The Thin Red Line*.

TOM CRUISE

TOM CRUISE

Tom Cruise was the determined pup who broke away from the Brat Pack and ended up king of the jungle. Like his cohorts Matt Dillon, Emilio Estevez, Rob Lowe, et al., he emerged from Francis Coppola's cult movie *The Outsiders*, but then he steadily moved up the cinematic ranks, transforming himself from young puck to the most expensive buck in the business.

In a 1992 feature on the millionaire's club, *Movieline* magazine wrote: 'If you're going to pay anybody too much to star in the movie you're spending too much to make, pay Tom Cruise. He's the only *bona fide* movie star of his generation.'

In 1986 and 1987, Tom Cruise was the number one top box-office attraction in the USA, bigger than Eddie Murphy, Sylvester Stallone or Clint Eastwood. In 1988 he dropped one place, but only after Jack Nicholson had nudged his way into the top spot. However, Cruise was to have the last laugh: in 1992 he not only walked

Tom Cruise in *A Few Good Men*

*As Hollywood's **Top Gun***

away with $12 million for *A Few Good Men*, but also top-billed Nicholson, who only received $8 million. Cruise, who was also reportedly paid somewhere between $10 million and $12 million for *Far and Away* – plus a percentage of the gross profits – was quick to point out: 'I don't have a set price. To me each film is different. The people who own studios didn't get to where they were by being dumb businessmen. They aren't going to pay me one penny more than I'm worth, especially in this marketplace. They wouldn't pay me if I wasn't worth it. And the day I'm not, they won't.' In 1996 he was paid $20 million to star in *Jerry Maguire*.

In spite of his price, Tom Cruise was in demand. So much so, that everybody thought they were working with him. In 1990 he was reputedly making *China Maze*, James Ivory's *An Innocent Millionaire*, *Out West*, *Top Gun II* and *What Makes Sammy Run?* – none of which saw the light of day. He was also due to star in *Backdraft*, *Edward Scissorhands*, *Prelude to a Kiss*, *Rush* and *Till There Was You*, all of which were filmed with other actors. Instead, Cruise made *Days of Thunder* and met his future wife, the 5'10", flaming-haired Nicole Kidman from Australia.

Very little about Tom Cruise is not known to his public. They know he is 5'9", a devout Scientologist, an ardent environmentalist, was married to Mimi Rogers for three years (1987–1990), divorced her, and then wed Nicole. They know he is the top gun, the leading star of his generation, the handsome, determined actor who fought and planned his way to the top, taking risks, working with the best.

Paul Newman, who played Cruise's mentor in *The Color of Money*, described him as: 'This kid [who had] the head and the balls to be one of the great ones ... the next Hollywood legend.' Dustin Hoffman, who co-starred with Cruise in Barry Levinson's *Rain Man*, said of him: 'There's no sense of a crest in Tom. His talent is young, his body is young, his spirit is young. He's a Christmas tree – he's lit from head to toe. He's the biggest star in the world.' But Barry Levinson believes: 'Tom is at a disadvantage. He's got a pretty face, so his abilities are underestimated. And he's not working a rebel image, which is associated with being a good actor.'

Indeed, far from being the sullen, paparazzi-punching rebel, Cruise is endearing in his eagerness to please. In person, he is surprisingly boyish, polite and modest. The cocky bravura that accompanies so many of his screen characters evaporates as he – ever so courteously – explains his case. Maybe Cruise is still covering his tracks, knowing that overnight superstardom can vanish as quickly as it materializes. He appears to be terrified of putting a foot wrong. Like Mitchell Y. McDeere, the character the actor so closely mirrors in *The Firm*, Cruise is a high-

achiever, a success story who has overcome insurmountable odds to make it to the top. For a start, he's dyslexic and never went to college, a drawback he surmounts by carrying a dictionary with him wherever he goes.

Born Thomas Cruise Mapother IV in Syracuse, New York, on 3 July 1962, the actor grew up surrounded by women. There was his mother, Mary Lee, and then his three sisters, Lee Anne, Marian and Cass. His father, Thomas Cruise Mapother III, was an electrical engineer and moved the family from Canada to New Jersey, from Missouri to New York. At kindergarten, Tom was forced to become right-handed, and by the age of 12 he had attended twelve schools in as many cities. At one academy his classmates voted him the boy least likely to succeed.

When he was young, his mother explained: 'Tom used to create skits and imitate Donald Duck and Woody Woodpecker and W.C. Fields – all when he was just a tiny tot. I guess I was his greatest audience. He had it in him then, but as he got older, he was more into sports, and it stopped completely.' Tom was 11 when his father walked out and Mary Lee Mapother took the family back to Louisville, her Kentucky hometown. Five years later, she re-married and the family finally settled down in Glen Ridge, New Jersey.

For a while Cruise contemplated becoming a priest and attended a year in a Franciscan seminary. He was also a keen wrestler, but when a leg injury

*With Oscar-winning Paul Newman in Martin Scorsese's **The Color of Money***

*With Oscar-winning Dustin Hoffman in Barry Levinson's **Rain Man***

forced him off the school team he auditioned for a play out of boredom. The part was Nathan Detroit in *Guys and Dolls*. It was his. 'It felt just right,' he explains. 'It felt like I had a way to express myself. I decided then and there that this was what I wanted to do. I packed my bags and went to New York. I didn't even attend my high school graduation.'

Master Mapother shortened his name to Tom Cruise, waded through auditions during the day and waited on tables at night. When there was time, he attended classes at the Neighborhood Playhouse, honing his craft. Within five months he landed a small role in Franco Zeffirelli's *Endless Love*, 18th-billed, as Billy. He had another bit part, playing the sidekick of headstrong military cadet David Shawn in *Taps*, an army drama starring George C. Scott, Timothy Hutton and Sean Penn. When the actor playing Shawn was considered too weak for the part, Cruise stepped in. Sean Penn recalls: 'Cruise was so strong that the other guy didn't have a chance. Cruise was overwhelming. And we'd all kind of laugh, because he was so sincere.'

Cruise next joined the cast of *The Outsiders*, playing the high-spirited buddy of C. Thomas Howell and Emilio Estevez, revealing his sculptured torso in an open shirt and brandishing the tattoo of an eagle on his considerable biceps. It was a negligible role, but he was in the right place at the right

time. He lost the part of Paul Newman's son in *Harry & Son* (because he was too young – the role went to Robby Benson), and then landed his first lead, playing the retiring, gauche, yet enterprising Joel Goodsen in *Risky Business*. Co-starring Rebecca De Mornay as the prostitute who conspires with Joel to run a one-night brothel in his parent's house, the film was a critical and popular hit, grossing $65 million in the USA. To this day, the scene people remember best is the one in which Cruise mimes to Bob Seger belting out 'Old Time Rock & Roll', wearing nothing but his socks, Y-fronts and shirt tails. It was the most sensational piece of beefcake posturing since John Travolta donned his white suit in *Saturday Night Fever*. On one famous occasion, Ron Reagan Jr parodied it in an episode of *Saturday Night Live*, TDK cassettes copied it for their magazine ads and Campbell's Soup borrowed it for a commercial.

'In the script, the scene was one line that said, "Joel dances in underwear through the house"',' Cruise explains. 'But I had tried it a couple of ways where it didn't work. Finally, I put on socks, waxed the floor, and then put dirt around the area so I could slide right out to the centre of the frame. Then we did the thing with the candlestick – using it as a microphone – and made it into this rock and roll number. And we just kept going, trying different things. [Paul] Brickman [the

director] would say, "I want something crazy here," so I'd jump onto the couch and, you know, just let loose. I saw Brickman after he saw the rushes on that scene and he said, "It's the most hysterical scene in the movie."'

Cruise was a star. He dated Rebecca De Mornay in the glare of the paparazzi's flashbulbs, and won top-billing in his second movie, *All the Right Moves*. The story of a steel-town jock who tries to win a football scholarship to make something of himself, the film was another hit.

However, the star's next venture, Ridley Scott's *Legend*, was less popular. Actually, it was a disaster. A misconceived fairy tale that failed to rise above its stunning 'look', the film proved to be a troubled one, aggravated by the set being burned down mid-shoot. Also, Cruise's father had just died. It was a rough time for the actor, who spent a year marooned in London while nursing filial guilt. And, to add injury to insult, he injured his back. In future, Cruise promised himself that he would have more control over the films he accepted. On his return from England he broke up with Rebecca. It was the actor's lowest point – moments before he turned from star to superstar.

When the actor was offered a project about an elite navy pilot, he liked the sound of it. However, he wouldn't commit immediately. Instead, he insisted on working on the script with producers Don Simpson and Jerry Bruckheimer before consenting to do the picture. Simpson and Bruckheimer agreed – in spite of the box-office failure of *Legend*. 'He was terrific,' Simpson offered. 'Tom would show up at my house, grab a beer, and we'd work for five or six hours on the script. Sometimes we'd act scenes out. The guy doesn't see things from just a couple of perspectives, he can really wrap his arms around something and see it from all angles. We had a lot of fun.'

Again, Cruise took his research to the extreme, studying and flying with real pilots. Sheepishly, he divulged: 'I came close to getting my licence, but didn't really have enough time.'

The film, called *Top Gun*, was the biggest money-making picture of 1986. Recruitment into the navy escalated. A song from the picture, Berlin's 'Take

As crippled Vietnam vet Ron Kovic in Oliver Stone's gut-wrenching **Born on the Fourth of July**

My Breath Away', held the number one spot in Britain for four weeks. Other actors in the movie – Kelly McGillis, Val Kilmer, Anthony Edwards, Meg Ryan and Tim Robbins – all went on to greater glory.

Having made the ultimate pop movie, Tom Cruise was now ready to prove his mettle as a serious actor. Working with Martin Scorsese, the most highly-acclaimed filmmaker in America, seemed the next logical step.

The Color of Money was Paul Newman's film, everybody knew that. It was a sequel to 1961's *The Hustler*, which starred Newman as 'Fast' Eddie Felson, pool shark extraordinaire. In the sequel, Newman is 25 years wiser, acting as mentor to Vince Laurie, a hot-shot hustler who reminds Felson of what he used to be: raw, hungry, brilliant. Cruise won equal billing to Newman – *and* his friendship (it was Newman who introduced him to motor racing). 'He's got a lot of actor's courage,' Newman conceded. 'He doesn't mind climbing up there and jumping off. It's nice to watch that.'

Although it was Newman who ultimately won the Oscar, Cruise revealed a new edge to his acting, exhibiting an innocence and vulnerability overlaid

with a stylish, steely braggadocio. His pool-playing, too, brought a fresh athleticism and flamboyance to the game. Needless to say, *The Color of Money* broke box-office records for Touchstone Pictures, eventually grossing $47 million in the USA.

After this, Cruise took some time off to pace himself and to wait for *Rain Man* to happen. The story of a flash, young salesman who discovers he has an autistic savant older brother, *Rain Man* was a project Cruise and Dustin Hoffman desperately wanted to do together, whatever it took. Martin Brest, who was hoisted onto the Hollywood A-list after directing *Beverly Hills Cop*, walked off *Rain Man* after fearing that it was turning into a two-man road movie. Next, Steven Spielberg wrestled with the screenplay, and then Sydney Pollack. They both walked away.

Meanwhile, Cruise was fielding other offers, became obsessed with motor racing and, on the morning of 9 May 1987, married the actress Mimi Rogers. He admired her strength and intelligence, and after eight months revealed: 'Mimi helps me. She was there with me whenever she could be on *Rain Man*. Yet she's got her own career, which is just as important as mine. I just really enjoy our marriage.'

While still waiting for *Rain Man* to happen, the actor worked on *Cocktail*, a glossy, lightweight beefcake vehicle in

which he played a womanizing, super-slick bartender. Characteristically, he worked hard on his performance, and toiled undercover in a couple of New York bars, learning to juggle bottles while he served up potent cocktails. According to the film's director, Roger Donaldson: 'When Tom and I decided to make this movie, we said, "Well, it might not make any money, but at least it'll get good reviews."' However, the critics dismissed the film – but the public turned up in their droves, earning *Cocktail* a handsome $75 million in the USA.

Eventually, Barry Levinson came on board the runaway train that was *Rain Man* and kicked the film into production. As it happens, the wait was worth it. Cruise was paid $3 million for his part, and *Rain Man* went on to gross over $171 million in the USA alone. It also won the Oscar for best film, best actor (Hoffman), director and screenplay. Cruise himself didn't get a nomination, but his co-star – who has been called 'exacting' by his kindest critics – had nothing but praise for him: 'I don't usually meet people with my work habits,' Hoffman admitted, 'but Tom and I both like to get up before dawn and exercise. We'd drive to the set together, using the time to rehearse. Neither of us much like lunch; [so] we both stayed in the trailer and worked on the material. At night, Tom was constantly knocking on my door. He'd

Top wheel: Tom Cruise in **Days of Thunder**, based on his own story

say, "Why don't we do it this way?" And he'd do my lines so well he could have played my part.'

It must have been an odd sensation for Tom Cruise to see his last two co-stars both walk off with an Oscar. So, having already served time with Coppola and Scorsese, he hitched up with America's other great celluloid maestro, Oliver Stone. Their film together was *Born on the Fourth of July*, based on Ron Kovic's harrowing real-life story, a project Al Pacino had previously walked off. Stone called the latter 'a schmuck' and accused him of getting 'cold feet', but Cruise had anything but. This was to be his Big One. Not only did the actor befriend Ron Kovic, but insisted on riding around in a wheelchair on and off-set. At nights he would wheel himself right up to bed, allowing Mimi to help him into his sheets. 'It was very difficult getting up on curbs,' he recalls. 'In fact, it was exhausting. Every day that I was in that chair, I built up different muscles – but I was still tired.'

Cruise also grew his hair long, cultivated a spindly moustache and totally turned himself over to the role, frequently enduring the most humiliating of scenes. The end result was nothing short of gut-wrenching, and the film went on to gain eight Oscar nominations, including a nod for Cruise as best actor. The odds were in his favour for winning the statuette, but to most people's surprise another chair-bound actor wheeled off with the award – Daniel Day-Lewis, for *My Left Foot*. Still, Cruise is obviously here for the duration and, like his old friend Paul Newman, will probably see many more Oscar nominations slip by before the award is his.

Next, he practised his skills on the circuit with *Days of Thunder*, a motor racing drama based on his own idea, produced by Don Simpson and Jerry Bruckheimer and directed by Tony Scott – all of whom had previously worked on *Top Gun*. 'It's not *Top Gun* on wheels,' Cruise defended his Formula One venture. 'The characters have depth. It's about America and America's sons, really. Cars symbolize to me creative greatness. These drivers are artists. It's not just about going out there and putting your foot on the pedal.'

Whatever else the film was, it was a well-oiled machine that moved with the precision of a turbo engine. And the racing sequences were sensational. The preliminary advertising played up Cruise's power as a household name. Full page ads devoted three quarters of their space to six letters: 'C R U I S E', followed by 'LIKE THUNDER' in smaller capitals. Although *Days of Thunder* was considered a box-office 'disappointment', it grossed $82 million in the USA and $230 million (including video sales) worldwide – which was nothing to cry about.

This time his leading lady was Nicole Kidman, who had made an enormous impression in the Australian thriller *Dead Calm*. She didn't receive the kindest reviews for her role in *Thunder*, but her love scenes with Cruise must have packed some punch, as the couple became engaged – even before the actor's divorce from Mimi Rogers was final. 'Instant lust, that's what I felt,' Cruise revealed. 'I thought she was amazingly sexy and stunning. It grew into love and respect. I just knew I couldn't live without her.' They married – secretly – in Telluride, Colorado, on Christmas Eve, 1990. And, like Mimi before her, Nicole is a keen disciple of Scientology, Cruise's chosen religion.

The tabloids moved in, and vicious stories circulated around Hollywood's latest spot-lit couple. One rumour suggested that Cruise married Kidman because his first wife couldn't give him children. Another story, much publicized, claimed that the star forced his new girlfriend to have fertility tests before he'd marry her. Another announced Kidman's pregnancy. 'It's very strange reading about your life and thinking it's not true,' Kidman offered. 'It's *not* true, I don't know where they get it from. What's unbelievable is how the stories get out of control. They spread all over the world to Australia ...' And, to set the record straight, she avowed: 'I did not marry into a marriage of convenience. I would never, ever do that. You marry for love.'

She also denounced the rumours suggesting that her husband was gay: 'We're both heterosexual. I'll bet all my money I've ever made, plus his, that he doesn't have a mistress, that he doesn't

Cruise sinking his teeth into his most adventurous role yet, in **Interview With the Vampire**

have a gay lover, that he doesn't have a gay life.' Well, that's final, then.

Meanwhile, Mimi Rogers could not contain her bitterness: 'I can complain about it now,' she confessed, 'but when you marry somebody, you love them and you realize the association is part of the deal. But you get to a point where it's enough already ... I'm waiting for the moment when I don't have to talk about that fucking name anymore. I've had it welded onto mine for years now.'

When Tom Cruise was signed up to play a brash, illiterate Irish farm hand opposite Kidman's rebellious aristocrat in *Far and Away*, director Ron Howard swears he didn't know they were an item. Cruise defends Howard by saying: 'You know, he lives in Connecticut – and he doesn't read the *National Enquirer*. Not that they ever get it right.'

Far and Away was a very personal project for Howard, who based the screenplay on stories from his own family's Irish background. Shot in Panavision Super 65mm, the film was a sweeping, old-fashioned romance, in

*With Emmanuelle Beart in Brian De Palma's **Mission: Impossible**, which Cruise also produced*

which Cruise and Kidman bickered at each other across their respective class barriers until the final, sunlit smooch. Budgeted at $42 million, the project was a sizeable gamble for Universal Pictures and, when it opened in the summer of 1992, it couldn't compete against *Lethal Weapon 3* and *Alien3*. However, the film did exhibit some staying power, and two months later it was making more money than either of these films. The reason for this was that cinemagoers were going back to see it *again*. Eventually, it clocked up $59 million in the USA – $4 million more than *Alien3* made.

In *A Few Good Men*, Tom Cruise played Lieutenant Daniel Kaffee, in the words of his superior, 'a fast food, slick-assed' navy lawyer. However, Kaffee is forced to re-examine his legal ethics when he teams up with Demi Moore to defend two marines accused of murder. Slouching around Washington DC in jeans and sports jacket, Cruise looked uncannily like Joel Goodsen in *Risky Business*, until, done up to the nines in full military uniform, he is dressed to kill. The problem with Cruise in the film is that he is so readily associated with his role as the crusading good guy that it was hard to believe he could be such an irresponsible cad (dishing out plea bargains in order to find time to play softball). Equally, it was predictably obvious that he was going to pull his socks up before the film's end. Still, the film was the biggest box-office hit over the 1992 Christmas period, which helped

refuel Cruise's standing as a bankable legend. Indeed, he was voted the biggest box-office star of 1992 by America's cinema managers.

He then landed another big movie, *The Firm,* based on John Grisham's number one bestseller of 1991. Robert Towne scripted, Scott Rudin produced and Sydney Pollack directed, with Cruise playing a hotshot law student signed up by a questionable – nay, *lethal* – law firm in Memphis. Gene Hackman, Jeanne Triplehorn, Holly Hunter and Ed Harris co-starred, and the picture went on to gross a phenomenal $158.3 million in the USA alone. In January 1993, Cruise took a brief leave of absence from the set to join his wife for a few days to bond with Isabella, the daughter they adopted in Miami (they later adopted a second child, Connor Antony). In spite of the secrecy surrounding the occasion, the *National Enquirer* turned up to take the first pictures of the happy trio, and the world was let in on the secret.

Future aspirations included the mandatory stab at directing, something many think Cruise has the focus to pull off – including Ron Howard. 'Can Tom Cruise direct a movie? Without a doubt,' the filmmaker conceded. 'Whether he will *like* it or not, that's another story. But as an actor who became a director myself, I can see that Tom thoroughly understands the process ... It's easy for him to shift and see the big picture. Most actors can't do that, even highly skilled, experienced ones.'

Sure enough, Cruise made his debut behind the camera on the 30-minute 'The Frightening Frammis', an episode of TV's *Fallen Angels*. Starring Peter Gallagher, Nancy Travis and Isabella Rossellini, the show premiered on Sunday, 5 September 1993, and demonstrated that Cruise had an unmistakable talent as a filmmaker, particularly a skill for shaping performances.

It was about this time that he began preparing for his role as Lestat in Neil Jordan's *Interview with the Vampire*, based on the novel by Anne Rice. The part had originally been offered to Daniel Day-Lewis and Johnny Depp (both of whom rejected it), and when Cruise signed on the dotted line, Rice publicly announced: 'Cruise is no more my vampire Lestat than Edward G. Robinson is Rhett Butler.' The author later retracted her statement with a written testimony that smacked of PR subterfuge: 'On September 16, 1994, I saw a videocassette of the up and coming film *Interview with the Vampire*, based on my first novel. I loved the film. I simply loved it. I loved it from start to finish, and I found myself deeply impressed with every aspect of its making, including its heartfelt and often daring performances by all the actors and actresses ... The charm, the humour, and invincible innocence which I cherish in my beloved hero Lestat are all alive in Tom Cruise's courageous performance.'

Be that as it may, this critic found the picture a pretentious, time-consuming wallow, desperately in need of a kick up its narrative bottom. Yet whenever Cruise was on screen (which wasn't that much), the movie came bounding to life. A heroic change of pace for the actor (who lost 18 pounds to 'look the part'), Cruise revelled in the charismatic evil of his character, whether sweeping up a rat and biting its head off, or plucking up a plague-riddled corpse, dancing round the room with it proclaiming: 'There's life in the old lady yet!' Not a typical Cruise vehicle, to be sure, but *Interview with the Vampire* amassed $105.3 million at US cinemas alone.

Next, the star not only returned to the more familiar terrain of clean-cut hero but, for the first time he also flexed his muscles as movie producer.

As **Jerry Maguire**, the part that won Cruise a Golden Globe and a second Oscar nomination

Jumping onto the whimsical bandwagon that converted TV cast-offs into box-office gold (*The Fugitive*, *Maverick*), Cruise took on the legend of CBS TV's *Mission: Impossible*. He played master of disguise Ethan Hunt (based on the Rollin Hand character played by Martin Landau) who, on a routine assignment in Prague, is left fighting for his life when his colleagues are wiped out in an elaborate double-cross. However, in spite of Cruise's considerable screen presence, the characters were so sexless and sketchily drawn that the audience was given little to latch on to. Furthermore, the film was cluttered by an unfathomable plot and undermined by pointless arty camera angles, courtesy of director Brian De Palma. In fact, much was made of the antagonism between producer and director, although Cruise went on record to say: 'That's bullshit. We had *one* bad argument on the phone. I don't even remember what we were fighting over. But suddenly we started yelling at each other and we hung up on each other. So I called him back and said, "Brian, we just had our first fight." We

were both exhausted and under a lot of pressure. It was no big deal.'

Whatever, the slick marketing and hit theme tune (remixed by Larry Mullen and Adam Clayton) helped *Mission: Impossible* to a staggering $452.6 million worldwide.

Indeed, 1996 was a good year for Tom Cruise. Particularly as real-life hero. In March he witnessed a woman knocked down by a car, phoned the paramedics and paid her hospital bill. In July he saved a boy from being crushed by the first-night crowd at the opening of *Mission: Impossible*. And in August he and Nicole came to the aid of five survivors of a burning yacht off the coast of Capri.

Furthermore, Cruise was, as ever, on the top of every producer's list. He turned down the David Caruso role in *Jade* (sensibly), the Gregg Kinnear part in *Sabrina* (wisely) and the George Clooney character in *One Fine Day* (no comment). Then, when Tom Hanks (for whom the part was written) dropped out of the title role in *Jerry Maguire*, Cruise ignored the coffee stains on the script and grabbed the role with both

hands.

Jerry Maguire was a self-confessed 'shark in a suit', a top-of-the-rung sports agent whose sudden stab of conscience sends his career into a tailspin. Fired from his job, he struggles gamely to win back his standing in the business while trampling over the very ethics that got him fired. Only the love of a good woman – the winning Renee Zellweger – can save Jerry Maguire, but only if he can learn to return that love. Working from a sharp, insightful script by director Cameron Crowe (*Fast Times*, *Singles*), Cruise strode through his customary paces with pizzazz, flailing his arms, flashing his killer smile and punching out some terrific speeches. But this was a different Tom Cruise, a can-do over-achiever who's slipping from his perch – an arrogant son-of-a-bitch grinning manfully on his way down the corporate ladder. The star invested his traditional stamina in the role, and this time caught his critics off-guard. On 10 December 1996 he was voted best actor of the year by the National Board of Review, and on 19 January 1997 he snatched the prestigious Golden Globe award.

He then teamed up with Nicole Kidman (for the third time) in Stanley Kubrick's erotic melodrama *Eyes Wide Shut*. Rumours of trouble quickly leaked from the London set, which, as ever, Cruise was eager to dispel: 'We're working 14-hour days. You work on a scene and you work on it and work on it. Stanley will do 20 takes – that's not unusual. You are *not* leaving until he gets it right. It's intense, but as an actor, that's exactly what you want.'

As a director, Cruise was considering making his feature-directing debut on an untitled project about the 16th-century explorer Alvar Nunez Cabeza de Vaca.

FILMOGRAPHY

1981: *Endless Love*; *Taps*. 1983: *Losin' It* (a.k.a. *Tijuana*); *The Outsiders*; *Risky Business*; *All the Right Moves*. 1985: *Legend*. 1986: *Top Gun*; *The Color of Money*. 1988: *Cocktail*; *Rain Man*. 1989: *Born on the Fourth of July*. 1990: *Days of Thunder* (also co-story-writer). 1992: *Far and Away*; *A Few Good Men*. 1993: *The Firm*. 1994: *Interview with the Vampire*. 1996: *Mission: Impossible* (also produced); *Jerry Maguire*. 1997: *Eyes Wide Shut*.

JAMIE LEE CURTIS

Jamie Lee Curtis has gone through a number of transformations. At first she was known as the daughter of Hollywood royalty, being the offspring of former heart-throb Tony Curtis and actress Janet Leigh. Then, when she became an actress herself, she was dubbed 'the Queen of Scream', thanks to her vocal roles in such shockers as *Halloween*, *Prom Night* and *Terror Train*. She graduated from teenage victim to a full-blown woman in *Trading Places*, and became famous for her breasts. Two years later, vacuum-sealed into a leotard in *Perfect*, she was the girl with the legs. She was about to be labelled a has-been when, in 1988, she returned with a bang in the surprise hit *A Fish Called Wanda*, playing a big-time crook sexually turned on by foreign languages. And, finally, she became famous as a TV star, in the acclaimed sitcom *Anything But Love* – as Chicago scribe Hannah Miller.

Jamie Lee Curtis was born on 22 November 1958 in Los Angeles. She was three years old when her parents

Jamie Lee Curtis in Mother's Boys

divorced, and 11 when her father was arrested in England for possession of marijuana. A gawky, flat-chested teenager, she was educated at Beverly Hills High School, Westlake School for Girls and Choate Rosemary Hall in Connecticut. She went on to attend the University of the Pacific, and as part of one of her courses there she auditioned for Universal Studios and won a seven-year contract. Aged 18, she dropped out of college and took small roles in such TV fare as *Quincy*, *Columbo* and *The Nancy Drew Mysteries*. Then, six months into her career, she won the part of Lieutenant Barbara Duran in the TV movie *Operation Petticoat* – a remake of her father's 1959 comedy classic and a pilot for a new TV show. She recreated her role in the series, playing the part for a total of 13 months. 'For somebody who was not a beauty, and had no discernible talent,' she says, 'I had amazing success very quickly. I was 18! I knew nothing! ... I was playing a woman who was supposed to be in her thirties. I had all this make-up and hair, but it didn't matter how dressed up I was, I was the "kid".' The actress is quick to point out, too, that she got her roles without the aid of nepotism: 'I always felt the need *not* to go to the people closest to me,' she insisted.

The month *Operation Petticoat* went off the air, John Carpenter's *Halloween* opened in the USA and changed the face of the horror film. Jamie Lee played Laurie Strode, an innocent teenager stalked by a psychotic killer known as Michael Myers. Donald Pleasence was top-billed as Myers' anxious psychiatrist, but it was Jamie Lee's screaming heroine that the public remembered. The film was decidedly Hitchcockian in tone, and the press played up the comparison between Jamie Lee's character and her mother's in *Psycho* in which she was famously stabbed to death in the shower.

Halloween led to more horror, but of lesser pedigree. There was Carpenter's mediocre *The Fog*, with Janet Leigh; the Canadian slasher *Prom Night*, with a serious Leslie Nielsen, and another Canadian entry in the genre, *Terror Train*, starring Ben Johnson.

If the actress's career was failing to make inroads into art, her personal life was suffering, too. Now in her early

twenties, she went on a three-year spree of substance abuse and drinking – a spell she later blamed on her father's influence. She recovered, but her career was still in the doldrums. There was a so-so TV movie, *She's In the Army Now*, with Melanie Griffith; an intriguing thriller with Stacy Keach, *RoadGames*, which failed to catch on; the disappointing *Halloween II* (although Curtis was now top-billed *above* Pleasence), and another TV outing, *Death of a Centerfold: The Dorothy Stratten Story* (in which she played the real-life, tragic *Playboy* centrefold), a story which was told better two years later in Bob Fosse's *Star 80*.

Her favourite movie up to this time was Amy Jones' low-budget romantic drama *Love Letters*, in which she played a woman who takes up with a married man (James Keach). However, in spite of good notices, the public stayed away. Nevertheless, they turned up in droves to see her play a golden-hearted hooker in *Trading Places*, a hilarious comedy with Dan Aykroyd and Eddie Murphy. Although she'd indulged in some steamy sex scenes in *Love Letters*, nobody had noticed, so when she took off her shirt in *Trading Places* the world went hog wild. 'All of a sudden I was "a sex girl",' she muses. 'All of a sudden people discovered that I had breasts. I mean, it was wild. To this day it's the topic of conversation when people meet me. So, I bared my breasts. Everybody does it. I don't want to start listing all the actresses that have done nudity in movies ... I was playing a hooker, and there was no question that nudity was in the movie. It turned out to be my avenue into a more main-stream audience. It took six seconds.'

Later, when promoting her role in *Fierce Creatures*, the actress expanded on her theme: 'Now my chest has a world of its own. It has an agent, a publicist, a fan club, a Web page. There's a whole city devoted to these breasts.'

For Jamie Lee, 1984 was an even more important year. In *Grandview, USA*, she played the owner of a demo-lition derby romantically wedged between C. Thomas Howell and Patrick Swayze but, more importantly, she picked up a copy of *Rolling Stone*. In it, she found a photograph of the chameleonic actor and writer Christopher Guest. 'He was wearing a

Jamie Lee with her co-stars from **A Fish Called Wanda**: Michael Palin, John Cleese and Kevin Kline

plaid shirt, he had a smirk on his face, and I thought he was just the most beautiful man,' she remembers. 'I called up his agent and sort of fumbled for words, trying to find out if he was single, and would he want to go out with me? I had never, *ever* done this before. Anyway, he never called. But, about two months later, I was having dinner in a restaurant, and he was there. We looked at each other, and he sort of signalled that he'd gotten the message by waving at me. He called me the next day. That was June 28. We went out July 2 and were married December 18.'

The following year she paid her debt to *Rolling Stone* by starring in *Perfect*, opposite John Travolta. She played an aerobics instructor (in those famous leotards), and Travolta was the reporter from *Rolling Stone* who romanced her. Columbia Pictures invested a small fortune in promoting the picture, but the critics retaliated with bile and the movie was a box-office stiff. Still, the attendant publicity had served Jamie Lee well. Now she

was even *more* famous. And more cautious: 'When *Perfect* bombed, I made a personal decision that I would let the script dictate my choices finally. I would only do things that appealed to me. It's what most good actors do.'

While she weighed up her career, Jamie Lee and her new husband adopted a 12-hour-old baby, Annie, as Curtis was unable to have children of her own. And while Annie brought new joy into her parents' lives, her mother's career stumbled.

Four films in three years failed to make an impression with critics or public alike, until a small comedy from England upped Jamie Lee's ante. This was the oddly-titled *A Fish Called Wanda*, starring and written by the oddly-proportioned English TV comedian John Cleese, with the unlikely supporting cast of Jamie Lee, Kevin Kline and Michael Palin. However, *Fish* had one thing in its favour – it was hysterically funny.

A superbly-structured crime caper with beautifully-realized characters, *A Fish Called Wanda* was loaded with canny observations of the love-hate bridge between America and Britain. It also boasted a cracking pace and priceless dialogue. All the actors on hand were on the top of their form, with Jamie Lee a particularly engaging temptress (Wanda Gershwitz) who seduces all three of her co-stars – in the name of greed. The film was a smash box-office success and every-

body's favourite comedy of the year.

The actress was on a roll. She next starred as Hannah Miller in the ABC sitcom *Anything But Love*, playing a journalist on the *Chicago Weekly*, platonically involved with co-writer Marty Gold (Richard Lewis). Although successful, the series suffered a bumpy ride, which included three separate pilot shows, alternative time slots, conceptual shifts and even cancellation, until popular demand brought the series back. It also won Curtis a Golden Globe and the People's Choice Award as 'America's favourite female performer in a new TV series'. The Golden Globe honour reduced her to tears, prompting her to write a thank you note to each of the judges: 'It's taken me 12 years for people to recognize my work,' she declared.

In the hard-hitting crime thriller *Blue Steel*, the actress was top-billed as a rookie cop pursued by a psychotic killer (Ron Silver), and she won more good reviews (her old ally, *Rolling Stone*, glowed: 'Curtis must be praised for a great performance filled with ferocity and feeling'). She was lost in the all-star cast of *Queen's Logic* (Kevin Bacon, Joe Mantegna, John Malkovich, Tom Waits), a labour of love which virtually sank without trace, and she then bounced back in the excruciating *My Girl*. A sugary vehicle for the photogenic allure of 11-year-old Anna Chlumsky and Macaulay Culkin, the film apparently appealed to American

*Mr and Mrs Schwarzenegger: Arnie and Jamie in James Cameron's wildly entertaining **True Lies***

Back with Kevin Kline in **Fierce Creatures,** *every inch an equal of* **A Fish Called Wanda**

family audiences and strolled away with $58 million in the bank (in the USA alone). Jamie Lee Curtis, decked out in a trampy 1960s wardrobe, looked too old to be convincing, and her attraction to Chlumsky's overweight father (Dan Aykroyd, as a mortician) was inexplicable.

Next, she was cast in the romantic, old-fashioned *Forever Young* as a single mother with the hots for Mel Gibson, unaware that he is actually old enough to be her grandfather. Hers was a beautifully judged performance, an adroit mix of humour and pain.

She then starred in *Mother's Boys*, a serviceable thriller in which she played Jude Madigan, the most despicable screen mother since Faye Dunaway raised a coat hanger in *Mommie Dearest*. Thankfully, the actress reined in the hysteria, and even by the film's end one was not entirely sure who had taken us for a ride – Jude or the scriptwriter.

She was wasted in the ghastly sequel to *My Girl*, but then her stock rose considerably with the hugely successful *True Lies*, in which she played the wife of Arnold Schwarzenegger. Posing as a sales rep for a computer company, Schwarzenegger is actually a world-class spy for a top-secret government agency formed to combat nuclear terrorism. Bored with her role as housewife, Curtis activates a clandestine affair with a conman (Bill Paxton)

before being drawn into a international incident presided over by her husband. Combining awkwardness with high-wattage sex appeal, Curtis was a perfect foil – both comically and romantically – to Schwarzenegger, and almost stole the movie from the exorbitant special effects.

She then wrote a book – *Tell Me Again About the Night I Was Born* – about adopted children relating their stories to their parents. 'It's a story taking adoption away from this Gothic sadness that people always seem to associate with it,' she explained. She won terrific reviews for her performance as the feminist Heidi Holland in an excellent TV movie, *The Heidi Chronicles*, with Tom Hulce, and then, in the embarrassing farce *House Arrest*, she played a mother in the throes of separation (from Kevin Pollak). While based on a reasonably funny idea – a father and mother locked in a basement by their children until forced to change their plans for divorce – the film substituted wit for gross physical farce and much repetition.

There was farce again in *Fierce Creatures*, in which Curtis was joined by her *A Fish Called Wanda* co-stars, John Cleese, Kevin Kline and Michael Palin. This time she played a bright American executive who is transplanted to a quiet, provincial zoo in England where she falls for the zoo's tyrannical

director – Cleese – whom she mistakenly believes to be an animal in bed. The formula of *Wanda* was largely repeated – Cleese flabbergasted, Curtis seductive, Kline maniacal, Palin loopy – but the circumstances were rather different.

According to countless press reports, Cleese was edgy and demanding and Kline plain difficult, while Curtis herself was cited as unprofessional. Whatever the facts, the film tested so badly in the USA that the Australian director, Fred Schepisi, was called in to shoot an estimated 45 per cent of extra material. Having originally completed production in August of 1995, *Fierce Creatures* didn't actually open until 24 January 1997. Curtis, who had just adopted a second child, Thomas, told a friend in her defence: 'John knew when I came on the film that I was worried about my children and wanted to spend time with them. I think he's being totally unreasonable.'

Nevertheless, the finished product tested well in the USA and was in fact a superbly-crafted piece of farce, brimming with wonderful sight gags and some terrific dialogue. Curtis was fabulous as the siren caught between Cleese and Kline, who, in addition, develops an affinity with an outsize gorilla. She then starred in the action-thriller *Virus*, with Donald Sutherland.

Meanwhile, her husband inherited an English peerage, enabling him to sit in the House of Lords. That makes Jamie Lee Curtis, actress, author and mother, also Lady Haden Guest.

FILMOGRAPHY

1977: *Operation Petticoat* (TV). 1978: *Halloween.* 1980: *The Fog; Prom Night; Terror Train.* 1981: *She's In the Army Now* (TV); *RoadGames; Halloween II; Death of a Centerfold: The Dorothy Stratten Story* (TV). 1982: *Money On the Side* (TV). 1983: *Love Letters* (a.k.a. *Passion Play*); *Trading Places.* 1984: *Grandview, USA.* 1985: *Perfect.* 1986: *As Summers Die* (TV). 1987: *Amazing Grace and Chuck* (UK: *Silent Voice*); *A Man in Love.* 1988: *Dominick and Eugene* (UK: *Nicky and Gino*); *A Fish Called Wanda.* 1990: *Blue Steel.* 1991: *Queen's Logic; My Girl.* 1992: *Forever Young.* 1993: *Mother's Boys; My Girl 2.* 1994: *True Lies.* 1995: *The Heidi Chronicles* (TV). 1996: *House Arrest.* 1997: *Fierce Creatures; Homegrown; Virus.*

JOHN CUSACK

John Cusack in 1989

John Cusack is the most unusual of leading men. A hive of contradictions, his gangly 6'2" frame is capped by a boyish face, itself stamped with a wisdom beyond its years. Look closer, and you notice an army of freckles washed back though countless nights in darkened cinemas and smoky clubs. Cusack, who paid his acting dues alongside the likes of Rob Lowe, Molly Ringwald and Demi Moore, boycotted Hollywood's glitzier parties in favour of the seclusion of blues bars in his native Chicago, preferring to soak up a nocturnal atmosphere with non-actors and other real people. He *is* a dedicated film buff, but his taste is decidedly non-mainstream, favouring 'great classics like *Plan 9 From Outer Space*. I love things that you can laugh at, but also things that are piercing and fierce that take on the establishment,' he professes.

His own early films were hardly in the same league as *Plan 9*, and when he swore he'd never do another 'teen pic', he played love-struck high school student Lloyd Dobler in his best film to date, *Say Anything ...* In his defence, Cusack explains: 'I really didn't want to graduate high school again. But then I thought, I'm 22, I'm only going to be this young once, I might as well close that part of my career on a good note.'

It was a very good note indeed, and

it led to the lead in Stephen Frears' critically saluted, hard-boiled film noir thriller *The Grifters*, in which the actor played a sleazy conman with an Oedipus complex. Frears volunteered: 'John is like a jazz musician. He zones off into these dark moods, then zaps out of it with no warning and goes on. There's a light blackness to his talent that I found extraordinary. Someone once described John to me as being Jimmy Stewart with an edge, and I think that description is quite accurate.'

Cusack's next big break was to be signed up by James Cameron (*Terminator 2*, *Aliens*) to play real-life multi-schizophrenic Billy Milligan in the eagerly-awaited film version of *The Crowded Room*. Virtually every star under 45 in Hollywood was after the part, but Cameron held out for Cusack. However, due to financial problems afflicting Cameron's production company, the film was put on hold. If or when the film does get made, it should turn Cusack's career around.

John Cusack, one of five children, was born on 28 June 1966 in Evanston, Illinois, an affluent suburb of Chicago. His father is the Emmy award-winning documentary filmmaker Richard Cusack, and his older sister, Joan, an

appealing and successful actress, who won an Oscar nomination for *Working Girl* and has also appeared in *Broadcast News*, *Nine Months* and, with her brother, *Grosse Point Blank*. John himself was encouraged to act at the age of nine and took classes at the Piven Theater Workshop in Evanston. At 12, he was already an old hand at commercials, promoting the joys of McDonald's on TV and the advantages of Heinz tomato ketchup on radio. While still in high school he wrote and staged two musical comedies which were later broadcast on local TV.

He was 16 when he breezed into the office of Chicago agent Ann Geddes and told her that he'd win any audition she set him up for. Impressed by his chutzpah, Ms Geddes put him up for a role as Rob Lowe's bright sidekick in *Class*. He got it.

A slew of 'teen pics' followed, but Cusack kept his dramatic focus by periodically returning to Chicago. In 1984, aged 18, he wrote and directed an award-winning programme for NBC TV and produced a stage production of *The Day They Shot John Lennon*. He later formed his own theatrical company, New Criminals, and won a local prize for best director.

Cusack with Meredith Salenger in the delightful wilderness yarn
The Journey of Natty Gann

Cusack with Ione Skye in Cameron Crowe's _Say Anything_

On screen, he starred in Rob Reiner's sleeper hit _The Sure Thing_, playing a 19-year-old Ivy League student who dreams of an easy lay. On a cross-country journey to find his 'sure thing', he's thrown together with fellow student Daphne Zuniga, whose patience has been frazzled by Cusack's chat-up lines on astronomy. Inevitability wins out, but not before we have warmed to these two sweet teenagers, misled by society to behave out of character. Cusack was an unlikely yet irresistible romantic hero, replacing beefcake swagger with a touching credibility.

The Sure Thing not only introduced Cusack to a new public, but to his best friend, Tim Robbins, who played Gary. The pair soon became inseparable, and on one famous occasion they set out to find Elvis Presley. 'We went from New York to Memphis before we found out that Elvis was actually dead, that he'd mated with a female bear, and their son – a half-man bear-child – was alive and heir to the throne,' he recalls. 'But it

wasn't until we ended up in Vegas twisted drunk that the trip really got dark.'

Back on film, he played a hobo in Disney's surprisingly distinguished outdoor adventure _The Journey of Natty Gann_, but then he succumbed to more teenage drivel. 'I must have been asleep,' he reveals reluctantly. 'I guess I had to learn that holes in scripts don't fix themselves.' The only decent title in the lot was Reiner's _Stand By Me_, in which the actor made a brief appearance as Whil Weaton's older brother. He was offered a pile of money to play Molly Ringwald's live-in boyfriend in _For Keeps_, but turned it down to escape to Africa. 'I had to get away,' he explains.

He was good as the principled baseball player George 'Buck' Weaver in John Sayles' _Eight Men Out_, but the film was terribly dreary; and then he turned down, then accepted, the lead in _Say Anything_ ... Although a box-office disappointment, the film was fresh, funny and achingly honest – and put a

new zing in Cusack's career.

He took a supporting role in Roland Joffe's _Fat Man and Little Boy_, a film he's deservedly proud of, in which he played a young scientist who works on the atomic bomb; and then came _The Grifters_. Cusack was unexpectedly at home in the sleazy milieu of author Jim Thompson's novel, playing a small-time con artist who plays the sexual affections of his mother (Anjelica Huston) off on his scheming girlfriend (Annette Bening). Both actresses were honoured by America's National Society of Film Critics, but Cusack came away empty-handed.

He then starred in Herbert Ross's _True Colors_, as a treacherous, social-climbing politician who clashes with his former law school buddy, James Spader. Cusack struggled manfully with the implausibilities of his role, but in the end the obvious plot strands and character manipulation capsized the film, Cusack and the entire cast (including such heavyweight players as Mandy Patinkin and Richard Widmark).

The actor then went on the cameo trail, proving most effective of all in Tim Robbins' _Bob Roberts_, in which he portrayed a recalcitrant TV host who refuses to kowtow to the ingratiating charm of the eponymous political candidate (Robbins). He also took small parts in _The Player_, _Roadside Prophets_, _Shadows and Fog_ and _Map of the Human Heart_, yet turned down sterling lead roles in the likes of _Sleeping With the Enemy_, _Indecent Proposal_ and _White Men Can't Jump_ (all hits). 'You have a clear view of what you think you are,' he tried to explain, 'what you feel you want, what you feel is right, what you feel you have to do. I don't like playing characters who are empty vessels.'

Of his subsequent roles, two stand out. In Woody Allen's _Bullets Over Broadway_, he played a neurotic, intellectual playwright who, in order to have his precious play staged, is forced to cast a gangster's girlfriend in it. In a cast that included Dianne Wiest, Jennifer Tilly, Chazz Palminteri and Mary-Louise Parker, Cusack had the lead – as Woody's alter ego – and seriously improved his profile when the film went on to land seven Oscar nominations.

Cusack, who had previously

John Cusack as the alter ego of Woody Allen in **Bullets Over Broadway**

Cusack as deputy mayor Kevin Calhoun in **City Hall**

appeared in Allen's *Shadows and Fog*, was obviously thrilled with the opportunity to work with the maestro again. 'That was the dream gig,' he marvels. 'The rest of the world doesn't apply to Woody. He's the best writer to ever work with. He would come up very often and say, "Improvise; say what you like – so long as it sounds like two people talking." I'd say, "Woody, the scene's so great. I want to hit all the beats." He'd say, "Trust me, it's not that good."'

Then, in *City Hall*, Cusack played Kevin Calhoun, the sharp-witted, silver-tongued deputy of Al Pacino's charismatic New York mayor. A slick, acccomplished, intelligently-written and extremely well-acted film about corruption in American politics, the film was another major boost for Cusack who, in spite of Pacino's presence, had the leading role (modelled on real-life spin doctor James Carville). 'I got a call to have lunch with Al and

the director Harold Becker,' the actor recalls, 'and after a couple of hours we all liked each other, and they asked if I wanted to do the movie and that was that. No matter how big the budget, the movie will have integrity – Al is the bohemian who lives the life he wants and makes the movies he wants. When Pacino wants to do a movie, you go. When Woody Allen calls, you go. If Schwarzenegger calls, you go to lunch just to see the show, not to make the movie.'

Cusack then wrote, executive produced and starred in the hilarious black comedy *Grosse Point Break*, in which he plays a hitman who undergoes an emotional reassessment at a high school reunion. 'Being a killer,' he says, 'is a metaphor for all the people who are killers in the business place, who walk all over people for money ...' Then he joined Nicolas Cage, John Malkovich and Steve Buscemi in the action-adventure *Con Air*, playing the good guy

(a US marshal) in a nest of volatile heavies, and signed to produce and star in *Arigo*, the true story of a reporter (Cusack) who covers the trial of a man charged with witchcraft.

FILMOGRAPHY

1983: *Class*. 1984: *Sixteen Candles; Grandview USA*. 1985: *The Sure Thing; The Journey of Natty Gann; Better Off Dead*. 1986: *One Crazy Summer; Stand By Me*. 1987: *Hot Pursuit; Broadcast News* (cameo). 1988: *Eight Men Out; Tapeheads*. 1989: *Say Anything ...; Fat Man and Little Boy* (UK: *Shadow Makers*). 1990: *The Grifters*. 1991: *True Colors*. 1992: *The Player* (cameo); *Roadside Prophets; Shadows and Fog; Bob Roberts*. 1993: *Map of the Human Heart; Money For Nothing; The Badger*. 1994: *The Road To Wellville; Bullets Over Broadway; Floundering*. 1996: *City Hall*. 1997: *Grosse Point Blank* (also co-scripted); *Anastasia* (voice only); *Con Air*. 1998 *Hellcab; Arigo* (also produced); *Midnight in the Garden of Good and Evil*.

D

CLAIRE DANES

*Claire Danes (left) with Trini Alvarado in **Little Women***

Steven Spielberg, who has yet to work with her, has called her 'one of the most exciting actresses to debut in the last ten years'. Jodie Foster, who *has* worked with her, notes: 'She's this wiser-than-her-years-seeming person and yet she's really, really, really a baby. And you forget, because she's this beautiful, demure lady.' And yet, 'she's so down-to-earth,' observes Foster. 'She has the emotional strength to take her celebrity for what it is, see it as a small sacrifice, and move on.' And Winnie Holzman, who wrote the award-winning TV series *My So-Called Life* – in which Claire Danes starred – volunteered: 'the first few days of seeing her on film, I realised that she would be a movie star. We all kind of knew where it was going.'

While this book aims to provide

background information on the current stars of the Hollywood firmament, Claire Danes has exhibited such a fine talent in the few films she has made that she has already secured her niche as a future dignitary of considerable standing. Pretty, bright and above all extraordinarily gifted, young Claire Danes won American television's highest honour – the Golden Globe award – at the tender age of 15, beating such competitors as Angela Lansbury, Jane Seymour and Kathy Baker. In her film debut, in *Little Women*, she lent a sober, serene dignity to the role of the tragic Beth March. In Jodie Foster's *Home for the Holidays*, she was a breath of fresh air as Kitt, the precocious 15-year-old daughter of Holly Hunter who breezily announces: 'Mom, I'm going to have sex with Tim.' But it was her luminous presence and effortless mastery of the prose in *William Shakespeare's Romeo + Juliet* that confirmed her status as a major, major talent.

The daughter of a photographer (her father) and a textile designer (her mother), Claire Danes was born in New York City in 1979. Revealing an artistic temperament from an early age, Claire was enrolled in classes for modern dance and then, aged ten, she joined Lee Strasberg's Theater Institute. 'All the other kids would just round around,' she says now. 'But I was trying to Feel The Moment,' she adds with some emphasis.

Acting classes followed at the Dalton and the Professional Performing Arts School, when her photograph speared her a part in *Dudley*, a TV pilot starring Dudley Moore and Joanna Cassidy. In it, she played 'the angst-ridden teenager, of course, because that's what I do. Even on a sitcom I had a morbid role.' She also had a small part in the TV movie *No Room For Opal*, and scenes in HBO's *The Coming Out of Heidi Leiter* and the NBC crime show *Law & Order*. Then came the big break.

In ABC TV's drama series *My So-Called Life*, Danes played Angela Chase, an awkward 15-year-old with compellingly recognizable traits. Herself 15, the actress brought the character vividly to life, playing her with complex layers of anxiety and intelligence. The series premiered on 25 August 1994, and the following January Claire Danes

was named Best Actress in a TV Series or Drama at the Golden Globes ceremony broadcast live from the Beverly Hilton in Hollywood.

By then *Little Women* had already opened in the USA to rave reviews (and enthusiastic audience response), and Danes was filming her second picture, Jocelyn Moorhouse's *How to Make an American Quilt*, in which she portrayed young Glady Joe, the character of Anne Bancroft in flashback, and then played Anne Bancroft's granddaughter in *Home for the Holidays*. However, on neither occasion did she share the screen with the great actress.

She then flew to Berlin to star with Jeanne Moreau and Robert Sean Leonard in Billy Hopkins' *I Love You, I Love You Not*, and was then chosen (over the likes of Alicia Silverstone and Natalie Portman) to play Juliet Capulet opposite Leonardo DiCaprio's Romeo. According to Baz Luhrmann, the director: 'Claire was strong with Leonardo and was someone you could believe was discovering the overpowering force of the love drug for the first time.' Unquestionably, Danes was a perfect choice, her passion, loveliness and, indeed, her youth, proving to be prerequisites for the role. 'Juliet is much more secure than I am,' she argues. 'She doesn't put herself down; she respects herself. Maybe that's because she's more of a child. I mean, she's pretty and smart and she has a lot going for her and she's OK with that. I'm not.'

Aimed at a teenage American audience, Baz Luhrmann's *William Shakespeare's Romeo + Juliet* relocated the 1594 tragedy to contemporary Mexico and pitted some impressive MTV visuals against the iambic pentameter. A surprise success at the box-office, the film – with its attendant hype – firmly established Claire Danes as a new star to watch. Indeed, the actress now possesses all the accoutrements of a major Hollywood celebrity, complete with an accountant, agent, a publicist and two managers, one being her mother. However, the burden of fame does not rest easily on her young shoulders. 'At this moment,' she says, 'I'm certainly not happy, but it's for a whole bunch of reasons. I miss having friends. There's not much fun in my life. There's no time for me. I don't want to sound whiny and lame, but I

*Claire Danes as Juliet Capulet in William Shakespeare's **Romeo and Juliet***

have few moments of happiness. Right now, for instance, it's been a week since I've seen a person my own age.'

To settle the balance she booked a place at Columbia University for the autumn of 1997, and then took on two more films. However, before that she starred in *To Gillian On Her 37th Birthday* and was genuinely moving as the introspective daughter of Michelle Pfeiffer and Peter Gallagher, prompting *Variety* to rave: 'Danes proves again that she's one of the most naturally gifted actresses of her generation.' She also completed a role in the romantic comedy *Polish Wedding*, with Lena Olin and Gabriel Byrne, before taking the female lead in Francis Ford Coppola's *The Rainmaker* (from the novel by John Grisham), with Matt Damon, Danny DeVito, Jon Voight and Mickey Rourke. She then joined the muscular cast of Sean Penn, Nick Nolte, Jennifer Lopez and Powers Boothe in Oliver Stone's Arizona-set drama *U-Turn*, described by the director as a story of 'murder, sex, betrayal and all that stuff'.

FILMOGRAPHY

1994: *Little Women*. 1995: *How to Make an American Quilt; Home for the Holidays; I Love You, I Love You Not*. 1996: *William Shakespeare's Romeo + Juliet; To Gillian On Her 37th Birthday*. 1997: *Polish Wedding; The Rainmaker; U-Turn*. 1998: *Victor Hugo's Les Misérables; Brokedown Palace*.

GEENA DAVIS

Facially, she is not perfect. Her eyes are too small, her teeth too pronounced, her jaw too square. Her lips, though, are volcanic, and when she smiles her mouth explodes. Her body, too, shatters thermometers. Six feet tall, she flows in all the right places and her legs go all the way to China. But it's her ebullient personality, comedy timing, business acumen and above all her acting talent that has made Geena Davis a star to reckon with. Such combinations of intelligence, sex appeal and genuine wit are virtually unheard of in Hollywood.

Following her Oscar for *The Accidental Tourist*, then the furore and critical plaudits surrounding *Thelma and Louise* (it made the cover of *Time* magazine) and the colossal box-office success of *A League of Their Own*, Geena Davis was one of the hottest properties in the USA.

Of course, she had already been famous, but was famous for all the wrong reasons. Famous for her eccentric marriage to Jeff Goldblum (they showered bizarre gifts on each other), famous for her collection of strange gadgets and tacky bric-à-brac and famous for her unconventional leading men. In a relatively short career, Geena Davis had starred opposite Bill Murray in a clown's costume, Dustin Hoffman in drag, a rocketful of aliens, a ghost with halitosis, a disobedient corgi, a vampire, a fly, Susan Sarandon and Madonna. This, some may say, was fitting for Hollywood's zaniest actress. But just don't say it to Geena. 'It is irritating to be perceived as kooky, or wacky, or zany, or whatever it is,' she complains. 'It's very limiting and somehow disapproving and certainly not how I perceive myself. I am not Pee-wee Herman; I'm a serious actor, a serious person doing something serious.'

True. She is a member of Mensa, the international society whose members' intelligence exceeds that of 98 per cent of the population. She can also speak fluent Swedish, is a talented cartoonist, small-time inventor and accomplished musician, able to play the drums, flute, organ and piano. She also ran her own production company, Genial Pictures, on the lot at Twentieth Century Fox, with whom she had

carved out a production deal. In 1992, Genial had 12 films in pre-production – all due to star Ms Davis. Not bad for an ex-model.

Virginia Elizabeth Davis was born on 21 January 1957 in Wareham, Massachusetts (near Cape Cod), the daughter of William Davis, a civil engineer, and Lucille, a teacher's assistant. Her one brother is a geotechnical engineer living in Las Vegas. Geena recalls: 'I knew when I was five or something that I wanted to be an actress. I can remember parts of my life where I was thinking, "Well, I'll be an actress, and I'll be a clothing designer, and an inventor, and a graphic artist." I thought, "I'll be each thing for ten years, and I'll switch professions, because there are so many things I want to be."'

She studied acting at Boston University, and moved to New York in 1979, where she initially worked as a waitress. Lying about her height (she wore high heels and said she was 5'10" without them), she got signed up by the prestigious Zoli modelling agency. In between catwalk assignments she took a job as a sales assistant in a dress shop, and to combat boredom posed with the mannequins in the window to confuse passers-by. The prank was a crowd-puller, and she was consequently

Geena Davis

*Come on baby, light my fire; Geena Davis in **Beetlejuice**, seen here with Alec Baldwin and a supernatural manicure*

Hallowe'en in the appropriate place of Las Vegas, Jeff Goldblum and Geena Davis exchanged wedding vows on a whim. A year later, Geena was in another hit, and back in the world of the unreal, in Tim Burton's fantastical *Beetlejuice*. This time she was a ghost, the ordinary kind who doesn't believe in tricks and has impeccable taste in interior design. But she and her spectral hubby, Alec Baldwin, are pushed to their limit by an obnoxious human family who move into their home. Enough is enough, so Geena and Alec call on Peoplebuster Betelgeuse (Michael Keaton) to rid them of their mortal pests. A nice twist on a familiar tale, *Beetlejuice* was consistently hilarious, and Geena made the most appealing spook in recent memory.

Now typecast as weird and wonderful, she played Valerie Dale in *Earth Girls Are Easy*, a dizzy manicurist who believes Finland is the capital of Norway. She also plays host to three furry extraterrestrials who take over her home and her libido. It was pure Goldblum-Davis territory (he co-starred as one of the aliens), but *too* wacky for most tastes.

She beat out a host of A-list actresses for the role of Muriel Pritchett in *The Accidental Tourist*, Lawrence Kasdan's film version of Ann Tyler's bestseller. Muriel, on the surface a zany scatterbrain, is in fact an extraordinarily complex character, a woman damaged by men but still in desperate need of them. It would have been easy to play Muriel's goofy physicality and to

hired to stand in the window every Saturday. She also married the manager of the store's restaurant, a liaison which lasted two years.

Before embarking on a modelling trip to Paris, she auditioned for a small role in the film *Tootsie* and, in France, received a telegram telling her she had won the part. Essentially her role was a visual joke, but she carried it off with aplomb. Wearing nothing but the skimpiest underwear, she played a TV starlet who shares a dressing room with Dustin Hoffman (5'6"), who was disguised as an actress. Her naked innocence was charming, Hoffman's embarrassment hilarious, the film an enormous success.

After terminating her marriage, Ms Davis moved to Los Angeles to pursue her career as movie star. Almost instantly she landed the role of Dabney Coleman's naive researcher, Wendy Killian, in the TV sitcom *Buffalo Bill* (Coleman had played her director in *Tootsie*), for which she contributed to the show as writer. The following year she starred in her own series, *Sara*, as single San Francisco attorney Sara McKenna.

In the Chevy Chase comedy *Fletch*, she played a newspaper morgue chief (a role originally written for a man), and she then joined Linda Hamilton as a Russian seductress trained by Sally Kellerman to be a spy in the dreadful TV movie *Secret Weapons*. In NBC's *Family Ties* she was Karen, the mixed-up housekeeper, and she then played a

horny vampire in the horror spoof *Transylvania 6-5000*, which was nothing to write home about, but it did introduce her to Jeff Goldblum, who seemed to share her lop-sided view of life and, at 6'4", was a physically suitable date. They returned to the world of the unreal in David Cronenberg's *The Fly*, a Beauty and the Beast tale in which Davis loved Goldblum in spite of the strange buzzing noise. The film was distinguished by some remarkable special effects, was very frightening (and often revolting), yet never lost sight of its sense of humour. Goldblum and Davis made an attractive, offbeat couple, and *The Fly* went on to become a sizeable hit.

In 1987, on the appropriate night of

*Geena and Susan Sarandon in **Thelma & Louise***

ignore the pain underneath, but Geena dissected her character with the precision of a surgeon and the tenacity of a bull terrier. She was also hilarious, as she forced her way into the affections of William Hurt's emotionally numb writer, only gradually revealing to him the truth about her troubled past. Kasdan, who at one stage had considered casting Melanie Griffith in the part, marvelled: 'Geena is like a lot of people with whom I've worked, in that it is impossible for them to lie. It's just absolutely impossible for them to do the cheap thing, so there is an enormous sense of integrity.'

Thankfully, Geena's fellow actors recognized this talent, and she was awarded the Oscar for best supporting actress – beating such rival nominees as Michelle Pfeiffer and Sigourney Weaver. Although she said at the time that Goldblum 'wasn't jealous for a second, only totally happy for me', some attribute the break-up of their marriage to Geena's Academy Award. A year later, in 1990, the actress filed for divorce from her husband. Since then, the tabloids have been full of gossip, exposing Geena's relationships with Brad Pitt, security specialist Gavin de Becker – and Jeff Goldblum (!). In the summer of 1993 she announced her engagement to the film director Renny Harlin. Ironically, Harlin had previously dated the actress Laura Dern, who was seeing Goldblum at the time of Davis's engagement.

After turning down the Annette Bening role in Stephen Frears' *The Grifters*, she starred opposite Bill Murray in one of the funniest films of 1990, *Quick Change*. Murray played a cynical and brilliant bank robber, with Davis his accomplice who steals for love. While Murray finds robbing the bank a cinch, getting out of New York is another matter entirely. Murray and Davis made a delightfully zany team, with Murray on particularly good form, while the dialogue, plot and comic improvisation all conspired to create a hilarious treat.

Then came Ridley Scott's *Thelma and Louise*, one of the most acclaimed and talked-about films of 1991. Davis was Thelma Dickinson, a brow-beaten housewife who's persuaded to go on a weekend fishing trip by her waitress friend, Louise (Susan Sarandon). When

*Geena discovers the true meaning of being a woman in Martha Coolidge's delightful **Angie***

Thelma is accosted by a redneck rapist, Louise shoots him dead, leading to a cross-country escapade in which the women discover their true identities. *Rolling Stone* magazine raved that *Thelma and Louise* was 'movie dynamite, detonated by award-calibre performances', and indeed, both Davis and Sarandon were nominated for best actress Oscars. In truth, they both deserved the award, but probably cancelled each other out, letting Jodie Foster win the prize in their place.

Geena was next offered the Sharon Stone part in *Basic Instinct*, but considered the script 'objectionable', instead accepting the central role of Dottie Hinson in the sentimental baseball comedy *A League of Their Own*, co-starring Tom Hanks and Madonna. While *Basic Instinct* went on to gross $117 million in the USA in 1992, *A League of Their Own* didn't do too badly itself, clocking up a handsome $107 million. She had less luck with *Hero*, a bright, provocative comedy from Stephen Frears in which she played a ruthless TV reporter. Saved from a plane crash by an unidentified figure (Dustin Hoffman), she starts a crusade to find the hero of the hour, and settles on saintly imposter Andy Garcia. A satirical take on the media and the marketability of false heroism, the film elicited favourable reviews (the American critic Scott Patrick called her performance 'sexy, bright and charming'), but failed to find favour with the public. Maybe the film's biting parody of American patriotism was too bitter a pill to swallow, or possibly Dustin Hoffman's grouchy anti-hero too unsympathetic.

Nevertheless, *Hero* was an extremely funny, well-made and moving piece, and was yet another jewel in Geena's crown.

Next, she was cast in the title role of Martha Coolidge's *Angie*, as a mousy, vulnerable Italian woman from Brooklyn, a part reportedly written for Madonna. Although Madonna was filming *Dangerous Game* at the time and couldn't fit it in her schedule, the singer publicly exhibited her distaste for Davis's casting. Nevertheless, Davis grabbed the part so wholeheartedly that one soon forgot the actress and ended up crying for the character in what turned out to be a warm, funny, moving and unexpected dramatic comedy. Audiences, though, more or less stayed away, leaving Davis with two duds in a row. However, critics were more generous to her next outing, Ron Underwood's *Speechless*, in which she and Michael Keaton played political speech writers who fall in love and out of politics. Yet so lukewarm was the public reception to this latest caper that it was dumped straight onto video overseas. Davis needed a hit. *Fast*.

Wielding a budget of over $100 million, husband Renny Harlin came to the rescue with a starring vehicle to die for. This was the role of Morgan Adams, a strapping pirate lass who ventures forth to avenge her father's death and secure a horde of golden treasure into the bargain. The film was *CutThroat Island* and, in order to boost the star power, Harlin had managed to persuade Michael Douglas to support his wife. However, Douglas jumped ship at the eleventh hour and last-

Give back my memory, or else: Geena Davis in **The Long Kiss Goodnight**

minute talks with Liam Neeson, Daniel Day-Lewis, Ralph Fiennes and Jeff Bridges all collapsed. Finally, Matthew Modine was recruited to play the male lead, which hardly helped the film's box-office chances. Despite this, the end result was a rollicking, gutsy pirate yarn that maintained a fine balance between playfulness and authenticity, while distinguished by some of the most eye-popping stunts ever to swoop across a screen. Davis herself was terrific in a gender-switch that scrambled the hormones and adrenalin into a heady cocktail – but she couldn't salvage what turned out to be year's biggest flop. Earning a miserable $2.3 million in its flagship weekend, the film plummeted to 15th place in the charts the following week, eventually limping off with an embarrassing $9.9 million.

A year later, Harlin and Davis were re-united on *The Long Kiss Goodnight*, a scorching action-comedy-thriller based on Shane Black's screenplay, which New Line Cinema had bought for a record $4 million. Davis played Samantha Caine, a loving wife and doting mother with 'focal retrograde amnesia' who gradually realizes that she

was a government assassin in her former life. A whole infantry of nasty characters turn up to keep Samantha's memory on ice as she gradually recovers her combatant skills, knocking the opposition for six. Slick, fast and rather sadistic – but above all very, very funny – *The Long Kiss Goodnight* turned out to be the most satisfying action-thriller in aeons, easily matching the testosterone-driven antics of *Die Hard* and *True Lies*. At last, thank God, Geena Davis had a bona fide vehicle that she could call her own (even if, in box-office terms, the film was not as big as it should've been – it cost $75 million and only grossed $33.4 million in the US).

She was then announced to play *The Politicians's Wife*, a Hollywood revamp of the award-winning British TV series that starred Juliet Stevenson.

FILMOGRAPHY

1982: *Tootsie*. 1985: *Fletch*; *Secret Weapons* (a.k.a. *Secrets of the Red Bedroom*) (TV); *Transylvania 6-5000*. 1986: *The Fly*. 1988: *Beetlejuice*; *The Accidental Tourist*. 1989: *Earth Girls Are Easy* (filmed in 1988). 1990: *Quick Change*. 1991: *Thelma and Louise*. 1992: *A League of Their Own*; *Hero* (UK: *Accidental Hero*). 1993: *Angie*. 1994: *Speechless*. 1995: *CutThroat Island*. 1996: *The Long Kiss Goodnight*; *Mistrial* (TV) (executive-produced only). 1997: *Looking For Eve*.

JOHNNY DEPP

In 1989, Johnny Depp was getting $45,000 an episode for the TV series *21 Jump Street*. He was being paid $1 million to star in John Waters' *Cry-Baby*. He was receiving 10,000 fan letters a month. And yet he refused to live up to his celebrity. In March 1989 he was arrested and jailed (for one night) in Vancouver on assault charges. He sported a tattoo on each arm and dressed in torn jeans (prompting Waters to eulogize: 'Nobody looks better in rags.'). Stranger still, Depp didn't own an apartment, a house or even a car. Later, when he moved in with Winona Ryder, it was into a series of hotel rooms. And if his address lacked permanency, so did his love life. He was married to his first wife, musician Lori Anne Allison, for two years (1983–85);

he was engaged to the actress Sherilyn Fenn for three (1985–88), and broke off an engagement to Jennifer Grey a year later. But to prove that his love for Winona was the real thing, Depp added a third tattoo to his collection, a double banner curling down his right deltoid: 'WINONA FOREVER'. Yet that engagement was broken, too (forcing Depp to remove the tattoo letter by letter, so at one point his deltoid read: 'WINO FOREVER'). He then embarked on a very public liaison with the willowy English model Kate Moss.

OK, so Johnny Depp was weird. But then he had an unusual childhood. Part Cherokee, he was born John Christopher Depp II on 9 June 1963 in Owensboro, Kentucky, the youngest of four children (he has two sisters and a brother). His father was a city engineer, his mother a waitress, and when Johnny Jr was seven, the family moved to Miramar, Florida. It was there that he began his life of rebellion. Once, he was suspended from school for exposing his buttocks to a teacher; by 11 he was into drugs. He was also known as a vandal and a thief and, at 13, he had his first sexual experience. By 14 he had kicked his drug habit, but suffered terribly when his parents divorced a year later. Shortly afterwards, he dropped out of school (in his junior year) and joined a rock group, The Kids, which was a minor sensation locally and opened for such big-name acts as the B-52s, Iggy Pop and Talking Heads. At 18, Depp married Lori Anne, the 25-year-old sister of a fellow musician, and the group upped sticks to try their luck in LA.

Nothing doing. To support himself and his wife, Depp became a ball-point pen salesman on the phone, but was divorced from Lori in 1985. Still, they remained amicable, and when she started dating actor Nicolas Cage, the guys became friends. Cage suggested Depp talk to his agent with a view to becoming an actor, and so Depp went up for his first audition – for a low-budget horror film called *A Nightmare On Elm Street*. The director, Wes Craven, was getting bleary-eyed viewing the same old posturing studs, when Depp ambled in. The filmmaker immediately saw something different. 'Johnny really had sort of a James Dean attraction,' Craven recalled, 'that quiet charis-

Scarfacial innocent: Johnny Depp lends an ethereal air to Tim Burton's wonderful Edward Scissorhands

ma that none of the other actors had.'

Johnny Depp got the part – as Glenn, the boy who's literally swallowed by a bed in a torrent of blood – and the film was a hit, spawning five sequels (at the last count). Depp then won the lead in the dreadful sex comedy *Private Resort* and, with The Kids disbanded, he decided to take this acting thing seriously. He started attending drama classes, but found the parts weren't exactly queuing up at his door. There were a couple of spots on TV, and then the cable movie *Slow Burn*, a dreary thriller starring Eric Roberts. However, he was inspired working with Oliver Stone on *Platoon*, in which he played the interpreter, Lerner. *Platoon* went on to become an enormous hit and won the Oscar for best film.

Thinking that he was made, Depp first turned down the lead in the TV series *21 Jump Street* ('I wasn't ready for that kind of commitment.'), and then took it when his replacement (Jeff Yagher) was excused. Depp played undercover high school cop Tom Hanson and, when the series was a success, he became a household name – at least in those households that contained

teenage girls. However, for a new face in town, Depp was surprisingly candid in his views on the show. He was happy with the first season, with the series' willingness to tackle such issues as AIDS, juvenile crime, sex, child molestation and the like, but he later became disenchanted. He started questioning the direction of his character, the story-lines, the show's moral viewpoint. Soon, his 'high-handed' behaviour leaked out to the press and Depp was branded 'difficult'. After four seasons, he left the show.

He still had his fans, and the revisionist filmmaker John Waters wrote the part of the delinquent biker Wade Walker in *Cry-Baby* especially for him (Waters also cast such unlikely icons as Iggy Pop, Traci Lords and Troy Donahue in the film). Explaining why he wanted Depp, Waters declared: 'First of all, he's a good actor, but secondly, he's handsome in a real way. He's just got that *thing* that makes a star.'

On the heels of *Cry-Baby*, Depp landed the title role in *Edward Scissorhands*, another very personal vision from a highly idiosyncratic filmmaker. Tim Burton was one of the hottest names in Tinseltown thanks to his direction of *Beetlejuice* and *Batman*, and was now in a position to realize his own fairy story. This was the occasionally hilarious, always wondrous and surprisingly touching tale of a man-boy-machine cursed with 12-inch blades for fingers. Facially scarred by his own hand gestures and dressed in black leather and studs, his was a fearsome presence, hiding the pathos and love underneath. Edward is desperate to give and to receive affection, but is unable to touch others without hurting them. Reportedly, the role was first offered to Tom Cruise, but he insisted on a cosmetically happy ending. So Depp stepped in, studying the silent films of Charlie Chaplin to bring a wordless expression and body movement to his role. He says: 'I think the script was one of the best things I'd ever read, so of course I jumped at the opportunity to play him. Because Edward is not human, and not a robot, I didn't think he would talk a lot. He would cut through everything and have the most honest, pure answer with all the clarity in the world.'

Burton was pleased with the result.

'He's great in it,' the director acknowledged. 'I really admired his performance very much. He just risked being – *simple*, you know? Like Edward, Johnny really is perceived as something he is not. Before we met, I'd certainly read about him as the Difficult Heartthrob. But you look at him and you get a feeling. There is a lot of pain and humour and darkness and light. I think it's a very mature and risky performance.'

Playing the girl who sees beyond Edward's blades, Winona Ryder made the perfect fairy tale heroine (albeit a product of America's suburban barbe-

Johnny Depp at the top of his form as the boy who would be Chaplin - in Benny & Joon

cue set). She was also Johnny Depp's girlfriend. The couple met through a friend, and Winona admits: 'I thought maybe he would be a jerk. I didn't know. But he was really, really shy.' They discovered a mutual fixation for J.D. Salinger and the soundtrack album of *The Mission*, and the rest was plain sailing. Burton, not entirely seriously, has called them an 'evil version of Tracy and Hepburn'. In fact, despite a hint of rebellion and a love of the offbeat, they were (for a while) an intelligent, loving couple just trying to survive in the

*Johnny Depp looking on the bright side as the talentless film-maker **Ed Wood***

glare of the spotlight.

Career-wise, Depp took a cameo (seen briefly on a TV screen) in *Freddy's Dead: The Final Nightmare*, and then worked with another highly individual filmmaker on *Arizona Dream*. This was the weirdest of movies, an oddly lyrical combination of whimsy and slapstick from Emir Kusturica, the Sarajevo-born director, rock musician and Columbia University lecturer. Depp played Axel Blackmar, a New York game warden summoned to Arizona to serve as best man at his uncle's marriage to a bride thirty years his junior. Jerry Lewis played the uncle, supermodel Paulina Porizkova played Lewis's bride, while the rest of an unlikely cast included Faye Dunaway, Lili Taylor and Michael J. Pollard. Depp received top-billing, and again proved he was more than just a pretty face.

Next, in the delightful, decidedly offbeat romantic drama *Benny & Joon*, he portrayed a dyslexic eccentric in love with black-and-white movies and Mary Stuart Masterson. Whether chasing his hat through the park, ironing his sandwiches or mashing potatoes with a tennis racket, Depp displayed an uncanny knack for physical comedy. He was also ethereal enough to get away with a line like, 'It seems to me that besides being mentally ill, Joon is pretty normal,' as he set about wooing the heart of the psychologically impaired Masterson.

He revisited the domain of the mentally unstable in Lasse Hallstrom's

What's Eating Gilbert Grape, this time playing a young man from a 'dyslexic family' with a 36-stone mother and a retarded brother. Leonardo DiCaprio was brilliant as the brother, but the film's look-at-me eccentricity and frequent longueurs failed to win it many admirers.

Yet, in spite of these cinematic equivalents of culinary 'side orders', Depp continued to dominate the tabloids. His tempestuous relationship with Kate Moss constantly made headlines. They split up. They got together again. He refused to let her appear in a

*The ultimate seducer: Depp as **Don Juan DeMarco***

video from his new album, believing her catwalk image to be too 'commercial' for his group, 'P', for whom he sings and plays bass guitar. Then, in a devastatingly romantic gesture, he stocked her room with several thousand fresh daisies. They got together again.

In addition, he was – and is – co-owner of The Viper Room, a trendy nightspot on Sunset Boulevard that is all mirrors, black walls and charcoal upholstery. It was there that in the early hours of Halloween, on 31 October 1993, River Phoenix collapsed outside on the pavement, having imbibed a lethal cocktail of valium, marijuana, ephedrine, cocaine and heroin. 'When River passed away, it happened to be at my club,' the actor acknowledges. 'Now that's very tragic, very sad, but the media made it a fiasco of lies to sell fucking magazines. They said he was doing drugs in my club, that I allow people to do drugs in my club. "Hey! I'm going to spend a lot of money on this nightclub so everyone can come here and do drugs!"'

Then there was the hotel incident. On 13 September 1994, Johnny Depp was staying at the $500 a night Mark Hotel in New York when he lost his temper and smashed up his room. 'I was having a bad day,' he said. 'I think we all will have those, but if somebody else does what I did it's not usually in the news.' But in the news it was, and Depp was arrested, imprisoned and forced to pay $9,767 for trashing a table and chair, a glass-topped coffee table and 17th-century picture frames holding valuable prints.

Not surprisingly, the actor remained obstinately famous – and was offered big roles to prove it. It was as if Hollywood went out of its way to forgive Depp for his odd behaviour and bizarre career choices. He was offered the starring roles in *Speed*, *Legends of the Fall* and *Interview with the Vampire*, and he turned down every one of them – only to see each make a bundle of money.

Instead, he decided to re-team with Tim Burton on *Ed Wood*, a black-and-white biography of the occasional transvestite and worst film director of all time, Edward D. Wood Jr. The film was overlong, depressing and oppressively deferential, and was hardly helped

*An accountant in wolf's clothing: Depp in Jim Jarmusch's **Dead Man***

by Depp's one-note performance and fixed grin. Still, critics seemed to relish the sight of the star in high heels and Angora sweaters, and he won the best actor award from the London Film Critics' Circle.

He then went from worst filmmaker to greatest lover in the charming, effervescent *Don Juan DeMarco*, in which he played a mysterious young man who thinks he's God's gift to women. Depp himself persuaded Marlon Brando to co-star as DeMarco's psychiatrist, and apparently the incongruous icons got on like a house on fire. So much so that they re-teamed for the whimsical, supernatural comedy *Divine Rapture*, with Debra Winger and John Hurt also along for the ride. But then, after two weeks of shooting on location in the tiny East Cork village of Ballycotton, the finance for the $13.8 million production fell through. 'It was like being in the middle of sex,' Depp disclosed, 'right at the peak, and a guy walks in with a gun: "Stop it now." That's when you feel shitty, because you remember it's the movie business, based on money.'

Talking of money, he priced himself out of the Val Kilmer role in *Heat* and then accepted $4.5 million to star in John Badham's *Nick of Time*. A genuinely suspenseful, Hitchockian thriller, the film cast the actor as a timid accountant forced into the role of assassin when his six-year-old daughter is kid-napped (by a menacing Christopher Walken). He took the role, he says, because 'it gave me the chance to play a straight, normal, suit-and-tie guy,' but audiences failed to embrace Depp as a normal human being, the film flopped at the US box-office and bounced straight to video in Britain.

He then did *Dead Man* so that he could work with his friend Jim Jarmusch, and, in his own words, was paid 'less than my expenses during the shoot'. He played William Blake, another mild-mannered accountant (from Cleveland) who becomes the most unlikely outlaw ever to lift a Smith & Wesson. The film was a quirky, black-and-white re-evaluation of the western, and a gift to Jarmusch devotees.

He swam into the mainstream again to take the title role in Mike Newell's *Donnie Brasco*, playing a real-life under-cover cop who infiltrates the Mafia. Revealing a new maturity and displaying some edge, he was a revelation as a man torn between professional duty, his wife (the divine Anne Heche) and the third-rate gangster he is hired to destroy. Al Pacino played the gangster, and it is a tribute to Depp's talent that someone of Pacino's stature would agree to support him in a subsidiary role. The film received ecstatic reviews and grossed $11.6 million in its opening weekend, finally confirming the arrival of Depp as a viable leading man.

He then made his directorial debut with *The Brave* – in which he cast his old friend Brando as a snuff filmmaker – and was announced as the star of the film version of Hunter S. Thompson's legendary *Fear and Loathing in Las Vegas*, with Terry Gilliam attached to direct.

FILMOGRAPHY

1984: *A Nightmare On Elm Street*. 1985: *Private Resort*. 1986: *Slow Burn* (TV); *Platoon*. 1990: *Cry-Baby*; *Edward Scissorhands*. 1991: *Freddy's Dead: The Final Nightmare* (uncredited cameo). 1993: *Arizona Dream*; *Benny & Joon*; *What's Eating Gilbert Grape* (UK: *What's Eating Gilbert Grape?*). 1994: *Ed Wood*; *Don Juan DeMarco*. 1995: *Nick of Time*. 1996: *Dead Man*. 1997: *Donnie Brasco*; *The Brave* (directed only). 1998: *Fear and Loathing in Las Vegas*.

LAURA DERN

For somebody so inextricably associated with sex, Laura Dern appears refreshingly normal. Sure, she can look ravishing, a sensual stream of hair, legs and arms. But she is not a Hollywood goddess in the sense that Michelle Pfeiffer, Sharon Stone and Julia Roberts are. At 5'10", Laura Dern can be both gawky and goofy. She reminds one of a frisky young colt – not entirely sure of its gravity, but none the less full of the joys of spring. Her attractiveness is her spirit, her youth, her acting skills. For one so young, she has been bestowed with an exceptional number of honours. The Los Angeles Film Critics gave her their New Generation Award for her performance in *Smooth Talk*; for *Rambling Rose* she was nominated for an Oscar, and she won the best actress award at the Montreal Film Festival; for her role as a crusading widow in the TV film *Afterburn*, she won the Golden Globe, and she landed a second best actress citation at Montreal for *Citizen Ruth*.

*Laura Dern in David Lynch's **Blue Velvet***

*With John Cusack in Roland Joffe's underrated **Fat Man and Little Boy***

Laura Dern specializes in playing innocents, yet she has become associated with cinematic sex. In *Smooth Talk*, she was a teenage virgin seduced by Treat Williams; in David Lynch's *Blue Velvet* she was the virtuous counterbalance in a plot full of depravity; in the same director's *Wild at Heart*, she was a lustful runaway sexually humiliated by Willem Dafoe; in *Rambling Rose*, she was a nymphomaniac who introduces a 13-year-old boy to the mysterious pleasures of her body. Off-screen, too, she had a succession of suitors, some of them famous. For four years she was partnered with Kyle MacLachlan (a 'tough but good' relationship); she was linked with Peter Horton, of TV's *thirtysomething*; she dated the Finnish filmmaker Renny Harlin (*Die Hard 2*, *Cliffhanger*), and she ended up with Jeff Goldblum.

She was born on 10 February 1967 in Santa Monica, California, the second of two daughters (her older sister drowned as an infant). The theatre was in her blood. Her parents, Bruce Dern and Diane Ladd, are both actors and Oscar nominees, no less. Tennessee Williams was a cousin, and Laura's great-uncle was the poet/playwright Archibald MacLeish, and, for the sake of versatility, her great-grandfather was a governor of Utah. However, her parents split up when she was two, and Laura became estranged from her father (one of her earliest memories of him was on TV in *Hush ... Hush, Sweet Charlotte*, in the scene in which his sev-

ered head bounces down the stairs). However, she revealed later: 'Now we're the best of friends.'

At first, Laura's parents discouraged her desire to become an actress. 'They thought I should be something like a psychologist or a doctor,' she recalls. 'They used to take me to the set hoping I'd get bored and hate it – but it didn't turn out that way.' Indeed, at the age of five she appeared in an episode of the daytime soap *The Secret Storm* with her mother, and at six she had a bit part in the Burt Reynolds actioner *White Lightning*, also with her mother. The following year she consumed nine banana-flavoured ice creams in nine takes in a scene from Martin Scorsese's *Alice Doesn't Live Here Anymore*. Recalls Ladd: 'I said, "She's gonna get sick," and Marty said, "No, she's not. She's gonna be an actress."' Ladd played Flo, the tough-talking waitress in the film – and won her first Oscar nomination for the part.

When Laura was 11, she dolled herself up to look like a precocious 14-year-old, nabbing a small role in Adrian Lyne's *Foxes*. At 13, she played a punk rock groupie in *Ladies and Gentlemen, The Fabulous Stains*, with Diane Lane; and a year after that she began taking children's classes at the Lee Strasberg Theater Institute. At school, she attained top grades and even found time to be class president and homecoming princess. At 16, she enrolled at RADA in London, and cut her teeth on Shakespeare, appearing in produc-

tions of *Hamlet* and *A Midsummer Night's Dream*. Back in America, she continued her career in movies, popping up in the TV films *Happy Endings* and *The Three Wishes of Billy Grier*. In *Teachers*, with Nick Nolte, she played a 16-year-old student who decides to have an abortion, and in Peter Bogdanovich's *Mask* she was the blind girl (Diana) unperturbed by Eric Stoltz's hideous deformity. She then took a dramatic U-turn, registering at UCLA to study child psychology. Two days into her course she won the starring role in Joyce Chopra's *Smooth Talk* and turned her back on academia forever.

In *Smooth Talk* she played Connie, a teenage girl coming to terms with her sexuality, and ran away with glowing reviews. When Molly Ringwald was maternally advised against participating in David Lynch's *Blue Velvet*, 'about S & M and bugs', she lost the most interesting film of her career. Laura Dern stepped in as the sweet, questioning Sandy Williams, and when the movie became an enormous cult success, her future seemed assured.

She was re-teamed with Eric Stoltz in *Haunted Summer*, an unconvincing take on the famous get-together between Lord Byron, Percy Shelley and Mary Godwin (with Dern as Claire Clairmont), and she took a supporting role in *Fat Man and Little Boy*, Roland Joffe's distinguished drama about the

*Simmering nicely as Lula Pace Fortune in David Lynch's **Wild at Heart***

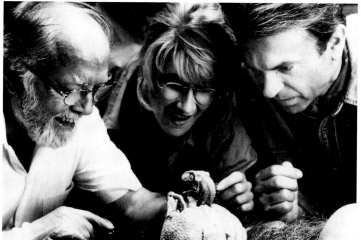

*Laura Dern flanked by Richard Attenborough and Sam Neill in the biggest money-making movie of all time, **Jurassic Park***

making of the atom bomb, in which she played the fictional Nurse Kathleen Robinson, who has an affair with scientist John Cusack, and then has to look on as he slowly dies from radiation sickness.

With a display of directorial loyalty, David Lynch called on Ms Dern again, this time to play a part diametrically opposed to Sandy in *Blue Velvet*. This time he cast her as Lulu Pace Fortune in *Wild at Heart*, a free spirit fleeing across America's South with her parole-jumping boyfriend, Nicolas Cage. Cage and Dern were on the run from Lulu's crazed mother – played with manic glee by none other than Diane Ladd – while Dern summed up the spirit of the enterprise with her famous declaration: 'The whole world's wild at heart and weird on top.' Indeed. The movie grabbed legions of devout followers by the throat, and even nabbed a second Best Supporting Actress Oscar nomination for Ms Ladd, whose luck continued a year later when she won a *third* nomination for *Rambling Rose*, proving that she acts best under the influence of her daughter. Laura played the rambling Rose of the title, a 19-year-old waif taken into the home and hearts of the genteel Hilliar family. Once rooted, Rose blossoms into an ingenuous nymphomaniac, seducing Mother (Ms Ladd), corrupting Father (Robert Duvall) and showing their young son (Lukas Haas) a thing or two. Based on Calder Willingham's autobiographical novel, the film was a superbly-crafted, well-acted drama in the tradition of

Driving Miss Daisy, but with enough ruffled taboos to give the British censor apoplexy. Although uncut in the USA, the film fell victim to the scissors in Britain.

Laura Dern was now very hot news indeed – helped, no doubt, by an Oscar nomination for *Rambling Rose*. She turned down the role of Andy – John Lithgow's wife – in the ecological epic *At Play in the Fields of the Lord* (replaced by Daryl Hannah), a wise decision as it turned out, and decided to make a TV movie instead. This was HBO's *Afterburn*, the true story of an American airman's widow who sets about clearing her husband's name after his death is blamed on pilot error. Again, Dern turned in a first-class performance as a strong, sympathetic woman, and won the Golden Globe award as best actress.

After that she landed the female lead in the biggest-grossing movie of all time, namely Steven Spielberg's *Jurassic Park*. She played Ellie Sattler, a paleobotanist who gets to cue in the film's most awe-inspiring moment, when, fingering a colossal leaf, she turns to Sam Neill, mouthing incredulously: 'Alan, this species of veriformans has been extinct since the Cretaceous period. I mean, this thing ...' Then she catches sight of the towering figure of an apatosaur sauropod (brontosaur, to you) and gives a perfect, elastic-jawed stare of utter disbelief. The actress reveals: 'I was surprised to find myself in the film, but I wasn't doing anything else at the time, so why not? Work is tempting, money is tempting.' So was

co-star Jeff Goldblum, who played the cynical mathematician Ian Malcolm (Goldblum's ex-wife, Geena Davis, had married Laura's ex-boyfriend Renny Harlin, so it was only natural). On Christmas Day 1995, Goldblum popped the definitive question and Laura responded in the affirmative. However, at the time of going to press the couple were still living in separate houses, and Laura was said to be dating Billy Bob Thornton.

Next, she appeared in the half-hour 'Murder, Obliquely', a segment of Showtime TV's *Fallen Angels*, in which she played a wallflower who becomes enmeshed with caddish blighter Alan Rickman. She wasn't very effective, but was better in Clint Eastwood's *A Perfect World*, as a state criminologist tracking an escaped convict (Kevin Costner). A tough movie of enormous tenderness that dared to address a number of substantial questions, the film was a surprising disappointment at the US box-office. 'Maybe people just want Kevin Costner to be the good guy, to be Robin Hood,' the actress reasoned. 'I don't know. Kevin's a very nice guy, and we got on fine, but I worked much more with Clint than with Kevin. I loved Clint.'

Then, after her mother made her directorial debut with the video feature *Mrs Munck* (which starred Ladd opposite Bruce Dern), Laura herself directed a short based on the making of the

*Dern as criminologist Sally Gerber in Clint Eastwood's **A Perfect World***

film. Thus fired, the actress then got behind the camera again, directing a short for TV called *The Gift*, with Ladd, Isabella Rossellini (Laura's best friend), Mary Steenburgen, Bonnie Bedelia and Peter Horton heading the cast.

In the acclaimed, harrowing, made-for-video movie *Down Came a Blackbird* she won excellent reviews for her role as a journalist who investigates a clinic for the victims of torture, and then she played Ruth Stoops in *Citizen Ruth*. An irreverent, biting satire of the abortion issue, the film starred Dern as a trashy, irresponsible mother of four who becomes pregnant a fifth time, inciting the rage of a judge who pressurizes her to have her unborn child terminated. Top-billing a cast that included Burt Reynolds and her mother, Dern walked off with the best actress prize at the Montreal Film Festival and was heavily promoted for an Oscar nomination.

FILMOGRAPHY

1973: *White Lightning*. 1974: *Alice Doesn't Live Here Anymore*. 1980: *Foxes*. 1982: *Ladies and Gentlemen, The Fabulous Stains*. 1983: *Grizzly II – The Predator* (unreleased); *Happy Endings* (TV). 1984: *The Three Wishes of Billy Grier* (TV); *Teachers*. 1985: *Mask; Smooth Talk*. 1986: *Blue Velvet*. 1988: *Haunted Summer*. 1989: *Fat Man and Little Boy* (UK: *Shadow Makers*). 1990: *Wild at Heart*. 1991: *Rambling Rose*. 1992: *Afterburn* (TV). 1993: *Jurassic Park; A Perfect World*. 1995: *Down Came a Blackbird* (TV). 1996: *Citizen Ruth* (a.k.a. *Precious/The Devil Inside/Meet Ruth Stoops*); *Bastard Out of Carolina* (voice only); *The Siege at Ruby Ridge* (TV).

LEONARDO DICAPRIO

Yes, Leonardo DiCaprio is pretty. Yes, Leonardo DiCaprio is cocky. Yes, Leonardo DiCaprio is wild. But can the boy act.

For his first notable role in a film – as the sullen teenager brutalized by his stepfather (Robert De Niro) in *This Boy's Life* – DiCaprio was voted Best Supporting Actor of 1993 by the National Board of Review, and Most Promising Actor by the Chicago Film Critics' Circle. In addition, he was short-listed by the National Society of

Leonardo DiCaprio flanked by Ellen Barkin and Robert De Niro in Michael Caton-Jones' **This Boy's Life**

Film Critics and the New York Film Critics' Circle. And, in the same year, he was nominated for an Oscar for his performance as Johnny Depp's retarded brother in *What's Eating Gilbert Grape*.

Besides these credentials, DiCaprio also has a prodigious female following. On location in Mexico, John Leguizamo (who, in *William Shakespeare's Romeo + Juliet*, played Tybalt to DiCaprio's Romeo) revealed: 'All the Mexican girls were going mad over him. They were hunting us down. We were trying to throw ourselves in their way, hoping that he would rub off on us.'

'He's what we call in England the thinking woman's crumpet,' volunteers Michael Caton-Jones, the Scottish-born director of *This Boy's Life*. 'He'll do intelligent material with depth, feel and range, but he also has lots of sex appeal. I saw his performance in *Gilbert Grape* – that's what separates movie stars from everyday actors, the ability to take a flying moment of madness.'

George DiCaprio was a big noise in the world of underground comedy and was holidaying with his wife, Irmalin, in Italy. They were viewing a painting by Leonardo Da Vinci when their unborn son lashed out his first foetal kick. A few months later, on 11 November 1974, Leonardo appeared, and a few months after that George disappeared – at least from his family's life. So little Leonardo grew up in the care of his mother, who struggled to make ends meet in a shabby corner of Hollywood Boulevard. 'We were in the poorhouse,' recalls Leonardo. 'I would walk to my playground and see, like, a guy open up his trench coat with a thousand syringes. I saw some major homosexual activity outside my friend's balcony when I was five. To this day it's

DiCaprio with Johnny Depp in **What's Eating Gilbert Grape**, the role that secured DiCaprio an Oscar nomination

As Jim Carroll in Scott Kalvert's harrowing **The Basketball Diaries**

an imprint on my mind.'

While Leonardo claims, 'I decided I wanted to be an actor so I could be cool,' it goes back further than that – to be exact, when his brother landed a commercial for Golden Grahams, the breakfast cereal. 'I asked my dad how much Adam made from it and he said, "about $50,000",' recalls the actor. 'Fifty thousand dollars! It just kept going through my head: My brother has $50,000 dollars! And that kept on being my driving force. I just remember for, like, five years thinking my brother was better than me because he had that.'

Leonardo went up for his first audition at the age of six – but was rejected on the grounds of his haircut. It was to be another eight years before he made his TV debut, in an episode of *Lassie*, followed by appearances in such small-screen fare as *Santa Barbara*, *Roseanne* and *The Outsiders* – and, finally, the recurring part of the 13-year-old Garry in *Parenthood*. Then, in 1991, he won the role of the homeless urchin, Luke, in the last season of ABC TV's family sitcom *Growing Pains*, going on to make his official film debut in *Critters 3*, as Leonard. There was also a nod and a wink in the overheated melodrama *Poison Ivy*, with Drew Barrymore, before he went up for the role of Toby 'Jack' Wolff – a bad kid with a good heart – in *This Boy's Life*.

Only now, in retrospect, does the actor grasp the significance of his audition. 'I didn't worry what De Niro thought,' he recollects, somewhat breezily. 'I went in, looked him in the eye and got the part. I was confident, even though I'd never done anything like it before. Now I realize that it was ignorant confidence. I had no idea.'

While De Niro rampaged through his performance stuck on the fast-forward button, DiCaprio was simply incandescent as the bruised apple of Ellen Barkin's eye. The subsequent deluge of plaudits were well deserved, even though the film itself – based on the autobiographical book by Tobias Wolff – was below par. Set in Washington State in the late 1950s, *This Boy's Life* strained too hard to capture the period, while De Niro's assaults on his co-star verged on the sadistic. Indeed, much of DiCaprio's discomfort on screen was for real. 'It was kind of hard not to get frightened,' he recalls. 'But I liked it when De Niro scared me. It helped me react.'

From De Niro, DiCaprio moved on to Depp – in *What's Eating Gilbert Grape*. Depp, too, seemed to delight in scaring DiCaprio into character, taking on the mantle of mischievous big brother. DiCaprio played Arnie Grape, the simple-minded 18-year-old brother of Gilbert, with a propensity for getting stuck in high places. In a film that flirted with self-conscious idiosyncrasy, DiCaprio stood out like a zit on a mannequin's neck – that is, he brought an astonishing realism, spontaneity and innocence to a role that could so easily have lapsed into bathos. 'I had to really research and get into the mind of somebody with a disability like that,' the actor explains. 'So I spent a few days at a home for mentally retarded teens. We just talked and I watched their mannerisms. People have these expectations that mentally retarded children are really crazy, but it's not so. It's refreshing to see them because everything's so new to them.'

DiCaprio was now a hot property in Hollywood – smouldering nicely from his Oscar nomination – and was being pitched for several high-profile roles. One was Robin in *Batman Forever*, the other was James Dean. Indeed, Michael Mann, creator of TV's *Miami Vice* and director of *The Last of the Mohicans* and *Heat*, was so knocked out by DiCaprio's performance in *Gilbert Grape* that he postponed his Dean biography (which had been variously attached to Brad Pitt, Gary Oldman and Brendan Fraser) so that the 19-year-old actor could grow into the part.

Meanwhile, DiCaprio succumbed to some powerful overtures from Sharon Stone, who was producing her first film, *The Quick and the Dead*. In fact, so keen was Ms Stone to have the hot newcomer on board that she paid for his salary out of her own: 'I wanted him bad,' she divulged. A rip-roaring, spectacular and raunchy parody of the spaghetti western, *The Quick and the Dead* was the most entertaining horse opera this side of *Westworld*. Ms Stone, trussed up in black leather, played Ellen, a mysterious gunslinger who rides into a town called Redemption to settle an old score. Gene Hackman was the ruthless, trigger-happy mayor who challenged all rivals to a shooting tournament, including his own son, 'The Kid' (DiCaprio), who had little to do but squint menacingly, but did so with conviction.

Meanwhile, the young actor had lost the role of the journalist in *Interview with the Vampire* (first to River Phoenix, then to Christian Slater) and saw Robin go to Chris O'Donnell. Then, to compound the folly, both films turned into massive hits. *The Quick and the Dead*, however, limped away from the US box-office with just $18.6 million in its saddlebag.

Next, DiCaprio took the lead in Scott Kalvert's *The Basketball Diaries*, based on Jim Carroll's searing autobiography. An uncompromising, dynamic look at one man's descent into heroin addiction, the film was a numbing vehicle for DiCaprio's burgeoning talent, which reached new heights here. Unfortunately, the film failed to stir up much interest, either critically or commercially, but it was at least better received than *Total Eclipse*, in which DiCaprio played the French poet Arthur Rimbaud – to David Thewlis's Paul Verlaine – in a film which was damned by the critic Todd McCarthy for its 'utter inability to link the men's self-destructive behaviour with anything touching upon their art'.

He had a fleeting cameo in Agnès Varda's star-laden, Anglo-French *A Hundred and One Nights* – a capricious tribute to 100 years of cinema (starring Michel Piccoli as Mr Cinema) – then

*As The Kid in Sam Raimi's **The Quick and the Dead***

Depardieu co-starring as Athos, Aramis and Porthos.

He was also at the centre of a tabloid frenzy over an alleged affair with Demi Moore, fuelled by a series of incriminating photographs. Then, to cap a remarkable three months, he was voted best actor at the 47th Berlin Film Festival for *Romeo + Juliet*.

FILMOGRAPHY

1991: *Critters 3*. 1992: *Poison Ivy*. 1993: *This Boy's Life*; *What's Eating Gilbert Grape* (UK: *What's Eating Gilbert Grape?*). 1994: *A Hundred and One Nights* (cameo). 1995: *The Quick and the Dead*; *The Basketball Diaries*; *Total Eclipse*. 1996: *Marvin's Room*; *William Shakespeare's Romeo + Juliet*. 1997: *Titanic*. 1998: *The Man in the Iron Mask*.

won the role of Hank in *Marvin's Room*. Re-teamed with Robert De Niro, DiCaprio played the pyromaniac son of Meryl Streep who returns with her to their home in Florida to patch up old wounds with Hank's sickly aunt (Diane Keaton). De Niro, playing bravely against type as Keaton's doctor, doubled as producer, but it was Streep that filled DiCaprio's eyes with stars. 'She was the coolest lady,' he confided. 'She doesn't take shit from nobody.'

Twentieth Century Fox were already considering a film version of *Romeo and Juliet* – with Ethan Hawke attached to play the Veronian Romeo – when the Australian-born Bazz Luhrmann entered the picture. The recipient of numerous awards for his first film, *Strictly Ballroom*, Luhrmann envisioned his version of Shakespeare's romantic tragedy with guns and gangs and Garbage on the soundtrack. Fox didn't get it, so Luhrmann lured DiCaprio to do a promo reel and changed the studio's mind. DiCaprio settled for a spartan fee of $35,000, and even flew economy to Australia to participate in a workshop exploring the mysteries of iambic pentameter.

DiCaprio was excited by Luhrmann's vision. 'Our *Romeo and Juliet* is a little more hardcore and a lot cooler,' he elucidates. 'I wouldn't have done it if I'd had to jump around in tights.' Swapping Verona, Italy, for Verona Beach in Florida, Luhrmann transported his cast and crew to

Mexico and came up against a heap of problems. No sooner had DiCaprio and his Juliet – Claire Danes – arrived than they went down with dysentery; a crucial fish tank – integral to the lovers' first meeting – shattered on the first day of filming, and a ferocious gale hammered the crew in Vera Cruz, necessitating re-shoots. To add to this, a make-up artist was kidnapped, ransomed for $400 and dumped out of a speeding car, while a friend of DiCaprio's was beaten up by security guards. Some shoot.

Despite this, this low-budget vision of a 400-year-old play directed by an unknown Australian opened at the top of the US box-office charts. Grossing $11.1 million over the weekend, *William Shakespeare's Romeo + Juliet* made three times more than the new Bill Murray comedy – at 1,157 fewer screens. Within a matter of weeks it had become the top-grossing Shakespearian film in American history.

Next, in *Titanic*, DiCaprio played a blue-collar youth sailing on the doomed luxury liner of the title who falls under the spell of an upper-class passenger (Kate Winslet). With a starting budget of $100 million, the film, directed by James Cameron (*The Terminator*, *The Abyss*, *True Lies*), was destined to become one of the biggest movies of all time. DiCaprio was then announced to play the title role in *The Man in the Iron Mask*, with John Malkovich, Jeremy Irons and Gerard

MATT DILLON

Matt Dillon in a typical pose

More than any other actor of his generation, Matt Dillon epitomizes urban cool. Physically tough, emotionally vulnerable, streetwise, brooding, intelligent and ingenuous, Dillon displays a persona of James Dean intensity without ever appearing to act. He just *is* this

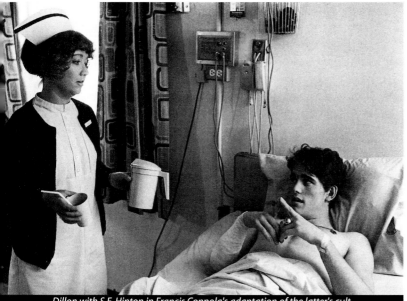

Dillon with S.E. Hinton in Francis Coppola's adaptation of the latter's cult novel *The Outsiders*

really cool guy who wound up in the movies because he couldn't get a job as a mechanic.

In the opening scene of *The Outsiders*, Dillon is seen in long-shot leaning against a traffic light igniting a cigarette. Nonchalant, wise beyond his years, he instantly conveys the image that he is a product and a survivor of the streets. Approached by C. Thomas Howell, he is asked, 'What do you want to do?' Dillon's reply is typical: 'Nothing legal, man.'

However, Kelly Lynch, Dillon's co-star in *Drugstore Cowboy* six years later, claims: 'People don't know how intelligent and gracious an actor he is. He's always the cool guy: cowboy hat, tight jeans, cigarette in the mouth, leaning on a wall, smoking and snarling. That's *not* Matt's energy. There's an innocence and ingenuousness, too. He's a comedian like you wouldn't believe.'

He's also a natural. 'The camera really does love him,' offers James Dearden, who directed the star in *A Kiss Before Dying*. 'It's extraordinary. I mean, every time he steps in front of the lens – *pow*!'

Matt Dillon *is* a natural. Born on 18 February 1964 in New Rochelle, New York, the second oldest of five boys and a girl, he was spotted in the corridor of his junior high school by a talent scout. He was 14 and sneaking out of school. Instead, he ended up in his first movie.

Until then, Dillon, the son of a salesman, had uttered one line in a play in fourth grade. Sports and shoplifting were more his line – and killing time with the boys. A former classmate volunteers: 'He hung out with a tough crowd – sort of desperadoes. He always wore his jacket collar turned up, and he had a black German shepherd.'

His first film was Jonathan Kaplan's *Over the Edge*, a gritty, unsettling view of rebellious youth, with Dillon cast as Richie White, an ill-fated ruffian with an attitude. His performance was frighteningly authentic for one so young, but it was his face that caught the attention of casting directors. In *Little Darlings* he played a boy called Randy, an under-age stud who is pursued by Kristy McNichol at summer camp. It was this performance that really got young hearts fluttering, aided by pin-up portraits in teen magazines and a spontaneous fan club.

After playing two variations on his persona of street tough, Dillon was the school bully in Tony Bill's *My Bodyguard*, forcing puny Chris Makepeace to hire brawny Adam Baldwin. He then turned to romance in *Liar's Moon*, a film that inspired so much confidence in its distributor that two versions were released, each with a different ending. He then segued into a PBS TV special, *The Great American Fourth of July and other Disasters*, before

embarking on his S.E. Hinton trilogy.

Susan Hinton was the guru scribe of disenchanted youth, whose slim novels suddenly gripped the imagination of filmmakers. The first to go before the cameras was *Tex*, the story of a teenage kid (Dillon) struggling to grow up under trying circumstances. It was directed by Tim Hunter, who had co-scripted *Over the Edge*, and co-starred Meg Tilly and Emilio Estevez.

Next came *The Outsiders*, directed by Francis Coppola and starring a who's who of future stars. Dillon played Dallas Winston, a social underdog looked up to by the likes of C. Thomas Howell and Ralph Macchio. The film was a hit, although not as popular as hindsight would suggest. *RumbleFish* was even less successful, but has earned itself a place as one of the most written-about movies of the 1980s. In this, Dillon played Rusty James, an outsider obsessed by his older brother, biker boy Mickey Rourke. Typically, Rusty is defined (by co-star Nicolas Cage) as 'a very cool dude', in spite of his propensity for getting beaten up and knifed and treating his girlfriend (Diane Lane) like trash.

Next, Dillon won critical raves for the title role in *The Flamingo Kid* and displayed an unexpected gift for comedy. Instead of lording it over impressionable younger kids, this time Dillon was the youngster striving to make it an adult world. He was top-billed as Jeffrey Willis, a gauche hustler who plays on his charm and angelic looks to make good at a Long Island beach club.

Dillon admits that comedy comes unnaturally to him, but he proved to be surprisingly good at it, aided no doubt by the adroit direction of Garry Marshall (who went on to win even greater acclaim with *Beaches* and *Pretty Woman*). 'I believe there was once somebody famous,' the actor points out, '– I don't remember who it was – that said on his deathbed, "Dying's easy, but comedy's hard." And I think that's true.'

Next came a string of flops that almost extinguished the actor's career. In *Target*, a run-of-the-mill spy thriller, he played Gene Hackman's son in search of his kidnapped mother; in the Australian *Rebel*, he was miscast as a 1940s GI in love with a cabaret singer;

As the low-life with a poet's heart: Dillon with Max Perlich in Gus Van Sant's idiosyncratic *Drugstore Cowboy*

and in the disastrous 1930s-set *Native Son* (based on the celebrated novel by Richard Wright) he played the Communist boyfriend of Elizabeth McGovern.

On paper, *The Big Town* looked like a prestigious star vehicle, with a supporting cast that included Diane Lane, Tommy Lee Jones, Tom Skerritt, Lee Grant and Bruce Dern. In fact, it was another turkey, featuring Dillon as a crap-shooter with a lucky streak courting notoriety in 1950s Chicago. He seemed considerably more at ease as a charismatic, gun-toting psychopath in the entertaining *Kansas* (with Andrew McCarthy), but nobody turned up to witness the event. The public also stayed away from *Bloodhounds of Broadway*, an ill-advised adaptation of a 1928-set Damon Runyan story, with Madonna, Jennifer Grey, Rutger Hauer and Randy Quaid.

Off-screen, Dillon kept a quiet profile, indulging his love of drawing and painting, and refusing to talk about his private life. For a while he dated a girl from one of his acting classes, and later frequented public events with a blonde model from London called Emma Woollard. He also spent some time with his family, which included his younger brother, Kevin, who has followed his famous brother's footsteps, starring in such films as *The Blob*, *War Party* and *The Rescue*.

According to Kaplan, who directed *Over the Edge*, the Dillon brood were

'close, but not cloying', adding: 'How many times do we have to hear about Drew Barrymore and Corey Feldman going through another dope treatment? Not the Dillon kids. That stuff doesn't interest them. They'd rather hang out with friends and family.'

The closest Matt Dillon came to serious drug taking was with his role as a junkie and thief in a small, low-budget picture called *Drugstore Cowboy* (set in 1971). Although stark and realistic in its depiction of pharmacy ghouls, the film did have a well-developed sense of humour that made it one of the most perversely irresistible independent American films of 1989. Dillon in particular received raves for his performance, and was subsequently re-embraced by the media.

He offset this return to favour with a dreadful remake of the 1956 Robert Wagner thriller *A Kiss Before Dying*. The film's lack of conviction, though, was due less to Dillon's portrayal of a charming serial killer than to Sean Young's double performance as twin sisters. River Phoenix had turned this one down, and so should Matt Dillon.

He then made a rare appearance on TV in the three-part, deftly-titled *Women & Men 2: In Love There Are No Rules*. He and Kyra Sedgwick (who previously played his girlfriend in *Kansas*) starred in the segment titled 'Return to Kansas City' (from a short story by Irwin Shaw), in which Dillon portrayed a boxer with marital problems.

In *Singles*, a beautifully-written look at Seattle youth, he accepted a supporting role, as Cliff Poncier, a would-be rock star who fails to appreciate his loving girlfriend (Bridget Fonda). Next, he teamed up with Danny Glover in Tim Hunter's *The Saint of Fort Washington*, a compassionate, credible drama focusing on the plight of the homeless in New York, which took nine years to bring to the screen. Dillon played Matthew, an emotionally disturbed schizophrenic who has only his battered camera for company, until befriended by Glover. Unlike anything he had attempted before, his portrayal of Matthew revealed a new depth and complexity to his craft.

After that, he took the lead in Anthony Minghella's *Mr Wonderful*, the funny, sharply-realized story of a

divorcee (Dillon) who tries to find Mr Right for his ex (Annabella Sciorra) – in order to relieve his alimony payments. Again, Dillon surprised his critics, this time by bringing a surprising comic freshness to his exasperated character.

Then, in slightly more romantic vein, he played the Caucasian ingredient in *Golden Gate*, an inter-racial love story with Joan Chen, a commercial and critical flop; he was Nicole Kidman's underachieving, ill-fated husband in the cult success *To Die For*, and he was terrible as a Texan GI who befriends an Irish dwarf in the woefully misconceived *Frankie Starlight*.

He was better in Ted Demme's well-written ensemble *Beautiful Girls*, as a snowploughman torn between Mira Sorvino and his ex, Lauren Holly; he then played a self-possessed surf music 'superstar' – married to Illeana Douglas – in *Grace of My Heart*, Allison Anders' affectionate, nostalgic portrait of the pop universe. He also starred in Kevin Spacey's suspenseful, accomplished directorial debut, *Albino Alligator*, as the wounded leader of a gang of aspiring thieves; and he then joined Kevin Kline, Joan Cusack and Tom Selleck in the Frank Oz comedy *In and Out*, play-

Dillon with Bridget Fonda in Cameron Crowe's *Singles*

In one of his best performances, as the down-and-out Matthew in Tim Hunter's **The Saint of Fort Washington**

ing an actor modelled on Tom Hanks.

At the date of going to press, he was dating the actress Cameron Diaz (*The Mask, She's the One*).

FILMOGRAPHY

1989: *Over the Edge*. 1980: *Little Darlings; My Bodyguard*. 1981: *Liar's Moon*. 1982: *The Great American Fourth of July and Other Disasters* (TV); *Tex*. 1983: *The Outsiders; RumbleFish*. 1984: *The Flamingo Kid*. 1985: *Target; Rebel*. 1986: *Native Son*. 1987: *The Big Town; Dear America* (voice only). 1988: *Kansas; Bloodhounds of Broadway*. 1989: *Drugstore Cowboy*. 1991: *A Kiss Before Dying; Women & Men 2: In Love There Are No Rules* (TV). 1992: *Singles; Malcolm X* (cameo); 1993: *The Saint of Fort Washington; Mr Wonderful; Golden Gate*. 1995: *To Die For; Frankie Starlight*. 1996: *Beautiful Girls; Grace of My Heart; Albino Alligator*. 1997: *In and Out*. 1998: *Wild Things*.

STEPHEN DORFF

With characteristic hysteria the media dubbed Stephen Dorff 'the next Christian Slater' – before he'd even asked his first supermodel for the time of day. Sure, he was hunky, spunky and young – with attitude to spare – but Christian Slater? As it happens, Dorff's career has followed a far more interesting trajectory and he's revealed a much more versatile talent. To appreciate the actor's range you have only to see three of his movies. In *The Power of One* he played an Anglo-Afrikaans teenage boxer. In *Backbeat* he was Stuart Sutcliffe, the Liverpudlian-born 'fifth Beatle'. And in *I Shot Andy Warhol* he assumed the persona of Factory superstar Candy Darling, magnificent in blonde wig and stockings.

Yet in other ways Stephen Dorff has undoubtedly followed the Slater route. He's a certified party animal, he has graced his fair share of teen magazine covers and he was up for the role of the interviewer in *Interview with the Vampire*, a part which finally went to, er, Christian Slater. Furthermore, after dating a catwalk of beautiful women (including Alicia Silverstone), Dorff settled on the South African model Georgina Grenville – at the same time as Slater was dating Christy Turlington. 'I'm so totally in love with this girl I can't even look at anybody else,' Dorff admits. Then, in his defence, he argues: 'obviously, I'm young and crazy and a hormonal psychopath for beautiful women. So why not, in my position, go out with gorgeous girls? If I didn't do that, I don't think I'd be normal.'

His talent, though, is far from conventional. Dennis Hopper, his co-star in *Space Truckers*, granted: 'Stephen is very intelligent and is dedicated to his work'; while director Bob Rafelson (*Blood and Wine*) added: 'Jack [Nicholson] thinks Stephen has some of the same qualities as Montgomery Clift: that is, he is sensitive and shy, but at the same time very, very invigorated.'

The son of the Grammy-winning musician and film composer Steve Dorff (*Pink Cadillac, Pure Country*), Stephen was born on 29 July 1973 in the San Fernando Valley, California. While his younger brother, Andrew, was attracted to their father's world of music, Stephen showed an interest in acting at an early age (at nine, to be precise). Later, however, he was also to dabble in composition, writing musical motifs for his film characters as a sort of emotional preparation.

While still young he studied drama at the Stock Workshop in Los Angeles and cut his milk teeth on a number of commercials. Then, as a teenager, he appeared in a variety of TV movies and such TV shows as *Married ...With Children*, *The Father Dowling Mysteries*, *Family Ties* and *Empty Nest*, and had a recurring role on *Roseanne*.

He landed the lead in the low-budget horror opus *The Gate* – as a bored schoolboy who stumbles across the doorway to Hell – which turned out to be his first hit. The film wasn't very

Stephen Dorff as the 'fifth Beatle' Stuart Sutcliffe, with Sheryl Lee, in **Backbeat**

*Stephen Dorff as rebellious hero in Jefery Levy's **SFW***

Mark Kamen (*Taps*, *The Karate Kid*), the star had 'to handle action, love scenes and lengthy dialogue. We wanted to be sure we found a young man who could handle the most of this part.'

The interviewing process was arduous to say the least, and Dorff sparred with a boxing coach for several weeks to prepare for his audition. Then, once he had the role, he trained in earnest: 'We'd go in at about eight in the morning and box, punching the bag and shadow-boxing until we were out of breath. And all that went on for about five hours. Then we'd break for lunch and come back and work out with weights all afternoon – a basic nine hours every day.' In all, Dorff packed on an extra 20 pounds of muscle. In addition, he was forced to adopt an English accent – dusted with Afrikaans – and found himself on location in Britain, Botswana and Zimbabwe. Zimbabwe in particular opened his eyes. 'The country changed me as a person,' he says in retrospect. 'Before, I was into the LA scene, thinking, "Hey, teen idol. I'm the top." But being in Africa really set me down.' It was unfortunate, then, that the film resembled an airport novel in style, varnished with an overbearing score and photographed like a tourist brochure. Still, Dorff stood up to his celebrated co-stars – John Gielgud, Morgan Freeman and Armin Mueller-Stahl – and Hollywood took note.

However, it was to be two years before he speared another role to write home about. Again, this was an English part, the role of the 'fifth Beatle' in Iain Softley's *Backbeat*. 'Stuart Sutcliffe was an amazing cult character to play,' the actor related, 'because nobody knows who the fuck he was. And he was an important element to what the Beatles became because he changed John Lennon's life.' This time the picture was a hit, although Dorff and his American co-star, Sheryl Lee (as the in-vogue German photographer, Astrid Kirchherr), failed to rustle up any on-screen chemistry. No wonder then that newcomer Ian Hart – in a wicked impersonation of Lennon – won all the good reviews.

In *SFW* Dorff moved into genuine Slater territory as a posturing, foul-mouthed youth who attains celebrity status when taken hostage. Smugly cap-

italizing on his catch phrase, 'So fucking what?', the rebel is immortalized on magazine covers, videos, CDs and T-shirts in a heavy-handed attempt to remind us how immoral the media is. Nevertheless, the director, Jefery Levy volunteered: 'There were dozens of people who wanted that part. The first person we saw was Dorff, and I just *knew* ... He turned out to be better than my wildest dreams.' Be that as it may, Dorff now insists, 'I don't really want to talk about *SFW*. I don't even think about that movie anymore.' The case rests.

Following a cameo in Agnes Varda's celebratory, Anglo-French *A Hundred and One Nights*, he starred in another Anglo-French vehicle, *Innocent Lies*, a bumbling endeavour to blend an erotic French thriller with Agatha Christie. There was then the inept adaptation of Craig Lucas's bizarre play *Reckless*, in

*A change of pace: Dorff reveals his sensitive side as Candy Darling in **I Shot Andy Warhol***

good and received terrible reviews, but at least it had a sense of humour and some decent effects, producing a sequel (minus Dorff) five years later. In *Rescue Me* he settled for second-billing as a youngster who joins forces with a Vietnam vet (Michael Dudikoff) to rescue his class princess (Ami Dolenz) from a pair of moronic hoodlums. Dorff was on good form, but the film itself was a leaden, hackneyed rites-of-passage affair that wasn't released until almost two years after *The Power of One* – a sweeping, big-budget saga based on the bestselling, semi-autobiographical novel by Bryce Courtenay. Dorff was selected for the lead out of several thousand hopefuls. The story of an English boy who grows up in South Africa and undergoes a series of hardships before finally learning to box his way to self-confidence, the film required an actor of uncanny ability. According to screenwriter Robert

Dorff in Bob Rafelson's Blood and Wine

which Dorff played the (fleeting) role of the son of Mia Farrow. Earlier, Dorff had failed to win the part of a drag queen in *To Wong Foo, Thanks For Everything! Julie Newmar*, but had sufficiently impressed the casting director Billy Hopkins to be put up for transvestite 'superstar' Candy Darling in Mary Harron's *I Shot Andy Warhol*. Harron was not convinced, but Hopkins pleaded: 'Trust me. Get Dorff in a dress and makeup and he looks just like Malibu Barbie.' She relented, and just four days before the start of filming Dorff metamorphosed into an eerily convincing princess of the New York underground. With his eyebrows waxed and his whole body shaved, Dorff displayed a facet of his talent that must've shamed Wesley Snipes and Patrick Swayze, the ungainly stars of *To Wong Foo*. But it was his quivering mannerisms and softly-spoken voice that truly transformed the Dorff of yore.

Securing his best reviews in aeons, the actor sashayed out of his career rut to encounter more praise as the disgruntled stepson of Jack Nicholson in *Blood and Wine*. A richly atmospheric thriller, the film was an actor's dream, and Dorff rose to the occasion magnificently, playing an emotionally isolated young man who shares his stepfather's

affections for a sexy Latin babysitter (Jennifer Lopez). Exhibiting a raw machismo matched with a confused naïveté, Dorff was totally credible in a role a million light years from Candy Darling.

He then joined Willem Dafoe, Nastassja Kinski and Irene Jacob in Hector Babenco's Argentina-set drama *Foolish Heart*, Harvey Keitel and Timothy Hutton in John Irvin's *City of Industry*, and Wesley Snipes in the special effects-enhanced actioner *Blade*.

Later, Dorff hopes to follow in the footsteps of such elders as Emilio Estevez, Matthew Broderick and Kevin Bacon as a director. To date he has already made a music video for the rock group Catherine Wheel, and he is mentally planning a full-length contemporary 'silent'.

FILMOGRAPHY

1987: *In Love and War* (TV); *The Gate*. 1989: *I Know My First Name is Steven* (TV). 1990: *Always Remember I Love You* (TV); *A Son's Promise* (TV). 1992: *The Power of One*. 1993: *An Ambush of Ghosts; Judgment Night; Rescue Me*. 1994: *Backbeat; SFW; A Hundred and One Nights* (cameo). 1995: *Innocent Lies; Reckless*. 1996: *I Shot Andy Warhol; Blood and Wine*. 1997: *Space Truckers; Foolish Heart; City of Industry*. 1998: *Blade*.

ROBERT DOWNEY JR

Everybody in Hollywood knew Robert Downey Jr had the talent. James Woods, who co-starred with him in *True Believer*, vouchsafed: 'Bob is the finest of the young actors. He really has that magic gift. I think I'm going to adopt him.' Dan Grodnik, producer on Downey's *1969*, went further: 'Robert's gonna be a big star. He's got the face, he's got the talent, and he's got the style.' Producer Scott Rudin echoed: 'I think of all his peers, Robert seems to be the one with the widest range and the most natural electricity. Very few actors have that combination of mercurial energy and emotional depth. He's now the guy that everybody in Hollywood wants.'

And yet Robert Downey Jr was at a standstill. He had paid his dues in a roll call of dud movies, playing flash young punks. He had shown his comedic prowess on the cult TV revue *Saturday*

Night Live. He had a relatively famous girlfriend, Sarah Jessica Parker, and he lived in a big house in Hollywood Hills built specially for Charlie Chaplin. And yet ...

In 1989 he told one journalist: 'I'm not going to work again until there's something that I'm really passionate about. I don't want to be thought of as someone who does progressively less good work because he's sort of just caught up in the flow.' He also

Robert Downey Jr

acknowledged: 'I'm just in the fetal stages as an actor.'

In 1990, Downey Jr slowed his workaholism down to a walking pace. He made one film: *Air America*. It had 'hit' written all over it. Not only did it have a blockbusting budget, it was a two-hander which gave Downey an opportunity to bounce off one of the most popular men in Christendom, Mel Gibson. It also took him to Cannes, where he got to meet other big stars, and where Arnold Schwarzenegger introduced him to Maria Shriver and Rob Lowe. All in all, it was a sobering experience. And, when the film opened on 10 August, it couldn't compete against *Flatliners* and *Ghost*, and quickly vanished from cinemas. He then resigned himself to another dud, *Into the Sun*, and a sup-

*Downey Jr showing his flare for comedy with Cathy Moriarty in Michael Hoffman's hilarious **Soapdish***

porting role in *Soapdish*, which failed to produce much of a lather.

Then Richard Attenborough cast him in the title role of *Chaplin* – the part of a lifetime. Attenborough, who described Downey as 'an extraordinary boy', predicted: 'He'll be a world figure as an actor within a month of the film opening.' Boasting a budget of more than $30 million, *Chaplin* had a supporting cast to die for: Dan Aykroyd, Geraldine Chaplin, Anthony Hopkins, Kevin Kline, Diane Lane, Penelope Ann Miller, James Woods and more. However, Downey, in spite of 22 films to his credit, was still considered an 'unknown'. And Attenborough wanted it that way. 'If you bring in a star, someone with other connotations,' the director argued, 'you start with a disadvantage.' But, Downey countered: 'My worry is – what do I do after this?'

Robert Downey Jr was born on 4 April 1965, in New York City, the son of an actress/singer and the independent filmmaker Robert Downey. At the age of five, he made his screen debut playing a puppy in his father's bizarre *Pound*. His first words on celluloid were: 'Got any hair on your balls?' The experience was not a happy one, and the child swore he would never act again, appearing two years later in Downey Snr's *Greaser's Palace*. He also popped up in his father's *Jive* and *Up the Academy*, moved to Los Angeles at 15 and dropped out of school (Santa Monica High) in the eleventh grade.

Moving back to New York, he waited on tables, worked as a shoe salesman and filled in as 'living art' in a SoHo nightclub (in an orange space suit). He then landed his first film without a parent, John Sayles' *Baby, It's You*. 'I think I had three weeks' work on it,' the actor recalls. 'I had scenes with Rosanna Arquette and I talked wild shit to everyone about how I was the next Dustin Duvall. Then they cut those scenes out, and I was in only one scene, being blocked by a very eager young actress leaning across the lens. So you can see me for just a second. My friends called it *Maybe It's You*.'

There was then a string of small parts in small movies before Downey Jr made an impact in the Rodney Dangerfield hit *Back to School*, playing Keith Gordon's wacky sidekick. He was also honing his comedic skills (and writing sketches) on *Saturday Night Live* alongside his pal, Anthony Michael Hall (they met on *Weird Science*), Joan Cusack, Jon Lovitz, Randy Quaid and

Damon Wayans. Then he gave his best performance yet in the title role of the Warren Beatty-produced *The Pick-Up Artist*. As the wise-cracking womanizer who chases Molly Ringwald, he was the best thing in a very bland movie.

He also won the kindest reviews in the poorly-received *Less Than Zero*, a story of everyday alienated yuppies, based on the cult novel by Brett Easton Ellis. Downey was the Beverly Hills cocaine addict, Julian, and gave a bravura performance of naked despair. There were two more disappointments – the execrable teen comedy *Johnny Be Good*, with Anthony Michael Hall; and Downey Snr's virtually unreleased *Rented Lips*, a porno spoof. There was also the self-indulgent *1969*, a nostalgic tale of disenchanted youth with Kiefer Sutherland and Winona Ryder, followed by the highly entertaining *True Believer*, in which Downey played an idealistic lawyer assisting James Woods in a murder case. The film failed to secure a theatrical release in Britain, as

Robert Downey Jr as Charlie Chaplin

The only one for Marisa Tomei? Downey Jr in Norman Jewison's **Only You**

did *Chances Are*, a romantic fantasy with Downey as the reincarnated love of Cybill Shepherd. Still, he won billing over Ryan O'Neal and Mary Stuart Masterson, which was some indication of his growing stature in the industry.

This led to *Air America*, an enjoyable action-adventure set in South-East Asia. Downey co-starred as an LA traffic cop transported to Laos to illegally airlift heroin on behalf of the CIA. Essentially a buddy-buddy movie, with Downey and Mel Gibson a charismatic duo, the film ultimately failed to exploit its explosive subject matter. Following the farcical *Too Much Sun*, he was hilarious as David Barnes, the unctuous, libidinous TV producer in *Soapdish*, a riotous comedy. Wearing dark-rimmed glasses and a lustful stare, he more than held his own in the midst of a top-notch cast: Sally Field, Kevin Kline, Whoopi Goldberg, Cathy Moriarty, Kathy Najimy, et al. The film should have been an enormous hit. It wasn't. Then came *Chaplin*.

Downey, a controversial choice for the title role in the long-awaited biog, exceeded all expectations. Thanks to an uncanny make-up job, he was the spitting image of Chaplin, complete with the mournful, lazy eyes and fleshy cheeks. He had the physical grace, the elastic motion, the melancholy stare. Even his accent was consistently

English, even though, on occasions, it slid across a few London streets (in one sentence). But even so, it was hard to picture *anybody* who could have been so perfect. The critics agreed, and in 1992, a year replete with stellar performances, Robert Downey Jr was nominated for an Oscar.

He then joined the all-star cast of *Short Cuts* (as a macabre make-up artist in cahoots with Lili Taylor), Robert Altman's highly-acclaimed ensemble piece based on the short stories of Raymond Carver. After that, he took the lead in Ron Underwood's drippingly sentimental but captivating *Heart and Souls*, and again proved what an engaging presence he was. Despite this, the film flopped.

Also in 1992, Downey married the actress Deborah Falconer, whom he had known for some years. The wedding was quick, quiet and painless, just the way Downey wanted it. But the marriage didn't last long, in spite of the birth of a son, Indio. Falconer left Downey in 1996.

Next, he took a supporting role in Oliver Stone's controversial *Natural Born Killers*, as a brash TV journalist (complete with Australian accent) who interviews serial killers Woody Harrelson and Juliette Lewis; he was on excellent form as Marisa Tomei's deceptive soul mate in Norman

Jewison's incurably romantic *Only You*; he played Holly Hunter's wise-cracking gay brother in Jodie Foster's hilarious *Home for the Holidays*, and he starred in Michael Hoffman's opulent costume drama *Restoration* – as a libidinous healer who wins favour with King Charles II (Sam Neill). *Restoration* won Oscars for its costume design and art direction, but it did little for Downey's standing as a star.

He next turned up in *Danger Zone*, starring Billy Zane and Ron Silver, a run-of-the-mill actioner which trickled straight to video. He then joined Sean Penn, Cathy Moriarty and Alan Arkin in his father's *Hugo Pool*, and teamed up with Wesley Snipes and Nastassja Kinski in Mike Figgis's *One Night Stand*, playing a theatre director with AIDS. Figgis, who had recently steered Nicolas Cage to an Oscar in *Leaving Las Vegas*, called Downey's performance 'mind-blowing'.

Then, in the summer of 1996, the actor leaped into the headlines when, in the space of four weeks, he was arrested on three separate occasions, for possession of cocaine and heroin, for being under the influence of 'a controlled substance', for driving under the influence, and for being in possession of a handgun. The press had a field day, citing Downey as an object lesson in the depravity of Hollywood, but the actor got off relatively lightly, ending up on felony probation, making salads and washing up dishes in a drug-treatment facility.

FILMOGRAPHY

1970: *Pound*. 1972: *Greaser's Palace*. 1976: *Jive*. 1980: *Up the Academy*. 1982: *Baby, It's You*. 1984: *Firstborn*. 1985: *Weird Science*; *To Live and Die in LA*; *Tuff Turf*. 1986: *America* (filmed in 1982); *Back to School*; *That's Adequate!* 1987: *Dear America* (voice only); *The Pick-Up Artist*; *Less Than Zero*. 1988: *Johnny Be Good*; *Rented Lips*; *1969*; *True Believer* (UK: *Fighting Justice*). 1989: *Chances Are*. 1990: *Air America*. 1991: *Too Much Sun*; *Soapdish*. 1992: *Chaplin*; *Short Cuts*. 1993: *The Last Party* (documentary); *Heart and Souls*; *Hail Caesar* (six-minute cameo). 1994: *Natural Born Killers*; *Only You*. 1995: *Home for the Holidays*; *Restoration*; *Richard III*. 1996: *Danger Zone*. 1997: *Hugo Pool*; *One Night Stand*; *Two Girls and a Guy*; *The Gingerbread Man*. 1998: *Wild Things*; *US Marshals*.

E

Apocalypse 1989: Anthony Edwards in **Miracle Mile**

Anthony Edwards is a likeable, all-purpose leading man who bears a passing resemblance to a young Jeff Bridges. He can appear witty without being obvious, and makes a passable hero when the occasion calls for it. However, few of his films have won a theatrical release in Britain.

Born on 19 July 1963 in Santa Barbara, California, Anthony Edwards was the youngest of five children. His maternal grandfather was an artist who worked for Cecil B. De Mille at Paramount in the 1930s and who helped design Walt Disney's new studio. His mother was also an artist (designing landscapes) and his father was an architect, but Anthony himself became frustrated whenever he picked up a pencil.

Instead, he submerged himself into the theatre programme at Santa Barbara High and at the Santa Barbara Youth Theater. By the time he emerged from high school he had appeared in 30 shows, mostly musicals. His idols were Gene Kelly and Joel Grey (and, apparently, hardware shops). 'From the time I was 11 until I was 17, I did theatre,' he swears. 'It was all I ever wanted to do.' At 16 he started acting professionally, swotting up on camera technique from his appearances in dozens of commercials. He also hung out with fellow future star Eric Stoltz, the pair of them ducking into movie theatres and paying children's admission prices due to their short statures (later, Edwards climbed to 6'2").

A fan of Olivier, Richardson and O'Toole, Edwards took a 1980 summer workshop at RADA, and followed it up with two years at the University of Southern California. After that he won a small role in the acclaimed, true-life TV movie *The Killing of Randy Webster* (playing Webster's friend), alongside other budding stars Jennifer Jason Leigh and Sean Penn. The three of them reunited for Cameron's Crowe's successful *Fast Times at Ridgemont High* (in which Edwards played Penn's dopehead sidekick), after which he followed with a bigger part in another celebrated movie, *Heart Like a Wheel*.

He turned to television with 23 episodes of the sitcom *It Takes Two*, playing Andy, the teenage son of Richard Crenna and Patty Duke Astin, and then established himself as the chief geek in *Revenge of the Nerds*. 'We all knew the *Nerds* film was shameless,' the actor owns up. 'It was a really silly script, but the reason it was successful was because we were all honest about it.' It was so successful, in fact, that it spawned two sequels, with Edwards taking a guest role in the first.

He played the best friend (John Cusack's) in Rob Reiner's delightful teen romance *The Sure Thing*, and then, on TV, took the title role of the champion downhill skier in *Going for the Gold – The Bill Johnson Story*, with Dennis Weaver and Sarah Jessica Parker in support. But it was the next two films that sealed his stardom.

In *Gotcha!* he skewered top-billing as an amiable college kid who finds himself embroiled in an espionage plot in Paris – thanks to femme fatale Linda Fiorentino. The movie was no masterpiece, but it was an enjoyable bit of hokum that was well played. Edwards then took fourth-billing in a film dedicated more to fighter jets than actors, but he stole the notices anyway as the movie soared into box-office heaven. Edwards played the easy-going Lieutenant Nick Bradshaw – 'Goose' to his friends – the ultimately tragic pilot who valued his wife and son above his testosterone level. The film was *Top Gun* – the highest grosser of 1986 – and the actress who played his wife was an unknown called Meg Ryan. She was also his girlfriend at the time.

The film's success naturally led to more leading roles, but the next three were all disappointments. *Summer Heat* was a turgid rural drama with Lori Singer; *Hawks* a misguided black comedy with Timothy Dalton, shot in London and Amsterdam, and *Miracle Mile*, an overly sincere romance set during nuclear panic. Nevertheless, Edwards was always good value for money.

His next picture, *Mr North*, was another box-office flop, but a delightful curio for all that. Based on Thornton Wilder's novel *Theophilus North*, the film was shot for under $4 million by Danny Huston, whose illustrious father, John, served as co-scripter and executive producer. Sadly, the elder Huston was to die before completion of the project, but a wonderful cast rallied round to show support: Robert Mitchum (replacing Huston Snr), Lauren Bacall, Anjelica Huston, Mary Stuart Masterson and Virginia Madsen. Edwards was totally engaging in the title role, playing a young academic whose surplus of personal electricity leads the community of Newport, Rhode Island, to mistake him for a faith healer. Enchanting whimsy.

Unfortunately, it was downhill from there. Over the following years Edwards found himself in a roster of pictures that saw little light of day: the teen comedy *How I Got Into College*; *Downtown*, a police melodrama with Forest Whitaker; *El Diablo*, a TV west-

Edwards with Anjelica Huston in **Mr North**

The famous face of Anthony Edwards: as Dr Mark Green in TV's ER

ern with Louis Gossett Jr, and a TV fable about the sins of lying, *Hometown Boy Makes Good.*

In 1992, the star reached a new low when he accepted second-billing to child actor Edward Furlong in the horror sequel *Pet Sematary Two.* Still, it wasn't as bad as its predecessor (which wasn't hard) – although nobody turned up to find out. He then starred in the one-hour TV special *Sexual Healing,* as a lonely man who falls in love with an unhappily married woman (Mare Winningham) through a telephone sex line.

TV, as it happens, turned out to be his saving grace. Not only did he land a recurring role in the successful series *Northern Exposure* – as a serious allergy case – but he secured top-billing in the top-rated hospital drama *ER.* Edwards played the guilt-plagued surgeon Dr Mark Greene, who juggled his scalpel with divorce papers while seducing the heart of a nation. Balding and bespectacled, he left the show's romantic escapades to co-star George Clooney, but established his own legion of fans who found his noble, hang-dog workaholic irresistible.

Before his new fame kicked in, he played Susan Sarandon's legal assistant in *The Client* (a hit), and then won enormous praise for his portrayal of the off-centre killer Dick Hickock in the mini-series *In Cold Blood,* Jonathan Kaplan's brilliant re-working of Truman Capote's book. He also pulled off a deal with Warner Brothers to produce, direct and act in projects of his own choosing.

FILMOGRAPHY

1981: *The Killing of Randy Webster* (TV). 1982: *Fast Times at Ridgemont High; Heart Like a Wheel.* 1984: *Revenge of the Nerds.* 1985: *The Sure Thing; Going for the Gold – The Bill Johnson Story* (TV); *Gotcha!.* 1986: *Top Gun.* 1987: *Revenge of the Nerds II: Nerds in Paradise; Summer Heat.* 1988: *Hawks; Miracle Mile; Mr North.* 1989: *How I Got Into College.* 1990: *Downtown; El Diablo* (TV); *Hometown Boy Makes Good* (TV). 1991: *Landslide* (TV). 1992: *Delta Heat; Pet Sematary Two.* 1993: *Sexual Healing* (TV). 1994: *The Client; Charlie's Ghost* (also directed). 1996: *In Cold Blood* (TV).

EMILIO ESTEVEZ

As the cinematic phenomenon of the Brat Pack gathered momentum in the mid-1980s, three seminal films were held responsible: *The Outsiders, The Breakfast Club* and *St Elmo's Fire.* Emilio Estevez was in all of them.

In the space of two years, Estevez was seen on screen wrestling with Tom Cruise, defending Molly Ringwald's honour and knocking back beers with Rob Lowe. Although he vehemently rejected the Brat Pack label, he was the living embodiment of it. He established considerable notoriety as a ladies' man, his best friends included fellow Brat Packers Cruise, Lowe and Sean Penn, he was engaged to Demi Moore, and he spent more hours at LA's Hard Rock Cafe than was good for him. He was, in the words of the media, a hell raiser.

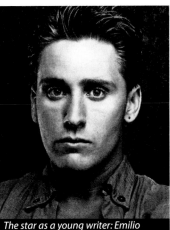

*The star as a young writer: Emilio Estevez on the set of **That Was Then, This is Now***

Later, the star rationalized: 'We were just guys being guys. We'd meet to let off a little steam, that was all. We all have to grow up.' His father, the actor Martin Sheen, took up the defence: 'They were just kids with a sense of humour.' Cruise was more succinct: 'It was just something the press made up.'

Nevertheless, the overt carousing helped keep Emilio's name in the papers – and, subsequently, in the public's mind. He was, however, an unlikely star. He was short (5'6"), he lacked the drop-dead good looks of Rob Lowe, the bravura acting talent of Tom Cruise and the innate sex-appeal of Matt Dillon. He was more often surly than smouldering, and he was hardly charismatic. Also, he had the misfortune (or poor judgement) to star in an impressive chain of box-office stiffs (*Nightmares, Maximum Overdrive, Wisdom, Men at Work, Freejack*).

He was equally unlucky with films that never materialized. For instance, he was due to play the man who organized the 1969 Woodstock rock festival in Warner Brothers' *Young Men With Unlimited Capital,* but according to leaked reports, the film never got made because of billing disputes between Estevez and his co-star, Ralph Macchio. He was then announced to direct *Clear Intent,* from his own screenplay – however, good intentions do not a movie make. Other projects – *El Niño* (with Martin Sheen directing), *Ask the Dust* (for French filmmaker Daniel Vigne) and *Secret Society* (again with dad) – all fell through.

Emilio Estevez's personal life was no more successful. The model Carey Salley sued the actor for palimony and child support, claiming he was the father of her two children, Taylor and Paloma. At the time, Emilio publicly denied his paternity, although court records revealed that he had been paying Salley $3,000 a month; she wanted more like $15,000. Meanwhile, Martin Sheen arranged for Taylor's baptism and provided extra financial support for his daughter-out-of-law. Estevez refused to talk about 'this personal stuff', but that was then. Now, he acknowledges: 'You turn your back on your kids and eventually you're going to regret it.'

There was also the Demi Moore situation. The couple met while filming *St Elmo's Fire,* fell in love, set the wed-

Young man with a gun: Emilio with co-star Richard Dreyfuss in one of his biggest hits, Stakeout

ding date for 6 December 1986, and sent out the invitations. Demi then had second thoughts, claiming: 'We were at two different junctures of our internal lives.' After a four-month courtship, she married Bruce Willis.

Emilio's romance with make-up artist Sheryl Berkoff was equally ill-fated. She ended up marrying Rob Lowe. Says Estevez: 'There's an unwritten rule between guys who are friends – you *don't* go out with your buddy's ex-girlfriend. And you certainly don't marry her.'

In the end, Estevez got hitched himself – to the singer Paula Abdul. But that didn't last long either.

On a positive note, Emilio Estevez does go down in the history books as the youngest Hollywood star to write his own script – for *That Was Then, This is Now*. The film also showcased his most powerful, bravura performance to date (and one of the best of 1985), playing a rebel without a cause who competes with his best friend (Craig Sheffer) for the affections of a girl (Kim Delaney).

On the strength of this, Estevez entered the history books again, this time as the youngest writer-director-star of a movie, although on this occasion he found himself a victim of the critics. The trade paper *Variety* wrote: '*Wisdom* marks 23-year-old actor Emilio Estevez' directorial debut – and it shows,' adding that the film suffered from 'a completely implausible script and unending sophomoric dialogue'. Estevez countered with: '*Fuck the critics* – because they tried to really break me down, and the only thing it did was make me stronger.' Nevertheless, he also admits, 'after *Wisdom*'s release, I was

devastated. If I'm watching TV now and the movie comes on, the first thing I do is change the channel to CNN.' Incidentally, the film co-starred Demi Moore.

Emilio's relationship with the press has never been an easy one. He has seemed easy prey. The media had a field day in 1992 when the star allegedly fired actress-model Kathy Ireland from his film *National Lampoon's Loaded Weapon 1* – because, it was reported, she was 5 inches taller than him. The story goes that he was invited to stand on a box, but turned the offer down. As it happens, the entire scenario was made up by the tabloids.

His loathe-hate relationship with the media is an old battle. When *Life* magazine presented a lavish feature on showbusiness families, he refused to endorse the article, leaving his father and siblings (Charlie Sheen, Ramon and Renee Estevez) to frolic happily for the camera on their own. Emilio Estevez is reluctant to acknowledge any debts. 'I'm much more ambitious than my father,' he has said. 'What I've got from him is the idea that, if I kept my feet firmly planted on the ground, I could achieve whatever I wanted. Everything that's come to me I've earned. I haven't been given stardom. I'm not a pretty boy who was told, "We're going to make you a star."'

Born Emilio Sheen on 12 May 1962, in New York City, the actor adopted his father's original (Spanish) surname as his first statement of independence. He wanted to act for as long as he could remember, and as a young teenager he made Super 8 films with his two brothers and boyhood friends Sean and Christopher Penn and Rob and Chad Lowe.

At the age of 20 he starred opposite his father in the highly-acclaimed TV movie *In the Custody of Strangers*, playing a 16-year-old imprisoned on a charge of drunken behaviour. He then made his theatrical debut in *Tex*, based on the cult novel by S.E. Hinton. On the set, he met the author, who suggested he would make the perfect Mark Jennings, the protagonist of her book *That Was Then, This is Now*. So he optioned the rights.

After he made his name in the surreal *Repo Man* (playing an uncharismatic punk who repossesses cars) – and did

time on the Brat Pack trilogy – he embarked on *That Was Then* ...: 'I thought I'd hire a writer to adapt the novel,' he explained, 'but I had some time on my hands, so I wrote a draft.' It was a good draft, but it was the fourth adaptation of a Hinton novel, and the public had tired of the familiar tale of the outsider fighting for his rights. The film was not a success.

Success *did* arrive, although belatedly, with John Badham's *Stakeout*, a ferociously entertaining buddy-cop saga, strong on romance, laughs and action. Richard Dreyfuss and Estevez played the cops, who stake out the girlfriend (Madeleine Stowe) of a vicious killer (Aidan Quinn). Estevez's role was originally intended for an older actor ('they were thinking of a James Garner type,' he says) but, according to the film's producer, Cathleen Summers, 'Once we had decided to play around with their ages, we immediately thought of Emilio.'

Comedy was certainly a change of pace for the actor, and the practical jokes he and Dreyfuss got up to were a joy to behold. Nevertheless, it *was* Dreyfuss's picture.

Another success was the Brat Pack western *Young Guns*, with Estevez top-billed as a nauseatingly cocky Billy the Kid. But, again, the actor was diluted by his co-stars (Kiefer Sutherland, Lou Diamond Phillips, Charlie Sheen, Terence Stamp, Jack Palance). He had

Still trigger-happy, Emilio top-bills in Geoff Murphy's futuristic flop Freejack

the lead in an excellent TV movie, *Nightbreaker*, as a naive doctor who witnesses government atomic testing (Martin Sheen played the same character in later years), and then he directed (and scripted) himself and Charlie Sheen in the risible comedy *Men at Work* (they played garbagemen who stumble on a murder). *Young Guns II – Blaze of Glory*, directed by Geoff Murphy, turned out to be better than the original, although Estevez was even *more* irritating as the cackling outlaw.

In Geoff Murphy's big-budget *Freejack*, based on Robert Sheckley's notable sci-fi novel *Immortality, Inc.*, Estevez proved he was not the stuff of macho heroism, and the film's limited glory went to co-star Mick Jagger as the heavy. He was more appealing as an arrogant lawyer forced to coach a children's ice hockey team in *The Mighty Ducks*, but the film was predictable and bland – albeit his biggest solo commercial success. In the USA, *The Mighty Ducks* went on to gross over $50 million. Estevez then tried comedy again, playing the 'Mel Gibson' part in *National Lampoon's Loaded Weapon 1*, a spoof of *Lethal Weapon*, *The Silence of the Lambs* and *Basic Instinct*. Samuel L. Jackson co-starred as 'Danny Glover', with such ready hams as Tim Curry and William Shatner in support. The film opened well, grossing $11 million in its first week, but it quickly lost steam. After that, Estevez continued his spate of workaholism and went straight on to star in *Judgment Night*, a tough thriller about four young guys who witness a mob killing (have you noticed that there are *always* witnesses at a mob killing?). He then rejoined Richard Dreyfuss and director John Badham for the predictable, farcical *Another Stakeout*, one of the worst sequels in cinema history.

If, on the whole, Emilio Estevez's career looks like a disaster area, it is not through lack of talent. He demonstrated his potential with the complexity and power of his performance in *That Was Then, This is Now*. He was also excellent as the pressurized jock in *The Breakfast Club*, and he showed some flair for comedy in *St Elmo's Fire*. Personally, he now seems more at ease with himself, and is less outspoken in front of the press. By all accounts, he is also a committed father to Taylor and

Paloma.

Then, on 29 April 1992, at the ripe old age of 29, Emilio Estevez finally declared his conjugal vows to Paula Abdul, the rock star one year his junior (and 4 inches shorter). The couple, who had been dating for five months and were engaged that February, married spontaneously and secretly in Santa Monica, California, surprising their friends, the media and even Paula's mother. On 19 September they splashed out on a second ceremony (reportedly costing $200,000), and invited the whole family and their intimates (although best man Tom Cruise chose not to show up, much to the amusement of the media). It was a shame, then, that the marriage collapsed so soon afterwards.

Commercially, Estevez hung on to the *Mighty Ducks* franchise, which not only managed to produce two fairly successful follow-ups, but retained the energy and fun quotient of the original (if you liked that sort of thing). However, with *Young Guns II* and *Another Stakeout* already under his belt, Estevez was reluctant to commit to another sequel. 'My kids really wanted me to do the movie,' he rationalized. 'They're very big on hockey. I didn't want to let them down.'

His excuse for the third one was that, in return for his services, Disney agreed to fork out 75 per cent of the budget for his next directorial effort, *The War at Home*. A low-budget ($4.2 million) drama about the after-effects of Vietnam on a subdued Texan family, the film lacked dramatic focus. Estevez himself, as the vet still haunted by the trauma of battle, failed to bring his character to life, although he did elicit a remarkable performance from his dad, who played his character's father.

He then took an unbilled cameo in *Mission: Impossible* (opposite his old friend Tom Cruise), in which he played a secret agent who meets a nasty end in an elevator shaft; and then he teamed up with Denis Leary in the low-budget drama *Sand*.

FILMOGRAPHY

1980: *Seventeen Going Nowhere* (TV). 1981: *To Climb a Mountain* (TV). 1982: *In the Custody of Strangers* (TV); *Tex*. 1983: *The Outsiders*; *Nightmares*. 1984: *Repo Man*. 1985: *The Breakfast Club*; *St Elmo's*

*Armed to the teeth: Emilio takes on a volley of bad jokes in **National Lampoon's Loaded Weapon 1***

Fire; *That Was Then, This Is Now* (also scripted). 1986: *Maximum Overdrive*; *Wisdom* (also directed and scripted). 1987: *Stakeout*. 1988: *Young Guns*. 1989: *Nightbreaker* (TV). 1990: *Men at Work* (also directed and scripted); *Young Guns II – Blaze of Glory*. 1992: *Freejack*; *The Mighty Ducks* (UK: *Champions*). 1993: *National Lampoon's Loaded Weapon 1*; *Judgment Night*; *Another Stakeout*. 1994: *D2: The Mighty Ducks*. 1996: *Mission: Impossible* (unbilled); *The War at Home*; *D3: The Mighty Ducks*. 1997: *Sand*.

*As smooth operator Gordon Bombay in **The Mighty Ducks***

F

JEFF FAHEY

In the late 1980s and early 1990s, Jeff Fahey displayed the hottest matinee idol looks around. With a chiselled jaw-line and pale blue eyes to die for, he was your prototypical leading man – albeit without a hit movie. Ironically, in his most successful film yet – the 'virtual reality' thriller *The Lawnmower Man* – he played a chap with the mental age of a six-year-old saddled with a fright wig. *Not* the sort of role to launch next year's heartthrob. In fact, it was co-star Pierce Brosnan who probably benefited most from the film's high profile. And there was another irony: Fahey and Brosnan look remarkably alike and could easily swap careers.

Jeff Fahey (pronounced 'Fay-hee'), one of 13 children of Irish-American parents, was born on 29 November 1956, in Olean, New York. When he was ten the family moved to Buffalo, and Jeff attended two local schools until graduation in 1972. After hitch-hiking to Alaska, he travelled round the

Jeff Fahey in his biggest hit yet, as **The Lawnmower Man**

The man with the see-through eyes: Jeff Fahey in Clint Eastwood's **White Hunter, Black Heart**

world – backpacking in Europe, working on a kibbutz in Israel and celebrating his 19th birthday in India. He also spent time as a crewman on a fishing boat, drove an ambulance in Germany, trekked across Afghanistan and the Himalayas, and returned to America to study ballet. He then danced with the celebrated Joffrey Ballet for three years. Stage work followed with the Broadway revival of *Brigadoon*, a tour of *Oklahoma!* and, in Paris, *West Side Story*.

On TV, he played Gary Corelli for two-and-a-half years in the daytime soap *One Life To Live*, and he made his film debut in Lawrence Kasdan's epic western *Silverado* – as Tyree, whom he later named his own production company after. Back on TV, he starred in *The Execution of Raymond Graham*, playing the convicted killer of the title, and a year later he began his film career in earnest.

In the jokey *Psycho III* he was the young male lead, as Duane, an aspiring musician holed up at the Bates Motel, and he then starred in *Backfire*, a classy film noir thriller, in which he played Donny McAndrew, a Vietnam vet plagued by recurring nightmares and Keith Carradine. In *Split Decisions* he was Gene Hackman's son, an arrogant boxer; he won top-billing (for the first time) in *True Blood*, a routine crime drama in which Fahey is falsely accused of killing a cop, and he then starred in *Out of Time*, a British-Egyptian romantic adventure in which he was cast as a zealous archaeologist who discovers a

rare bust of Alexander the Great. In the Australian family western *Outback* he portrayed a mysterious American businessman, and he then joined Brian Dennehy as one of *The Last of the Finest* – honest LA cops battling a government conspiracy (borrowing its plot from the Iran-Contra affair).

In *Impulse*, directed by Clint Eastwood's former actress girlfriend, Sondra Locke, Fahey played an assistant DA who teams up with undercover cop Theresa Russell. He then won good reviews in the TV movie *Parker Kane*, as a gutsy ex-policeman uncovering a toxic waste-dumping scam.

In spite of his obvious demand, Jeff Fahey was still a star without a hit picture. This finally arrived with Clint Eastwood's *White Hunter, Black Heart*, a critically revered look at the making of John Huston's *The African Queen*. A success at Cannes, the film starred Eastwood (who also directed) as a recalcitrant filmmaker more interested in shooting elephants than film. Fahey played Pete Verill, the director's biographer, from whose point of view the story is told. Eastwood made a brave stab at character acting but lacked the vocal depth needed to capture the charisma of the man. Ironically, it was Fahey himself who supplied the movie's greatest magnetism, the actor's weathered good looks making him an ideal candidate for any John Huston movie.

It was back to low-budget mediocrity with the Japanese-produced whodunnit *Iron Maze*, with Bridget Fonda, and then a better-than-average TV movie, *Iran: Days of Crisis*, an impressive co-production from the USA, Britain and France. Fahey co-starred as presidential aide Hamilton Jordan, on whose book the film was based, observing the Iranian revolution through American eyes. *Body Parts* was not good, a tired re-working of the old killer limb routine (remember Michael Caine in *The Hand*?), but then *The Lawnmower Man* saved the day; at least it was a box-office success, thanks to some spectacular computer graphics. Jeff Fahey had the title role – a gardener and village idiot who becomes a supernatural threat when a game of 'virtual reality' unleashes hidden powers in his brain.

This was followed by *Sketch Artist*, another B-movie, but one deserving more attention than it received. Fahey had the title role, an LA police artist who sketches suspects from eye-witness memory. Things hot up considerably when witness Drew Barrymore describes Fahey's wife (Sean Young) as the suspect leaving the scene of a brutal murder. Fahey has never been better than as a man descending into his own private hell, a hero with demons to hide. If the actor's prospects were based on *Sketch Artist* alone, Fahey should be a major star very, very soon.

Next, he was joined by Bo Derek and Robert Mitchum aboard a luxury yacht in the erotic mystery-thriller *Woman of Desire*, and he then popped up in Rick King's *Quick*, with Martin Donovan. After that, he played a bodyguard in the thriller *The Hit List*, co-starring with James Coburn. The next few years provided little relief from the video fodder that consumed him, although he made a compelling Ike Clanton in Lawrence Kasdan's *Wyatt Earp* (unrecognizable behind a handlebar moustache) and starred in the ABC TV series *The Marshal*. Most recently, he was top-billed in the Florida-set drama *Catherine Wheel*, with Maria Conchita Alonso.

FILMOGRAPHY
1985: *Silverado*; *The Execution of Raymond Graham* (TV). 1986: *Psycho III*. 1987: *Backfire*. 1988: *Split Decisions*. 1989: *True Blood* (a.k.a. *Edge of Darkness*); *Out of Time*; *Outback*. 1990: *The Last of the Finest* (UK: *Blue Heat*);

Impulse; *Parker Kane* (TV); *White Hunter, Black Heart*. 1991: *Iron Maze*; *Iran: Days of Crisis* (TV); *Body Parts*. 1992: *The Lawnmower Man*; *A Feel For Murder*; *Sketch Artist*. 1993: *Woman of Desire*; *Quick* (UK: *Crossfire*); *The Hit List*; *In the Company of Darkness*; *Freefall*. 1994: *Wyatt Earp*; *Temptation*. 1995: *Sketch Artist II: Hands That See* (TV); *Sweeper*. 1996: *Darkman III: Die Darkman Die*; *Small Time* (a.k.a. *Waiting For the Man*); *Lethal Tender*; *Addicted To Love* (TV). 1997: *Serpent's Lair*; *Operation Delta Force*; *Catherine's Grove*. 1998: *Growing Up*; *When Justice Fails*.

BRIDGET FONDA

Just because your father is Peter Fonda, your aunt is Jane Fonda and your grandfather is Henry Fonda doesn't mean you're going to be a star. Just because you're beautiful and you don't have to go through aerobic hell to own a lissom body doesn't mean you're going to be a star. Just because you're surrounded by artistic forces with all the right contacts doesn't mean you're going to be a star. But of course, it helps.

Bridget Fonda's lineage, she concedes, 'may have affected me slightly, but only because I grew up around creative people,' but, 'in high school I got into a play, and I *knew*. I felt it right away.' Sometimes, however, she admits: 'I wish my dad was maybe a bum actor or something like that. It would have

made it a lot easier for me.' And, on the subject of her famous aunt, Bridget asks: 'Wouldn't you be insecure if she were *your* aunt? I saw her one Christmas and she told me that I have no muscle tone in my thighs!' She adds: 'I've never worked out to any of Jane's videos. I have a hole in my heart, so I have to be careful.'

Bridget Fonda has all the credentials to be another overnight, flash-in-the-pan flavour of the month. She's pretty, well-connected and she lives in Los Angeles. But Fonda has transcended all that, has taken risks, down-played her heritage. Hell, if she's going to become a star, she's going to do it on her own terms, and her decisions are going to be intelligent ones.

Turning her back on Hollywood, Fonda honed her craft in British movies, opposite British stars (frequently John Hurt), working with British intellects. When she was ready, she returned to LA to steal some of the plummest parts on offer.

Born in LA on 27 January 1964, Bridget had an enchanted childhood, living a carefree life of hippie liberation. Her mother, Susan (née Brewer), was the daughter of an industrialist; her father, Peter Fonda, the star and producer of *Easy Rider*, the hippest movie of the 1960s. Until her parents' divorce in 1972, Bridget lived in California's Coldwater Canyon, and then divided her remaining formative years between Los Angeles (with Peter) and Montana (with her mother and common-law

Fonda (right) with Joanne Whalley-Kilmer in **Scandal**

*(above) Victim of the small ads: Fonda in Barbet Schroeder's chilling **Single White Female***

*(below) For the first time with her name solo above the title: Bridget Fonda as **The Assassin***

stepfather). She and Peter would also hang out in New Mexico, letting their hair down with Dennis Hopper and *his* kid, Marin. Bridget was, Marin says, 'a tomboy in beat-up sneakers', and was happiest riding bikes or sitting around listening to Monty Python records.

At school she appeared in a production of *Harvey* and decided to act professionally. She then moved to the East Coast to study acting at New York University and with the Lee Strasberg Theater Institute. She also studied cinema and played the lead role in *PPT*, a graduate student film.

For a while Bridget worked in the theatre, and then made her film debut (not counting a cameo in *Easy Rider*) in the British-produced *Aria*, a ten-part collection of cinematic interpretations of famous operatic pieces. John Hurt tied the pieces together as an anonymous character wandering around the deserted streets of Cremona in Italy, while Bridget made a striking impression in the seventh segment, *Tristan and Isolde*. Directed by Franc Roddam, the episode featured Fonda and James Mathers as teenage lovers who slash their wrists in a Las Vegas bathroom after a very explicit coupling.

The film was not well-received, but Bridget had turned enough heads to land the female lead in the perfectly awful *You Can't Hurry Love*, a romantic comedy set in the LA singles scene. She was better served by the British-produced *Shag*, a rites-of-passage comedy set in 1963 in Myrtle Beach, South Carolina, where four girlfriends sow their wild oats before emigrating to university and/or marriage. Phoebe Cates won top-billing, but Fonda caught the spotlight as the brash, all-over erogenous zone who enters a Miss Sun Queen Pageant wearing nothing but a bikini and the American flag.

She remained in 1963 for Michael Caton-Jones' *Scandal*, the controversial, seedy take on the Profumo affair – replacing Emily Lloyd in the role of showgirl and key witness Mandy Rice-Davies. John Hurt starred as the fall guy Stephen Ward, with Ian McKellen as Profumo and Joanne Whalley-Kilmer as the catalytic Christine Keeler. Although Fonda made a brave stab at her English accent, she was, on this occasion, upstaged by her British co-stars. Still, she *was* nominated for a

Golden Globe award as best supporting actress.

It was her role in *Shag*, however, that caught the attention of playwright-filmmaker David Hare, who cast her in his third and best film, *Strapless*. It was also Fonda's best screen performance to date. Hare's American girlfriend, Blair Brown, played a London radiotherapist courted by an enigmatic German (Bruno Ganz), while Fonda co-starred as her rebellious younger sister, Amy. It was a plum part, and Fonda executed it with verve. 'It was a strange film,' the actress concedes. 'The more you see it, the more you see. Each time there's an extra layer. I loved that movie.'

She returned to America – at least, to Rome's Cinecitta studios – to join the all-star cast of Francis Coppola's *The Godfather Part III*, playing Andy Garcia's ill-fated photojournalist girlfriend. She stayed in Italy (in and around Milan) to play Mary Godwin Shelley – opposite a time-travelling John Hurt – in Roger Corman's preposterous, heavy-handed *Frankenstein Unbound*.

Considering her European schedule, it's hard to believe that Fonda was actually living in New York at the time with her British fiancé, actor-writer Lee Drysdale (they have since separated). For him, she co-starred in *Leather Jackets* – alongside English actor Cary Elwes, then played an incest victim-turned-murderess in Gary Winick's *Out of the Rain*, and joined Jeff Fahey as a murder suspect in *Iron Maze*, a tiresome, *Rashomon*-style whodunnit. And for her good friend Phoebe Cates she did a one-day cameo on *Drop Dead Fred* (as the girlfriend who discovers Rik Mayall staring up her skirt).

The major Hollywood studios had yet to take Jane's niece to their collective bosom, although the actress did have a neat part as a predatory Southerner in *Doc Hollywood*, opposite Michael J. Fox – but then, it was directed by her old *Scandal* colleague, Michael Caton-Jones.

The star-making turn arrived with *Single White Female*, a prestigious thriller from Columbia Pictures, with Fonda top-billed as Allison Jones, a smart, sexy computer software expert. Let down by her boyfriend, Allison advertises for a flatmate, the latter arriv-

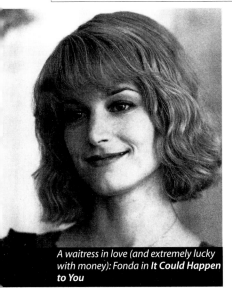

*A waitress in love (and extremely lucky with money): Fonda in **It Could Happen to You***

ing in the homely shape of Hedra Carlson, played by Jennifer Jason Leigh. At first the two girls get on famously, but gradually Allison sees that Hedra is not all she says she is. Although Jason Leigh had the meatier role, it was Fonda who hogged centre stage, deftly blending her character's vulnerability with a steely inner resolve.

She played a flighty young thing in *Singles*, Cameron Crowe's perceptive look at twentysomething life in Seattle, with Fonda gooey-eyed over would-be rock star Matt Dillon. She had a guest spot in Sam Raimi's *Army of Darkness: Evil Dead 3* ('she absolutely *loves* Raimi's films,' explained Fonda's agent), and she then landed the starring role (wresting the part from Kim Basinger) in John Badham's *Point of No Return*, the Americanization of the French hit *Nikita*. With Gabriel Byrne, Harvey Keitel and Anne Bancroft in support,

Bridget Fonda was no longer the decorative sex kitten in the corner. She was a major star.

Next, she was excellent in the 'existential romantic comedy' *Bodies, Rest and Motion*, with Tim Roth as the boyfriend who leaves her to find a better life in Montana, only to return to wrest her from the arms of Eric Stoltz (her real-life boyfriend, who also produced the movie). Then, in *Camilla*, she played a songwriter who embarks on an incredible journey with an 84-year-old Jessica Tandy, the two of them getting up to all sorts of mischief, including a skinny dip. She had less to do in Bernardo Bertolucci's sweeping, cinematically invigorating *Little Buddha*, as the American mother of the next Chosen One, but she made up for it in a subsequent burst of major activity.

In the sweet, fact-based romantic comedy *It Could Happen To You*, she played a New York waitress who gets to share $4 million from the state lottery with a love-struck Nicolas Cage. In Alan Parker's elegantly scatological *The Road to Wellville* she was Eleanor Lightbody, a liberated young wife seeking to improve her health and marriage at the notorious Battle Creek Sanitarium. And in the screwball, somewhat inane *Rough Magic* she was a magician's assistant tied up with sorcery and romance in deepest Mexico.

In Harold Becker's articulate political thriller *City Hall* she was virtually glossed over by her male co-stars (John Cusack, Al Pacino), in spite of the fact that she was paid $3 million. She then took a priceless cameo in *Grace of My Heart*, Allison Anders' affectionate tribute to female singers, playing a superficial, emotionally unsteady songstress

(and lesbian) reputedly modelled on Lesley Gore. Next, she was the love interest of faith healer Skeet Ulrich in Paul Schrader's comic-noir fable *Touch*, from the novel by Elmore Leonard, and played Marilyn Monroe to Harvey Keitel's Elvis in the Memphis drama *Graceland*.

She remains philosophical about her place in the Hollywood firmament. 'There's a children's book by, I think, Shel Silverstein,' she relates. 'It's about a pile of caterpillars, or worms, and they're just piled sky high. Everyone's just climbing to get to the top. You look for that thing that you think of as fame, that raises you out of the pile of worms. In reality, there's no big difference. You're just another worm.'

FILMOGRAPHY

1969: *Easy Rider* (bit part). 1987: *Aria*. 1988: *Light Years*; *You Can't Hurry Love*; *Shag*. 1989: *Scandal*; *Jacob I Have Loved* (TV); *Strapless*. 1990: *The Godfather Part III*; *Leather Jackets*; *Roger Corman's Frankenstein Unbound*. 1991: *Drop Dead Fred* (cameo); *Out of the Rain*; *Iron Maze*; *Doc Hollywood*. 1992: *Singles*; *Single White Female*; *Army of Darkness: Evil Dead 3* (cameo). 1993: *Point of No Return* (UK: *The Assassin*); *Bodies, Rest and Motion*; *Little Buddha*. 1994: *Camilla*; *It Could Happen To You*; *The Road to Wellville*. 1995: *Rough Magic*; *Balto* (voice only); *City Hall*. 1996: *Grace of My Heart*; *Touch*. 1997: *In the Gloaming* (TV); *Graceland*. 1998: *Jackie Brown*; *The Breakup*.

JODIE FOSTER

She made her professional debut aged three. At eight, she appeared in her first film. At 12, she won an Oscar nomination. At 27, an Oscar. Three years later, she won a second. At 28, she turned film director. A former child star, Jodie Foster was famous before anybody else in this book. But not only did she survive her pre-adolescent celebrity, she surpassed it. Today, she is better known and more respected than ever.

Evelyn 'Brandy' Foster was three months pregnant when she was divorced from Lucius Foster III and, on 19 November 1962, she gave birth to her fourth child, Alicia Christian, in the Bronx, New York. However, the baby's older siblings didn't see their new sister

*Fonda with John Cusack in **City Hall***

as Alicia, so they took it upon themselves to dub her 'Jodie'. Strapped for money, Brandy helped pay the bills by finding advertising assignments for her son, Lucius 'Buddy' Foster IV. On one occasion, Buddy was waiting to audition for a Coppertone sun tan commercial, when Jodie, aged three, was spotted. 'Well, they decided to change the campaign,' Jodie reveals. 'They called up and said they wanted me as the Coppertone girl.' As commercials went, it was one of the most visible of the decade, showing a sun-tanned little girl with her knickers pulled down by a dog to reveal a white bottom. Ten years later that same little girl had appeared in nearly 50 commercials, eight movies and had starred in the TV series *Paper Moon*. But Jodie almost didn't make it.

She was eight when she made her film debut (as Samantha) in Disney's *Napoleon and Samantha*. Her co-stars included Michael Douglas, Will Geer and a lion called Major. Jodie recalls: 'I got too close. His mane sort of reached around my body, took me up by my hip, turned me sideways, and started shaking me. I thought it was an earthquake. And everybody ran away!' To this day she has the scars to remind her of the ordeal, but after a spell in hospital she returned to work two weeks later. 'It was smarter for me to go back,' the actress rationalizes now, 'you know, to get back on the horse that bucked me.'

On TV, she was a regular on the sitcoms *The Courtship of Eddie's Father* and *Bob and Carol and Ted and Alice*, and she popped up in episodes of *Gunsmoke* and *The Partridge Family*. Also, thanks to her appearance in a number of Disney films, she had gained a reputation as a rather sweet, wholesome thing. She changed this popular view of herself when, at the age of 11, she played a streetwise, wine-guzzling ne'er-do-well in Martin Scorsese's *Alice Doesn't Live Here Anymore*. Her performance marked the arrival of a remarkably natural, major character actress, and Scorsese, obviously delighted, signed her up to play a 12-year-old hooker in *Taxi Driver*.

'I had never thought of making movies as anything but a nice little hobby that I would probably give up when I was 15,' Jodie explained, 'until

Jodie in her first Oscar-winning role, as rape victim Sarah Tobias in Jonathan Kaplan's disturbing **The Accused**

Taxi Driver. It was the first time that someone didn't say to me, "OK, now be yourself." I was asked to create a character.' But before she could play the part she was submitted to four hours of psychological tests at the insistence of the California State Welfare Department as, in her words, 'They had to see if my morals would hold up during filming,' adding: 'Kids talk like sailors today – and adults just don't want to know.'

1976 was a good year. *The Washington Post* declared her 'a prodigious movie talent in the making', and for her role in *Taxi Driver* she was voted best supporting actress by the National Society of Film Critics and the Los Angeles Film Critics. She was also bestowed with an Oscar nomination.

Taxi Driver was just one of three Jodie Foster films screened at the Cannes Film Festival that year. There was also Alan Parker's kid musical *Bugsy Malone*, in which she played Tallulah, a sexy nightclub singer; and the Canadian thriller *The Little Girl Who Lives Down the Lane*, in which she por-

trayed a pint-sized killer. For the latter she was required to undress for the camera, but the idea so repulsed her that her older sister, Connie, supplied the flesh. Jodie carped: 'I didn't think people wanted to see a girl my age naked.'

Her mother disagreed. As Jodie returned to the Disney stable to make such routine family pictures as *Freaky Friday* and *Candleshoe*, Evelyn Foster was pushing her daughter for the role of Vickie La Motta in Scorsese's *Raging Bull*. She decided that Jodie needed to prove her sex appeal, so she signed up photographer Emilio Lari to take some revealing pictures. According to Lari the actress 'was dead set against doing it. But she was only 15, after all. And she only came round after a lot of persuasion from her mother. But I thought, "Oh, my God, I'm in trouble." You see, Jodie was just a small fat baby, not very attractive or sexy.'

Nevertheless, the photographs were taken and years later came back to haunt the actress as they circulated the tabloids and girlie magazines. But she didn't win the role in *Raging Bull*, a film that was later voted best picture of the decade in innumerable critical polls.

In 1980, Jodie Foster gave up acting to go to college. No ordinary college, of course. She went to Yale University, where she studied literature (in particular, African-American works). 'I always thought all actresses were stupid,' she confessed, 'and believed if I went to college I wouldn't turn out that way. But I realized what I really wanted was to be an actress and there was nothing stupid about it at all. It's like going to another country – you learn about chopsticks and all that, but what you really learn about is yourself.'

Her self-knowledge was pushed to the limit when, on 30 March 1981, John Hinckley Jr shot President Ronald Reagan outside the Hilton Hotel in Washington. He did it, he said, to impress the love of his life – Jodie Foster. He had sent countless letters to the star, followed by death threats, and claimed he had seen *Taxi Driver* 15 times. She was on campus when the news broke, and in hours she became a media sensation. Her new celebrity and inadvertent notoriety unearthed fresh weirdoes, and one crazed fan, Michael Richardson, threatened to end her life. After an extensive search, the Secret Service picked him up in New York City and found a loaded gun on him.

Jodie Foster was shell-shocked and retreated inside herself. Security guards followed her round campus, as did reporters and fellow students looking for a scoop. The actress resorted to drinking and on one occasion was arrested for possession of cocaine. But, in spite of these distractions, Jodie earned her BA from Yale and graduated with honours. She could also now speak Italian and – thanks to her mother enrolling her at the Los Angeles Lycée Français – was fluent in French. In 1984, when she starred in Claude Chabrol's *Le Sang des Autres*, she looped all her own dialogue.

But her career was in a slump. In the virtually unseen *O'Hara's Wife* she was billed beneath Ed Asner and Mariette Hartley; she turned producer with an absurd Anglo-Australian-New Zealand costumer, *Mesmerized* (another dud), and she had a meagre role in the dreadful *Siesta*, in which she played a lascivious English socialite and was

required to lick Julian Sands all over. He later became her boyfriend.

She was good in *Five Corners*, an unusual British-financed drama set in the Bronx in 1964, with Tim Robbins and John Turturro; but she was wasted in the wordy, muddled *Stealing Home*, as Mark Harmon's dead girlfriend (but she was great in the flashbacks).

When Kelly McGillis turned down the role of Sarah Tobias, the rape victim

*Jodie Foster in her second Oscar-winning role, as FBI trainee Clarice Starling - in Jonathan Demme's **The Silence of the Lambs***

in Jonathan Kaplan's *The Accused*, Foster moved in for the kill. 'I did everything I could to get it,' the actress reveals. The film's producers, Stanley Jaffe and Sherry Lansing, could not see Foster in the role, but after gentle nudging from Kaplan agreed to let her screen test. She got it. And she got the part.

The Accused was the film Jodie Foster had been waiting for. Although second-billed to McGillis (who played Sarah's icy attorney), Foster dominated

the drama as the real-life good-time Charlene who flirts the night away in a seedy bar and then gets gang-raped on a pinball machine. The scene was harrowing to watch – and a nightmare to play. Kaplan reported: 'It was horrendous and really traumatized people. Actors were breaking down in tears. What Jodie said to me was, "Look, I'm going to be upset, OK, but don't worry about me. Your job is to take care of everyone else."' The scene took five days to film, but Jodie remembered little of the ordeal, with only her cuts and bruises to remind her.

On 29 March 1989, Jodie Foster ran up to the podium at the Shrine Auditorium in Los Angeles, and, accepting the Oscar from presenters Dustin Hoffman and Tom Cruise, she declared: 'This is such a big deal – and my life is so simple. There are very few things. There is love, and work, and family ...' She praised her mother and thanked her for 'making all my finger paintings seem like Picassos'.

Next, she starred in the wildly entertaining, eccentric thriller *Backtrack*, and was excellent as a sexy, doughty 'neon artist' hunted down and then romanced by Mafia hitman Dennis Hopper. Hopper also directed, but had his name removed from the credits when the producers re-cut his finished product. Foster ducked behind the camera herself and wrote and directed a short piece called *Hands of Time*, which was shown as part of the *Time-Life*/BBC documentary series *Americans*. This whet her appetite for bigger things, and she set about preparing her first full-length feature to direct – *Little Man Tate*. But first she needed to capitalize on her new kudos as an Oscar-winning actress.

Michelle Pfeiffer was first choice for the role of FBI trainee Clarice Starling in Orion's *The Silence of the Lambs*, but turned it down on the grounds that she found it 'too chilling'. Once again, Foster went into action. She tracked down the director, Jonathan Demme, in New York and told him she wanted to be his 'second choice'. She also revealed: 'It's not a flashy part, not the Oscar kind of part. But I don't make movies for flashy, juicy performances. I have to find something in the story that's part of my progress, part of this little train I'm on. In order for me to

*Jodie as one of the boys in Richard Donner's enormously successful **Maverick***

star in, direct and produce films for them. Sadly, the company's subsequent cash-flow problems stymied the deal. But Jodie wasn't finished yet.

The Silence of the Lambs opened to ecstatic reviews in 1991, and went on to gross a phenomenal $130 million at the US box-office alone. That same year also saw the actress, aged 28, receive a lifetime achievement award from the Boston Film Festival. And, later in 1991, *Little Man Tate* also opened to favourable reviews.

In the spring of 1992, Jodie Foster won her second Oscar (for *Lambs*), much to the surprise of insiders, who had predicted an incontestable win for Susan Sarandon in *Thelma and Louise*. And to cement the film's victory, it went on to win Oscars for best film, best director, best actor (Hopkins) and best screenplay.

Taking to the stage for a second time, Jodie laughed loudly before announcing: 'This has been such an incredible year! I'd like to thank all of the people in this industry who have respected my choices and who have not been afraid of the power and the dignity that that entitled me to.' And, after much distribution of gratitude, the actress glowed: 'and most of all I'd like to thank my mother Brandy, my friend, the person who has loved me so much and so well that she taught me in inimitable *Little Man Tate* fashion to fly away. Thank you.'

She then starred opposite Richard Gere in *Sommersby*, an elegant, gut-wrenching romantic drama based on the 1982 Gerard Depardieu vehicle *The Return of Martin Guerre*. Foster played Laurel Sommersby, a woman who falls in love with her own husband (Gere) when he returns home from the American Civil War after an absence of six years, only he is so changed by his experience (for the better) that he is charged with being an imposter. Foster and Gere generated considerable chemistry during their love scenes, and in spite of its pastoral background (a box-office no-no), *Sommersby* performed well commercially.

Then, when Meg Ryan baled out of the jokey western *Maverick*, Foster moved in – playing a determined con artist. However, in what seemed a desperate attempt to keep up with her male co-stars (Mel Gibson, James

Garner, James Coburn), the actress never seemed entirely at ease. Still, the movie went on to gross an astounding $101.6 million in the USA. She co-produced her next venture, *Nell*, a moving, intelligent and thought-provoking tale about an Appalachian recluse. Here, Jodie was simply brilliant as a woman who's impenetrable speech patterns attract the attention of the scientific world, which fails to see the gloriously unspoiled woman beneath the specimen. For the fourth time Foster was honoured with an Academy Award nomination, but this time lost out to Jessica Lange (for *Blue Sky*).

She was due to receive $5 million for her starring role in *Crisis in the Hot Zone*, an adaptation of the frightening real-life bestseller by Richard Preston about a killer virus that actually broke free just outside of Washington. But after much pre-production procrastination, the pressure of a similar movie in the pipeline (*Outbreak*) and the prospect of Foster's part being cut in order to build up Robert Redford's, the actress jumped ship. Instead, she took up megaphone duty again with the Thanksgiving comedy *Home for the*

*Yet another Oscar nomination: Jodie Foster in the title role of **Nell**, which she also produced*

spend three months on something, to understand it, it has to speak to me personally.'

In order for Clarice Starling to hold her own against the evil charisma of the film's other major character – top psychiatrist and serial killer Dr Hannibal Lecter, played by Anthony Hopkins – the film needed a strong actress, and Foster threw herself into the role. Adopting a Southern accent, she displayed an admirable mix of steel and brain, but never lost sight of her character's human centre. Demme noted it was: 'the first part Jodie's ever played in which she hasn't had to mask her intelligence'.

In the summer of 1990, Foster buckled down to directing and starring in *Little Man Tate*, and revealed a new talent. She played Dede Tate, a struggling waitress and single mother who finds she is rearing a seven-year-old child prodigy. Foster, a former child star and prodigy herself, knew her subject well, and produced a mature, thought-provoking work.

Following completion of the picture, Orion Pictures signed the actress to a two-year, first-look agreement to

Holidays. 'I had such a good experience on *Little Man Tate*,' she says, 'that directing is something I'm really interested in pursuing more now.' As it happens, the film, 'was a very healing experience for all of us. Each one of us had come from difficult films. Somehow, we just got together and it was like being a gift.' Indeed, juggling a variety of comedy styles and a stellar cast – Holly Hunter, Robert Downey Jr, Anne Bancroft, Geraldine Chaplin, Steve Guttenberg – Foster never pushed a joke too far, while using the film's humour to illuminate some painful home truths.

She was due to star opposite Michael Douglas in the psychological thriller *The Game*, but clashed with the producers over the details of her role. As reports filtered out that she had stormed off the movie, she hit back with a £36 million lawsuit claiming unfair dismissal. Meanwhile, she signed on as the star of the sci-fi thriller *Contact*, playing a radio astronomer who tunes into an extraterrestrial communiqué. Matthew McConaughey, James Woods, Rob Lowe and Angela Bassett co-starred under the direction of Robert Zemeckis.

FILMOGRAPHY

1972: *Napoleon and Samantha; Kansas City Bomber; Menace on the Mountain* (TV). 1973: *Rookie of the Year* (TV); *Tom Sawyer; One Little Indian*. 1974: *Smile, Jennie – You're Dead* (TV). 1975: *Alice Doesn't Live Here Anymore*. 1976: *Echoes of a Summer; Taxi Driver; Bugsy Malone; The Little Girl Who Lives Down the Lane*. 1977: *Freaky Friday; Il casotto* (UK: *The Beach Hut*); *Moi, fleur bleue* (US: *Stop Calling Me Baby!*); *Candleshoe*. 1980: *Carny; Foxes*. 1983: *O'Hara's Wife; Svengali* (TV). 1984: *The Hotel New Hampshire; Le Sang des Autres (The Blood of Others)* (TV). 1986: *Mesmerized* (also co-produced). 1987: *Siesta*. 1988: *Five Corners; Stealing Home; The Accused*. 1989: *Backtrack* (UK: *Catchfire*). 1991: *The Silence of the Lambs; Little Man Tate* (also directed). 1992: *Shadows and Fog* (cameo). 1993: *Sommersby; It Was a Wonderful Life* (narrated). 1994: *Maverick; Nell* (also produced). 1995: *Home for the Holidays* (directed and co-produced only). 1997: *Contact*.

MICHAEL J. FOX

In John Badham's *The Hard Way*, Michael J. Fox played an extremely successful, very popular and unimaginably rich film star who wants to be taken seriously, so he teams up with a real-life cop (James Woods) to find out what it's *really* like on the streets of the Bronx – all the better to prepare for a role that will change his image. *The Hard Way* was a fast-paced, funny and thoroughly enjoyable action-comedy full of in-jokes. In fact, it was a typical Michael J. Fox movie. Fox, who was an extremely successful, very popular and unimaginably rich film star, had himself been trying to change his image by

*The debonair lycanthrope: Michael J. Fox with Susan Ursitti in his 1985 **Teen Wolf***

starring in such gritty, dramatic films as *Light of Day*, *Bright Lights, Big City* and *Casualties of War*. But they had all bombed at the box-office. In short, Michael J. Fox needed to return to the genre for which he was known.

Also, *The Hard Way* surfaced during the Gulf War, and at the time Fox felt: 'People desperately needed to laugh.' And, with the birth of his son, Sam Michael, on 30 May 1989, his priorities had changed. He had a family to provide for, a new life to live. As he put it: 'To be a happy, healthy, family-orientated person is more important than trying to be the Boy Prince of Hollywood.'

But his fame was hard to escape. His Vermont wedding to actress Tracy Pollan on 16 July 1988 turned into a media circus. A *National Enquirer* journalist attempted to abduct the bride's grandparents by car to quiz them on their wedding plans. Dozens of

reporters offered bribes to locals and disguised themselves as tourists. Others camouflaged themselves in nearby woods. Six press helicopters hovered over the 'secret' ceremony. One security specialist estimated that the tabloids invested almost $250,000 in covering the nuptials, but thanks to a decoy car ('complete with tin cans tied to the fender and a slip of wedding gown caught in the door', said Fox), they failed to get their story. Shortly afterwards, Michael J. and his new bride were recovering from the media onslaught on a private beach at Martha's Vineyard. Unbeknown to them, a frogman emerged from the sea with a waterproof telephoto lens and

took a series of photographs. The pictures appeared in publications throughout the world. The media had won after all.

But why all the attention? Well, Fox was one of those rare personalities who had successfully crossed over from TV celebrity to Hollywood glory. For seven years he starred in the sitcom *Family Ties*, for which he won three Emmy awards, the highest accolade TV can bestow. On film, he was equally successful (if not more so), starring in the highest-grossing movie of 1985, *Back to the Future*, as well as its two sequels and such hits as *Teen Wolf* and *The Secret of My Success*. In 1985 he was voted the fourth biggest box-office draw in America, and two years later was placed third (after Eddie Murphy and Michael Douglas). For the period 1989–90, according to *Forbes* magazine, he earned $33 million. Ironically, Fox was only paid $250,000 for the first

Back to the Future, but was able to ask $5 million for each sequel. He also had a lucrative deal with Pepsi, the joys of which he promoted in a number of TV and cinema ads. Asked why he undertook such an artistically demeaning enterprise, he answered with typical self-deprecation: 'I drink it. They give it to me free, so it'd be stupid not to.'

On top of that, Fox cut a deal with Universal Pictures which enabled him to make his own films and to move into television production. Indeed, in 1991 he directed a segment ('The Trap') of the HBO horror omnibus

Michael J. Fox in his most famous role, Marty McFly, in the phenomenally successful **Back to the Future**

Tales from the Crypt, which featured Bruce McGill, Bruno Kirby, Teri Garr and Carroll Baker. Later, he was due to direct the theatrical feature *Thirty Wishes*, in collaboration with Universal and his own production company, Snowback Productions, although this fell through. In his spare time, he acted as National Chairman of Public Awareness for the Spina Bifida Association and worked on his skills as a modern father.

Michael Andrew Fox was born on 9 June 1961 in Edmonton, Canada, the fourth son (of five children) of an army officer and a payroll clerk. As his family moved from one army base to another, his childhood was fragmented, and he dreamed of becoming a professional hockey player and/or a rock guitarist.

While living in Vancouver, he played rhythm guitar in a local band and discovered acting. At 15, he was cast as a ten-year-old in the Canadian TV series *Leo and Me*, and more or less remained typecast for the rest of his career as a younger man than himself (he is, after all, 5'4").

At 17, he dropped out of school and started working regularly in local TV, theatre and radio. He made his film debut in the critically celebrated TV movie *Letters From Frank*, the story of a newspaper man replaced by a computer. It was his veteran co-stars, Art Carney and Maureen Stapleton, who suggested he try his luck in Hollywood and, in 1980, aged 18, Michael Fox headed south. Not long after his arrival in LA, he secured a small part in a dire Disney film, *Midnight Madness*, and became a regular on the TV series *Palmerstown USA*, playing Willie-Joe. He also auditioned for the Timothy Hutton role in *Ordinary People*, but clashed with the film's director, Robert Redford.

A fan of the character actor Michael J. Pollard, Fox adopted the 'J' in his name, and started popping up in such TV fare as *Trapper John, MD* and *Lou Grant*. However, following the Screen Actors' Guild strike of 1981, he found himself in debt to the tune of $10,000. Salvation arrived in the shape of NBC's sitcom *Family Ties*, the story of caring, liberal parents played by Michael Gross and Meredith Baxter Birney. Fox was their Nixon-worshipping son, Alex P. Keaton, and he stole the show from them.

Gary David Goldberg, the series' creator, volunteered: 'Even if Michael was onstage for just a few minutes, it was electric. We'd look around and say, "Why is the audience leaning forward?" Michael has an ability to let the audience in, to get people to breathe with him. I don't want to say we were fighting his stardom, but it wasn't what we had in mind.'

The show had been going for three years when Eric Stoltz was fired from *Back to the Future*. Although Fox was already up to his eyes in TV work, he signed on to play Marty McFly in the movie, produced by Steven Spielberg and directed by Robert Zemeckis. During the day, he worked on his sitcom between 10 a.m. and 6 p.m., and

then rushed off to film *Back to the Future* until 2 a.m. His schedule was exhausting, but Fox was determined not to miss out on the opportunity of playing McFly, the affable all-American teenager transported back in time to his parents' courting days of 1955.

The film was a deserved success (it grossed $350 million worldwide) and coincided with the release of *Teen Wolf*, a low-budget comedy about a high school student who becomes a success with the girls when they discover he's a werewolf. The film's concept was more imaginative than its delivery, but Fox's

Sending himself up rotten, Fox plays a movie star researching the role of a cop in John Badham's entertaining **The Hard Way**

amiable performance made it a hit – so much so that it spawned an animated TV series and a sequel.

Tired of his image as a lightweight comic actor, Fox next tried something heavier – Paul Schrader's *Light of Day*, a tough Cleveland-set story of rock 'n' roll and domestic blues. However, the film was neither a critical nor a box-office success, and the only good reviews going went to co-stars Joan Jett and Gena Rowlands. 'I did *Light of Day* for the wrong reasons,' Fox admits now. 'I did it because I wanted to do something that wasn't expected of me, and I wanted to do a dramatic film and goof around and play the guitar for five months.'

He returned with a bang in *The Secret of My Success*, playing a country

Kansas boy who makes good on Wall Street, defeats his crooked uncle and runs away with the heart of the drop-dead gorgeous Helen Slater. This was designer slapstick at its slickest, with all its commercial ingredients polished to a high shine. Fox himself performed with such joyful energy that one couldn't help but sit back and relish the proceedings.

Then the actor tried to be taken seriously again. He played yuppie cocaine addict Jamie Conway in *Bright Lights, Big City*, a big movie based on Jay McInerney's 'important novel' about alienated New York youth. Tom Cruise had originally been sought for the starring role and, quite frankly, would have made a more convincing Conway. Fox retaliated: 'My natural response after I do something successful is to do the antithetical thing. Because if you only do what you do best and you fail, you're screwed. But if you do something that you're not sure about and you succeed, it's from heaven.'

He was serious again in Brian De Palma's brutal but simplistic *Casualties of War*, playing a real-life combat GI who brings his unit to court martial for the kidnap, rape and murder of a Vietnamese village girl. Sean Penn co-starred as Fox's commanding officer and was about as mean as Fox's private was saintly. Frankly, *Casualties of War* just didn't seem convincing, even if the carnage was.

In 1989, Fox filmed the two sequels to *Back to the Future* back-to-back, reuniting him with director Zemeckis and producer Spielberg. In the first, McFly and his faithful companion, Doctor Emmett Brown (Christopher Lloyd), are transported into the year 2015, where McFly confronts his own future. Fox had extra fun playing McFly at 47, as well as his own son and daughter! In *Part III*, he and Brown find themselves shuttled back to 1885, where Fox dons a stetson, buckles on his guns and adopts the appropriate pseudonym 'Clint Eastwood'. Audiences quibbled over which was the better of the two sequels, but whichever way you looked at it, they were both first-rate exercises in escapism.

Next came *The Hard Way*, a box-office disappointment, and then Fox used his clout to get *Doc Hollywood* off

the ground. 'It was the first movie I was able to con a studio into making,' the actor revealed proudly. 'It's very low key, there are no car chases and it's just a sweet story. I told them, "Trust me."' Indeed, *Doc Hollywood* was a delightful romantic comedy with buckets of charm to spare, in which a would-be plastic surgeon finds himself waylaid in a South Carolina backwater. Fox was agreeable as ever, finding true love with a feisty local ambulance driver (Julie Warner) while getting his values fine-tuned. Also, with a US gross of $52 million, it showed that with the right star, a gentle comedy like this could make money.

Next, in Barry Sonnenfeld's inoffensive, undemanding *For Love or Money*, he played the ambitious employee of a grand New York hotel asked to 'babysit' a beautiful young woman (Gabrielle Anwar) in return for a loan to start his own business. As the can-do charmer, Fox was as watchable as ever and was backed up by a snappy script, classy direction and a fine supporting cast. He then returned to Canada for James Lapine's *Life With Mikey*, a flop co-starring Cyndi Lauper, and partnered Kirk Douglas in the predictable, lightweight but frequently funny *Greedy*, a comedy loosely adapted from Dickens' *Martin Chuzzlewit*.

He joined the ensemble cast of Woody Allen's TV debut, *Don't Drink the Water* (as the inept son of the ambassador to a communist regime), and more or less stayed in supporting vein from then on. He contributed a priceless, scatological cameo in Wayne Wang and Paul Auster's *Blue in the Face* (going unrecognized to many critics), and had little to do as the domestic policy adviser to *The American President* (a role he modelled on George Stephanopoulos), which was a hit. He had the lead in Peter Jackson's black horror comic *The Frighteners* (a New Zealand-American co-production), which was poorly received, and he then took another supporting role, in Tim Burton's *Mars Attacks!* (as a TV journalist who, literally, loses his hand to Sarah Jessica Parker).

With his last successful star vehicle a distant memory, Fox wasn't letting preconceived ideas of accomplishment get to him. Apparently relishing the mantle of fatherhood (besides his son, Sam, he

now had twin daughters, Schuyler and Aquinnah), he returned to the medium that made him a star. In ABC TV's sitcom *Spin City*, he played spin doctor Mike Flaherty, whose job it is is to varnish the image of New York's doltish mayor (Barry Bostwick) – a character not a million miles removed from *Family Ties*' Alex P. Keaton. Fox served as executive producer himself (in collaboration with Gary David Goldberg), which may account for the show's tendency to over-play the jokes. However, according to Fox: 'Nothing comes close to being as fun and fulfilling as this. It's 1996 and I'm still here, still making a good living and having a good time. Now I'm more comfortable and at peace with who I am. The greatest part of that is that I'm not the centre of my life anymore. My family is.'

FILMOGRAPHY

1979: *Letters From Frank* (TV). 1980: *Midnight Madness*. 1982: *Class of 1984*. 1983: *High School USA* (TV). 1984: *Poison Ivy* (TV). 1985: *Back to the Future*; *Teen Wolf*. 1986: *Family Ties Vacation* (TV). 1987: *Light of Day*; *The Secret of My Success*; *Dear America* (voice only). 1988: *Bright Lights, Big City*; *Casualties of War*. 1989: *Back to the Future Part II*. 1990: *Back To the Future Part III*. 1991: *The Hard Way*; *Tales from the Crypt* (TV; also directed); *Doc Hollywood*. 1993: *Homeward Bound: The Incredible Journey* (voice only); *For Love or Money* (UK: *The Concierge*); *Where the Rivers Flow North*; *Life With Mikey* (UK: *Give Us a Break*). 1994: *Greedy*; *Don't Drink the Water* (TV); *Coldblooded* (also produced). 1995: *Blue in the Face*; *The American President*. 1996: *Homeward Bound II: Lost in San Francisco* (voice only); *The Frighteners*; *Mars Attacks!*

Psychic conman: Michael J. Fox in New Zealand for Peter Jackson's scare fest, **The Frighteners**

G

ANDY GARCIA

*As Vincent Mancicni, nephew of Al Pacino's Michael Corleone, in Francis Coppola's **The Godfather Part III***

Andy Garcia has been on the brink of stardom for more years than he'd care to remember. After *The Untouchables*, he was on everybody's lips as the next Al Pacino. Then came *Black Rain*, whose producer, Sherry Lansing, promised it would make him 'a major, major star'. *The Godfather Part III*, though, was the film that would discharge him into the stellar stratosphere. Well, almost. And then of course there was Stephen Frears' *Hero*, with Dustin Hoffman and Geena Davis. What a cast! What a director! What a concept! It was a bomb.

Garcia was also getting a reputation as a support system. He says of his colleague, Michael Douglas, who starred in *Black Rain*: 'Every time I see him he says, "So when are you gonna carry a movie? Come *on*. You guys come in, work two scenes, steal the movie!"' Sure enough, Andy's co-stars were more famous than he, the real big boys

of Hollywood: Douglas, Kurt Russell, Jeff Bridges, Kevin Costner, Sean Connery, Richard Gere, Al Pacino, Dustin Hoffman ... But Garcia was holding his own corner, projecting the steely charisma of a star-regent.

Andy Garcia is also extremely selective when it comes to choosing scripts. 'There's a danger,' he says, 'of young actors being in total submission to the industry, in accepting the audition process as a do-or-die situation, where it can affect your emotional state. The only way to survive the process is by concentrating on your craft, on your passion for the work.'

Garcia is passionate about his work alright, although he can be spectacularly modest at the same time. 'I've survived,' he admits of his stubbornly burgeoning career. And yet if Garcia had refused to ever play a cop, that career would be non-existent. He's rather good at playing men on the right side of the law ('I do *look* the part.'), although his first showy role was as a cocaine dealer, and his most famous part that of the psychotic Vincent Mancini in *The Godfather Part III*.

Andres Arturo Garcia Menendez was born on 12 April, 1956, in Havana, Cuba, the youngest of three children. His father, known as 'The Mayor', was a lawyer who owned considerable property, while his mother, Amelie, taught English. When the Americans invaded in the notorious Bay of Pigs debacle, Amelie and her children

boarded a plane for Miami. At Miami Beach Senior High, Andres Garcia excelled at sport and admitted: 'If I could have made a living as a basketball player, I would have.' However, following a bout of mononucleosis, he was knocked sideways, and at a mere 5'11" he was too short for college basketball anyway.

Instead, he turned to drama, left school in 1977 and faffed around in the Caribbean before moving to Los Angeles to take his craft seriously. In the tradition of all future stars, he became a waiter – and started getting bits parts here and there. While performing with an improvisational group, he played a young gang leader in the TV pilot of *Hill Street Blues* and got small roles in the features *Blue Skies Again*, *A Night in Heaven* and *The Lonely Guy*.

If his professional life wasn't exactly going places ('I was rejected,' he says with some bile), his personal life was. He met, courted and then married Maria Victoria (Marivi for short) back home in Miami. Ironically, that was where Phillip Borsos was filming *The Mean Season* with Kurt Russell and Mariel Hemingway, and the director signed Garcia to play Ray Martinez, a Hispanic homicide detective. This led to another sizeable role in Hal Ashby's *8 Million Ways To Die*, in which the actor played Angel Maldonado, an urbane, ponytailed cocaine lord.

Garcia's villainous turn impressed

*Garcia with Geena Davis in Stephen Frears's very funny, thought-provoking **Hero***

Brian De Palma, who was then casting the role of Frank Nitti, the Mafia hitman in *The Untouchables*. In order to avoid typecasting, Garcia asked if he could play the good guy instead. De Palma agreed, and the actor found himself billed alongside Kevin Costner and *above* Sean Connery and Robert De Niro. Garcia was the Italian cop, George Stone – a.k.a. Giuseppe Pedri – and his opening scene was a classic. Connery and Costner are recruiting crack shots for their team of 'untouchables' to combat Al Capone. Connery, unimpressed with Stone's pseudonym, calls him a 'wop'. Garcia whips out a gun, pushes it into Connery's Adam's apple and slowly – hesitantly – murmurs: 'You stinking Irish ... *pig*.' With a flippant 'He'll do!', Connery enlists him on the spot.

The film was a colossal hit for Paramount Pictures, and the studio took note of Garcia as a man worth grooming for stardom.

He won top-billing in the dire British-Australian political thriller *American Roulette*, and took a supporting role in the fact-based, hard-hitting *Stand and Deliver* – as a favour to its director, Ramon Menendez (no relation). He was then top-billed again, and made an engaging leading man, in the cable movie *Clinton and Nadine*. Garcia was Clinton, a magnetic gun-smuggler; Ellen Barkin was Nadine, a classy prostitute. Jerry Schatzberg, who directed, offered: 'It's very difficult not to get along with Andy.'

Paramount gave him second-billing to Michael Douglas in Ridley Scott's *Black Rain*, a big-budget, hard-hitting thriller set in Osaka, Japan. Garcia was another cop, Charlie Vincent, who is brutally beheaded by a gang of Yakuza thugs. The role of Sergeant Raymond Avila, a new recruit in LA's *Internal Affairs* department, was written specially for him. Richard Gere played the rogue cop Garcia has to tame, and it was a welcome switch in stereotypes to see the Hispanic cop on the side of the angels.

Paramount was also packaging Francis Ford Coppola's third instalment in *The Godfather* saga, and there was much speculation in the press as to who was going to play the young Vincent Mancini, heir to the bloody Corleone throne. Such names as

Sylvester Stallone and John Travolta had been bandied about, while Alec Baldwin and Matt Dillon looked like more serious contenders. Even Robert De Niro was after the part, but was dismissed as being too old. Garcia got it, and was paid his first million for the honour.

Family man: *Garcia with Meg Ryan and family (Casey Green, Tina Majorino) in Luis Mandoki's heart-stopping* **When a Man Loves a Woman**

He was then brought in to replace Nick Nolte in George Miller's *Lorenzo's Oil*, as Augusto Odone, the father who struggles to find a cure for his dying six-year-old son. But Garcia's interpretation of the gentle Italian banker grated with Miller's vision of the character (he knew the real Augusto). According to the director, Garcia 'went off on a completely different track. It would have meant the story would have had to shift enormously.' As it happens, Nolte suddenly became available again and Garcia dropped out of the project in the spring of 1991. Instead, he did a couple of cameos – in the ill-fated *A Show of Force*, with Amy Irving, and in the Kenneth Branagh hit *Dead Again* – and he then turned down the lead in *The Mambo Kings* (the role went to Armand Assante). Next, he played *another* cop – in Bruce Robinson's atmospheric, intelligent thriller *Jennifer Eight*. This time he had a romance on the side (with a blind Uma Thurman) as an LA sergeant who moves to a small northern Californian town to escape the rat race. There he stumbles onto a vicious serial killer who specializes in dicing

up blind girls. Robinson cast Garcia, he says, because: 'Andy has a very potent star quality – and I thought he would be very interesting in this country environment.'

The actor then teamed up with Dustin Hoffman and Geena Davis in the satirical *Hero*, directed by Stephen Frears – the *sixth* English director Garcia had worked with. Frears originally saw the part of John Bubber – a homeless Vietnam vet who falsely claims a hero's reward – as a vehicle for Kevin Costner. But Garcia's vision of Bubber as a man 'propelled into a role by destiny' impressed the director and he got the part. He'd also gone up for the Hoffman role – but that is another story. Although a critical success, the film was not embraced by the public, which was surprising. It was both funny and poignant and raised a lot of important issues, not least the dichotomy of good and evil in all of us. It should have been the movie that turned Garcia's career around.

Next, he was in another terrific movie, teamed opposite Meg Ryan in the romantic drama *When a Man Loves a Woman*. This time it was a hit – and Garcia was top-billed. A startlingly truthful examination of a marriage sliding into hell, the film boasted sensationally credible performances from Garcia and Ryan. In fact, seldom has a major American picture dared to give its characters so much room in which to pause, think and breathe.

His next outing, *Things To Do In Denver When You're Dead*, received even better reviews and became something of a cult attraction. Garcia played the smooth, inappropriately named Jimmy the Saint, a man who has fallen foul of the law more times than he'd care to remember. However, he's now an upstanding member of the community in Denver, Colorado, operating a bizarre video business in which he records parting words of comfort from the dying. However, when The Man With the Plan (Christopher Walken) enlists him in a little 'action', Jimmy's life takes a nasty turn. Written with a superb ear for the offbeat line, the film manoeuvred its predictable path with a fresh, quirky step.

Garcia had also teamed up with Michelle Pfeiffer for Disney's classroom drama *Dangerous Minds*, playing her ex-husband. However, Disney decided that his role hampered the impetus of the narrative, so his contribution was completely junked. Another blow came with the disastrous *Steal Big, Steal Little*, a tiresome, whimsical comedy in which the actor attempted to extend his range by playing twin brothers of opposing natures – evil and saintly. His two stock expressions of benevolent smile and stony stare did little to resolve the audience's confusion over which brother was which.

Then, following his starring role in Sidney Lumet's New York-set drama *Night Falls On Manhattan* and the Puerto Rico thriller *Death in Granada*, he made his directorial debut on *The Lost City*, starring himself, Robert Duvall, Edward James Olmos and Isabella Rossellini.

FILMOGRAPHY

1981: *Hill Street Blues* (TV; pilot). 1983: *Blue Skies Again; A Night in Heaven*. 1984: *The Lonely Guy*. 1985: *The Mean Season*. 1986: *8 Million Ways To Die*. 1987: *The Untouchables*. 1988: *American Roulette; Stand and Deliver; Clinton and Nadine* (a.k.a. *Blood Money*). 1989: *Black Rain*. 1990: *A Show of Force; Internal Affairs; The Godfather Part III*. 1991: *Dead Again*. 1992: *Jennifer Eight; Hero* (UK: *Accidental Hero*). 1994: *When a Man Loves a Woman*. 1995: *Things To Do In Denver When You're Dead; Steal Big, Steal Little*. 1997: *Night Falls On Manhattan; Death in Granada; The Lost City* (also directed); *Hoodlum; Desperate Measures*. 1998: *The Scalper*.

*Bad egg: Garcia as the bad brother in **Steal Big, Steal Little***

H

Woody Harrelson

Few actors have made the transition from TV to the large screen with much success, which makes Woody Harrelson's achievement all the more remarkable. He had only done one small film part when he landed a supporting role in NBC's *Cheers* during its fourth season. He was brought in to replace the regular character of 'Coach' (played by Nicholas Colassanto, who died in 1985), and he had mixed feelings about doing TV. His dream was to appear on Broadway. Still, it was a part, and the show was a winner, so he took it. He was 23 when he first played Woody Boyd, the slow-witted barman who could turn a non sequitur into a jewel of wisdom – and then miss the point. And he was outstanding. His naive charm proved to be the perfect antidote to the barbed asides of Rhea Perlman and the roguish scheming of Ted Danson, and in 1987 Harrelson won the American Comedy Award and in 1989 the Emmy as 'Outstanding Supporting Actor'.

Woody the Emmy-winner feels a strong allegiance to Woody the barman, which probably accounts for the character's lasting success. He may be dumb, but he's no instant-mix caricature. 'Actually, I've always considered

Woody naive, not dumb,' the actor argued. 'If anything, he's an idiot savant. He has an amazing knowledge of trivia and can beat anybody at chess.'

Woody, the actor, was a savant himself when he started courting Hollywood. He started with a well-placed cameo – as a crazy TV producer in Steve Martin's hip, hilarious *LA Story* – and followed it with a good character role in *Doc Hollywood*, as the redneck companion of Bridget Fonda and rival to Michael J. Fox. Fox was already a friend from their days on the Paramount lot, where Fox was shooting NBC's *Family Ties*. Harrelson was rather good at making influential allies. When he dated the actress Carol Kane, ten years his senior, he felt at home in the company of her intimates, Jack Nicholson and Anjelica Huston, and later, when he appeared opposite Glenn Close in the play *Brooklyn Laundry*, he became more than close to his co-star. Despite their 14-year age difference (and Woody's reputation as a brawler and womanizer), the distinguished actress (and mother) accepted his proposal for marriage. However, the engagement was short-lived.

Harrelson was also careful when it came to the parts he played on screen. 'I have turned down roles – like a rapist, once – in which I would be too different from Woody. I've looked for parts that are an appropriate transition, like my character in *Doc Hollywood*. He had some of Woody's innocence, but he was *considerably* more in touch with his sexuality.' Indeed, the first starring film role the actor accepted was yet another variation on the dimwit. In the basketball comedy *White Men Can't Jump*, the actor played Billy Hoyle, a sartorial disaster area in baggy shorts and sagging socks, who used his nerdish image to con black jocks into competing with him on the court. Hoyle is, of course, a phenomenal bounder in both senses of the word, proving that at least one white man *can* jump. The film was an enormous success, grossing $19 million in its opening week in the USA, and clocking up $70 million in less than three months. Thanks to his astute planning, Woody Harrelson was a movie star.

The second of three boys, Woodrow T. Harrelson was born on 23 July 1961 in Midland, Texas, into a strict

Presbyterian family. When he was seven, his father left home and his mother moved the family to Lebanon, Ohio, where Woody was looked after by his grandmother and great-grandmother. His father's departure, the actor says, 'didn't seem to make much of a difference,' but when Harrelson Snr was imprisoned in 1982 for two life sentences (for the assassination of a federal court judge), Woody believed in his innocence. 'The truth will out,' he says simply.

As a child, his great loves were reading, writing poetry and picking fights. 'I wanted to be a minister,' he says, 'I was the head of the youth group and used to lead Bible studies. But I also fought a lot.' He then became interested in drama, did the requisite number of school plays and, on a Presbyterian scholarship, enrolled at Hanover College in Indiana, where he majored in theatre arts and English. It was around this time that he lost faith in organized religion and dedicated himself to a career in the theatre. Moving to New York, he landed an understudy job in Neil Simon's *Biloxi Blues* and, in 1986, he made his film debut in the comedy *Wildcats*, in which

*A conman with legs: Woody with Wesley Snipes in the surprise hit **White Men Can't Jump***

he was 13th-billed as Krushinski and got to hoist football coach Goldie Hawn onto his shoulders. Interestingly, the film also marked the screen debut of Wesley Snipes, Woody's co-star in the far more successful sports comedy *White Men Can't Jump*.

Cheers followed *Wildcats*, and Woody embarked on his career as rabble-rouser and womanizer. Besides his 18 months with Carol Kane, the actor

consequential things in life. For starters, he now puts his spirituality above his sexuality. 'That's a big step,' he concedes, 'because the only thing sacred about my physicality prior to this was the frequency of it.' He is now an outspoken critic of the American government, was an active campaigner against the Gulf War and, like Ted Danson, is contributing considerable effort on behalf of such environmental groups as

ruckus when he jumped at the chance to star in Oliver Stone's *Natural Born Killers*, from a white-hot script by Quentin Tarantino. Michael Madsen, who played Mr Blonde in Tarantino's *Reservoir Dogs*, thought he was a definite for the lead, then fired his manager and agent when Harrelson got the role. But that was just the beginning. The film, the story of a glamorous white-trash couple (Harrelson and Juliette Lewis) who go on a killing spree, was intended as a satire on the promotion of violence by the media. However, Oliver Stone's multi-media freak show – employing tilted camera work, black-and-white photography, video, animation and sitcom inserts – was virtually unwatchable. Still, some people watched it – and liked what they saw. At least ten real-life murders, committed between New Mexico and France, were attributed to the film. One 14-year-old boy accused of cutting off the head of a 13-year-old girl allegedly told friends that he wanted to 'be famous like the *Natural Born Killers*'. Somewhat nettled by all this negative publicity, Warner Brothers decided to delay the release of the film in Britain, resulting in even more negative attention. And, as any film distributor knows, any publicity is good publicity.

James Ferman, director of the British Board of Film Classification, ventured: 'To be honest, I'm not sure what all the fuss is about. Every other board in Europe has passed it.' And in his introduction to the BBFC's annual report, the board's president, the Earl of Harewood, wrote: 'The Board delayed its certification long enough to research the facts and found no significant basis for the claims. When the film opened in Britain in February [1995], those months of media attention added a great deal to the box-office takings, but by that time the press seemed as bored by the issue as they were by the film itself ... Britain appears to be the only country in which the risk of anti-social influence was seriously argued.'

In the interim, Woody Harrelson – sporting a shaved head and sunglasses – leered from every corner of the media. Woody Boyd had become a bloodthirsty icon.

Next, Harrelson starred opposite Kiefer Sutherland in the painfully inept *The Cowboy Way*, a farce about two

*Pimp or lover? Woody Harrelson as Demi Moore's deserted husband in Adrian Lyne's efficient romance, **Indecent Proposal***

was romantically linked with Brooke Shields, Moon Unit Zappa and Ally Sheedy. Earlier, when he was understudying *Biloxi Blues*, he had married the daughter of Neil Simon, Nancy, when they happened to be in Tijuana, Mexico. Later, the actor explained: 'The whole point was doing something just for the fun of it. I do a lot of things on a whim that maybe wouldn't be kosher.' However, by 1993 it looked as if he had finally settled down when, on 26 February, his girlfriend, Laura Louie, gave birth to a seven pound baby girl, Deni Montana.

He also indulged his love of the theatre, writing the baseball-themed one-act play *2 on 2*, in which he starred, in a double-bill with Edward Albee's *The Zoo Story*. He was also showing an interest in matters beyond showbusiness, sparked by a trip to Machu Picchu, the mountain city in Peru which has become something of a spiritual mecca. He came back a changed man, took up vegetarianism and began exploring, for him, the more

the Earth Communications Office and the American Oceans Campaign.

Film-wise, his career was going from strength to strength, although not always without a hitch. He was signed to play the part of Benny in MGM-Pathe's *Benny & Joon*, opposite Johnny Depp and Mary Stuart Masterson, when he pulled out to take the role of Demi Moore's husband in Adrian Lyne's Paramount thriller *Indecent Proposal*. MGM head Alan Ladd Jr hit back with a lawsuit indicting Harrelson, Paramount, Lyne and the film's producer, Sherry Lansing. MGM claimed that Harrelson had signed a pay-or-play contract to star in their film, and that the actor, Paramount, Lansing and Lyne 'knowingly and wilfully entered into an agreement or agreements whereby they conspired to induce Harrelson to breach their contractual obligation to Pathe and/or deny the existence of such a contract'. Eventually, Aidan Quinn was signed up for the role Harrelson had vacated.

Next, the actor created another

King of controversy: Woody and Juliette Lewis as Oliver Stone's **Natural Born Killers**

The People vs. Larry Flynt: *Woody with Courtney Love in the role that won him his first Oscar nomination*

gant cancer specialist who is kidnapped by a New Age hoodlum, but the film died at the box-office. Then, when Michael Keaton bowled out of *Kingpin* (to take on four roles in *Multiplicity*), Harrelson moved in. As it happens, Harrelson was a former roommate of the director, Peter Farrelly, who was still glowing from the success of *Dumb & Dumber*. However, *Kingpin*, a dark comedy which featured Harrelson as a one-armed, former bowling champion, failed to score a strike.

Then there was *The People vs Larry Flynt*. Long in gestation, the project about the *Hustler* publisher and First Amendment activist was originally to have been directed by Oliver Stone, but the filmmaker passed when he got bogged down with *Nixon*. Instead, Milos Forman (*One Flew Over the Cuckoo's Nest*) climbed on board what was to be his first picture in seven years, and Forman chose Harrelson to play Flynt. Says Harrelson: 'Initially, when I heard of the project, I thought, Larry Flynt? I thought he was kind of a slimeball. But I was flattered, almost to the point of being aghast, that Milos wanted me. There aren't that many poor white-trash guys working with a sense of humour, maybe. I don't know. Poor white-trash, that's me, all the way. You can't take that out of somebody, can you?'

Harrelson embraced the part with brio, going so far as to actually move in with the real Larry Flynt. 'Once I was comfortable with Larry,' he says, 'I was able to ask him some very pointed questions. He always gave me the most candid reply, even to questions that would insult most people. With Larry, you may not like the fact that he's a pornographer, and you may not respect some of his outrageous antics, but you have to respect his honesty. He says what he thinks, even when it's crazy.' At last, Harrelson had found a role that would win him the respect of his critics, and to prove the point he was nominated for an Oscar as best actor. He then joined Robert De Niro and Dustin Hoffman in Barry Levinson's comedy-drama *Wag the Dog*.

When he is not acting, romancing or saving the planet, the star performs and writes songs for his own band, Manly Moondog and the Three Kool Kats.

rednecks who clash with city slickers, and then he was paid $5.5 million to re-team with Wesley Snipes in *Money Train*. An agreeable, light-hearted comedy-thriller, *Money Train* attracted almost as much controversy as *Natural Born Killers* when two real-life psychos re-enacted a scene from the movie (in which a subway cashier is set alight).

In Michael Cimino's *The Sunchaser*, the actor was on good form as an arro-

Kingpin: *Woody in the part Michael Keaton turned down*

FILMOGRAPHY

1986: *Wildcats*. 1987: *Bay Coven* (TV). 1989: *Casualities of War* (bit part). 1991: *LA Story* (cameo); *Doc Hollywood*; *Killer Instinct* (video); *Ted and Venus*. 1992: *White Men Can't Jump*. 1993: *Indecent Proposal*. 1994: *I'll Do Anything* (cameo); *Natural Born Killers*; *The Cowboy Way*. 1995: *Money Train*. 1996: *Kingpin*; *The Sunchaser*; *The People vs Larry Flynt*. 1997: *Welcome to Sarajevo*; *Wag the Dog*. 1998: *Palmetto*; *The Thin Red Line*; *The HiLo County*.

ETHAN HAWKE

Ethan Hawke is not so much a star as a useful leading man. He is an accomplished actor, displaying the same range of sensitivity as River Phoenix did – but without the quirks. He has made few films, yet they are notable for their critical kudos. Even the teenage comedy *Mystery Date* is better than its title would suggest, being a dark, inspired exercise in mistaken identity.

Jeremy Irons, who played Hawke's professor in the critically lauded *Waterland*, volunteered: 'Ethan is great. He's like all of the best actors. You can't tell when he starts and when he stops. And he's far too good-looking for his age!'

Ethan Hawke was an only child born in Austin, Texas, on 6 November 1970. His parents divorced when he was young, his mother moving to Connecticut, Vermont, Georgia and Brooklyn, before settling in Princeton, New Jersey, with a new husband.

*Ethan as Sgt. Will Knott in Keith Gordon's masterly **A Midnight Clear***

There, she produced two more children, providing Ethan with a stepbrother and stepsister. He was eight years old when he saw a production of *Annie* and decided to become an actor, making his stage debut in *St Joan* and, at 14, landing the lead in Joe Dante's sci-fi fable *Explorers*, which, as it happens, also marked the theatrical film debut of River Phoenix. 'It was such an amazing experience to be 13 in California, the lead in a movie,' the actor recalled later, but, 'when it got released, I went from being a big celebrity in my town to being the big fool in my town in a period of about two days.'

Although *Explorers* was exceptionally well acted by its young cast and full of inventive twists and sly movie references, the film's increasing departure from reality (not to mention an overblown climax) sent it spinning to an early grave. At 14, Ethan Hawke retired from acting: 'I had a rough time after *Explorers*, so I wasn't really interested in the theatre, but this teacher got me back into it.'

Ethan continued his studies at the British Theatre Association in England and, fleetingly, at Carnegie-Mellon University in Pittsburgh, which he left after being thrown out of his very first class. He was 19 when he won the role of the shy, soft-spoken Todd Anderson in Peter Weir's *Dead Poets Society* – and the film changed his life. 'It allowed me to continue to work,' he says. '[Director] Peter Weir had all this confidence in us, let us goof around and put it together so that it told a great story. Then I started to realize that if I

didn't keep working, I wouldn't get better.'

Ethan got better, and in *Dad* he was terribly good as Ted Danson's independent, rebellious son, Billy Tremont – in what threatened to be a Kleenex festival. Sure, *Dad* exuded its share of sentimentality, but it didn't drown in it, thanks largely to director Gary David Goldberg's insightful, heartfelt screenplay and to the high standard of acting (Hawke, Danson, Jack Lemmon, Olympia Dukakis). Next, Ethan speared the starring role in *White Fang*, a beautifully photographed but ponderous version of Jack London's classic love story of a boy and the half-wolf/half-dog he adopts.

In *Mystery Date* he repeated his turn as a painfully shy youth, this time unable to summon up the courage to ask his comely neighbour (Teri Polo) out on a date. When he does get up the nerve (thanks to his older brother's suit, car and credit card), his dream liaison turns into a nightmare as he finds himself mistaken for his brother, the latter being in trouble with the police, the Chinese Mafia and a fuming flower delivery boy.

In *A Midnight Clear*, Hawke was the callow, 19-year-old commander of a bedraggled squad of young soldiers up against the Nazis during Christmas of 1944. Directed and adapted from William Wharton's novel by the former actor Keith Gordon, the film was a surprisingly tender, compassionate look at men at war, drawing its power not from guns and bloodshed but from the quality of its acting. 'That part, more

than anything I've ever done, it just *me*, you know?' Hawke explains. 'It was all very simple and very honest and very quiet, and that's ultimately why I think it works.'

He took a supporting role in *Rich in Love*, Bruce Beresford's starry tale of a dysfunctional Southern family, playing the confused outsider who falls for Kathryn Erbe (Albert Finney, Jill Clayburgh and Kyle MacLachlan were also in the cast) – but the movie was not well received.

Waterland, however, was critically cherished. Like *A Midnight Clear* and *Rich in Love*, this was another adaptation of a literary work (Graham Swift's novel), in which Hawke played Mathew Price, a bright, outspoken Pittsburgh student who questions his history professor's teaching methods. Filmed partly in America and partly in England's fen district, *Waterland* was directed by the American Stephen Gyllenhaal, who described Ethan as a 'fabulous young actor emerging as a major movie star'. Jeremy Irons was top-billed as the teacher, teaching his young colleague how to draw on his own experiences. 'Working with Jeremy Irons gave me a lot more respect for the profession than I originally had,' Hawke acknowledges 'with the amount of freedom and discipline that he approaches his work with. It

*Ethan as Uruguayan survivor Nando Parrado in Frank Marshall's riveting **Alive***

*Ethan with Winona Ryder in **Reality Bites***

makes it seem like a worthy thing to do with your life.'

Hawke then took his most demanding role to date, as Nando Parrado, a 22-year-old Uruguayan rugby player in Frank Marshall's harrowing true-life drama *Alive*, based on the bestselling account by Piers Paul Read. Parrado and his college team mates find themselves struggling for their lives when their plane crashes into the Andes, killing 18 passengers and crew. Rationed to one piece of chocolate and a sip of wine a day, the survivors find themselves abandoned, frozen and starving, forced to eat their dead to stay alive. Hawke, playing a character older than himself for the first time, lost over 20 pounds to look right for the part. Marshall (who had previously produced such films as *Raiders of the Lost Ark*, *Back to the Future* and *Dad*) offered: 'I didn't know this until I met him, but Ethan is very serious about his work. He's very sincere, and he studied very hard. I look at him as a young Harrison Ford. He has that silent strength and mystery.'

The actor is also keen to pursue a career as filmmaker and, in 1992, directed a 30-minute short starring his *Alive* co-star (and friend) Josh Hamilton as a Texas honeymooner. He was also impatient to write – but first there were more films.

In Ben Stiller's *Reality Bites* he played Troy Dyer, an aspiring musician

with a serious attitude problem. In Lelaina Pierce (Winona Ryder), he sees a kindred spirit but cannot reconcile himself to her innate snobbery. Although what follows is essentially a predictable and old-fashioned love story, it is dressed up with such good dialogue and lively music that one forgives it everything.

Next, he took a cameo in the stingingly observant *Floundering*, a piquant story of contemporary malaise, and had a small role as the assistant of Dennis Hopper, a self-help guru, in the woefully misconceived *Search and Destroy* (directed by New York artist David Salle).

He then teamed up with director and fellow Austin native Richard Linklater for *Before Sunrise*, a meditative, two-character love story set in Vienna. Hawke played Jesse, a 24-year-old American travelling through Europe, who is drawn into a conversation with a young French student (Julie Delpy) and then invites her to spend the next 14 hours with him before his plane leaves. Thanks to Linklater's singular ear for dialogue and the captivating performances of Hawke and Delpy, the film proved to be an unexpected, sharp and perceptive diversion.

While the actor became more and more selective about the films he chose to appear in, he courted some media attention by (briefly) dating Julia Roberts and then buried himself in his

writing. His first novel, *The Hottest State*, hit the book stands in 1996 and elicited some positive reviews. Britain's *Daily Telegraph* noted that it: 'provides some fascinating reflections on the business of acting ... even the minor characters are well defined in Hawke's impressive debut ... a substantial achievement.'

Hawke then returned to acting, almost playing Romeo in a straight adaptation of Shakespeare's tragedy for Twentieth Century Fox. However, when Baz Luhrmann, the director of *Strictly Ballroom*, proposed a more outrageous version starring Leonardo DiCaprio, the studio switched allegiance. Instead, Hawke starred in the sci-fi drama *Gattaca*, with Uma Thurman, and then played a modest fisherman-turned-artist who takes on New York in *Great Expectations*. The latter, which co-starred Gwyneth Paltrow and Robert De Niro, was an update of Dickens' classic, with Hawke in the modernized role of Pip Pirrip.

FILMOGRAPHY

1985: *Explorers*. 1989: *Dead Poets Society*; *Dad*. 1991: *White Fang*; *Mystery Date*. 1992: *A Midnight Clear*; *Rich in Love*; *Waterland*;*Alive*. 1994: *White Fang 2: Myth of the White Wolf* (unbilled); *Reality Bites*; *Floundering*. 1995: *Search and Destroy*; *Before Sunrise*. 1997: *Gattaca*; *Great Expectations* 1998: *Newton Boys*.

*Talk of the town: Julie Delpy and Ethan Hawke in Richard Linklater's **Before Sunrise***

H

HOLLY HUNTER

Holly Hunter as Ed, the cop with the maternal instinct - in the Coen brothers' wonderful Raising Arizona

Holly Hunter could not be described as a versatile actress, but what she does she does very well indeed. She is hilarious in comedy, she can wrench your guts out in drama, and she can skip between the two with the finesse of one of the most skilled performers of her generation. Most famous for playing Southern firebrands on screen, Holly Hunter has done Ibsen on stage, played Henry Higgins' mother in a production of *Pygmalion*, and still aspires to Chekhov. However, she is best at playing variations of herself: spunky, sexy, feisty Southern women who speak their mind and can hold their own against any man (or woman). And then, damn it, she went and won an Oscar for playing a mute Scottish mother in the New Zealand period drama *The Piano*.

Steven Spielberg, who directed the actress in *Always* and found himself romantically linked with her in the tabloids, says: 'She shatters all stereotypes. She has an enormous amount of firepower. This is someone no taller than my mom [she's 5'2"], but on the screen she is overwhelming.'

Albert Brooks, Hunter's co-star in *Broadcast News*, added: 'With Holly, there's no bullshit. Period. You know where you stand. If you spend three minutes with her, you get to see who she is.'

Holly Hunter was born on 20 March 1958 in Conyers, Georgia, the youngest of seven children (she has five brothers and one sister). Her father was a sporting goods sales rep who raised his children on a 250-acre cattle-and-hay farmstead. 'My father did not approve of my learning to drive a tractor,' Holly reveals, 'which is probably why I'm so stubborn. He made the rules, and I broke them. But, like everyone who grows up on a farm, I got a working knowledge of life and death and what goes on in between.'

There were few theatrical influences in Holly's young life, and the local cinema had been transformed into a revivalist meeting house – although, as the actress relates, 'When they spoke in tongues and became possessed by the Lord, it was more fun than a movie.' Holly discovered acting at 16, and decided to go to drama school, when she got a role in a high school production of *The Boyfriend*. Her grades weren't good enough to get her into a leading drama academy, but she knew if she could only land an audition she could get in anywhere else. She got an audition, and enrolled at the Carnegie-Mellon University in Pittsburgh for four years, concentrating solely on acting.

She graduated in 1980 and moved to New York where, two weeks later, she won her first film role, saying, 'Hey, Todd, over here!' in *The Burning*, a Z-grade slasher (notable only for Tom Savini's bloody special effects and a score by Rick Wakeman). Nevertheless, casting director Joy Todd was impressed: 'She read a couple of lines in this accent you could spread on a piece of bread. I just sat up and took notice. She was so good she could do whatever she wanted.'

One play Joy Todd sent Hunter up for was Beth Henley's *The Wake of Jamey Foster*. But on the way to the audition the actress found herself trapped in an elevator – with Beth Henley. The two became inseparable, Holly won the role in *Jamey Foster*, and on top of that was asked to replace Mary Beth Hurt in *Crimes of the Heart* – on Broadway. 'She picks up a script of mine,' Henley offered, 'and it becomes alive. Holly and I share a Southern sensibility: that joyous-despairing view of life.'

Holly received rave reviews for *Jamey Foster*, and two years later was given the lead in Henley's *The Miss Firecracker Contest*, another triumph, which was later filmed – with Holly repeating her stage role. But before the actress was big enough news to star in her own movie, she had a few turkeys to pluck first.

For a while she shared an apartment in the Bronx with fellow actress Frances McDormand, who later became the wife of filmmaker Joel Coen. Furthermore, Hunter's boyfriend, the photographer John Raffo, shared office space with Joel and his producer-writer brother Ethan. In 1984, while Holly took a small role in the TV movie *With Intent to Kill*, saw her part in Jonathan Demme's *Swing Shift* trimmed to just a few scenes, and appeared in the awful *Animal Behaviour*, Frances McDormand got to star in the Coens' critical triumph *Blood Simple*. But Holly had made some useful friends. Says Joel Coen: 'Ethan and I got to know Holly well, and when *Blood Simple* was finished, we thought it would be fun to write something for her. *Raising Arizona* developed out of that.'

Holly Hunter in the part that made her a star - as TV executive Jane Craig in James L. Brooks' Broadcast N

In *Raising Arizona*, Holly Hunter played the highly emotional Edwina McDonnough, an infertile cop who marries a habitual criminal (Nicolas Cage), and then orders him to steal a baby. Combining a number of film genres, *Raising Arizona* was a miracle of style over content, a rollercoaster ride of belly laughs and imagery, a touching fable of contemporary America married with a Gothic, surreal nightmare vision. Above all it was a hilarious original, which – paradoxically – grew funnier with repeated viewings. The film

Holly Hunter as Ada, the role that won her an Oscar - in **The Piano**, with Anna Paquin

was chock full of memorable moments, but the scene in which a pissed-off Hunter confronts a grotesque, heavily-armed bounty hunter with the words, 'Gimme dat buy-bay, you wart hog from hay-ell,' was a classic.

Sadly, *Raising Arizona* was *too* original to catch on with mainstream audiences, but it did become a cult phenomenon on its own terms. Meanwhile, Hunter had to make do with her burgeoning stage career, a good part in Volker Schlondorff's excellent TV movie *A Gathering of Old Men* and a secondary role (as a redneck's wife) in the capricious *End of the Line*, executive produced by the actress Mary Steenburgen.

To James L. Brooks, who had won

an Oscar for directing *Terms of Endearment*, Holly Hunter was still an unknown. He was currently casting the role of Jane Craig in *Broadcast News*, his sophisticated and satirical look at the world of TV news. He already had his male stars lined up – William Hurt as a slick but intellectually lacking anchorman, Albert Brooks as a hard-working, hard-sweating correspondent, and Jack Nicholson, in a cameo, as a super-powerful news presenter. Jane Craig was the movie's central character, an intelligent, highly-focused TV executive caught off guard by the love of Hurt and Brooks, a part the director had written with Debra Winger in mind. When Winger became pregnant, Brooks considered Sigourney Weaver, Judy Davis, Elizabeth Perkins, Elizabeth McGovern, Christine Lahti and Mary Beth Hurt, but none of them seemed to fit the bill. He hadn't heard of Hunter and, frankly, didn't think a Southern actress adept at comedy sounded ideal but, with 48 hours left before the start of filming, he was willing to see anybody.

When Holly turned up for the audition, she wasn't in the least bit nervous, as she recalls: 'There was no way in hell I was going to get that role.' She arrived early, and when Brooks turned up, he looked straight through her. 'I missed her completely,' he admits, 'I thought she was a researcher or something.' But when the actress started bouncing her lines off Hurt, he remembers, 'Five lines into the reading I knew she was the one.' Afterwards, Hurt couldn't stop himself proclaiming: 'We've found her, we've found our Jane! And she's an actress – not a movie star!' Brooks himself added: 'She read her part like a dream. No, wait. I'm building legends here. She read *better* than a dream. She read like a gifted actress.'

The film was a hit, and an immensely intelligent, entertaining and well-acted one. For her role, Holly Hunter was voted best actress by the New York Film Critics, the Los Angeles Film Critics and the National Board of Review, and was nominated for an Oscar. She was a star.

Next came *Miss Firecracker*, the film version of Beth Henley's play about a small-town beauty contestant, and again Hunter gave a performance of unlimited depth, cramming her small

features with pain, humour and passion, demanding the audience never to take their eyes off her (in spite of a cast that included Tim Robbins, Mary Steenburgen and Alfre Woodard).

Active with the National Abortion Rights League since the early 1980s, the actress jumped at the chance to play Norma McCorvey in the TV movie *Roe vs. Wade*. McCorvey (who was fictionalized as Ellen Russell in the film) took on the Texas judicial system in 1970 in order to have an abortion, hiding under the pseudonym of Jane Roe. An unmarried Texas mother desperately looking for work (at the film's outset she is the presenter of a travelling freak show), Hunter's Jane Roe was a woman with no pat answers, yet armed with an overriding passion for what she knew was right (the right of a woman to choose whether or not she is fit to bear a child). The film, which also starred Amy Madigan and Kathy Bates, astutely avoided soapbox lecturing and revealed both sides of the abortion issue with articulate level-headedness, while letting Hunter carry the story's human passion. For her performance, she won the Emmy for best TV actress of the year.

Steven Spielberg's desire to update the 1943 romantic fantasy *A Guy Named Joe* (which starred Spencer Tracy and Irene Dunne) had suffered many false starts, but when the filmmaker settled on Hunter to play the lovelorn girlfriend of forest firefighter Pete Sandrich (Richard Dreyfuss), he kicked the film into high gear. The result was a whimsical, touching and magical love story, with Dreyfuss and Hunter making an irresistibly offbeat couple. They teamed up again to grand effect in Lasse Hallstrom's *Once Around*, a moving dramatic comedy about an overbearing salesman (Dreyfuss) who creates waves when he romances an inhibited Hunter and then alienates her family.

Next, she starred in the TV movie *Crazy In Love*, directed by Martha Coolidge, in which she and Frances McDormand played sisters with unfaithful husbands. However, the movie was sabotaged by a cloying gentility, and Hunter was at her most strident. She then went to New Zealand to star in Jane Campion's *The Piano*, a chamber work of enormous power and

Tough cookie: Holly holds her own in Jon Amiel's cuticle-chewing Copycat

beauty, in which the actress made an extraordinary transition as Ada McGrath, a mute Scottish woman dispatched down under for an arranged marriage (to Sam Neill). For her performance, she won the best actress prize at the 1993 Cannes Film Festival, while the film itself snatched the Palme d'Or.

Next, she took a supporting role (fifth-billed) in the big-budget legal thriller *The Firm*, based on John Grisham's phenomenal bestseller. She played Tammy Hemphill, a ditzy platinum-blonde secretary who lends Tom Cruise a hand in uncovering the nefarious deeds of a Memphis law firm. She acted the Guccis off the rest of the cast.

It was a phenomenal year. Not only was *The Firm* a resounding hit (grossing $158.3 million in the USA alone), but Hunter won the Emmy for best actress in the fact-based (and highly comical) TV movie *The Positively True Adventures of an Alleged Texas Cheerleader Murdering Mom*. She was also voted best actress in *The Piano* by the Australian Film Institute, the British Academy of Film and Television Arts, the Los Angeles Film Critics' Association, the National Board of Review and the New York Film Critics' Circle, capping it off with a Golden Globe.

And it didn't stop there. In February 1994 she was nominated for not one, but *two* Oscars – for best actress in *The Piano* and for best sup-

porting actress in *The Firm*. And, on 21 March, after Al Pacino had announced, 'and the Oscar goes to ... Holly Hunter,' the actress strode up to the stage to make a simple, awe-struck speech: 'I'm so overwhelmed – to be with that group of actresses [fellow nominees Angela Bassett, Stockard Channing, Emma Thompson and Debra Winger]. It just slays me.' Then, after the obligatory thank yous: '... and just thank you all so much for letting this movie in ... and ... thank you.'

At the same ceremony, the Polish-born cinematographer Janusz Kaminski received an Oscar for his stunning work on *Schindler's List*, and to complete Hunter's second incredible year in a row, the couple were engaged that November. The following May they tied the knot in a secret ceremony in Malibu, attended by only their closest friends. 'I'm very protective of my marriage,' Hunter revealed. 'It's a fortification. It fortifies me but it doesn't make me change my global plan, you know. Certainly not thus far. Janusz is a person who utterly understands my commitment. He's in the movie business, too. We have a mutual understanding of what it takes ... I don't talk about if I'm going to have kids. If I do, I do. If I don't, I don't.'

Meanwhile, she concentrated on her career, returning to comedy to play a mother caught in the domestic crossfire of a calamitous Thanksgiving weekend in Jodie Foster's hilarious *Home for the Holidays*. According to Jodie: 'What I love most about Holly – as an actress and as a person – is that she is the most disciplined, focused and intense *listener*. When she commits to something, she commits to it 175,000 percent. There's loyalty to that. If you treat her well, she'll die for you.'

In Jon Amiel's gripping, intelligently-conceived thriller *Copycat* (another complete about-face for the actress), she played spunky homicide detective M.J. Monahan, a part written for a man. Hunter, as always, was terrific and was good enough reason alone to see the movie, the story of a cop (Hunter) who teams up with a criminal psychologist (Sigourney Weaver) to track down a serial killer re-enacting 'celebrated' murders.

She was in the news again as the star of David Cronenberg's controver-

sial *Crash*, in which she played the widow of an auto crash victim who later gets it off with the driver of the other car (James Spader). Perhaps predictably, the powers that be in Britain tried to have the film banned, contributing enormously to its public profile. She then signed on for *A Life Less Ordinary* – for the director, producer and writer who brought us *Shallow Grave* and *Trainspotting* – portraying an angel who plays Cupid to Ewan McGregor and Cameron Diaz. And then she joined Sean Penn, Kevin Spacey and Robin Wright in *Hurlyburly*, the big-screen adaptation of David Rabe's highly-acclaimed play.

FILMOGRAPHY

1981: *The Burning*. 1983: *An Uncommon Love* (TV); *Svengali* (TV). 1984: *With Intent To Kill* (TV); *Swing Shift*; *Blood Simple* (voice only); *Animal Behaviour* (released 1989). 1987: *Raising Arizona*; *A Gathering of Old Men* (TV); *End of the Line*; *Broadcast News*. 1989: *Miss Firecracker*; *Roe vs. Wade* (TV); *Always*. 1991: *Once Around*. 1992: *Crazy In Love* (TV). 1993: *The Piano*; *The Positively True Adventures of an Alleged Texas Cheerleader Murdering Mom* (TV); *The Firm*. 1995: *Home for the Holidays*; *Copycat*. 1996: *Crash*. 1997: *A Life Less Ordinary*; *Hurlyburly*. 1998: *The Kiss*.

TIMOTHY HUTTON

*Timothy Hutton in his Oscar-winning performance as Conrad Jarrett in Robert Redford's **Ordinary People***

A ferociously dedicated actor and a stickler for research, Timothy Hutton was a star by the time he was 20. Although his subsequent career has never topped his early promise, his consistently high standard of performance has kept him in the good books of the best directors. There were decidedly sticky patches, to be sure, but it was easy to see why Hutton made the choices he did.

When he agreed to star in the romantic fantasy *Made in Heaven*, it was to work with the celebrated maverick filmmaker Alan Rudolph. Likewise, when he surprised his peers by playing a Russian aristocrat in the picture-postcard *Torrents of Spring*, it was under the guidance of the acclaimed Polish director Jerzy Skolimowski. And Hutton proved he was up to the challenge. To prepare for his role, the 6'1" star learned to ride, play the piano, dance Russian-style and worked hard on his accent. The resultant performance was only jarring for those who entered with preconceived notions of who the actor was. For Timothy Hutton, it was a courageous move to prove that he could do something different.

Hutton was born on 16 August 1960 in Malibu, California, the son of Maryline Adams and Jim Hutton. His father was a relatively successful, if lightweight actor, whose films numbered *Where the Boys Are*, *Bachelor in Paradise* and *The Horizontal Lieutenant*, and was best known on TV as the canny detective *Ellery Queen*. Timothy was two when his parents divorced, moving with his mother and older sister, Heidi, to Cambridge, Massachusetts, and then to his mother's home town of Harwinton in Connecticut. He was 14 when the family left for Berkeley, western California, and there Hutton enrolled at LA's Fairfax High School, moving in with his father two years later. It was a tumultuous time – and one that left its mark. 'My friends and I stole cars from hotel parking lots,' he admits now. 'We broke into newspaper machines for pocket money. We even got people to leave their cars with us to be washed, and we'd take them out for joy rides. I don't glorify or romanticize what we did. It was idiotic and irresponsible.'

He was five when he made his film debut in the domestic comedy *Never Too Late*, starring his father and Connie Stevens, but he explained: 'At five, acting wasn't my primary goal. It wasn't until I was 17 that I decided I wanted to act. My father was very supportive, but he told me that I would have to do it on my own. No nepotism.' Nevertheless, Hutton allows: 'I left school to do a show with my dad, and then I started to get television work.'

The 'television work' was a string of TV movies, starting with a small part in *Zuma Beach*, a corny surf-and-sand caper co-scripted by John Carpenter and featuring Suzanne Sommers, Michael Biehn, Rosanna Arquette, P.J. Soles and Tanya Roberts. His second TV film, the real-life-based *Friendly Fire*, was altogether better, winning four Emmys, including an award for Outstanding Drama. Carol Burnett and Ned Beatty (both nominated) starred, with Hutton as their frightened, bewildered son who watches the family fall apart after the death of his brother in Vietnam. It was this performance that prompted Robert Redford to sign up the young actor to play the central role of Conrad Jarrett in his directorial debut, *Ordinary People*. Again, Hutton was the son in a disintegrating family unit, again caused by the death of an older brother. This time Mary Tyler Moore and Donald Sutherland played his parents, but it was Hutton, at the tender age of 20, who walked off with the Oscar, the Golden Globe and the Los Angeles Film Critics' award. And yet there was a sadness to Hutton's glory. Four months before he began work on *Ordinary People*, his father died, aged 45, of cancer of the liver. Clutching his Oscar at the podium of the Dorothy Chandler Pavilion in Los Angeles, the actor concluded his thanksgiving speech with a simple: 'I'd like to thank my father. I wish he were here.'

There was another TV movie, the highly-acclaimed *A Long Way Home*, in which he played a young man searching for his brother and sister, both of whom had been sequestered in foster homes, and then he was signed up to play the lead in the military drama *Taps*, co-starring George C. Scott, Sean Penn and Tom Cruise. To prepare for his role as Brian Moreland, the senior cadet who leads his men on a rebellion to keep their academy open, Hutton spent two months in military school. The film was a box-office success, and the actor was nominated for a Golden Globe for his performance.

After that, the commercial stature of his films was iffy, but his commitment to his roles was never less than admirable. In Sidney Lumet's *Daniel*, adapted by E.L. Doctorow from his own novel (*The Book of Daniel*), Hutton was electric as the anguished son of a man and woman (Lindsay Crouse, Mandy Patinkin), executed for leaking secrets to the Russians. For his role as a

As Jack in Gregory Nava's florid **A Time of Destiny**

scientist in Fred Schepisi's underrated *Iceman*, he took courses in anthropology and an Eskimo language.

In August of 1983, Hutton was scheduled to star in MGM's contemporary western *Roadshow*, opposite Jack Nicholson. The terms of his 'pay or play' contract stipulated that he would receive $1.5 million whether the film was made or not. But when MGM cancelled the picture in the spring of 1983, they failed to inform Hutton, who had turned down other projects in the interim. Meanwhile, Nicholson was paid an undisclosed sum out of court, while Hutton was completely overlooked. However, the actor had the last laugh. Eventually a Los Angeles Superior Court jury found MGM guilty of breach of contract, awarding Hutton $2.25 million in compensation and $7.5 million in punitive damages.

Meanwhile, his career chugged on undramatically. He was re-teamed with Sean Penn in John Schlesinger's mildly diverting, fact-based spy drama *The Falcon and the Snowman* (this time *he* was leaking to the Russians), and he then attempted to change his solemn image with the goofy *Turk 182!* This was an innocuous enough, fairly amusing fable about a graffiti artist who fights for his right to mess up the neighbourhood, becoming a mythical figure in a highly-publicized war with the Mayor of New York (Robert Culp).

Earlier, Hutton had met the actress Debra Winger, five years his senior, at an intimate Los Angeles party. He remembers: 'We ended up talking to each other and it was as if no one else was there.' A year passed and they met again, and again – at a Farm Aid concert. The tabloids had tried in vain to find a key to unlock Hutton's private life, and gaily reported his dates with a chain of famous women: Rosanna Arquette, Elizabeth McGovern, Tatum O'Neal, Kristy McNichol, Patti Davis Reagan, Belinda Carlisle, Diane Lane ... but, in truth, they were all just friends, not girlfriends. Then, on New Year's Eve 1985, he and Winger clicked. But it was their secret.

Ironically, the media was busily exposing the 'affair' Winger was having with Hutton's old mentor, Robert Redford, on the set of *Legal Eagles* – but they were way off target. On New Year's Day 1986, Hutton rang the actress, and just over ten weeks later they were married. On their wedding night, Winger got pregnant, but miscarried, and got pregnant again shortly afterwards. They named their son Emmanuel Noah Hutton. 'I'd never met anyone like her,' the actor revealed, 'and I don't imagine I ever will again. She's an original. I loved spending time together in a way I hadn't experienced before.'

The following year he starred in the sickly-sweet romantic fantasy *Made in Heaven*, a surprising hiccough from the iconoclastic filmmaker Alan Rudolph, and, as an in-joke, Winger cropped up in an unbilled cameo as – wait for it – a male angel called Emmett! Hutton then starred in the well-made, soap-operatic epic *A Time of Destiny*, as William Hurt's wartime buddy who,

unbeknown to Hurt, accidentally killed his father in a car accident. He took third-billing in the equally soapy *Everybody's All-American*, as the star-struck nephew of football icon Dennis Quaid, secretly in love with Quaid's wife, Jessica Lange. Quaid and Lange provided the acting, but Hutton was by far the most effective, as the 'serious' writer who narrates the story. The film spanned 25 years in the lives of these all-American folk, providing Hutton with an opportunity to age for the first time on screen. He was even older – and far from American – in Jerzy Skolimowski's lush adaptation of Ivan Turgenev's 1872 novel *Torrents of Spring*, as an old Russian man reflecting on his tempestuous romance with two women (Nastassja Kinski, Valeria Golino). After one got over the shock of seeing Hutton in top hat and sideburns (and speaking in a thick Russian accent), the film was an engrossing romance – and looked stunning.

In June 1990, Hutton and Winger were divorced, and the star's career showed no signs of box-office improvement. But he was still a good actor, and he was still attracting the attention of major filmmakers. In Sidney Lumet's gritty, commanding New York drama *Q & A*, he played a conscientious assistant DA pitted against Nick Nolte's malevolent rogue cop, and he then starred in George A. Romero's far-fetched *The Dark Half* (adapted from Stephen King's 1989 bestseller), as a novelist who encounters the human manifestation of his *nom de plume*.

He then embarked on another 'commercial' venture, playing a young executive who suspects his temporary secretary (Lara Flynn Boyle) of murder in Tom Holland's derivative thriller *The Temp*. Unfortunately, the actor looked out of place in this manipulative, tacky piece, and the film took a header at the box-office.

Timothy Hutton also acted frequently in the theatre, explaining: 'I like to split my time between screen and stage. It is as exciting for me to receive an enthusiastic round of applause on stage as it is to have my screen work acknowledged.' He is also a talented musician and an avid collector of art, having acquired works by Picasso, Warhol, Calder, Magritte, Dali and James Wyeth.

On screen, his most notable role of late was as the pianist Willie Conway, in Ted Demme's funny, affectionate *Beautiful Girls*. Although basically a let's-hug-and-make-up ensemble piece, the movie starred Hutton as the emotional linchpin, the prodigal son who returns to his flock and, with the perspective of the outside world, sees his old friends (and himself) in a new light. According to Demme (nephew of the more famous Jonathan): 'Timmy related to the material immediately and just had a great take on it. He's an amazing actor, so the chance to work with someone like that was exciting to me. Tim brought so many dimensions to the character that were amazing, just from being a confused guy, to being one of the boys, to this really sweet relationship with the girl next door [Natalie Portman].'

The film also marked the professional consummation of Hutton's relationship with Uma Thurman, an off-again-on-again affair that the actor is loath to talk about. He'd far rather discuss *Mr and Mrs Loving*, the TV movie he executive produced himself in which he and Lela Rochon portray a real-life couple who, in the 1950s, went to the Supreme Court to defend their inter-racial marriage. He then played a villain in the thriller *Playing God*, starring opposite David Duchovny's drug-addicted surgeon, and joined Harvey Keitel and Stephen Dorff in John Irvin's *City of Industry*.

FILMOGRAPHY

1965: *Never Too Late.* 1978: *Zuma Beach* (TV). 1979: *Friendly Fire* (TV); *The Best Place To Be* (TV); *And Baby Makes Six* (TV); *An Innocent Love* (TV); *Young Love, First Love* (TV). 1980: *Father Figure* (TV); *Ordinary People.* 1981: *A Long Way Home* (TV); *Taps.* 1983: *Daniel; Iceman.* 1984: *The Falcon and the Snowman.* 1985: *Turk 182!* 1987: *Made in Heaven; A Time of Destiny.* 1988: *Everybody's All-American* (UK: *When I Fall In Love*). 1989: *Torrents of Spring.* 1990: *Q & A.* 1992: *The Dark Half.* 1993: *The Temp; Katya; Zelda* (TV). 1995: *French Kiss; The Last Word.* 1996: *Beautiful Girls; Mr and Mrs Loving* (TV); *The Substance of Fire.* 1997: *Playing God; City of Industry.*

K

NICOLE KIDMAN

Nicole Kidman

Nicole Kidman was doing very well, thank you, receiving heaps of critical praise and accumulating a number of awards in her native Australia. But then everything went right. She met Tom Cruise, married him and became a household name. Suddenly, the critics were not so sure about her. They dipped their pens in vitriol to describe her performance in *Days of Thunder*, but then the film did provoke a good deal of mud-slinging. Her next picture, *Billy Bathgate* (an even bigger box-office disappointment), at least landed her a Golden Globe nomination as best actress. But still the critics carped. Nicole's main problem was that she was Australian. Furthermore, she was an Australian playing Americans. *And* she had married the all-American, super-clean crown prince of Hollywood.

But you only have to re-wind to 1988 to see Kidman's performance in the Australian ocean thriller *Dead Calm* to know that the lady can act. Her flaming red hair blowing in the sea breeze, she immediately reminded one of Sigourney Weaver in *Aliens*, a strong, tall woman facing impossible odds – and coming out on top. Nicole was only 20 years old at the time, but she had already been voted best actress of the year by the Australian public. And the following year she was to be nominated best supporting actress by the Australian Film Institute for her role in *Emerald City*, on top of her two best actress awards for the mini-series *Bangkok Hilton* and *Vietnam*.

George Miller, the producer of *Dead Calm*, could sense something special: 'Nicole is not just someone who is acting for the short term,' he ventured. 'She's an absolutely serious actor. Some ten years ago I met Mel Gibson fresh out of drama school. I had this same gut feeling about him. He had this presence on film one couldn't stop watching. I feel that quality in Nicole.'

Robert Benton, director of *Kramer vs Kramer* and *Billy Bathgate*, would seem to confirm this opinion. 'She was just astounding,' he said. 'She's an astonishingly gifted actress, even more so

when you consider how young she is. There was not one person in the movie who did not adore her. She's truly one of the most amazing actors I've worked with.' And this from a man who directed both Meryl Streep and Sally Field in Oscar-winning turns.

The daughter of a biochemist and psychology lecturer (her father) and a nurse and teacher (her mother), Nicole Kidman was born on 20 June 1967 in Hawaii, a descendant of the Australian cattle baron Sir Sidney Kidman. Hers was a tall family. Her father is 6'10", her mother and sister 5'10", and by the time Nicole was 13 she was also 5'10". She swears: 'I wanted to act from the moment I was born. No really, it was always a fantasy. But my growth took over everything. I hated my looks. What with my height *and* hair – weird, curly, messy – I was considered a bit odd.' Nevertheless, Nicole pursued her fantasy. 'I did street theatre and mime when I was seven. I did ballet when I was three – I did that for many years. When I was 12 I joined a local theatre group and worked with them and did plays and was a stagehand.'

In fact, Nicole made her acting debut aged four, playing a sheep in a local nativity play. 'I wore car-seat covers, I bleated through the whole show, and I got my first laugh. I was this stupid kid trying to upstage baby Jesus. That was it. I thought, "Wow, this is fun!"'

At ten, she persuaded her parents to

let her attend drama school, and at 14 she made her film debut in *Bush Christmas*. In the popular *BMX Bandits*, she played a supermarket girl who teams up with a pair of young bikers, and she then played a rock singer in love with Tom Burlinson in *Windrider*. In the Disney Channel mini-series *Five-Mile Creek*, she was 'a little roughie who herded sheep'. Then she played a schoolgirl who becomes an anti-war protester in the mini-series *Vietnam* (1986), directed by Phillip Noyce. Noyce explained: 'We first became aware of Nicole from several Australian TV productions – what we call "domestic movies" – films hardly seen outside Australia. We felt she would be right for a key role in *Vietnam* that we [the Kennedy Miller organization] were developing. Little did we realize that in just three nights she would become a household name across the entire country.'

A slew of local awards followed, including a nod from the Sydney Theatre Critics, who, for her performance in *Steel Magnolias*, voted her Best Newcomer. Next, she nabbed the lead in Noyce's breath-catching thriller *Dead Calm*, in which she played the wife of Sam Neill stranded on an 80-foot ketch with psycho Billy Zane for company. *Dead Calm* was the year's surprise treat, a stylish movie with fresh faces that sent the pulse on overdrive. Warner Brothers released the film in the USA, and Hollywood jumped.

Nicole (right) with Thandie Newton in John Duigan's superb evocation of adolescence, **Flirting**

Meanwhile, Kidman won more local acclaim for her role as a heroin addict in the BBC-Australian miniseries *Bangkok Hilton*. For her, it was another breakthrough. 'It's a great role,' she said back then. 'I may look terrible, with my hair pulled back and sack-like dresses, but it's what acting is all about.' The late Denholm Elliott played her father, and volunteered: 'Nicole was a joy. She not only took the work seriously, but could always turn up the brilliance when she had to.'

Following her two AFI awards for *Vietnam* and *Bangkok Hilton*, Kidman was nominated best supporting actress for *Emerald City*, as the live-in girlfriend of a ruthless writer (Chris Haywood). Based on the hit play by David Williamson, the film was a witty satire on the Australian film industry, but proved too insular for international tastes. She also had a delicious supporting role in John Duigan's *Flirting*, a magical, painfully accurate homage to boarding school life, a surprisingly superior sequel to the director's 1987 *The Year My Voice Broke*. Kidman played Nicola Radcliffe, a 17-year-old head prefect. 'Blonde wig, loads of make-up, flirts like crazy and all the boys are in love with her,' the actress summarized her part succinctly. The film went on (deservedly) to sweep the Australian Film Critics' Circle Awards, winning

statuettes for best film, best director, best actor (Noah Taylor) and best cinematography.

By now, *Dead Calm* had left its mark on the international market, and Nicole was duly signed up to play the romantic interest in the $55 million stock-car racing actioner *Days of Thunder*. Directed by Tony Scott and starring Tom Cruise and Robert Duvall, the film was burdened with enormous expectations, which it duly failed to fulfil. It truth, it was a skilful, frequently wry piece of escapism with some fantastic racing sequences. OK, so Kidman looked out of her depth and her accent was enigmatic, but she did have her moments. And the film's worldwide gross of $230 million was no tragedy. Neither was Nicole's new liaison with her leading man. It was, she revealed, her first real romance. Earlier, she had confessed: 'Although it embarrasses me to admit it, I have not had a serious relationship. I wanted to establish my own independence first without having to depend on a man.'

The character of Drew Preston in E.L. Doctorow's celebrated novel *Billy Bathgate* was described as: 'so blindingly beautiful under that cut gold hair, her eyes were so green and her skin was so white, it was like trying to look into the sun, you couldn't see her through the brilliance and it hurt to try for more than an instant.' Robert Benton's big-budget film version of the book was to star Dustin Hoffman, and Kidman was desperate to play Miss Drew. Three weeks before her audition, she spent four hours a day studying with a dialect coach to get the aristocratic New York accent down pat. To be honest, nobody thought she could carry it off but, according to Benton, 'When she walked into my office, everyone was knocked out by her.' The film was not a commercial success, but Nicole got her Golden Globe nomination.

In Ron Howard's sweeping 1890s romantic epic *Far and Away*, the actress played a stiff Irish heiress opposite her new husband, who played a cocky, illiterate farm hand. Again, there were doubts about her handling the accent, and again, she came through with flying colours. The film was glossy, romantic tosh, but was executed with such technical verve, and if taken in the

right spirit, was a good, old-fashioned romantic wallow. And, with a domestic gross of $59 million, it was apparent that audiences adored it.

Next, the actress won the female lead in Harold Becker's corkscrew thriller *Malice*, an enjoyable, unpredictable genre piece in which Alec Baldwin played a sinister surgeon who rents out the top floor of Nicole and Bill Pullman's Victorian abode. It was a good deal better than *My Life*, a sugary vehicle for Michael Keaton as a PR man dying of cancer, with Nicole's part (as Keaton's pregnant wife) seriously under-written.

Meanwhile, shortly after completion of *Malice*, the actress rushed to Miami to collect the baby girl she and Cruise had put in for adoption. A nurse at the scene revealed: 'In 20 years of working with adoptions, I have never seen anyone so overjoyed as Nicole was when she first held her new daughter [Isabella Jane]. There were tears of happiness in her eyes as she held that child close to her.'

Film-wise, Kidman was criminally wasted as criminal psychologist Dr Chase Meridian, Bruce Wayne's romantic interest in *Batman Forever* (the top-grossing film of 1995), and she promptly set out to remedy the creative deficit. When Meg Ryan dropped out

Kidman as the hot-blooded Shannon Christie in Ron Howard's epic romance, **Far and Away**

*Fair weather before the storm: Nicole in her award-winning performance as Suzanne Stone in Gus Van Sant's **To Die For***

of the leading role in Gus Van Sant's *To Die For*, Kidman moved in for the kill. The part was Suzanne Stone, an ambitious young woman who will do anything to get her way, to secure her rightful place in the spotlight. Kidman rang the director at home in Portland, Oregon, and auditioned over the phone. 'When Nicole called,' Van Sant relates, 'I realized that she had great resources at her disposal, in terms of agents and knowledge about what was going on within our own camp. She told me straight out that she knew that she was not the person I wanted to play the role, and when I said, "That's not necessarily true," she goes, "Look, I just know this, OK?" I don't know how she knew that. She was right, actually, but I couldn't admit it. Then she said, "I'm *destined* to play this character." I guess it was Nicole's enthusiasm, her knowledge of the type of character Suzanne was, and her conviction that finally sold me on her.'

As it happens, it was a wise move on Van Sant's part, as Nicole Kidman

was the best thing in the movie. When her character asks, 'What's the point of doing anything worthwhile if nobody's watching?', the actress gave the line such conviction that you believed her. Because Suzanne Stone (who was modelled on real-life megalomaniac Pamela Smart) is determined to become famous so that she can justify her own shallow existence. And, if necessary, she'll kill to achieve her aims. Kidman was quick to point out: 'I was *acting*. I am *not* Suzanne Stone' – and the press agreed. She was voted best actress by the London and Boston Film Critics' Circles and won a Golden Globe into the bargain. Why she wasn't even nominated for an Oscar remains one of life's great mysteries.

Following her and Cruise's adoption of a second child, an Afro-American boy called Connor Antony, the actress set her sights on her next big role. And again, she did the courting.

Kidman had known Jane Campion, director of *The Piano*, since Campion was studying in film school in Sydney. In fact, Kidman, then aged 14, was cast in Campion's graduation film, but had to bow out due to scholastic commitments. Nevertheless, Campion wrote to her, saying, 'she would love to do a classic with me sometime, and to protect my talent,' the actress recalls. 'When I heard she was thinking about doing *The Portrait of a Lady*, I called her.' As it happens, Campion was already planning to contact Kidman.

The Portrait of a Lady, following on the heels of *The Piano* and Kidman's Golden Globe, should have been the movie that established Kidman as a

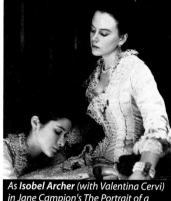

*As **Isobel Archer** (with Valentina Cervi) in Jane Campion's The Portrait of a Lady*

front-ranking actress and star. However, while a pictorially handsome adaptation of Henry James' powerfully interior novel, the film proved less than cinematic, was completely devoid of passion and humanity, and was crippled by long passages of inertia and pretentious camera work. Kidman herself, with the complexion bleached from her cheeks and her accent all over the place, could not compete with the acting of her co-stars, John Malkovich and Barbara Hershey.

She then took a cameo in *The Leading Man* (as herself) – a favour to the director, fellow Australian John Duigan (*Flirting*) – and then teamed up with George Clooney in the terrorist drama *The Peacemaker* and joined Tom Cruise for Stanley Kubrick's contemporary erotic drama, *Eyes Wide Shut*. Most recently, she was signed to star opposite Oscar-winner Frances McDormand in Paramount's *The Trade*.

Outside her film commitments, Nicole acts as Chairperson of the Advisory Board for the UCLA Women's Reproductive Cancer Research and Treatment Program and is Australia's Goodwill Ambassador for UNICEF.

FILMOGRAPHY

1982: *Bush Christmas*. 1983: *BMX Bandits*. 1986: *Windrider*. 1988: *Dead Calm; Emerald City*. 1990: *Flirting; Days of Thunder*. 1991: *Billy Bathgate*. 1992: *Far and Away*. 1993: *Malice; My Life*. 1995: *Batman Forever; To Die For*. 1996: *The Portrait of a Lady; The Leading Man* (cameo). 1997: *The Peacemaker; Eyes Wide Shut*.

With Val Kilmer in Batman Forever

VAL KILMER

Val Kilmer

Val Kilmer has been a stone's throw away from being a major star. But his films have never been quite the successes they could have been. He had the lead in his very first movie, *Top Secret!*, from the same directorial trio that reaped gold with the daffy comedy *Airplane!* But *Top Secret!* failed to catch on, even though the team's *next* picture, *Ruthless People*, was another hit. Four years later he had the lead in Ron Howard and George Lucas's ambitious $30 million fantasy-adventure *Willow*, but again it failed to live up to expectations. And three years after that he won the coveted role of Jim Morrison in Oliver Stone's much-anticipated *The Doors*. Both critically and commercially it was a disappointment.

Val Kilmer was definitely out there. He just wasn't hitting any home runs. Yet.

Born on 31 December 1959 in Los Angeles, Kilmer, part Cherokee Indian, was raised in California's San Fernando Valley. There, he attended the Hollywood Professional School and later became the youngest student ever admitted (at the time) to the drama division at Julliard, in New York. A keen amateur poet, he also tried his luck as a dramatist, co-writing the play *How It All Began*, which Joseph Papp

later presented at the Public Theater with Kilmer in the leading role. After graduation, he honed his skills on Shakespeare, appearing in Joseph Papp productions of *Henry IV, Part 1* and *As You Like It*, while on Broadway he co-starred with fellow unknowns Kevin Bacon and Sean Penn in *Slab Boys*.

On screen, Kilmer made a dashing, straight-faced hero in Jim Abrahams, David Zucker and Jerry Zucker's barmy farce *Top Secret!*, playing an Elvis-like rock star who encounters Nazis while touring East Germany. A joint spoof of World War II melodramas and Elvis Presley musicals, the film's silliness was a bit too much at times, and the jokes were pretty hit-or-miss. Still, Kilmer got a chance to display his singing talents, and did a good job with such classic numbers as 'Are You Lonesome Tonight?', 'Tutti Frutti' and 'How Silly Can You Get?'

He was given the lead in Martha Coolidge's *Real Genius*, playing a college whiz-kid exploited by a villainous William Atherton, but the film's novel satirical angle was diluted by cliche and stereotypes. This led to a supporting role, but a flashy one, as the gum-chewing 'Iceman' in *Top Gun*, the biggest movie of 1986. Kilmer didn't have *that* much screen time, but his glacial posturing made him a memorable villain, and he won billing over Anthony Edwards and Tom Skerritt.

There was a decent TV movie, *Murder in the Rue Morgue*, with George C. Scott and Rebecca De Mornay, and then another lead, in *The Man Who Broke 1,000 Chains*, also for TV. The latter was only so-so, with Kilmer cast as real-life convict Robert Eliot Burns (first created by Paul Muni in the classic *I Am a Fugitive from a Chain Gang*). He was then given the biggest opportunity of his career yet: the starring role in *Willow*.

Willow was the dream child of George Lucas, who thought up the idea even before he had embarked on his ground-breaking *Star Wars* trilogy. But, back then, his vision of fairies, magic spells, two-headed monsters and general sword and sorcery could not be realized with the available technology. As it happens, *Willow* required more than 400 individual special effects, supplied courtesy of Lucas's own Industrial Light and Magic. Kilmer, his muscular

chest bared and his hair flowing down his back, played Madmartigan, a roguish thief and rather good swordsman who reluctantly teams up with the goblin of the title (Warwick Davis) to combat an evil queen (Jean Marsh). The film proved to be a little frightening for children, and overly familiar for adults (it resembled *Star Wars* in enormous detail), but had enough verve and gusto to skate over the cliches. *Willow* grossed in the region of $54 million in the USA, which was less than anticipated, but hardly anything to cry over.

Also in the movie was the English actress Joanne Whalley, who played the witch's wilful but beautiful daughter, Sorcha. To date, Ms Whalley was best known for her performance as Nurse Mills in the BBC's acclaimed musical series *The Singing Detective*, but she had enjoyed enough exposure that Kilmer was already besotted before they met on the set of *Willow*. He admits that she took some persuading ('No, I can't, no,' he mimics her), but she eventually succumbed to his charms and the couple were married in March of 1988.

After a bout of domestic bliss,

*With the ex-wife: Val and Joanne Whalley-Kilmer on the set of **Kill Me Again***

His greatest role? Kilmer as Jim Morrison in Oliver Stone's **The Doors**

Kilmer starred in another TV movie, *Gore Vidal's Billy the Kid*, as the young outlaw, and then teamed up with his wife (now going under the professional name of Joanne Whalley-Kilmer) in the film noir thriller *Kill Me Again*. This was an enjoyable, taut yarn that refused to stop for a tea break, distinguished by some unusual locations and a charismatic, laid-back turn from Kilmer (as a double-crossed private eye at the mercy of femme fatale Joanne).

Around this time, the actor had grown tired of the movie business and was concentrating on his poems (he had a book of verse published), the stage (he played *Hamlet* at the Colorado Shakespeare Festival) and writing screenplays (he knocked out several). He was also working on a documentary dealing with nuclear issues.

And then he heard Oliver Stone was casting the role of Jim Morrison in *The Doors*. The film had long been in gestation, and such names as John Travolta and Timothy Hutton had already been announced to play the rock legend. But Kilmer felt an affinity with the tragic star and set about preparing for the role. After a meeting with Stone, the actor put together a rock video in which he sang Morrison's 'The End', 'LA Woman', 'Peace Frog' and 'Roadhouse Blues.' It won him the part.

Growing his hair to Morrison's length and squeezing his legs into tight leather trousers, Kilmer absorbed the persona of the singer and revealed an uncanny resemblance. The film, like Morrison's life, was not exactly easy to sit through, but Kilmer's performance was nothing short of admirable. It was, in acting terms, his magnum opus. And, yet, in spite of all the publicity, merchandising, books and successful re-release of The Doors' hit single 'Light My Fire', the film failed to make an impact at the box-office.

In *Thunderheart*, directed by Michael Apted and produced by Robert De Niro, Kilmer played a dedicated FBI agent from Washington DC who's dispatched to an Indian reservation to solve a murder. The movie, based on an amalgam of events that occurred in the 1970s, looked great but suffered from an overbearing self-importance. It was not a hit.

The actor then co-starred in Russell Mulcahy's offbeat romantic thriller *The Real McCoy*, playing a small-time thief who idolizes a master bank robber called Karen McCoy (Kim Basinger). He then took a cameo as the ghost of Elvis (!) in Tony Scott's thoroughly entertaining action-comedy *True Romance* (from a script by Quentin Tarantino), and signed up to play Doc Holliday to Kurt Russell's Wyatt Earp in the western *Tombstone*. As it happens, Kilmer was the best thing in this cut-price shoot-out, bringing an uncharacteristic eccentricity to the role of the jaundiced gunslinger and dentist. The film went on to gross a handsome $55.9 million in the USA, $30.8 million more than its direct competitor, the far superior *Wyatt Earp* (with Kevin Costner).

In *Dead Girl* he played an unorthodox psychologist, and then he joined Virginia Madsen and Christopher Walken in Julien Temple's *Galatea* – neither of which saw the light of day. He also pushed for the role of astronaut Jack Swigert in Ron Howard's *Apollo 13*, but lost the part to Kevin Bacon. The timing was perfect, then, for *Batman Forever*.

There was talk of Michael Keaton asking for $15 million to reprise his role as the Caped Crusader (he'd previ-

*As the Caped Crusader in **Batman Forever***

ously played him in *Batman* and *Batman Returns*), but the official story is that Keaton and the new director, Joel Schumacher, pleaded 'creative differences'. Anyway, a new actor had to be found.

Schumacher says: 'It was while I was watching *Tombstone*, around Christmas of '93, that I knew. Val did an extraordinary job as Doc Holliday, and seeing him on screen I thought this guy would make a great Batman.' Schumacher's dream came true, and with a supporting cast that included Tommy Lee Jones, Jim Carrey, Nicole Kidman, Chris O'Donnell and Drew Barrymore, the vision was complete.

Plastered inside the rubber prison of his Batsuit, there was little Kilmer could do with the role, but his jutting jaw was pretty enough, and the film blew the box-office away with a record $53.3 million in its opening weekend – in the USA it ended up as the top-grossing picture of the year. However, in spite of new toys, a new boy and a lighter touch courtesy of Schumacher, the sequel was nothing more than an incomprehensible and self-satisfied two-hour music video.

As a show of his new stellar status, Kilmer dropped out of *Johnny Mnemonic* (a sensible move, as it turned out) and joined Al Pacino and Robert De Niro in Michael Mann's *Heat*, an impressive and critically sanctioned crime epic (although Kilmer had little to do). He then signed up to star opposite another icon, Marlon Brando, in *The Island of Dr Moreau*. But, according to the film's scenarist and original director, Richard Stanley, Kilmer decided a few weeks before the start of production that he wanted his role cut by 40 per cent.

'He put me in an impossible situation,' griped Stanley, so the director was forced to cast Kilmer in the lesser part of Montgomery, Moreau's assistant. The English actor David Thewlis was flown in at the eleventh hour to take over the lead, although it was Kilmer and Brando who registered star billing. Then, to add insult to injustice, Kilmer turned up on set two days late with his lines unlearned. The subsequent rushes betrayed the shambles, and Stanley was relieved of his duties, replaced by John Frankenheimer. Needless to say, the film was an embarrassing flop.

Next, word leaked out that Kilmer behaved abominably on the set of the historical action-adventure *The Ghost and The Darkness*, a hokey and one-dimensional affair with Michael Douglas, when the actor really put the wind up Warner Brothers. He had already signed a contract to reprise his role as Batman, when he accepted a $6 million offer from Paramount to star in *The Saint*. But with Warner's film starting production on 1 August 1996, there was no way that Kilmer could don his Paramount halo as well. Furthermore, Kilmer objected to the title of *Batman and Robin* as, he said, it detracted from his own character. However, insiders put the fracas down to a matter of money, as Kilmer only pocketed $2 million from *Batman Forever*. In the end, the star reneged on his contract and went with the juicier offer, prompting Warner to offer George Clooney a walloping $10 million as his replacement.

While all this was going on, Kilmer was in the throes of an acrimonious divorce from his wife (in spite of the recent birth of their son), and was seen in the company of a number of women. He then, allegedly, popped the question to supermodel Cindy Crawford. Over the years he had romanced the likes of Michelle Pfeiffer and Cher (saluting the former in his published poetry), but proved no luckier with Cindy. She told reporters: 'I'm not a woman who *needs* to be married.'

When asked which sequel of any movie he would like to star in, Val Kilmer summed up his own appeal. 'I'd have to say *The Last Temptation of Christ*,' he revealed. 'If you're going to be in it, you might as well play Christ.'

FILMOGRAPHY

1984: *Top Secret!* 1985: *Real Genius*. 1986: *Top Gun; Murders In the Rue Morgue* (TV). 1987: *The Man Who Broke 1,000 Chains* (UK: *Unchained*) (TV). 1988: *Willow*. 1989: *Gore Vidal's Billy the Kid* (TV); *Kill Me Again*. 1991: *The Doors*. 1992: *Thunderheart*. 1993: *The Real McCoy; True Romance; Tombstone*. 1994: *Galatea; Wings of Courage; Dead Girl*. 1995: *Batman Forever; Heat*. 1996: *The Island of Dr Moreau; The Ghost and the Darkness*. 1997: *The Prince of Egypt* (voice only); *The Saint*.

*Into Africa: Val Kilmer waits for his pride and joy in **The Ghost and the Darkness***

L

JENNIFER JASON LEIGH

*The Whore: Ms Leigh as Tralala in the melodramatic **Last Exit to Brooklyn***

Small (5'3"), delicate, almost sparrow-like in appearance, Jennifer Jason Leigh can transform herself before your eyes. On good days, she can resemble a vixen in heat. She is also accomplished at playing tough, and has bared her emotional armour on a myriad of occasions. But she's also the mouse, the pathetic, stepped-on rodent, reluctant to part from her gutter. It is this chameleon quality that made the actress ideal casting as the dowdy, pitiable roommate of Bridget Fonda in Barbet Schroeder's thriller *Single White Female*. Soft, gentle, a little awkward, Leigh's Hedra Carlson was a sympathetic if slightly unappetizing creation, who, after layer on layer of narrative had been stripped away, was revealed as a ruthless, psychologically tormented monster – who would go to any lengths to satisfy her warped sense of justice. Had it not been for Leigh's performance, *Single White Female* would have ended up a very hollow thriller indeed.

But then Jennifer Jason Leigh has lent distinction to a vast number of dubious projects. Constantly seeking the underside of the characters she plays, she explains her predilection thus: 'It's a fantastic feeling, because you go in new territories that most people really try and stay away from. You get to explore these extremes without losing yourself. It's exhilarating. Everyone is fascinated with the dark side. I mean, I know a few people who don't look when they pass an accident, or who won't read the most sordid, horrific newspaper story, but not many.' She then suggests: 'Maybe I'm drawn to strange characters because my life is so boring.'

Barbet Schroeder, who has directed both Glenn Close and Fay Dunaway, puts Leigh in the same class. 'She has the same intelligence and mad, creative temperament,' he offered. 'It's a combination of being totally possessed and lucid at the same time.'

The writer Hubert Selby Jr, on whose novel *Last Exit to Brooklyn* was based, was reduced to tears when he watched Leigh recreate his tragic heroine – the prostitute Tralala – in the film's epic gang-rape finale. 'What Jennifer gets you to experience is Tralala and her suffering,' he said. 'The fact that she brings such humanity to such a degrading situation is an indication of her magnificence as an actress.'

Maybe it is her all-consuming obsession for changing herself from role to role that has kept Leigh out of the public eye for so long. She considers it a compliment not to be recognized from the films she's appeared in, and is fiercely protective of her secrecy. After *People* magazine did a cosy photo-report on her and the actor David Dukes (she was 19, he was 35), Leigh avowed: 'Reading that *People* article made me want to throw up.' For a while she was romantically involved with Eric Stoltz, whom she met while filming the Gothic thriller *Sister, Sister*, so when she played opposite Stoltz's girlfriend, Bridget Fonda, in *Single White Female*, the tabloids moved in. Leigh says the reports of friction between her and her co-star were totally unfounded: 'I told Bridget the press would have a field day. But it wasn't an issue at all. We loved working together.'

The actress's relative anonymity has enabled her to research roles that otherwise might have been closed to her. To prepare for *Heart of Midnight*, she talked to abused children and attended crisis clinics. To play a performance artist in *The Big Picture*, she became a regular on the Los Angeles performance circuit. For Hedra Carlson, she interviewed inmates of mental institutions and quizzed their psychiatrists. And for Robert Altman's *Short Cuts*, she hung out at a bustling phone-sex office, to get just the right feel for her character (a mother and part-time phone-seductress).

She does, however, admit that the intensity of her research intimidates some people: 'I know, for instance, it frightened [director] Lili Zanuck on *Rush* – at first. The prep I do isn't for anyone else but me. It gives me a place of truth to draw upon. I often discover something that could inspire a scene.' She also acknowledges: 'Things have upset me – but I always assume that that's a good thing.'

Jennifer Lee Morrow was born on 5 February 1962 in Los Angeles, the

*The Cop: as Kirsten Yates in the hardboiled **Rush***

The Psycho: The deranged Hedra Carlson in the flashy hit **Single White Female**

second of three girls. Her mother, Barbara Turner, a TV actress-turned-scriptwriter, and father, the actor Vic Morrow (TV's *Combat*), divorced when she was two. She was never close to her father, and when he lost his life in 1982 on the set of *Twilight Zone – The Movie* (he was decapitated by a helicopter), he only left her $78.18 in his will (although he left $600,000 to his oldest daughter, Carrie Ann).

A few years after her divorce, the ex-Mrs Morrow married the TV director Reza Badiyis, who cast Jennifer in a non-speaking role in his movie *Death of a Stranger*. 'I wanted to take acting lessons right away,' Jennifer recalled, 'but my mother said I had to wait until I was 14 – because she didn't want me to develop bad habits.' However, at the Pacific Palisades High School, Leigh acted in and directed numerous plays and, true enough, aged 14, she won a part in *The Young Runaway*, a Disney TV movie. Two years later she became a member of the Screen Actors Guild and changed her name to Jennifer Jason Leigh, to avoid any association with her father. She took her middle name from Jason Robards, a family friend.

She was then approached to play Tracy – a deaf, dumb and blind girl stalked by a psycho – in the feature *Eyes of a Stranger*, and learned Braille. 'When I was offered the film, I left high school promising my mother that I would take the equivalency exam –

which, of course, I never did.'

When Jodie Foster was considered too fat to play an anorexic in the TV movie *The Best Little Girl in the World*, Leigh won the role and dieted down to 86 pounds. There were more TV movies – the commendable *Angel City* and *The Killing of Randy Webster*, the latter featuring Sean Penn in his film debut – and then she was offered the starring role of Stacy Hamilton, a virgin who seeks love and finds sex, in the comedy *Fast Times at Ridgemont High*. The film, which top-billed Penn and co-starred Phoebe Cates (now a bosom friend), was a hit and Jennifer Jason Leigh was on the way.

She had supporting roles in *Wrong Is Right*, with Sean Connery, and in the

Rodney Dangerfield hit *Easy Money*, and was top-billed as a white slave transported to Japan in *Girls of the White Orchid*, for TV. She was a gum-chewing bimbo in *Grandview, USA*, with Patrick Swayze, and she then starred opposite Rutger Hauer in Paul Verhoeven's sword-and-sex epic *Flesh + Blood*, as a princess violated by thugs. While developing her role, she employed a historical researcher but, as it turned out, this was not preparation enough. 'We all thought we were going to die,' she recalls. 'It was colder that year than it was in Russia. During the rape scene, which took five nights to shoot in zero-degree weather, they wouldn't even let me wear underwear to cover myself while I was lying on the ground.'

She was back with Hauer in the contemporary thriller *The Hitcher*, as a sexy, small-town waitress who ends up – literally – being torn apart by a trac-tor-trailer, and in *The Men's Club* she played a foul-mouthed whore who models herself on Jean Harlow. She was a copper's nark in *Under Cover*, directed by the actor John Stockwell, a dis-turbed young woman manacled and sexually ravaged in *Heart of Midnight*, and an eccentric performance artist – who befriends Kevin Bacon – in Christopher Guest's hilarious satire on Hollywood, *The Big Picture*. Guest, a malleable actor himself, commented: 'She looks different every time I see her in person.'

She then played Tralala, the tough prostitute in *Last Exit to Brooklyn*, and another hooker in the Jonathan

The Slut: Jennifer talking dirty in Robert Altman's superlative **Short Cuts**

The Journalist: as Amy Archer in the Coen brothers' sublime **The Hudsucker Proxy**

Demme-produced *Miami Blues*, who dreams of becoming a housewife and ends up being used and abused by ex-con Alec Baldwin. For her two performances she won the New York Film Critics' Circle award as best supporting actress.

If Jennifer Jason Leigh seemed to be concentrating on movies slightly off the beaten track, it wasn't because she was an unknown quantity in Hollywood – or that she was avoiding the big names. She did go up for the lead in *Basic Instinct*, but lost the role because director Paul Verhoeven 'thought I was way too young for it, and though Sharon Stone isn't much older, she looks like a woman'. She talked herself out of *Pretty Woman* (she referred to the film as 'a recruiting movie, the *Top Gun* of prostitution'), refused to read for *A League Of Their Own* and turned down *sex, lies, and videotape* to do *Miami Blues*.

After Alec Baldwin came Billy Baldwin, with whom she made love on top of a fire engine in Ron Howard's big-budget *Backdraft*, and then she had to compete against some major actresses for the role of Kristen Cates in *Rush*. This was the gruelling film version of Kim Wozencraft's semi-autobiographical novel about an undercover cop who becomes a heroin addict in the course of duty. The film was far too

bleak to become a box-office property, but Leigh was sensational in probably the best performance of her career.

However, *Single White Female* was a huge hit, and brought the actress the spotlight she so rightly deserved. Her co-star, Bridget Fonda, was originally ear-marked for the female lead – opposite Tim Robbins and Paul Newman – in Joel and Ethan Coen's 1950s fantasy *The Hudsucker Proxy*, but the part fell to Ms Leigh, who exhibited an unexpected knack for screwball comedy, perfectly taking off Katharine Hepburn.

Returning to mimicry, she played Dorothy Parker in Alan Rudolph's dreary biography, *Mrs Parker & the Vicious Circle*. However, she became so engrossed in her interpretation of the suicidal, hard-drinking writer that she was virtually incomprehensible. Then, for her role as a lousy, alcoholic club singer in *Georgia* (scripted by her mother), she received the best actress award – *again* – from the New York Film Critics' Circle. And deservedly so. To train for her role, Leigh hung out in Seattle, submerged herself in the music of Sinead O'Connor and Janis Joplin, and spent two gruelling weeks rehearsing her climactic delivery of Van Morrison's 'Take Me Back'. Memorizing every grunt and quaver of Morrison's own rendition of the ballad, the actress spilled her guts out in front of an audience of 3,000, giving one of the most naked, emotionally charged displays of her career.

She had little to do in Taylor Hackford's dour adaptation of Stephen King's *Dolores Claiborne* – as a chain-smoking reporter who suspects her mother (Kathy Bates) of murder – and then re-teamed with Robert Altman for *Kansas City*. Altman volunteered: 'She doesn't care whether the camera is up her nostrils, on the back of her head, or on her foot. She's absolutely professional, she's very easy to work with and has great confidence about what she does. I just have to turn the switch on and she does it. I don't know anybody who's better.' Nevertheless, Leigh's turn as a hard-boiled kidnapper seemed strangely at odds with the film's evocative, Depression-era tone. An ill-judged delivery of sneers and barks, the actress's performance came off like a bizarre caricature in an otherwise accomplished and atmospheric jazz-

driven drama.

She then played a troubled wife and mother in Anjelica Huston's much-praised directorial debut, *Bastard out of Carolina*, based on Dorothy Allison's novel about poverty and child abuse in the South – and she won laudatory reviews. Next, she played the plain and awkward Catherine Sloper in Agnieszka Holland's adaptation of Henry James' *Washington Square* (previously filmed in 1949 as *The Heiress*) and starred opposite Michelle Pfeiffer and Jessica Lange in Jocelyn Moorhouse's powerful family drama, *A Thousand Acres*. She then joined Tom Cruise and Nicole Kidman in Stanley Kubrick's erotic drama, *Eyes Wide Shut*.

FILMOGRAPHY

1967: *Death of a Stranger* (bit part). 1977: *The Young Runaway* (TV). 1980: *Eyes of a Stranger; Angel City* (TV). 1981: *The Best Little Girl In the World* (TV); *The Killing of Randy Webster* (TV). 1982: *Fast Times at Ridgemont High* (UK: *Fast Times*); *Wrong Is Right* (UK: *The Man with the Deadly Lens*). 1983: *Easy Money; Girls of the White Orchid* (later *Death Ride to Osaka*) (TV). 1984: *Grandview, USA*. 1985: *Flesh + Blood*. 1986: *The Hitcher; The Men's Club*. 1987: *Sister, Sister; Under Cover*. 1988: *Heart of Midnight; The Big Picture*. 1989: *Last Exit to Brooklyn; Miami Blues*. 1990: *Fire Princess; Buried Alive* (TV). 1991: *Backdraft; Crooked Hearts; Rush*. 1992: *Single White Female; The Prom*. 1993: *Short Cuts; The Hudsucker Proxy*. 1994: *Mrs Parker & the Vicious Circle; Vanished*. 1995: *Georgia; Dolores Claiborne; Kansas City*. 1996: *Bastard out of Carolina*. 1997: *Washington Square; A Thousand Acres; Eyes Wide Shut*.

The Kidnapper: as Blondie O'Hara in Altman's **Kansas City**

JULIETTE LEWIS

*Juliette with Woody Allen in the latter's controversial **Husbands and Wives***

Barely old enough to say 'I do', Juliette Lewis was launched into the headlines thanks to three men: Robert De Niro, Woody Allen and Brad Pitt. An undeniable beauty who knew how to act, Ms Lewis hit paydirt when she won a key role in Martin Scorsese's *Cape Fear*. The film was a hit (Scorsese's biggest), and starred De Niro, Nick Nolte, Jessica Lange, Robert Mitchum and Gregory Peck. Come Oscar time, De Niro received his customary vote of confidence and Juliette Lewis was nominated best supporting actress. The rest of the cast was ignored.

A breakneck thriller top-billing De Niro as a convict exacting a terrible revenge on the lawyer who put him behind bars (Nolte), *Cape Fear* gave its quietest and most sympathetic moments to Lewis. As Danielle Bowden, Nolte's 15-year-old daughter tormented by De Niro, Lewis was an innocent, faltering and credible heroine, a blossom not yet in flower – waiting to be crushed by the force of evil. De Niro, who had casting approval on the movie, suggested Lewis to Scorsese after their first meeting. 'I met her at the Beverly Hills Hotel for a preliminary chat,' he revealed, 'and I had an interesting feeling about her. She had a natural thing. You have to have a certain kind of awareness of yourself to be an actor, and I was impressed with how she handled the highly emotional stuff in *Cape Fear*. It's not easy to pull that out of yourself, to know where to get it. Some people don't even know how to begin to do it.'

A year after she shot *Cape Fear*, Juliette Lewis was chosen by Woody Allen to replace Emily Lloyd in *Husbands and Wives*, his 22nd picture as writer-director. She was cast as 'Rain', a 21-year-old student who falls under the spell of an English professor, played by Woody himself. The irony of this was that Juliette was 18 at the time, the same age (journalists argued) as Soon-Yi Previn, Woody's lover and the adopted daughter of Mia Farrow. The actor-filmmaker maintained Soon-Yi was nearer 21, but his stand made little difference in the face of the public furore that surrounded his separation from Ms Farrow. Opening in the wake of the court case (Woody fighting for child custody), *Husbands and Wives* captured its share of the media spotlight, further establishing Juliette Lewis as a household name.

Cape Fear and *Husbands and Wives* aside, the actress was accumulating more print mileage thanks to her romantic liaison with Brad Pitt, the coolest new male star of 1992. Six months before *Cape Fear* opened to ecstatic reviews in the USA, Pitt appeared in *Thelma & Louise*, a film of equal critical clout. When the couple started turning up at premieres together, their separate morsels of fame fed off one another. Soon, the tabloids were hailing them as the hottest new couple since Johnny Depp and Winona Ryder.

Brad and Juliette first met under less than romantic circumstances. She was starring in the true-life TV movie *Too Young To Die?* as Amanda Sue Bradley, a 14-year-old girl raped by her stepfather, discarded by her mother and abandoned by her 18-year-old husband. Enter Brad Pitt, who, by comparison, seems something of a saviour. But before you can say 'hard luck story', he's bashing her in the face, pumping her full of drugs and selling her on the streets. It was love at first sight.

Thankfully, the romance lasted longer than the movie, the latter being a brutal, artless and totally pointless piece of audience manipulation. Still, Juliette Lewis held our attention – if not our sympathies – revealing the potential of a very fine actress. But then she'd had a head start.

Born at home on 21 June 1973, in southern California, Juliette Lewis is the daughter of Geoffrey Lewis, the veteran character actor of such movies as *Heaven's Gate*, *Every Which Way But Loose* and *The Lawnmower Man*. He and Juliette's mother, Glenis Batley, a graphic designer, divorced when she was two, and she moved to Los Angeles with her father, along with her older brother, Brian, and younger sister, Brandy. Between the ages of six and nine she lived with her mother in Florida, although she frequently visited her father on movie sets. On one such occasion, aged seven, she even made a brief appearance in Clint Eastwood's *Any Which Way You Can* and was instantly branded 'a natural'.

A self-confessed troublemaker at school, she made her official acting debut aged 12, in the two-part TV movie *Home Fires*. Although an uninspired look at the trials of an American family, the film won Lewis an Emmy nomination as best supporting actress. She then co-starred in the ABC sitcom *I Married Nora*, as Nora's stepdaughter.

At 14, she sought legal emancipation and moved to Hollywood, where

*With then-boyfriend Brad Pitt in **Kalifornia***

she stayed briefly with the actress Karen Black, a family friend. She had a recurring role in the comedy-drama series *The Wonder Years*, and made her official film debut – as 'Lexie' – in *My Stepmother is an Alien*, after which she was launched onto the cinemagoing public.

In 1989 she had a small part in *The Runnin' Kind*, played Cindy Hollowhead in *Meet the Hollowheads* and was Audrey Griswold, Chevy Chase's daughter, in *National Lampoon's Christmas Vacation* (a hit). In the NBC sitcom *A Family For Joe*, she was Robert Mitchum's adopted daughter, Holly, and then she won the role that accelerated her career – the lead in *Too Young To Die?* After that there was a small part in the domestic drama *Crooked Hearts*, and then came *Cape Fear*.

In *That Night* she had another starring role, as an animated teenager impregnated by local undesirable C. Thomas Howell. However, there was little animation between the two stars. Of his colleague, Howell volunteered: 'The biggest problem was just getting around her. I mean, she sometimes wouldn't show up for rehearsals. She's very talented, but she doesn't really know where it comes from – or why. If you don't know what you're doing and that makes you feel uncomfortable, it makes everybody else feel uncomfortable.'

Meanwhile, the film's first-time director, Craig Bolotin, added: 'She's very opinionated about how to do things, and there was a clash,' but, 'out of that clash came a really terrific performance.'

There was a better rapport between her and her leading man on the set of *Kalifornia*, the powerful, stylish tale of a 'white trash couple' seriously into serial killing. Her leading man was Brad Pitt, who confessed: 'It was a fun shoot, because it was so easy and I got to hang out with my love,' adding: 'A lot of it is really sweet, believe it or not.' Ms Lewis played the killer's moll, a part Pitt describes as 'a little bird with a clipped wing'. Again, she was frequently humiliated and beaten by her co-star – and was sensational. However, her liaison with Pitt (which had already faltered once) did not last long afterwards.

She auditioned to play the wildly flirtatious Lucy Westenra in *Bram Stoker's Dracula*, but lost the part to British unknown Sadie Frost. However, she did get to act opposite Gary Oldman in his next film, the gritty black comedy *Romeo is Bleeding* (in which she played his pathetic mistress). After that she had the central role in Susan Seidelman's *Yesterday*, with Dianne Wiest (Brad Pitt's favourite actress), and skewered the role of Becky, a precocious itinerant, in Lasse Hallstrom's quirky, aimless *What's Eating Gilbert Grape*, alongside Johnny Depp.

Then she became an international icon. But first she resisted. It took five sessions with director Oliver Stone before she agreed to play the white-trash serial killer Mallory Knox in his *Natural Born Killers*. For a start, she didn't like the script, or at least, its depiction of her character. 'I asked Oliver – *told* Oliver – "you've got to show that something happened to this girl ..."' Callousness and cruelty come from pain, not because you don't give a shit.' So Stone agreed to insert a flashback in which Mallory is abused by her father (played – of all people – by Rodney Dangerfield), and the director turned it into a parody of a TV sitcom.

Stone declared that he found Lewis 'difficult. You have to wrangle her a little bit. She's an animal. Wild. She has tremendous instincts, but she hasn't been to acting school as far as I know. She either feels it or she doesn't. She was becoming a woman during this movie. I could feel it. Young and mean and hungry, stretching her muscles, wanting to get away from that nagging little portrait that she has always done in the past: girl with a finger in her mouth.'

The film sparked an extraordinary backlash from moral minorities and censors alike, particularly as it was accused of inciting a series of copycat killings (ten, by one count). Whatever, Juliette was sickeningly good – coquettish, vulnerable, lovesick, evil – choosing her next victim with a child-like glee: 'Eenie, meenie, miney, mo ...'

She took supporting turns in *Mixed Nuts* (as the pregnant girlfriend of an ex-con) and *The Basketball Diaries* (as a white-trash junkie hooker), and then, in Kathryn Bigelow's intellectual acid trip, *Strange Days*, she played Faith, an up-and-coming singer and former girl-

friend of ex-cop Ralph Fiennes. She was also in *From Dusk Till Dawn*, another nightmare scenario (scripted by Quentin Tarantino), as the daughter of the Reverend Harvey Keitel who is subjected to no end of unpleasantness (such as a lurid courtship from co-star Tarantino and an unseemly assault from an army of vampires).

Then, in *The Evening Star* – the sequel to *Terms of Endearment* – she played Debra Winger's daughter, Melanie Horton, who runs off to LA to escape the claustrophobic clutches of her grandmother, played by Shirley MacLaine. Sporting big hair and packing a big mouth, she displayed the spunk of Winger's Emma Horton, but it was hard to believe that she was a product of MacLaine's blue-blooded household. The film itself slaved too hard to pull the same strings as its predecessor, and only a fistful of good lines saved it from the video bin.

FILMOGRAPHY

1980: *Any Which Way You Can* (bit part). 1987: *Home Fires* (TV). 1988: *My Stepmother is an Alien*. 1989: *The Runnin' Kind*; *Meet the Hollowheads*; *National Lampoon's Christmas Vacation* (UK: *National Lampoon's Winter Holiday*). 1990: *Too Young To Die?* (TV). 1991: *Crooked Hearts*; *Cape Fear*. 1992: *That Night* (a.k.a. *One Hot Summer*); *Husbands and Wives*. 1993: *Kalifornia*; *Romeo Is Bleeding*; *Yesterday*; *What's Eating Gilbert Grape* (UK: *What's Eating Gilbert Grape?*). 1994: *Natural Born Killers*; *Mixed Nuts*. 1995: *The Basketball Diaries*; *Strange Days*; *From Dusk Till Dawn*. 1996: *The Evening Star*. 1997: *Full Tilt Boogie*.

Another hair-do, another film: Lewis with Gary Oldman in *Romeo is Bleeding*

Ray Liotta

Considering the wattage of the critical spotlight trained on Ray Liotta, the actor has exhibited a remarkably low profile in Hollywood. His career has consisted of a series of dramatic break-throughs, but it has failed to transform him into a household name. He avoids the glitzy parties of LA, the media-saturated premieres, the famous girlfriends. And he is refreshingly open about his belated intimacy with the movies – and acting.

'Becoming an actor wasn't a big, burning passion for me,' he revealed. 'I just did the whole jock thing in high school. Acting was sort of just something to do, but I liked it.' In fact, Liotta preferred playing baseball to anything else. He occasionally went to the cinema, but gleaned little from it. 'I was never really into movies enough when I was growing up to understand who Robert De Niro or Martin Scorsese were. I wasn't in awe. I just thought they were filmmakers who worked hard. And I don't think that's being arrogant, it's just because I never really wanted to do this, even when I was taking acting in college. I didn't know

anything about them.'

It is ironic, then, that it was De Niro who suggested Liotta for the part of gangster-wannabe Henry Hill in Scorsese's *GoodFellas*, the film that turned Liotta into a major contender for Hollywood stardom.

Exuding a sexual charisma that could stop a gangster's moll at twenty paces, Liotta acted De Niro off the screen. Dangerous, edgy, psychotic, Liotta's amoral womanizer was a character that actors would have killed for. OK, so Tom Cruise turned the part down, but reportedly the likes of Alec Baldwin, Nicolas Cage and Val Kilmer were fighting for the role. Yet Liotta almost didn't get it – because he was perceived as *too* dangerous, too manic. And still he managed to make Henry Hill likeable, which was no small feat.

The film's producer, Irwin Winkler, admitted: 'Frankly, I didn't want him in the movie. I felt that the character needed a lot of sympathy. I had just seen Ray in *Something Wild*, so I kept saying to Marty, "Jeez, are you really sure?"' Only after meeting Liotta did Winkler change his mind. 'We started chatting, and I realized that Marty was absolutely right. Ray was warm and gracious and had a lot of the qualities that Marty wanted for his character.'

Something Wild was another Liotta vehicle that promised instant stardom. And it was another role that the actor had had to declare war for. Eventually, he went direct to the film's star, Melanie Griffith, and begged her to let the film's director, Jonathan Demme, see him. A meeting was arranged and Liotta got the role (even though the part had been earmarked as 'a star vehicle'). As Ray Sinclair, Griffith's psychotic, redneck husband, Liotta again walked off with the acting honours. He won the Boston Critics' award for best supporting actor, and was nominated for a Golden Globe to boot. 'I like to play people who feel deeply about something,' the star explained, 'and that's pretty much what Ray Sinclair was about. And I was angry, waiting around for five years to be in a movie. I was *primed*. I worked my ass off.'

Born on 18 December 1955 in Union, New Jersey, Ray Liotta was the adopted child of an auto-parts shop owner. He was raised in a quiet, middle-class suburb and dismisses his

upbringing as: 'Fine. It was a nice life. I grew up nice.'

He enrolled at the University of Miami to study drama because, he says, that's where his good friend Vinny was and because the weather was nice. At least it was better than working in his father's store or tending cemetery grounds in New Jersey. Moving up to New York to become an actor, Liotta was out of work for two days before landing a K-Tel record commercial. This was going to be easy. Next, he won a regular spot on the daytime soap *Another World*, playing Joey Perrini, 'the nicest guy in the world,' he says. 'I couldn't have been any sweeter. It was sickening.' For three years, no less, he was the nicest guy.

He had a starring role in the TV movie *Crazy Times*, alongside Michael Pare and David Caruso, a nostalgic and mediocre look at three teenage friends growing up in 1955. And then the work stopped.

Liotta as the manic Ray Sinclair in Jonathan Demme's **Something Wild**

Liotta moved to Los Angeles, befriended two other unemployed actors – Andy Garcia and Kevin Costner – and played a lot of paddle tennis. He also got a girlfriend, former championship skier and stuntwoman Heidi Von Beltz, who was paralysed from the neck down (she had doubled for Farrah Fawcett in *The Cannonball Run*). By all accounts, Liotta was devoted to the beautiful blonde, an intimate of Melanie Griffith's. At the time, Liotta saw a lot of Griffith, too, who was married to another good friend, actor Steven Bauer (Al Pacino's sidekick in *Scarface*), from their days together at Miami University.

And so, after a miserly bit part in the awful *The Lonely Lady* (as the

Liotta (centre), surrounded by **GoodFellas** Robert De Niro and Paul Sorvino in Martin Scorsese's masterpiece

assailant who strangles Pia Zadora in the shower), the script of *Something Wild* fell into Liotta's hands. The film was a hit, and Liotta was a hit in it. The screwball tale of yuppie Jeff Daniels ensnared by wildcat Griffith, the film changed track dramatically half-way through when Liotta gate-crashed their dream. An ex-con from hell, Liotta trashes the couple's romance and makes Jeff Daniels confront his own manhood. So convincing was Liotta in the part that journalists at the film's press junket gave him a wide berth. It was the start of some serious typecasting.

Determined to make the most of his new standing, Liotta turned down every psycho role in Hollywood (and the large salaries that went with them). Finally, he opted for the role of Tom Hulce's caring brother, Gino, in Robert M. Young's brave little story of fraternal commitment, *Dominick and Eugene*. Again, he nearly didn't get the part. The producer, actor Mike Farrell, caught a screening of *Something Wild* and blanched. Farrell recalls: 'I called my partner and said, "Wait a minute! This murdering, outrageous, satanic, bastard guy scares the shit out of me!" So we took Ray out to lunch, and he was so sweet that he instantly erased all my fears.'

Dominick and Eugene was not a suc-

cess, and any good reviews the film got concentrated on Hulce's part as the retarded Nicky. However, as the medical student struggling to find the balance between his own life and his brother's, Liotta was also very good.

Next, he was announced as the star – opposite Linda Fiorentino – of *The War at Home*, but the film never materialized, and then came a supporting role in *Field of Dreams*. Liotta played the ghost of baseball legend 'Shoeless' Joe Jackson, and his old friend, Kevin Costner, was the farmer who heard voices in the cornfields ('If you build it, He will come.'). The film was a hit, but nobody seemed to notice Liotta. 'Maybe it was the hat,' he reasons.

GoodFellas changed all that. Martin Scorsese's picture was voted best film by the Los Angeles, New York and US National Society of Film Critics and by BAFTA, and that was just for starters. Joe Pesci, who played fellow gangster Tommy DeVito, won the Oscar, and the film proved to be a milestone for all concerned – including Scorsese.

For once, Liotta was able to pick and choose his scripts, and in another bid to beat typecasting he played the heroic Dr Leonard Sturgess in *Article 99*, a black comedy-drama set in a VA hospital. This time he was top-billed (above Kiefer Sutherland, Forest Whitaker, Lea Thompson, Kathy Baker and Eli Wallach), but the public were not yet ready to see their favourite psycho as a good boy. However, the movie did have its champions. The trade paper *Variety* thought it 'a timely and provocative' piece, and said: 'Liotta

shows inexhaustible spirit and convincing leadership qualities as the crusading doctor ...'

On TV, he played a concerned husband in the three-part *Women & Men 2: In Love There Are No Rules*, in the episode labelled 'Domestic Dilemma'. Andie MacDowell played his alcoholic wife, but the segment was the weakest of the three (Matt Dillon and Scott Glenn starred in the other two). If Liotta was to grab people's attention, he had to stride down the psycho path again.

This he did with a vengeance in Jonathan Kaplan's chilling *Unlawful Entry*, the story of a yuppie couple who call the police when an intruder breaks into their dream house. Kurt Russell and Madeleine Stowe were the couple, and they wished they'd never called the police. Liotta played Pete Davis, a handsome, highly-decorated police officer who sets up the couple's security system and then turns nasty. At first shy, aloof and sexually dangerous, Liotta's maniac cop never *acts* crazy, which makes him all the more of a lethal opponent. Only in the film's final passage does Liotta allow his psycho to snarl. Released during the aftermath of the Rodney King furore in Los Angeles, *Unlawful Entry* was a hot potato and made audiences particularly uneasy in the scene in which Davis lays into a black man with a baton. Ray Liotta found himself in another hit.

He also started dating the actress Michelle Johnson, the former wife of baseball star Mark Grace (of the Chicago Cubs). They met at a game in 1992, but Liotta edged towards first base with gentlemanly reticence. 'We built a friendship first,' he maintained. 'It was a slow start. And then it blossomed.' Four years later the couple were wearing engagement rings.

Professionally, he returned to playing the hero, albeit one convicted of murdering his commanding officer. In *No Escape* he was marine captain John Robbins, a tough cookie dumped on a jungle island-cum-penitentiary where the inmates are left to die. Of course, Robbins is made of sterner stuff and is quickly sorting out the human scum from the boys. 'Most of my parts had been so dark, so I was interested in doing something more heroic,' he explained.

*Ray Liotta in rare heroic mould, in Martin Campbell's **No Escape***

He changed gear even more dramatically in the warm, intelligent human drama *Corrina, Corrina*, loosely based on the childhood of its writer-director-producer, Jessie Nelson. Whoopi Goldberg played Corrina, a black maid who develops a unique friendship with a handsome widower and jingles composer (Liotta). However, it was hard to reconcile Whoopi and Liotta as amorous partners, however subtly they played it.

Next, he teamed up with Danny Glover and Denis Leary in *Operation Dumbo Drop*, Disney's candyflossing of the Vietnam War, a true story in which the US Army attempted to shuttle an elephant to a Vietnamese village. He then finally got to team up with Linda Fiorentino in John Dahl's sci-fi drama *Unforgettable*, in which he played a forensic pathologist accused of murdering his wife. Fiorentino, who had won enormous acclaim as the predatory bitch in Dahl's *The Last Seduction*, confessed: 'I don't scare easily, but if anybody could scare me, it would be Ray. He reminds me of a cat: one minute

purring and sitting on your lap, the next moment out killing something.'

He was then back in serial killer mode ('your basic nut job,' he concedes) in *Turbulence*, a cliché-plagued action-thriller with Lauren Holly and Ben Cross. Liotta was Ryan Weaver, who, on his way to a Los Angeles prison on a 747 jet, goes ballistic as the plane heads for the epicentre of a ferocious storm. He then joined the starry company of Sylvester Stallone, Robert De Niro, Harvey Keitel and Annabella Sciorra in James Mangold's police corruption drama, *CopLand*.

FILMOGRAPHY

1980: *Hardhat and Legs* (TV). 1981: *Crazy Times* (TV). 1983: *The Lonely Lady*. 1986: *Something Wild*. 1988: *Dominick and Eugene* (UK: *Nicky and Gino*). 1989: *Field of Dreams*. 1990: *GoodFellas*. 1991: *Women & Men 2: In Love There Are No Rules* (TV). 1992: *Article 99*; *Unlawful Entry*. 1994: *No Escape*; *Corrina, Corrina*. 1995: *Operation Dumbo Drop*. 1996: *Unforgettable*; *Turbulence*. 1997: *Copland*. 1998: *Phoenix*.

ROB LOWE

Whether he warranted it or not, Rob Lowe was the star representative of the Brat Pack. He went to school with Emilio Estevez, Charlie Sheen and Sean Penn. He made his film debut in *The Outsiders*, alongside Estevez, Tom Cruise and Matt Dillon. He surfaced in the requisite amount of teen fodder alongside such distaff regulars as Jodie Foster, Ally Sheedy, Demi Moore, Winona Ryder and Meg Tilly. He was seen at parties and premieres with a steady stream of famous women: Princess Stephanie of Monaco, Jodie Foster, Nastassja Kinski, Marlee Matlin, Fawn Hall, Chynna Phillips, Jane Fonda, Brigitte Nielsen, Grace Jones, Brooke Shields and his on-off love of six years, Melissa Gilbert. And he was a bad boy. He once claimed: 'If I haven't been with 'em, I know 'em, or I've been engaged to 'em. I looked at my calendar and said, "Shit, it's a few weeks into the new year and I haven't been engaged to anyone yet. I'd better get to work."'

But appearances can be deceptive. Underneath the pretty face, the moulded jaw-line and those penetrating blue eyes, Rob Lowe was just a regular guy

who wanted to be loved. He claimed: 'It's really weird, but I am the most shy when it comes to girls. *Really* shy.' He also wanted to prove that he was more than just a cute façade, and he worked hard to find challenging roles. In fact, he was only 19 years old when he was nominated for a Golden Globe award for his role as a boy undergoing a heart transplant in the TV movie *Thursday's Child*. Three years later, he was nominated a second time, for playing a retarded 21-year-old Texan in the movie *Square Dance*. And he had his champions. The celebrated New York critic Andrew Sarris wrote: 'I don't think Lowe gets enough credit. He has a real talent. He could be like Alain Delon, playing high-quality villains – interesting, complex people. I could see him playing Ted Bundy.' And Lowe was the first person not to take himself seriously. At the 1989 Oscar ceremony he poked fun at himself, singing 'Proud Mary' with Snow White, but the prank backfired when Disney sued the Academy for breach of copyright.

And there was that Atlanta scandal in 1988 involving two young women and a video camera – the night that turned Rob Lowe into the laughing stock of the world, the personal cata-

Rob Lowe in 1983

strophe that all but hammered the last nail into the actor's faltering career (see below). The media smirked when the star was reduced to accepting a supporting role in a Feydeau stage farce in New York. But Lowe was savvy enough to face the problem head-on, ironically daring to play a sleazy hustler who covertly videos a couple having sex in the movie *Bad Influence*, and, to add pepper to the stew, the guy having sex was James Spader, fresh from *sex, lies, and videotape*.

Then, when even that failed to save him, Lowe did something that he was strongly cautioned against: he took a supporting role in a film starring two unknowns based on a TV sketch. The film was *Wayne's World* and, grossing $132 million on its first US release, it became the most successful movie of Rob Lowe's career. Once again, the Romeo of Malibu was back where he belonged: on the cover of countless magazines.

Robert Hepler Lowe, the eldest of three children, was born on 17 March 1964 in Charlottesville, Virginia. The son of a lawyer, he grew up in Dayton, Ohio, and at five months old suffered an infection that rendered him completely deaf in his right ear. He remained in Dayton until his parents divorced – and his mother remarried. But he already knew he wanted to be an actor, inspired by a local production of the musical *Oliver!* He was nine when he made his first stage appearance in summer stock, following it up with commercials and bit parts on local television. When he was 12, his mother married a third time, and the family moved to Malibu. Behind him, Lowe left his two best friends, both brothers: one dead, killed in a car chase with the police, the other a young dad at 17 who'd been in and out of jail. Lowe realizes that, had he stayed, 'I don't know what I would have become.'

In Malibu he went to school with Emilio and Charlie, and they, together with Rob's younger brother, Chad (also an actor), became obsessed with making home videos. Rob continued his career in real showbusiness, but found the LA competition tough. He got a Coke commercial, and then, in 1979, landed a regular spot on the domestic TV sitcom *A New Kind of Family*, playing Tony Flanagan, the son of a wid-

owed Eileen Brennan. A year later he was the lead in the Afternoon TV Special *Schoolboy Father*, and he also appeared in the Emmy-winning *A Matter of Time*.

Lowe's big-screen debut arrived with *The Outsiders*, in which he played gas attendant 'Sodapop' Curtis, brother of C. Thomas Howell and Patrick Swayze. He had little to do, but he was naturalistic and pretty, and the scene in

*Lowe in his Golden Globe-nominated performance as the retarded Rory, in Daniel Petrie's **Square Dance***

which he arm-wrestled Tom Cruise got him noticed. Next came the TV movie *Thursday's Child*, and its attendant critical attention, and then top-billing in the romantic teen comedy *Class*. This was no small feat, as the movie was essentially about the romance between Lowe's roommate, Andrew McCarthy, and his mother, played by Jacqueline Bisset. In *Hotel New Hampshire*, based on the John Irving novel, he romanced Nastassja Kinski and Jodie Foster, the latter playing his sister (!), and he went to England to play an amorous jock in *Oxford Blues*. He was good in *St Elmo's Fire*, as a sax-playing philanderer who

neglects his wife and child, and he learned to smoke for the role. In *Youngblood* he was re-teamed with Patrick Swayze, in which they played ice hockey players, and he then wooed Demi Moore in *'About Last Night ...'*, a trashy film version of David Mamet's serious play, *Sexual Perversity in Chicago*. Lowe has said: 'I really have a great affection for that whole movie. Danny was hobbled by his fear of intimacy and commitment – which are issues I struggle with on a daily basis.' But as co-star Jim Belushi told Lowe's character, Danny: 'You know what your problem is? Your face. Come on, wise up, man. You're too good-looking.'

Lowe tried to remedy this by making a brave career move, taking a pay cut and accepting fourth-billing in the low-budget drama *Square Dance* (starring Jason Robards, Jane Alexander and Winona Ryder). He even had to audition for the part. 'I hadn't read for a role in a long time,' the actor admitted. 'It was scary. They were not sure someone perceived as a leading man could do a role such as this without damaging the project.' Unfortunately, in spite of all Lowe's efforts, it was hard to separate the star from the stammering, drawling, retarded youth he played. Still, he was nominated for a Golden Globe, which was more than he got for his next film, the courtroom farce *Illegally Yours*, in which he attempted broad comedy to disastrous effect. He was much, much better in Bob Swaim's *Masquerade* (a yuppie *Body Heat*), in which he played a 'two-dollar gigolo' preying on rich women. At the time, he admitted: 'The character's a real stretch for me. He is the kind of man people might never imagine I'd play. He's a sponge, a chameleon. He doesn't feel guilt and he doesn't see any reason to.' Swaim was impressed. 'Rob's underestimated by a lot of people,' the director offered. 'They ought to give him a break. He's a very bright kid, a director's dream.'

The year was 1988, and it was an emotionally bruising time for the actor. He had been dating the actress Melissa Gilbert (of TV's *Little House on the Prairie*) on and off for six years when she suddenly married actor-producer-director Bo Brinkman. Obviously stung by the break-up, Lowe revealed: 'Melissa chose to let me hear about it by calling up a radio station and broadcasting it to the public. I had never met the guy and have no idea who he is.'

But the year wasn't over yet. On 17 July 1988, Lowe was in Atlanta for the Democratic National Convention. After attending a party thrown by the media tycoon Ted Turner (now Jane Fonda's husband), he ventured on to the Club Rio. There, he was asked to prove his age at the door – so it never occurred to him that anybody else would be under-age. He had several drinks, talked to a lot of girls, and noticed that one in particular was making a play for him. By the time he left the club, he was accompanied by the girl, Lena Jan Parsons, and her friend, Tara Siebert, and they all went back to his hotel room. What followed became household news, and because of it a civil suit was filed against the actor, claiming that Lowe 'used his celebrity status as an inducement to females to engage in sexual intercourse, sodomy and multiple-party sexual activity for his immediate sexual gratification and for the purpose of making pornographic films of these activities'.

Jan Parsons, 16, was recovering from the collapse of her parents' marriage and was a confirmed truant. Tara Siebert, 22, was, according to court documents, a known lesbian. Following their sexual marathon in Lowe's hotel room, they slipped off while he was in the bathroom, taking with them $100 from his wallet and the minicassette from his video camera. The following day they couldn't contain themselves, telling friends of their experience. A month later, Jan's mother, Lena, found the video and all hell broke loose. In January 1989, Lena's lawyer contacted Lowe and court proceedings commenced. Lowe's attorney suggested a $35,000 'take it or leave it' offer, but it was rejected. It was too late, anyway. Copies of the video had mysteriously started to circulate, and before the whole ugly thing was over, Lowe had been threatened with 20 years in prison and a fine of $100,000. Meanwhile, parts of his home movie had been broadcast on network TV (on *A Current Affair*) and the X-rated cable show *Midnight Blue*. As it happens, no charges were brought in the end, but Lowe was a changed man. He also enrolled in a 12-step Alcoholics

Anonymous programme and entered a clinic to stem his voracious sexual appetite.

Later, he told *Rolling Stone* magazine: 'It was one of those quirky, sort of naughty, sort of wild, sort of, you know, drunken things that people will do from time to time. I had people come up to me on the street afterward and say, "Hey, you know, I do it all the time. The difference is you got caught."'

Career-wise, Rob Lowe couldn't top his home movie (which was fetching $250 a copy on the black market), with Arsenio Hall quipping: 'At last Rob Lowe has made a film everyone wants to see.' Nobody was particularly interested in *Bad Influence*, *If the Shoe Fits*, *The Dark Backward* (in which he had a jokey cameo as a broken-nosed Hollywood hustler) and *The Finest Hour*, all box-office duds.

In 1991 he secretly married make-up artist Sheryl Berkoff (former girlfriend of Emilio Estevez), whom he first met in 1983 and later became reacquainted with on the set of *Bad Influence*. They now have two sons. In addition, he played the villain in *Wayne's World*, the surprise hit of early 1992. As smarmy TV executive Benjamin Oliver (who sells Wayne and Garth down the river), Lowe brought a studied smoothness to the proceedings that gave the film a much-needed edge. Furthermore, it was the most successful movie of his career.

In 1993 he portrayed lobotomy pioneer Dr Cukrowicz in a BBC production of Tennessee Williams' *Suddenly Last Summer*, joined Molly Ringwald and Gary Sinise in the four-part mini-series *Stephen King's The Stand* (as a deaf mute who finds himself immune to a deadly virus), and he then co-produced the dark western *Frank and Jesse*, playing the notorious outlaw Jesse James to Bill Paxton's Frank.

TV producer Lorne Michaels (*Saturday Night Live*), who had cast him in *Wayne's World*, re-hired the actor for *Tommy Boy*, a vehicle for the overweight comic Chris Farley. 'The character was originally written as a sort of cousin to my character in *Wayne's World*,' Lowe explains, 'another Yuppie villain. But I think we've come up with someone very different and certainly more interesting for me to play. He's

conniving. He's surly. He's a little nasty. But underneath it all he's just one incredible buffoon.' While the idea of Lowe (who was uncredited) playing Bo Derek's son (yes, really) was fun, *Tommy Boy* was guilty of recycling old jokes and failed to set the box-office alight.

He was up for the role of Darcy in the BBC's *Pride and Prejudice* (but lost out to Colin Firth), had a fleeting unbilled cameo in *Mulholland Falls* (as a hood) and, according to *Variety*, was 'distressingly miscast' as a James Bond-type hero in the TV mini-series *Jack Higgins' 'On Dangerous Ground'*. The rest of his films crawled straight to video.

FILMOGRAPHY

1983: *The Outsiders*; *Thursday's Child* (TV); *Class*. 1984: *The Hotel New Hampshire*; *Oxford Blues*. 1985: *St Elmo's Fire*. 1986: *Youngblood*; *'About Last Night …'*; *Square Dance*. 1987: *Illegally Yours*. 1988: *Masquerade*. 1990: *Bad Influence*; *If the Shoe Fits*. 1991: *The Dark Backward* (UK: *The Man With Three Arms*) (cameo). 1992: *The Finest Hour*; *Wayne's World*. 1993: *The Stand* (TV). 1994: *Frank and Jesse*. 1995: *Tommy Boy*; *First Degree*. 1996: *Mulholland Falls* (cameo); *Jack Higgins' 'On Dangerous Ground'* (TV). 1997: *Contact*; *Hostile Intent*.

Lowe as the smarmy TV executive Benjamin Oliver in the smash-hit comedy **Wayne's World**

*Andie in her greatest role, as the suppressed housewife Ann Millaney in Steven Soderbergh's brilliant **sex, lies and videotape***

Andie MacDowell had three problems. She was beautiful, she was making good money and she had an accent as thick as molasses. Hollywood has never taken kindly to models who think they can act, and when MacDowell's voice was dubbed by Glenn Close in her first film – *Greystoke, The Legend of Tarzan, Lord of the Apes* – Tinseltown laughed. Andie MacDowell had a nervous breakdown, took a small part in a Brat Pack movie and then disappeared.

Four years later she played a brittle, sexually repressed Southern wife in a small, low-budget feature made by a first-time director. 'My thought was that I would at least get something on tape that I could show to casting directors,' she explained. But then the unexpected happened. The film, blessed with the intriguing title of *sex, lies, and videotape*, won the Palme d'Or at Cannes and gained a huge critical following. 'Its success only sank in properly,' she says, 'when I began to be offered films without being asked to audition.'

Better still, the Los Angeles Film Critics' Circle voted her best actress of the year (in a tie with Michelle Pfeiffer), and she was nominated for a Golden Globe award. Soon, MacDowell was starring in some very classy pictures opposite some very classy actors, not least John Malkovich, Gerard Depardieu and Ray Liotta. There was one hiccough, the $55 million box-office turkey *Hudson Hawk*, but this time most of the blame was shovelled onto co-star Bruce Willis.

She was born Rosalie Anderson MacDowell on 21 April 1958 in Gaffney, a small town in South Carolina. When the director James Cameron shot *The Abyss* at a disused nuclear power plant there, he told *Rolling Stone*: 'Filming in Gaffney is like filming in Tibet, but at least Tibet would be *interesting*.'

MacDowell, who was known as 'Rosie' as a child, was the youngest of four girls. Her father worked in the lumber trade and her mother was a music teacher. They divorced when Rosie was six. After her father remarried, the ex-Mrs MacDowell began drinking heavily, lost teaching jobs and was reduced to working in fast-food joints (she died in 1982). Meanwhile, Rosie and her sisters modelled at local shops, and Rosie began a secret portfolio. She left Gaffney to attend college in Winthorpe, South Carolina, but dropped out to pursue her modelling career in New York. There, she was signed up by the Elite Modelling Agency almost immediately and had her name changed to 'Andie'. She tired of the work after a month ('I'd done all this stuff already, when I was 15.'), so the agency sent her to Paris, where she became an enormous success and appeared on the cover of countless magazines. She returned to New York 'a star', and landed a lucrative contract with L'Oreal Cosmetics, who paid her $500,000 for 12 days' work a year for modelling their make-up. She also posed for The Gap, where she met former model Paul Qualley and three months later married him. Subsequently, he became a successful singer (reaching Italy's top ten as P.J. Qualley) and she became the mother of his son, Justin.

She was Jane in Hugh Hudson's visually sumptuous *Greystoke*, dressed not in a chamois leather but in Victorian lace and frills, and was romanced by a gentrified Tarzan (Christopher Lambert). The film was a success, but when MacDowell's Southern vowels were dubbed over by Glenn Close, she revealed: 'I was furious. I had a nervous breakdown about it. It was the worst thing I could imagine. I called my manager. I called everyone.'

A year later, she was ninth-billed in *St Elmo's Fire*, playing the heart's desire of Emilio Estevez, but she felt ostracized from the rest of the cast (Rob Lowe, Andrew McCarthy, Demi Moore, Ally Sheedy). Although the film was a success, few remember that MacDowell was in it.

She joined Ben Kingsley in the little-seen Italian mini-series *The Sahara Secret* and continued modelling. In a series of Calvin Klein ads on TV, she appeared as herself and wrote her own

*Andie and Gerard Depardieu in Peter Weir's winning romantic comedy **Green Card***

script – in which she addressed the camera with intriguing tales of the South. It was the first time people were genuinely aware of her accent.

She then read Steven Soderbergh's screenplay for *sex, lies, and videotape*. 'I was so touched by the role [of Ann Millaney],' she recalls, 'I wanted to live her, I wanted to *be* her so badly. And then I learned later that I almost didn't get to go up for it, because Steven, judging by my history, wasn't that enthusiastic about me.' Soderbergh admits: 'There were some people who weren't willing to consider her. But at the audition she completely blew me out. I went to my producers and said, "I think Andie's it," and they exchanged looks like, "Uh, oh." I knew people would be caught off guard by her work, which means now I get to look like a smart guy.'

*Andie MacDowell in a little English film called **Four Weddings and a Funeral***

Shot on a budget of $1.2 million, the film was a ferociously honest look at sex and the stagnation of marriage, and MacDowell (who was then pregnant with her second child, Rainey) was perfect as the emotionally constipated wife of Peter Gallagher, who is cheating on her with her sister (Laura San Giacomo). Soderbergh, who may have been aware of the irony, begins the film with a voice-over from MacDowell, who is talking to her therapist. 'Garbage,' she drawls, 'all I've been thinking about all week is garbage.'

She wasn't asked to audition for the role of Tina in the British black comedy *The Object of Beauty*, in which she played a skittish American tourist trapped in a London hotel with John Malkovich. 'At first, I wasn't really sure if I liked the script or not, because Tina is weak – or can seem weak,' she mused. 'Then I looked beyond that weakness and I saw that Tina is very colourful and fun.' The film was a delightful comedy of manners, and MacDowell exposed a new, playful side to her persona (as well as a shapely bottom).

She was repressed again in Peter

Weir's utterly charming and touching romantic comedy *Green Card*, in which she was an aristocratic New Yorker who marries a French lump (Gerard Depardieu) in order to qualify for the apartment of her dreams. The outcome was predictable enough, but it was a sheer joy to follow the film to its five-Kleenex conclusion. *Green Card* was a success, and MacDowell won another Golden Globe nomination.

When the Dutch actress Maruschka Detmers had to withdraw from *Hudson Hawk* because of back troubles, the *National Enquirer* claimed she was removed from the film at Demi Moore's insistence. 'Bullshit,' scoffed Bruce Willis, the film's star and Demi's husband. Anyway, Andie MacDowell was hastily flown in to replace her. For MacDowell, her role as 'a hip nun in Ray-Bans' was 'a whole new departure for me, to be in a real broad, screwball comedy.' Unfortunately, few were amused, and the $55 million movie was christened *Hudson the Duck* by the media and became the year's biggest bomb.

Her next role, in the omnibus TV feature *Women & Men 2: In Love There Are No Rules*, was a brave one. In the segment entitled 'A Domestic Dilemma', co-starring Ray Liotta as her concerned husband, MacDowell faced the spectre of her own mother's alcoholism by playing a woman who succumbs to the bottle. The only shame was that she didn't have more time to develop her character in the half hour allotted her.

Next, she played herself in Robert Altman's acclaimed *The Player*, and then won top-billing in the romantic mystery *Ruby Cairo*, as a woman searching for her husband across LA, Mexico, Egypt and Germany – assisted by Liam Neeson. In Harold Ramis's successful, high-concept comedy *Groundhog Day*, she was delightful as a smart, fun-loving TV producer tenaciously courted by a cynical weatherman (Bill Murray), and she then top-billed the all-star cast of Robert Altman's blue-collar satire *Short Cuts*, as a housewife whose young son is run over by waitress Lily Tomlin. In Mike Newell's enchanting, hilarious *Four Weddings and a Funeral* she was romanced by Hugh Grant's serial monogamist, and the film went on to become the highest-grossing British

picture of all time. Ironically, it was knocked off its No. 1 post in the USA (after just one week) by *Bad Girls*, in which MacDowell played a whore on the run, and which the critics hated. She hated it too ('I thought I was awful.') and confessed that she took the role, 'because I had huge mortgage payments due. I had just done *Four Weddings* for no money, even though I had points. Later on, it was absolutely fabulous because I ended up making over my normal amount – enough to pay for my pregnancy and my year off.'

She christened her third child Sarah Margaret, and next opted to star in a small-scale film, *Unstrung Heroes*, for first-time feature director Diane Keaton. Although top-billed, her role was a small one – as the bed-ridden wife of John Turturro – but the film was a charmer, a gentle, unassuming and frequently amusing adaptation of Frank Lidz's semi-autobiographical novel.

*Andie MacDowell in **Michael***

She then went mainstream again, returning to work for director Harold Ramis in *Multiplicity*. Michael Keaton starred as an overworked construction foreman and father who has himself clandestinely cloned in order to cope with his schedule. While Keaton was soundly praised for his multi-character performance, MacDowell, as the wife who becomes increasingly confused by her multiplying husbands, had the more difficult part. Indeed, her sharp, observant performance was the stuff of great reacting.

She was less effective in Nora Ephron's awkward fantasy *Michael*, in which she played an ersatz angel expert who falls for tabloid reporter William Hurt. The sexual chemistry just wasn't there, although MacDowell did have a wonderful scene in which she stood up in a crowded bar and sang a country & western number about her three ex-husbands. She then headed the cast of Wim Wenders' *The End of Violence*, with Gabriel Byrne and Bill Pullman.

FILMOGRAPHY

1984: *Greystoke, The Legend of Tarzan, Lord of the Apes*. 1985: *St Elmo's Fire*. 1987: *The Sahara Secret* (TV). 1989: *sex, lies, and videotape*. 1990: *The Object of Beauty; Green Card*. 1991: *Hudson Hawk; Women & Men: In Love There Are No Rules* (TV). 1992: *The Player* (bit part). 1993: *Deception* (a.k.a. *Ruby Cairo*); *Groundhog Day; Short Cuts*. 1994: *Four Weddings and a Funeral; Bad Girls*. 1995: *Unstrung Heroes*. 1996: *Multiplicity; Michael*. 1997: *The End of Violence*. 1998: *The Scalper* (aso ex prod.).

MADONNA

By the early 1990s, what the world didn't know about Madonna wasn't worth knowing. Not only was she the pop phenomenon of her time, but also an actress, songwriter, dancer, business-woman, sex symbol, fashion queen and, above all, self-publicist. Spike Lee, who knows about such things, proclaimed: 'Marketing is something I'm very proud of. The only artist that does it better than me is Madonna. She's the champ.'

Indeed, she was *the* commodity of the sex-starved 1990s, a golden-throated siren who understood the currency of lust. She also recognized the dangers of over-exposure, and consequently spread her celebrity over increasingly diverse domains. In 1992, a year which saw the release of her eighth album, *Erotica*, and her appearance in two films, she brought out a book succinctly titled *Sex*. A compilation of erotic photographs celebrating the joys of bisexuality and sado-masochism, the tome displayed Madonna in various

Madonna as Susan in Susan Seidelman's **Desperately Seeking Susan**

degrees of undress, accompanied by her arbitrary thoughts on anything and everything erotic. Bound in aluminium foil and accompanied with a CD, *Sex* cost a cool £25 in Britain and sold out instantly. In Germany they were flogging it for the equivalent of $65, and it sold out there, too. In short, it was the publishing sensation of the year.

In another attempt to flex her versatility, the star took to the New York stage in David Mamet's critically celebrated play *Speed-the-Plow*. Although she was not happy with the way her part turned out ('It ended up being a plot manipulation,' she complained), her director, Gregory Mosher, was impressed. 'It is not Madonna's habit to lie,' he revealed. 'Her habit is to be truthful. And that is the essence of being an actor – to tell the truth in imaginary circumstances. She tells the truth in her life. In her dancing. In her lyrics. I love her straightforwardness.'

If any far-flung corner of the Madonna machine revealed a weak link, it was her movie career. After a promising film 'debut' in *Desperately Seeking Susan*, in which she proved she could be as comfortable in front of a camera as a microphone, the singer embarked on a series of cinematic flops that grew in magnitude as her fame increased. *Shanghai Surprise* was a vehicle for her and her husband, Sean Penn, and both of them were embarrassing in it. *Who's That Girl* was a farce so moronic that it defied belief, while *Bloodhounds of Broadway* was so bad it didn't even get a British release. However, when Madonna replaced

Sean Penn with Warren Beatty in her life, she was given the female lead – as Breathless Mahoney – in the latter's *Dick Tracy*. Although the seventh highest-grossing movie of 1990, *Dick Tracy* was considered a box-office disappointment by Buena Vista, its distributor. Of all Madonna's films, only *A League of Their Own*, in which she had a supporting role, could be considered an out-and-out home run. Until *Evita*, that is.

The star was born Madonna Louise Veronica Ciccone in Detroit, Michigan, on 16 August 1959, the daughter of a Chrysler engineer. The third child of eight, she was immediately immersed in the strict, authoritarian rule of her strict, Italian Catholic family. When she was six her mother died of cancer, which transformed her into a hypochondriac and daddy's girl. When her father later remarried, it almost destroyed her. 'I said, "OK, I don't need *anybody*," and I hated my father for a long, long time,' she revealed. 'And I made a promise to myself that no one was going to hurt me again. I was going to be somebody, I was going to rise above it.'

At school she dreamed of becoming a nun, but her desire for boys eventually clouded her more pious aspirations. The day after she ditched her vision of sisterhood she landed her first kiss – in a convent, naturally. It was, she recalls, 'incredible'.

She was a bad girl, stealing kisses from her girlfriends' boyfriends, setting up shoplifting contests and going to church naked under her coat. After

*As mischievous Mae Mordabito in the huge 1992 hit **A League of Their Own***

'Please let's not talk about it. OK, so it was one big fat flop. But that is beside the point. For me, after the darkness of *At Close Range*, it seemed like a rather extravagant and exciting opportnity to do something totally crazy. Now, I'm trying very hard not to think of it in commercial terms.' And, almost in apology: 'You know, there's more than one way of looking at a movie.'

Any way you looked at *Bloodhounds of Broadway*, it was a flop. Devoid of wit or charm, the film was an amalgamation of four Damon Runyan stories, with Madonna a nightclub singer in love with gambler Randy Quaid. At least Madonna seemed to have a grip on her material, which is more than can be said for the rest of the cast, which included Matt Dillon, Rutger Hauer and Jennifer Grey. For some

school, she trained as a dancer in Detroit, and in 1978 moved to New York, where she worked on choreography in Alvin Ailey's dance troupe. It was around this time that she made her 'unofficial' film debut in the underground movie *A Certain Sacrifice*, later dismissed as 'a sex-slave romp'. For her part, she was paid $100 and played a teenage drifter out to revenge the men who gang-raped her. Later, when the film was released directly on video, Madonna sued the distributors, but to no avail.

She followed this with an excursion to Paris with the Patrick Hernandez Revue, and then returned to the USA to cut a series of demo tapes. Sire Records signed her, and soon she was pumping out singles, racking up such number one hits as 'Like a Virgin', 'Material Girl', 'Crazy For You', 'Into the Groove', 'Open Your Heart', 'Papa Don't Preach', 'True Blue', 'La Isla Bonita', 'Who's That Girl', 'Like a Prayer', 'Lovesong' (with Prince), 'Vogue' and 'Justify My Love'. With that lot she became the hottest female singer of the 1980s, with her records reportedly selling an average one million copies a week worldwide. To provide an indication of her popularity, when her 1987 Wembley concert in London was announced, all 144,000 tickets sold within the space of 18 hours and 9 minutes. Between the years 1986 and 1990 it was estimated that she earned a phenomenal $90 million and, in 1992, she cut a deal with

Time Warner that was to net her a further $60 million. Madonna not only made records, she broke them.

In 1985, with two albums under her belt (*Madonna*, *Like a Virgin*), she appeared briefly in *VisionQuest* singing 'Crazy For You', and then landed a central role in Susan Seidelman's *Desperately Seeking Susan*, as Susan. Playing a zany, man-devouring slut, Madonna could not have found the part too much of a stretch, but she did it extremely well and helped the low-budget comedy become a huge cult.

A year later, she played a 1930s missionary in the British-American *Shanghai Surprise*, an adventure yarn inspired by *The African Queen* and *Casablanca*, produced by George Harrison and co-starring her new husband, Sean Penn. The press declared war on the film, and the public stayed away, and all for perfectly good reasons: the movie was a stiff, with Madonna delivering the worst performance of the year.

Who's That Girl was equally dumped on by the critics, but at least it generated three hit singles to help pump up its box-office. A cliche-ridden farce about a zany jailbird (Madonna) reluctantly escorted by a hapless Griffin Dunne, the film was cluttered by obvious stereotypes and tired plot devices. Its director, James Foley, had previously directed Penn in *At Close Range* (featuring Madonna on the soundtrack), and obviously felt a rapport with the Penns. However, even he pleaded:

*Madonna in her most naked performance to date, in Abel Ferrara's searing **Dangerous Game***

extraordinary reason, the media greedily exploited the rumour that Madonna was having an affair with Ms Grey, no doubt prompted by Madonna's teasing appearance on TV's *Late Night With David Letterman* show. She and her good friend, Sandra Bernhard, decided to 'have some fun' and owned up to a lesbian affair – which the media took at face value and milked to the full.

Snubbing her critics, Madonna embarked on a whirlwind romance with the ultra-straight Warren Beatty, following an equally tempestuous divorce from Sean Penn. Neither actor-director relished the attention of the press, so it was odd that they both chose to court such a public figure. Still, Beatty found her irresistible. He said: 'Madonna is simultaneously touching and more fun than a barrel of monkeys. She's funny, and she's gifted in so many areas and has the kind of energy as a performer that can't help but make you engaged.'

Beatty's last picture, *Ishtar*, had been a box-office bomb, due – according to popular theory – to the star's reluctance to publicize it. So no doubt it helped that Beatty cast Madonna in his next, which he not only starred in but directed and produced. Beatty took the title role, Dick Tracy, and Madonna played Breathless Mahoney, a sultry nightclub singer who, in the film's most famous line, purred to her leading man: 'I know how you feel: you don't know if you want to hit me or kiss me. I get a lot of that.' In spite of a starry cast that included Al Pacino, Dustin Hoffman and James Caan, it was Madonna who stole the show – along with the film's amazing make-up effects.

Dick Tracy, backed up by an enormous publicity and marketing campaign, was a resounding hit, and won Oscars for best make-up, art direction and the song 'Sooner or Later', composed by Stephen Sondheim and delivered by Madonna.

The following year she found herself in another success, *Truth or Dare*, an eye-opening documentary chronicling the singer's 'Blonde Ambition' world tour. Packed with provocative, showstopping Madonna hits, the film also revealed the star in private – backstage with Beatty, flirting with her male dancers and making fun of Kevin Costner. She also disclosed her inexhaustible obsession with sex and told how she handled the pressures of stardom. Some accused the film of being a set-up job, but it was none the less as entertaining a rockumentary as you could find.

In 1992 she took a cameo in Woody Allen's *Shadows and Fog*, as a trapeze artist who conducts an affair with John Malkovich's clown. She then took a supporting role in the baseball hit *A League of Their Own*, directed by Penny Marshall, in which she played the streetwise, knicker-flashing 'All the way' Mae, and gleefully announced: 'May. That's not a name, that's an attitude.' Although Geena Davis and Tom Hanks had the bigger roles, Madonna added some much-needed grit to the sentimental stew, and the film stormed off with $105 million at the US box-office.

As Marias Eva Duarte Peron, the role that won her the Golden Globe (but no Oscar) in Alan Parker's **Evita**

Next, she starred in the erotic thriller *Body of Evidence*, with Willem Dafoe and Joe Mantegna, in which, in the words of director Uli Edel, 'She plays a woman accused of murdering her lover ... with sex.' However, critics dismissed the film as a bargain-basement rip-off of *Basic Instinct*, and at a private screening in New York the audience greeted it with jeers and laughter. Worse still, her acting was called into question. Although a Hollywood executive vouchsafed, 'they are going to edit a good performance out of her,' Madonna's acting coach on the movie offered: 'This girl will never be an actress. She is too vulgar and she thinks she knows it all.'

Next, the singer was announced as the star of the low-budget *Dangerous Game*, a drama set in the world of moviemaking and created by Madonna's own production company, the Maverick Picture Co. As part of her lucrative deal with Time Warner, the film co-starred Harvey Keitel and was directed by Abel Ferrara (who had directed Keitel in the highly controversial *Bad Lieutenant*). Also, there was the role of a Brooklyn girl in *Angie* (written especially to show off her range as an actress), but when pre-production conflicted with the shoot of *Dangerous Game*, Geena Davis was brought in to replace her. Madonna reportedly faxed Joe Roth, the film's producer, saying: 'I can understand why you had reservations about my ability. I can see why you would think Geena Davis is the better actress for the part. After all, she's Italian and has an edge.' Roth, ignoring this sarcasm, simply explained: 'She was offered the role but chose to do *Dangerous Game* instead.'

Madonna was also announced to play the title role in the long-awaited film version of the stage hit *Evita*, beating Meryl Streep to the part. Before she knew the role was hers, the singer announced: 'I've decided that if anybody's going to do it, I'm going to do it – I'll kill Meryl Streep.' As it happens, Walt Disney Productions couldn't come to terms with the film's enormous budget, and *Evita* was put on hold. But then many Madonna projects met similar fates. At various points in her career she was due to do a remake of Dietrich's *The Blue Angel*, *Blessings in Disguise* (a love story to be produced by Warren Beatty) and *Leda and Swan*, with Demi Moore. She was also famous for deserting films at the eleventh hour, having been inked to appear in such projects as *Soapdish*, *Three of Hearts*, *The Bodyguard*, *Boxing Helena* and *Even Cowgirls Get the Blues*. But then everybody wanted Madonna.

While waiting to play Evita, the star sharpened her acting ability on a trio of cameos, namely in Wayne Wang's wonderful *Blue in the Face*, the disastrous *Four Rooms* (in which she played a witch) and Spike Lee's execrable *Girl 6*. Meanwhile, Oliver Stone had taken over the directorial reins of *Evita* and virtually came to blows with Madonna, who called him a 'pig'. Stone signed up Michelle Pfeiffer instead, but when Pfeiffer refused to film outside the USA and the promised Argentinean locations fell through, Stone jumped ship. Alan Parker (*Bugsy Malone*, *Fame*, *Pink Floyd – The Wall*) then took over the helm and immediately snapped up an eager Madonna, in spite of the reservations of the show's composer, Andrew Lloyd Webber. 'I don't think she's right for it,' Lloyd Webber announced. 'Perhaps ten years ago when she was younger, but I think she's a bit old for it now, because Evita died when she was 33.' True, Madonna was already 36 and had to play the Argentinian icon from her early days in poverty. But then Madonna was in remarkable shape – and she had Carlos Leon, her own personal fitness trainer, to prove it. Indeed, in April 1996, she announced from the *Evita* set in Budapest that Leon was the father of her unborn child.

In certain scenes in the finished picture, an embryonic tummy is noticeable, but this barely detracted from the role that Madonna was born to play. Both she and Maria Eva Peron (née Duarte) struggled free from their humble beginnings, and both women exhibited a strong will and take-charge attitude that shaped their respective careers. They even shared a subtle facial resemblance, and both dyed their naturally dark hair blonde, the colour with which they later became associated. To the astonishment of her detractors, Madonna proved that she could rise to the material and brought a subtlety and resonance to the Tim Rice-Lloyd Webber songs that was awe-inspiring. At last, Madonna had conquered the medium that had for so long eluded

her, and she stormed off with the Golden Globe to prove it.

Then on Monday 14 October 1996, she completed the most perfect year of her life. Her daughter, Lourdes Maria Ciccone Leon, entered the world weighing 6 pounds 9 ounces. Madonna noted: 'I don't have any plans. I'm reading scripts for other movies, but I haven't seen anything I love. Plus, I don't know what it's going to be like to have a baby. But I have a job – I have many jobs – which means I'm not going to be around changing diapers 24 hours a day.' We never suspected it.

Four months later, she signed up to play the photographer and revolutionary Tina Modetti in a film biography to be produced by Mick Jagger.

FILMOGRAPHY

1983: *A Certain Sacrifice* (filmed 1978–81). 1985: *VisionQuest; Desperately Seeking Susan*. 1986: *Shanghai Surprise*. 1987: *Who's That Girl*. 1988: *Bloodhounds of Broadway*. 1990: *Dick Tracy*. 1991: *Truth or Dare: On the Road, Behind the Scenes & In Bed With Madonna* (UK: *In Bed With Madonna*). 1992: *Shadows and Fog; A League of Their Own*. 1993: *Body of Evidence; Dangerous Game*. 1994: *Blue in the Face*. 1995: *Four Rooms*. 1996: *Girl 6; Evita*.

MATTHEW MCCONAUGHEY

Matthew McConaughey as he appeared in A Time to Kill

In the summer of 1996 a ferocious tug-of-war erupted between the major Hollywood studios: Warner Brothers, Twentieth Century Fox and Universal Pictures found themselves jostling for the services of an actor that only the most dedicated film buff might have heard of. While rumours that Matthew McConaughey was being offered a pay cheque worth $20 million were preposterous, they none the less reflected the heat of this overnight sensation.

Universal approached McConaughey to star in their *Day of the Jackal* (now just called *The Jackal*). Fox wanted him to replace Keanu Reeves in *Speed 2*. Warner Brothers were determined that their 'find' was going to honour his contract for a two-picture deal, following his starring role in Joel Schumacher's *A Time to Kill*. McConaughey turned a blind eye to the mounting dollar signs and opted to star in Warner's *Contact*, opposite Jodie Foster – not a bad choice, considering the sci-fi thriller (adapted from the bestseller by Carl Sagan) was one of the most hotly anticipated projects of 1997.

The actor also formed his own production company, J.K. Living, named after a line he improvised in the cult comedy *Dazed and Confused*: 'Just keep living.' The director of this film, Richard Linklater, snared McConaughey for the starring role in his *Newton Boys* (opposite fellow Texan Ethan Hawke), and Joel Schumacher joined hands with J.K. Living to direct the actor in *South Beach*, a comedy-drama about a gang of bank robbers. McConaughey was also snapped up by Steven Spielberg – to star alongside Anthony Hopkins and Morgan Freeman in *Amistad* – and by Sandra Bullock.

'I've learned more from Matthew than he has from me,' asserts the actress, who shared his bed in *A Time to Kill*. 'He's an exceptional human being and is so talented and raw; he doesn't make excuses. He's great, and he's become a powerful force in my life – we have fabulous chemistry together.'

In spite of remarks like this, Bullock insisted that her relationship with McConaughey was purely chummy – but if couples want the media to believe this, they shouldn't walk out of airports holding hands or do their grocery shopping together. One witness at a New York nightclub told the *National Enquirer*: 'They couldn't take their hands off each other. They were smooching all night and got up and slow-danced together.' Sounds like chemistry all right.

The point is that Matthew McConaughey, the country boy from Texas, took one year to graduate from being the peg-legged psycho in *The Return of the Texas Chainsaw Massacre* to being as hot as a jalapeño banquet.

Born in 1969 in Ulvade, Texas, and raised in Longview, 25 miles south of Lone Star, Matthew McConaughey emerged a million miles from show-business. Indeed, his mother was a kindergarten teacher and his late father an oil pipe salesman, an occupation that Matthew's two older brothers also took up. 'My whole youth was about the outdoors,' the actor confirmed, 'building tree houses and swimming – not about arts and stuff. We were only allowed to watch one hour of television a day, and that was *The Incredible Hulk*.'

*McConaughey in an early role as a Tucson cop, with Drew Barrymore and Whoopi Goldberg, in **Boys on the Side***

At the University of Texas, McConaughey settled on psychology and philosophy, then switched his wavering attention to law – then dropped out: 'I met a bunch of guys who were into storytelling, and I

thought, "What am I doing at law school?" I didn't have a passion for it, so I took myself off to film school.'

He was still there when, in a bar in Austin, he met Don Phillips, who was producing the 1970s high school comedy *Dazed and Confused*. McConaughey approached him, hoping for a job, maybe as a production assistant. 'We got on so well,' he recollects, 'that three hours later we were kicked out of the bar for being too rowdy.'

In spite of his lack of experience, McConaughey was cast in the film as Wooderson, the lascivious pothead who refuses to grow up. 'He's a kind of has-been,' the actor noted at the time. 'His high school years were the salad days for him, and he's not ready to give that up.' The character was written into just three scenes, but McConaughey improvised so well that the part was extended and became one of the major roles in the film. Indeed, McConaughey got to utter the movie's most immortal line: 'That's what I like about freshman girls, man – I get older, they stay the same age.' He also landed a walk-on part in the retarded teen fantasy *My Boyfriend's Back*, and then returned to complete his film course at university, directing a 12-minute short, *Chicano Chariots*, set in the Hispanic neighbourhoods around Austin, Houston and San Antonio.

He then took time off, riding 'around Europe with a couple of guys on bikes', and returned to Hollywood to make his name. He played Ben in the sugary, ludicrous baseball fantasy *Angels in the Outfield* (a remake of the 1951 comedy) and was 'Abraham Lincoln' in *Boys on the Side*, a Tucson cop who arrests and romances Drew Barrymore.

Next, he landed the lead in *The Return of the Texas Chainsaw Massacre* (the fourth instalment of the series), in which he played the psychotic Vilmer, a tow-truck driver with a high-tech false leg who terrorizes Renee Zellweger (of *Jerry Maguire* fame).

He was excessive again in the woefully misconceived Bill Murray vehicle *Larger than Life*, in which he played another crazed truck driver with an accent you could cut with a chainsaw. While initially the character proved a nice counterpoint to Murray's laid-back demeanour, McConaughey quick-

ly became tiresome as the script relegated him to the status of running gag.

In John Sayles' *Lone Star*, he changed tack dramatically, as legendary lawman Buddy Deeds. Appearing in flashback sequences alongside Kris Kristofferson, he gave a thoughtful, measured reading in a film rippling with atmosphere and nuance. While perhaps too subtle for its own good, *Lone Star* failed to draft any major awards but popped up in a remarkable number of critics' 'ten best' lists of 1996.

For the central role of Jake Brigance, the Mississippi lawyer in Schumacher's *A Time to Kill* (based on the novel by John Grisham), Warner Brothers were eyeing Brad Pitt, Woody Harrelson, Alec Baldwin and Val Kilmer, but Grisham (who had loosely modelled Brigance on himself) had casting approval and dismissed all of them. 'We went through everybody from Macaulay Culkin to George Burns,' recalled Schumacher. 'John, however, did not agree with me about any of them. When I saw Matthew in *Dazed and Confused*, he just jumped off the screen. His appeal is that on first glance he looks like the perfect boy next door that every mother would like her daughter to marry, and then on second look you find a dangerous wild guy and you tell your daughter to stay in the house. That is what makes him thoroughly fascinating.'

McConaughey was already in place as the Ku Klux Klan thug Freddie Cobb (a role which later went to Kiefer Sutherland), when he put himself forward for the lead. Schumacher agreed to a private screen test, which he duly sent to Grisham. They were both bowled over: the part was McConaughey's. 'I was on the set of *Lone Star*,' the actor recalls, 'when Joel called and said, "We're making a movie together." I went outside and said a prayer. I then went home that night and celebrated, just me and my dog, Miss Hud.'

McConaughey was paid $250,000 to play Brigance, and the film went on to gross $153 million, sealing the actor's future as a grade-A star. With his sandy hair and piercing blue eyes, he resembles a young Paul Newman, but it isn't until the climax of *A Time to Kill* that the true strength of McConaughey's

McConaughey with Ashley Judd in
A Time to Kill

talent explodes. Grabbing the emotional moment, he holds a Mississippi jury by the jugular as he sums up his defence of a black man charged with the murder of his daughter's white rapists. Throwing his legal training out of the window, Brigance jumps into the void. He begins his summation softly, turning to his audience with the words, 'I want to tell you a story.' He then recounts the horrendous details of the little girl's rape – and is unable to hold back the inevitable, silent tears. Finally, turning to the jury, he hands them a burning torch: '... then imagine she is white.' The case for Matthew McConaughey rests.

FILMOGRAPHY

1993: *Dazed and Confused; My Boyfriend's Back*. 1994: *Angels in the Outfield* (UK: *Angels*). 1995: *Boys on the Side; The Return of the Texas Chainsaw Massacre*. 1996: *Larger Than Life; Lone Star; A Time to Kill; Making Sandwiches* (40-minute short). 1997: *Scorpion Spring; Contact; Amistad*. 1998: *Newton Boys*.

MATTHEW MODINE

Matthew Modine was doing something right. With filmmakers like Robert Altman, Jonathan Demme, Stanley Kubrick, Alan J. Pakula, Alan Parker, Tony Richardson, Alan Rudolph and John Schlesinger queuing up for his services, he had to be pretty damn good.

Modine had very little to do in his first film, *Baby, It's You*, but his naturalness caught the attention of director Harold Becker, who had previously made stars of Tom Cruise and Sean Penn in 1981's *Taps*. 'Matthew's a natural,' Becker noted, 'and I've always used that term for him from the first time I saw him. You never felt you were watching somebody who wasn't already completely accomplished. There were no rough edges on him.'

Alan Parker, who directed Modine in the title role of *Birdy* – William Wharton's story of a boy obsessed with becoming a bird – added: 'He is a wonderfully natural actor with a built-in phony-detector, which makes it difficult for him to make a dishonest move. Birdy's obsession had to be strange but believable – I still wanted audiences to keep in touch with him, to care for him, to like him.'

In John Schlesinger's romantic thriller *Pacific Heights*, the actor played Drake Goodman, a young man head-over-heels in love (with Melanie Griffith), who is forced to re-evaluate his human priorities when a psychopathic conman (Michael Keaton) takes over their new home. Schlesinger explained: 'Drake is the type of person who is always trying to organize things, but sometimes flies off the handle too soon. For that, I needed someone with a certain character and youthfulness, but still able to cope with the violence that occurs. Matthew was my choice. He is a man, yet he still has a boyish charm, a certain naïveté about his personality. And he's a *very* good actor.'

The youngest of seven children,

Matthew Modine was born on 22 March 1959 in Loma Linda, California, but grew up in Utah, where his father was the manager of a drive-in theatre. 'I saw so many movies,' he recalled, 'that I'm sure it influenced my desire to be an actor.' Matthew's father was also a Mormon, which conflicted with his professional calling. 'The church leased the land, but they said they'd take back the lease if my dad showed restricted films,' Modine noted. 'There wasn't much else to show. They didn't want *Rosemary's Baby* shown, and now it's on TV! I think my parents recognized the tremendous amount of prejudice the Mormons have against *everything*.' Indeed, when he was 12 they left the Church.

He was 18 when he headed for New York to study acting with the legendary drama coach Stella Adler. He then appeared in the obligatory commercials and performed in such stage productions as *Our Town, Tea and Sympathy* and *The Brick and the Rose*. On TV, he had a role in *Texas*, a daytime soap modelled on *Dallas*, and in 1981 he appeared in the ABC Afternoon Special *Amy and the Angel*.

Two years earlier, in 1979, he had bumped into a woman, Caridad Rivera, on the street, helped carry her packages, took her to a movie and then to the altar. She understood his vocation to be an actor, and soon he was able to support her in the manner to which she was about to become accus-

*Matthew Modine (right) as the unusual hero of Alan Parker's extraordinary **Birdy**, with Nicolas Cage*

tomed. They are married to this day, and have two children, a son, Boman, and daughter, Ruby.

Four years later he made his film debut in John Sayles' *Baby, It's You*, and in his first scene on celluloid he had the pleasure of Rosanna Arquette throwing up over him. He was a star. Well, not quite. Harold Becker, fresh off *Taps*, earmarked him for *VisionQuest*, but first Modine had the humiliation of appearing in the limp sex comedy *Private School*, starring Phoebe Cates. At the time he was still studying acting in New York, and explained: 'I had a chance to go to Hollywood.' His big break arrived with the central role of Billy, the sexually ambivalent soldier in Robert Altman's screen version of David Rabe's anti-war play *Streamers*. The entire cast were jointly awarded the best actor prize at the 1983 Venice Film Festival. In *Hotel New Hampshire*, Tony Richardson's breezy film of John Irving's bestseller, Modine had *two* roles, as Chip Dove, the idol and rapist of Jodie Foster, and as Ernst, her radical German seducer. Few realized it was the same actor playing both roles.

Next came *VisionQuest* – the story of a 'mystical' high school wrestler who sets his sights on the state championship – a film Modine is not proud of ('We all have to work,' he said), and then Gillian Armstrong's downbeat *Mrs Soffel*, based on real events that occurred in 1901, in which he played Mel Gibson's younger brother, Jack Biddle, who is sentenced to hang as an accessory to murder, but is then sprung from jail by the warden's wife (Diane Keaton).

Then came Alan Parker, who was casting *Birdy*. Parker, who prepares his films with the care and foresight of a Utopian interior minister, explained: 'I met with every possible young actor who could play the part, and my video tapes were starting to take up more room than my luggage. In Philadelphia, we saw over 2,000 in one day, each one reading a couple of pages of the script, smiling for the Polaroid and being shown the back door. Winnowing through the video tapes, we gradually zeroed in on Matthew Modine for Birdy. Originally I read the part of Al with him [which eventually went to Nicolas Cage], but Matthew's gentle, introverted and honest qualities seemed

to say "Birdy". He never could understand how I had cast him without reading a single word of the Birdy part, but I had worn out the rewind button on my tape machine.' For Modine, *Birdy* was a very special experience. 'I *love* Alan Parker,' the actor volunteered, 'because he's, like, an inventor. They're ready to close the patent office and he comes along with something new and they have to open it up again.'

The film was a genuine original, a magical, funny and supremely well-crafted evocation of lost innocence that swept through the 1985 Cannes Film Festival with the force of a tornado. That year, *Birdy* won the Special Grand Jury Prize for 'its originality and spirit of research'.

From the brilliance of Parker, Modine found himself in the clutches of an even greater cinematic legend – Stanley Kubrick. Kubrick propelled the actor into the middle of his searing Vietnam War epic *Full Metal Jacket*, a brutal, numbing accomplishment that managed to meld cinematic mastery with emotional impact. Modine played Private Joker, the story's narrator, and it was the star's most rewarding experience yet. 'Stanley doesn't pay people much,' Modine explained, 'but I don't know any actor who doesn't want to work with him. It's a great apprenticeship.'

In *Orphans*, Alan J. Pakula's efficient film version of the play by Lyle Kessler, Modine played Treat, an urban outcast who kidnaps a genteel mobster (Albert Finney), prompting *Esquire* magazine to observe: 'Modine goes head-to-head with Albert Finney and takes your breath away.' He turned to comedy for Jonathan Demme's offbeat, eminently enjoyable *Married to the Mob*, as an FBI agent and master of disguise who falls in love with the gorgeous, edgy widow of a Mafia gangster. Modine was surprisingly engaging as the incompetent G-man who will go to any lengths to prove the innocence of his ward (which, as she was played by Michelle Pfeiffer, was hardly surprising).

He was less successful as a trainee doctor in the dramatic comedy *Gross Anatomy*, set in medical school, which *Variety* thought 'about as exciting as a pop quiz', but he had another hit (at least in Britain) with *Memphis Belle*. Produced by David Puttnam, this was

the polished, gung-ho story of ten young Americans who crew the B-17 of the title, a 'Flying Fortress' that flew 25 bombing missions over Nazi Germany. Modine was Captain Dennis Dearborne, but he had little opportunity to shine in the face of the World War II hardware and a cast of young actors all trying to top each other.

He had more screen time in *Pacific Heights*, an effective if unlikely thriller which, surprisingly, was inspired by real events. The film was a modest hit, and Modine was very good as a hapless first-time house buyer – but it was Michael Keaton's menacing tenant that cinemagoers remembered. He was an unexpected ingredient in the banal

As Private Joker in Stanley Kubrick's gut-kicking **Full Metal Jacket**

Italian costume melodrama *La Partita*, and although he contributed much enthusiasm as a young cad, he was madly miscast (Faye Dunaway, camping it up as a scheming noblewoman, seemed far more at home).

For Alan Rudolph, the acclaimed, maverick director of *Choose Me* and *The Moderns*, Modine starred in *Equinox* as identical twin brothers. Separated at birth, the doubles, Henry and Freddy, are as different as chalk from cheddar in character, one being a timid nerd, the other a strutting thug. As in all Rudolph's films, the blessings were mixed, but there was enough charm and innovation to keep enthusiasts for the unusual happy, while Modine himself was at the top of his form.

In *Wind*, he had little to act on, playing an introspective sailor who loses the Americas Cup and his girl-friend (Jennifer Grey), forcing him to re-think his values, etc. This was famil-iar territory, and banal at that, while (by all accounts) the film was a pain to work on. A better experience was Altman's brilliant, excoriating, all-star *Short Cuts*, a series of loosely-related tales based on the short stories of Raymond Carver. Modine played

As Dave, philandering divorcee, in Sam Weisman's amusing, perceptive **Bye Bye, Love**

Ralph Wyman, a doctor married to Julianne Moore, who, naked from the waist down, subjects him to a ferocious tongue-lashing.

He was in more stellar company in Roger Spottiswoode's intelligent and riveting TV movie *And the Band Played On*, and this time he had the lead. Heading a cast that included Richard Gere, Alan Alda, Phil Collins, Anjelica Huston, Steve Martin, Ian McKellen and Lily Tomlin, he played Don Francis, a pioneering researcher at Atlanta's Center for Disease Control who strives to identify and isolate a deadly virus that is devastating America's homosexual community. More significantly, he finds that it is up to him to teach the world that the virus (AIDS) is not a political or gay issue, but a health and human one. While the part offered him little emo-tional scope, it none the less got him nominated for both an Emmy and a Golden Globe.

He was third-billed in the awkward update of the classic Terence Rattigan play *The Browning Version* (as a likeable

chemistry teacher ensnared by Greta Scacchi), and he then directed a short called *Smoking*, which premiered at the 1994 Sundance Film Festival. Next, he took the title role in the biblical TV movie *Jacob*, which he described as: 'a great story: how Jacob is cheated by his uncle, tricked into marrying Leah instead of her sister Rachel, whom he loves, and how he perseveres.' In *Bye Bye Love*, a refreshing, funny look at the chaotic roundabout of child custody, he was a divorcé juggling girlfriends and fatherhood, and then he starred in the beguiling, poignant fantasy *Fluke* in which, he explained: 'I die and come back as a chocolate-brown Labrador – only to find that my best friend [Eric Stoltz] and my wife [Nancy Travis] have gotten together, and I'm their dog.'

When Michael Douglas jumped ship on the $100 million swashbuckling pirate epic *CutThroat Island*, the film's production company, Carolco, entered into a frenzy of casting sessions to find a replacement. And, after Liam Neeson, Daniel Day-Lewis, Ralph Fiennes, Jeff Bridges and Gabriel Byrne had all turned the part down, Modine climbed on board. At the time the actor was unaware that he was not first choice for the role, but countered: 'If someone said they'd be taking you away for six months, put you on a ship, let you swing around, have sword fights and kiss Geena Davis – well, that wouldn't be so bad, would it?' Indeed, Modine cut a dashing, mischievous figure as William Shaw, an athletic swindler and cheat, even when saddled with lines like: 'I'm all at sea when it comes to things nautical.' However, the film was a catastrophic bomb, which was a shame as it was a breathless, handsome and entertaining yarn that could have found an enormous audience.

He then went on a work binge, starring in Tom DiCillo's *The Real Blonde*, Abel Ferrara's *The Blackout* and Tim Hunter's *The Maker*.

FILMOGRAPHY

1983: *Baby, It's You*. 1983: *Private School*; *Streamers*. 1984: *The Hotel New Hampshire*; *VisionQuest*; *Mrs Soffel*; *Birdy*. 1987: *Full Metal Jacket*; *Orphans*. 1988: *Married to the Mob*; *La Partita* (a.k.a. *The Gamble/The Match*) (released 1991). 1989: *Gross Anatomy* (UK: *A Cut Above*). 1990: *Memphis*

Belle; *Pacific Heights*. 1992: *Wind*. 1993: *Equinox*; *Short Cuts*; *And the Band Played On* (TV; UK: theatrical). 1994: *The Browning Version*; *Smoking* (short) (directed); *Jacob* (TV). 1995: *Bye, Bye Love*; *Fluke*; *CutThroat Island*. 1997: *The Real Blonde*; *The Blackout*; *The Maker*.

DEMI MOORE

Demi Moore just couldn't keep her name out of the papers.

It all began when she became engaged to Emilio Estevez and can-celled the wedding after the invitations had already been sent out. She explained: 'There were things I needed, like security, that Emilio wasn't in a position to offer me.' She then married Bruce Willis on a whim, after a whirl-wind, four-month courtship. Following a Las Vegas boxing match, the couple rang for a priest at 11.15 p.m. and were exchanging vows by midnight.

Then there was the story that sur-faced about her former marriage. On a TV chat show, she informed viewers that Willis was her first husband, and that her wedding licence backed up the fact. But then her *real* first husband, rock musician Freddy Moore, exposed the sham. 'She's probably very embar-rassed that she made a mistake,' he revealed to the press. 'It's so interesting that she lied – perhaps she never told Bruce about me.' The musician claims she also lied about her age when she married him, saying she was 21 when, in fact, she was only 16. Three years

Demi in her biggest hit - **Ghost** *- with Patrick Swayze*

after the wedding, she walked out on him and became engaged to Emilio while she was still married.

Then there was the furore over her posing naked for the cover of *Vanity Fair* while seven months pregnant. News stands in Britain and the USA refused to display – or even sell – the magazine, deeming the cover pornographic. However, Demi stuck to her guns, saying: 'To me, being pregnant is the sexiest thing in the world. I feel proud and my intention of doing those photos was to convey that pride.' The issue became the most talked-about edition in the magazine's history and was a sell-out.

Then there were the well-publicized threatening phone calls and one ominous note, fashioned out of newsprint, that warned Mr and Mrs Willis: 'Watch out for your darling daughter.' This was apparently provoked by an injudicious comment Willis made, blaming the unions for the high cost of filmmaking in Hollywood – which was rich coming from a man who was reportedly charging Twentieth Century Fox $16 million to star in *Die Hard 3*. To back up the threats, an anonymous car forced Willis onto the curb of an LA street.

Then more outraged newsprint was devoted to Mrs Willis, declaring that she was going to give birth to her second child in front of her husband, brother, sister-and-law *and* her three-year-old daughter, Rumer Glenn. The actress countered by saying: 'I wanted Rumer there to share the joy of her sister's birth.'

And, just in case the public had failed to read about her for a month or two, Demi appeared on the cover of *Vanity Fair* again, this time naked save for a prudently-placed thong and a layer of body paint patterned after a man's suit and tie. Much publicity followed, and the issue was another bestseller.

Such was her standing in the garish corridors of the media that when she shaved her head to play a navy rating in *G.I. Jane*, her follically-challenged appearance at the premiere of *Striptease* became the talk of the week. Oh, and for Pete's sake, don't even mention *Striptease*.

Demi Moore was famous, alright, and the press had a heyday reporting

her prima donna behaviour, going on about her ubiquitous entourage and revealing her insistence that she be chauffeured in limousines and private jets. But she has her defenders. Ezra Litwak, who co-scripted *The Butcher's Wife*, volunteered: 'Demi is very much a movie star. Everything revolves around that fact. She knows what she wants and how to get it. She's a very focused woman.' More succinctly, the director Alan Rudolph (*Mortal Thoughts*) described her thus: 'She's like a beautiful ballerina who can also kick-box.'

Francis on the daytime soap *General Hospital*, playing cub reporter Jackie Templeton. She also got married.

On the big screen, she made her film debut in *Choices*, a small-scale drama about a deaf teenager; she had a cameo in the comedy *Young Doctors in Love*, and then battled a giant slug in a 3-D *Alien* rip-off called *Parasite*. Then she was signed up to play Michael Caine's daughter in the vacation comedy *Blame It On Rio*, and spent four months in Brazil. When she returned to Los Angeles she had outgrown her marriage.

Demi as Lt. Cdr. JoAnne Galloway - in Rob Reiner's $200 million plus earner **A Few Good Men**

But Demi Moore's world has not always been big news and big cars. She started life as Demi Gene Guynes on 11 November 1962, in Roswell, New Mexico (not insignificantly, the site of a notorious UFO landing). Hers was an unhappy childhood. Born to teenage parents, she was carted around the country by her stepfather, newspaper ad man Duane Guynes, who had married her mother, Virginia, when she was pregnant. In the space of 13 years, Demi was uprooted 48 times ('At a wild guess, I went to 30 schools,' she says). She also underwent an operation to correct a squint, resulting in total blindness in her left eye. When she was 15, her mother left Guynes, who committed suicide two years later – a month before Demi's 18th birthday. At 16, Demi quit school and left home to pursue a modelling career, appearing nude in *Oui*. After landing two words on the TV series *W.E.B.*, she got her big break when she replaced Genie

She had the female lead in *No Small Affair* (replacing Sally Field), playing a struggling rock singer worshipped by Jon Cryer, and made an impression. Craig Baumgarten, who cast her in the film, marvelled: 'I knew from the very, very beginning Demi was going to be a movie star. I knew it when I saw dailies on *No Small Affair*. She can rip your heart out, make you care. That's a rare quality and part of what makes a star. When she was in pain, you just wanted to make her feel better.'

Demi *was* in pain, struggling against a ruinous alcohol and drug addiction. 'When I was in school, doing Quaaludes and smoking pot and drinking was what a majority of the kids did,' she disclosed. But it had got out of hand.

She was in the thick of it when, at Universal Studios, she was spotted by the director Joel Schumacher, who was casting *St Elmo's Fire*. 'I just saw this beautiful girl with long dark hair flashing by my office,' he recalls. 'She was running around a corner. I said to my assistant, "Get that girl!" He chased her down in the parking lot.'

She was signed up to play Jules, a young banker addicted to cocaine. But when Schumacher caught wind of her real addiction, he threatened to fire her. Demi immediately attended rehab, turned herself around and delivered the most attention-grabbing performance of her career to date: playing a beautiful, tough-on-the-outside, vulnerable-on-the-inside beauty careening out of control in the fast lane. Emilio Estevez was also in the film, and the couple started dating.

More pictures followed – *One Crazy Summer*, a comedy with John Cusack; '*About Last Night ...*', a romantic drama with Rob Lowe, and *Wisdom*, with Emilio co-starring, scripting and directing. *Wisdom* was a formidable flop, and marked the end of Demi and Emilio's relationship. In the mean time, she married Bruce, and was carrying his daughter when she starred in *The Seventh Sign*, a flashy, apocalyptic thriller. Demi played a pregnant mother haunted by a very disturbing Jurgen Prochnow, and endured many violent scenes (causing some concern for her real-life, unborn child). She even did a nude scene, setting the pattern for events to come. The role was a showy one, and the actress disported herself well. If Steven Spielberg had directed *The Omen*, it might well have looked like *The Seventh Sign*.

She was in good company – with Robert De Niro and Sean Penn – in the dramatically unfunny comedy *We're No Angels*, and then she was cast in the starring role of *Ghost*. While Patrick Swayze and Whoopi Goldberg had to fight to get in the movie, Demi was first choice in what turned out to be the biggest-grossing film of 1990. As the loving wife of Swayze (who is killed by a mugger, but returns to express his love), Demi, with her hair cropped short, had never looked more beautiful, and she delivered a star-making performance.

At this point Bruce Willis was also doing well, top-billed in *Die Hard 2*, the most successful action movie of the year. Mr and Mrs Willis were ordained 'the hottest couple in Hollywood'. But the good fortune was short-lived.

While Bruce found himself in three monumental flops – *Bonfire of the Vanities*, *Hudson Hawk* and *Billy Bathgate* – Demi turned producer with *Mortal Thoughts* (co-starring Willis), another fiasco, and then teamed up with Chevy Chase, Dan Aykroyd and John Candy in *Nothing But Trouble*, which lived up to its name. She replaced Meg Ryan in

*Demi as Diana Murphy, the woman who thought she couldn't be bought - in Adrian Lyne's **Indecent Proposal***

The Butcher's Wife, a delightful, magical romantic comedy, but was miscast as a naive clairvoyant, and the film died at the box-office.

But then her career took a turn for the better. In Rob Reiner's box-office hit *A Few Good Men*, she played a fastidious, passionate trial lawyer, teamed with Tom Cruise to defend two marines accused of murder. The film, budgeted at a colossal $41 million, was one of the most prestigious of 1992, and boasted a supporting cast that included Jack Nicholson, Kevin Bacon and Kiefer Sutherland. As Cruise's senior officer determined to stick to the rule book, Demi made a feisty, formidable operator, but never lost sight of her vulnerability. After that, she secured the female lead in Adrian Lyne's controversial *Indecent Proposal*, playing a married beauty bought by millionaire Robert Redford for one night of passion. Derided by the critics, the film

went on to gross a staggering $250 million worldwide.

In February 1993, the *National Enquirer* claimed that the actress had secretly visited a divorce lawyer to end her five-year marriage to Bruce Willis. There were also reports of rows in public places, while one insider revealed: 'They've already moved into separate quarters in their New York condo. She's living on one floor with the children, and he's living on the other.' Moore retaliated with a passionate defence in *Hello* magazine, saying: 'We have never taken any of this Hollywood gossip stuff seriously. But these latest stories have hit too close to home. We started getting calls from friends, asking us if everything was all right. We have to let the truth be known. Bruce and I both make a great effort to compromise and our marriage continues to grow stronger and stronger.'

She received a walloping $5 million to star in *Disclosure*, a film which, dealing with the topical subject of sexual harassment, captured even more headlines than *Indecent Proposal*. But, being an adaptation of a Michael Crichton bestseller, the movie flipped the argument on its head, with Demi the sexual predator, accusing Michael Douglas of harassment in order to further her own career. Fluidly directed by Barry Levinson and breathlessly edited, *Disclosure* was the cinematic equivalent of a genuine page-turner, and grossed a resounding $80.6 million in the USA alone.

Next, she took on the demanding role of Nathaniel Hawthorne's famously persecuted heroine, Hester Prynne, in *The Scarlet Letter*, and was inexplicably savaged by the critics. A loose adaptation of Hawthorne's turgid 1850 novel, the film, directed by Roland Joffe, was a handsome, passionate look at the prejudice and injustice of early American history, and was well served by excellent performances from Gary Oldman and Robert Duvall.

She had better luck with the sentimental and nostalgic reunion sudser *Now and Then* – a sort of distaff *Stand by Me* – which she co-produced. She, Melanie Griffith, Rosie O'Donnell and Rita Wilson played childhood friends who meet up to reminisce on the good old days. However, the picture really

*Open and shut case: Demi flaunts her power in Barry Levinson's **Disclosure***

belonged to the quartet of actresses who played the stars at 12 years of age, with Gaby Hoffmann delightful as the younger Demi.

She turned down the lead in *While You Were Sleeping* (a mistake), and instead starred in *The Juror*, for which she received $7 million. A polished thriller in which Demi played an avant-garde sculptress and single mother (who is threatened by mob hitman Alec Baldwin), the film certainly had its moments, but it was a little too glossy for its own good, and performed poorly at the box-office.

Then, in a flurry of publicity, Demi became the highest-paid actress in history when she accepted $12.5 million to take her clothes off for *Striptease*. As she had just disrobed for *The Scarlet Letter*, somebody was obviously duped, but then Demi did do a lot of athletic dancing as well. By now the mother of three (Rumer, Scout and Tallulah Belle), Demi had to train particularly hard to tighten up her stomach muscles, but rather overdid it. Her legs looked more masculine than feminine, and when she was not strutting her stuff on stage she was giving the worst performance of her life. Still, she did have the one comfort that her co-star, Burt Reynolds, was even worse. The film was a real turkey, but nevertheless managed to lure over $113 million in international revenue.

She also supplied the voice of Esmeralda in Disney's animated *The Hunchback of Notre Dame* (her singing dubbed by Heidi Mollenhauer), appeared in the '1952' segment of the TV movie *If These Walls Could Talk* (which she executive-produced) and took the title role in Ridley Scott's *G.I. Jane*, as a navy rating who undergoes a government experiment 'to become the first woman to participate in a special reconnaissance training programme as an experiment to integrate female combat fighters'. She then joined Judy Davis, Amy Irving, Mariel Hemingway and Woody Allen in Woody's *Deconstructing Harry*, her fee of $450,000 making her the highest-paid performer ever to to appear in a Woody Allen film.

At the time of going to press, Demi and Bruce were expecitng their fourth child, a boy, when the actress attracted a wave of publicity over her alleged affair

*Gimme the $12.5 million or else! Demi as Erin Grant in **Striptease**, the film that made her the highest paid actress in the business (until Sandra Bullock came along, that is)*

with Leonardo DiCaprio. Needless to say, her lawyers denied the intimacy, even though DiCaprio was photographed leaving her house the morning after they had spent a very romantic day together on the streets of Los Angeles.

FILMOGRAPHY

1981: *Choices*. 1982: *Young Doctors in Love*; *Parasite*. 1983: *Blame It On Rio*. 1984: *No Small Affair*. 1985: *St Elmo's Fire*. 1986: *One Crazy Summer*; *'About Last Night …'*; *Wisdom*. 1988: *The Seventh Sign*. 1989: *We're No Angels*. 1990: *Ghost*. 1991: *Mortal Thoughts* (also co-produced); *Nothing But Trouble*. 1991: *The Butcher's Wife*. 1992: *Tales From the Crypt Volume 3* (UK: video); *A Few Good Men*. 1993: *Indecent Proposal*. 1994: *Disclosure*. 1995: *The Scarlet Letter*; *Now and Then*. 1996: *The Juror*; *The Hunchback of Notre Dame* (voice only); *Striptease*; *If These Walls Could Talk* (TV). 1997: *G.I. Jane* (also executive produced); *Deconstructing Harry*.

EDDIE MURPHY

In the early 1980s, Eddie Murphy rose like an unstoppable warhead. And, like all meteoric phenomenons, he found that both his image and his personal life suffered badly for it. He has been bashed by the critics, attacked by the black community and hit by more lawsuits than featured in an entire series of *LA Law*. He has been sued for sexual harassment, at least three women have claimed to have had his baby and, most famously, the humorist Art Buchwald (and his partner, Alain Bernheim) sued Murphy and Paramount for $6.2 million for reputedly stealing Buchwald's storyline to *Coming to America*.

Murphy estimates that he has paid out several million dollars settling 'spurious lawsuits', but reserves his greatest contempt for the media. 'The press builds you up and tears you down,' he told *Playboy* in 1990. 'I'm in the teardown stage right now … Most of the people who want to talk with me, I feel, want to get me.'

But things got worse. When he was filming *Boomerang* in 1992, the trade paper *Variety* reported that on one occasion the star never showed up for a re-shoot in Atlanta – which cost Paramount Pictures $300,000. Another time he arrived to the location so late that the crew had started filming another scene. Furious, he walked off again. On yet another instance the star decided to see *Cape Fear* on the way to the set, and kept the crew waiting and guessing as to whether or not they'd ever see Murphy again. Sources estimated that overall *Boomerang* lost almost 100 working hours due to Murphy's tardiness. The producer, Brian Grazer, acknowledged that *Boomerang* actually went '$2 million to $3 million over budget'.

The most popular black screen idol of all time, Eddie Murphy has been criticized – particularly by the filmmaker Spike Lee – for not helping the black cause more. Indeed, racism has never been a big issue for Murphy: 'I grew up in a black neighbourhood and did not stray from the block,' he says. 'Consequently, I did not encounter any racism until I was 18. Everybody is

Murphy as Axel Foley in the megahit Beverly Hills Cop

preoccupied with the system and injustice and shit like that. But I am very nonchalant about everything. There's a lot wrong, but it's getting better.'

'Eddie doesn't want to be viewed as The Black Messiah,' added the star's personal assistant, Mark Corry. 'He'll do as much as he can to open doors for minorities, but he thinks the best way to do that is [through] good "colourless" TV and films.'

However, while shooting *Boomerang*, Murphy did persuade Paramount to fund ten paid positions for the Black Filmmaker Foundation Observer Program. According to the film's co-producer, Warrington Hudlin: 'This is the first time in 25 years, by my count, where a major studio has financed a learning experience for people of colour.'

With a star as big as Eddie Murphy it's hard to evaluate the true picture. Constantly surrounded by five bodyguards, and at one point employing as many as 52 people, he is not so much a recluse as an enigma blurred by contradictory media reports. As eccentric as any celebrity of his standing, Murphy has admitted that, when he's not working, he likes to get out of bed between 2 p.m. and 4 p.m., and goes back to sleep around 8 a.m. He also admits: 'I wash my hands 100 times a day.' Today, he is wary of talking to the press, and certainly doesn't need the publicity. While Murphy is reputed to be impossible to work with, his *Boomerang* co-star, Halle Berry, acknowledged that she was terrified at her screen test. 'I was a wreck,' she confided. 'I had read all those horror stories. But when I walked in, he just looked like a little boy with a big smile on his face, and all those fears went away.'

Another co-star, David Alan Grier, volunteered: 'What freaks you out is that his talent is so deep. He can mimic, he can mime, he can do physical comedy, he can do verbal comedy, and then he'll sit down at the piano and play just beautifully. Not rock 'n' roll, but serious piano. This guy is really, really heavy.'

Eddie Murphy was born 7 pounds, 2 ounces, on 3 April 1961, in Bushwick, Brooklyn. The son of a New York cop, he lived with his mother, a switchboard operator, and his stepfather, an employee of an ice-cream factory. He was a poor student, and his mother despaired of her son's future. 'Don't worry, Ma,' he comforted her, 'I'm going to be famous.'

At 15 he was fat and bespectacled and performed impromptu comedy routines in the school playground to gain favour. It was then that he first stepped on to a stage – at the Roosevelt Youth Center on Long Island. He continued his stand-up

comedy routine at local bars, and joined New York's Comic Strip following graduation. He would do mime, tell dirty jokes, impersonate the likes of Elvis Presley, Michael Jackson and Richard Pryor, grab his crotch and pepper his humour with a roll call of profanity. And then he would laugh that big, self-possessed, open laugh, inviting the audience to laugh along with him – *at* him.

At 19 he joined the 1980–81 season of TV's cult *Saturday Night Live*. Previously a springboard for such comic talent as Chevy Chase, John Belushi, Dan Aykroyd and Bill Murray, the revue was undergoing a rocky patch. At first Murphy was just a 'featured player' and could not stem the show's escalating disfavour with the public. However, when he was brought on board as a regular, he won three Emmy nominations in four years and turned the revue around. He was a star.

Cashing in on his TV popularity, Paramount paid Murphy $200,000 to appear opposite Nick Nolte (who was paid $2 million) in *48 HRS*, Walter Hill's hard-hitting comedy about a tough cop (Nolte) and a wily crook (Murphy) who spend two days insulting each other. The public loved the sinewy mix of broad comedy and violence, and *48 HRS* went on to gross over $30 million in the USA alone. Worldwide, it amassed almost $100 million.

A year later, Paramount paid Murphy $300,000 to replace Richard Pryor in *Trading Places*, John Landis's high-concept comedy about a pampered financier (Dan Aykroyd) and a street-smart bum (Murphy) who change places for a bet. Again, the public lapped up Murphy's high-octane display of comedy, and the film grossed over $40 million in the USA.

With two smash-hits to his name, Eddie Murphy could do no wrong, and he accepted $1 million to support Dudley Moore in the catastrophic *Best Defense*. 'They started offering me all this money,' he explained later. 'I was 21 years old. I said to hell with it and went for it. I knew the script for *Best Defense* was horrible, but I got talked into the movie by Paramount.'

He was offered considerably more – $4.5 million, plus a percentage of the profits – to play unorthodox cop Axel

Foley in *Beverly Hills Cop*, a film he was *very* happy with. Originally intended as a vehicle for Sylvester Stallone, the film had a muscular storyline alleviated by some high comedy playing from Murphy. It was a winning combination.

As Prince Akeem in John Landis's entertaining (but litigation plagued) **Coming To America**

'I think I could play Foley forever,' he says. 'I really enjoy him and I'm grateful audiences seem to feel the same way.' Indeed, *Beverly Hills Cop* grossed a phenomenal $350 million worldwide, and some say Murphy hasn't stopped playing Foley since.

Still, it's a formula that works – the rule-breaking smart-ass with the Grand Canyon laugh – and Murphy has mined it like gold. Paramount paid him $6.5 million to star in *The Golden Child*, another palpable hit, but this time one lambasted by the critics. He got $8.5 million for *Beverly Hills Cop II*, another critical bomb, but the highest-grossing movie of 1987. Paramount paid him the same again for *Coming to America* (in which he played four different characters and wrote the story), and once more critics and public disagreed.

At a time when the Hollywood star system was supposedly dead, Eddie Murphy was breaking the rules. While other icons were counting their flops and licking their wounds, Eddie triggered box-office queues for whatever he starred in. And he was now critic-proof.

Besides starring in his record-breaking movies, Eddie was spreading his tal-

ent elsewhere. He produced two comedy albums, the Grammy-nominated *Eddie Murphy* and Grammy-winning *Eddie Murphy: Comedian*; started a singing and songwriting career (his LPs number *How Could It Be*, *So Happy* and *Love's Alright*); taped a concert, *Delirious*, for HBO (now a bestselling video), and executive-produced the film of his one-man show, *Eddie Murphy Raw*, which became the most successful filmed concert in history.

Although now one of the richest stars in Hollywood, Eddie Murphy was still unhappy with his Paramount contract. He renegotiated his $15 million, five-picture deal with the studio *twice*, and told *Playboy*: 'I have a *horrible* deal at Paramount. Whoever's gonna give me the most lucrative deal, that's where I'm going' (later, he received $12 million, plus 15 percent of the gross, for *Boomerang*). Reputedly, he was furious that Tom Cruise, Arnold Schwarzenegger and Jack Nicholson were getting paid more than he was.

Then came the fall. Eager not to lose face with his Afro-American peers (Spike Lee, Keenen Ivory Wayans, Robert Townsend), Murphy decided to direct and produce his next picture, the period gangster comedy *Harlem Nights*. Based on his own screenplay, and co-starring his idols, Richard Pryor and Redd Foxx, the film was dumped on *hard* by the critics and is an unpleasant memory for the star. '*Harlem Nights* was the first time I did a movie that flopped,' Murphy acknowledges. 'It didn't flop on a monetary level, but it was, like, "Ugh, did you see that piece of shit?" And I had never gone through that before.'

Eddie Murphy had slumped to No. 22 in the box-office polls, even though his reunion with Nick Nolte in *Another 48 HRS* (trashed by the critics) grossed a resounding $89 million in the USA. But even Eddie was now aware of his professional slump, in spite of a new deal with Paramount that promised a much-ballyhooed $50 million. 'I walked through *Another 48 HRS*. I was depressed. I was fat. I was, like, 185 pounds.' By now, he also knew he'd been ego-tripping. However, he rationalized: 'There's no such thing in this business as someone who is successful *and* humble.'

Ensconced in Bubble Hill, New

Jersey, his 4 acre, $3.5 million answer to Elvis Presley's Graceland, Murphy worked out in his private gym, played with his little daughter, Bria (by Murphy's live-in girlfriend, model Nicole Mitchell), worked on his third album and occasionally showed up on the set of *Boomerang*. Loaned a new lease of life by Nicole, Bria and his music, Murphy shed 15 pounds.

Boomerang, the story of a self-centred, womanizing marketing executive who meets his match when he's employed by the gorgeous, ruthless Robin Givens, was admired by two critics in Washington and earned $13.7 million in its first weekend on release. One insider grumbled: 'It's too bad the movie's so good, because Murphy behaved so awfully and there'll be no reason for him to shape up. He's magic on screen.'

Boomerang grossed an agreeable $67 million in the USA, but his next comedy, Disney's *The Distinguished Gentleman*, a broad satire on Washington politics and chicanery, only attracted $46 million. This fact, coupled with Murphy's salary of $12 million, was bad news to everybody. However, the star was perfect as the slick conman

Murphy with Robin Givens in Reginald Hudlin's **Boomerang**

who tricks his way into Congress, although the supporting cast of Caucasian character actors were encouraged to mug shamefully.

Then, on Thursday 18 March 1993, Eddie Murphy married his long-time girlfriend, Nicole Mitchell. Among the 500 guests at the lavish ceremony were Quincy Jones, Bill Murray, Stevie Wonder, Bruce Willis and the bride

Fangs for nothing: Eddie teams with horror maestro Wes Craven for **Vampire In Brooklyn**

and groom's children, Bria, three, and Myles, four months.

Next, he received $15 million to reprise Axel Foley for *Beverly Hills Cop III*, a $45 million re-working of the old formula. When Foley's friend and mentor is murdered in a Detroit shoot-out, the grinning detective tracks down the killer to LA – whereupon the film shifts into a *Die Hard in Disneyland* scenario. In fact, the true star of the picture was the elaborate theme park built for the film, where the good guys and bad guys fight it out in a myriad of fantastic sets, ducking around dinosaurs, simulated floods, train rides and the like. However, you didn't have to be an accountant to work out that if a film costing $45 million made $42.6 million (in the USA), you didn't have a lot left over after the exorbitant expense of marketing, distribution and hidden costs.

Meanwhile, Murphy proved so keen to work with horror maestro Wes Craven on *Vampire in Brooklyn* that he deferred his considerable salary – a mistake, as it happens. The film barely limped off with $18.9 million. Still, *Vampire* was a labour of love for Murphy. He not only co-produced the picture (with Mark Lipsky), but he concocted the original story with his brother, Charles, who co-scripted. 'I've always been entertained by scary movies,' Murphy revealed, 'and particularly intrigued by vampire tales. I'm real familiar with Wes Craven's work.' In fact, Murphy not only played the title character, Maximilian, but also the parts of doddery Preacher Pauly and

Guido, a small-time hood. 'It was terrific to be able to do this kind of entertainment again, like the characters I did on *Saturday Night Live*,' he enthused. 'The audience can expect the unexpected in this movie.'

While *Vampire* proved to be an ill-fated marriage of guffaws and gore (and terribly derivative at that), it at least paved the way for the star's next multi-charactered exercise, *The Nutty Professor*. A special effects-enhanced remake of Jerry Lewis's most famous film, the comedy featured an unrecognizable Murphy as Professor Sherman Klump, a pioneering scientist with an excruciating weight problem.

The director was Tom Shadyac, who had guided Jim Carrey through his paces in *Ace Ventura: Pet Detective*. 'We had an image of this big, overweight family sitting around a table,' Shadyac recalls, 'with a crusty old father, a spacey and quite eccentric grandmother, a loving mother and a hard-edged brother. Eddie took it to the next step by suggesting he play *all* of the characters around the table, *including* the women.'

Thanks to the ingenuity of three-time Oscar-winner Rick Baker, Murphy was physically transformed. Each day the star was required to sit in the make-up chair for four hours while Baker cast his magic, employing layers of foam rubber latex, special wigs and a body-suit modelled from a 400 pound man. Shadyac was knocked out. 'What Eddie and Rick achieved with all these characters is truly amazing,' he noted. 'With Sherman Klump, the make-up job is seamless with the real character. Sherman Klump is a real person. Eddie brought a voice and physicality to Rick Baker's make-up and made Sherman Klump real.'

In its first week in the USA, *The Nutty Professor* grossed a staggering $42.3 million, by the second it had amassed $68 million and in just over four had passed the magical $100 million mark. Not only was Murphy basking in the financial glory of his first original hit since *Coming to America*, but he also received glowing reviews. Furthermore, he was voted best actor of the year by America's National Society of Film Critics and was honoured with a Golden Globe nomination.

Then, in *Metro*, he returned to *Beverly Hills Cop* terrain to play a wise-cracking hostage negotiator who meets his match in a cold-blooded jewel thief (Michael Wincott). Sporting braids in his hair and a slightly more weathered look, Murphy brought a surprising gravity to his role as a heroic, sharp-shooting and sharp-witted cop. 'This is the most physical role I've done in a movie,' he avowed. 'I tip my hat to Stallone, Schwarzenegger and Bruce Willis – I don't know how they can do movies like this all the time, because you really get beat up doing them. But it's great when you finally see the results up on screen.'

Indeed, *Metro* was a highly-accomplished piece of gung-ho escapism, its conventional moves glossed over with some astonishing stunts and rat-a-tat direction (from Thomas Carter). Murphy himself seemed perfectly at ease with the formidable demands of the script, establishing a likeable character with honour, guts and a winning sense of humour.

He then signed on to star in a remake of the 1967 Rex Harrison vehicle *Doctor Dolittle*.

FILMOGRAPHY

1982: *48 HRS*. 1983: *Trading Places*. 1984: *Best Defense; Beverly Hills Cop*. 1986: *The Golden Child*. 1987: *Beverly Hills Cop II*. 1988: *Eddie Murphy Raw; Coming to America*. 1989: *Harlem Nights*. 1990: *Another 48 HRS*. 1992: *Boomerang; The Distinguished Gentleman*. 1994: *Beverly Hills Cop III*. 1995: *Vampire in Brooklyn*. 1996: *The Nutty Professor; Metro*. 1997: *Doctor Dolittle*. 1998: *Holy Man*.

As **The Nutty Professor**, a performance which put Murphy back in favour with the public and won him the best actor trophy from the National Society of Film Critics

O

CHRIS O'DONNELL

He was the closest thing to a new Tom Cruise that Hollywood could find: good-looking, clean-cut and perfectly preppie. But there were other things, too. O'Donnell attended an all-boys Jesuit high school; Cruise spent a year in a Franciscan seminary. O'Donnell's first film was *Men Don't Leave*, directed by Paul Brickman; Cruise's first leading role was in *Risky Business*, directed by Paul Brickman. O'Donnell starred opposite Al Pacino in *Scent of a Woman*, for which the latter won the Oscar for best actor; Cruise starred opposite Dustin Hoffman in *Rain Man*, for which the latter won the Oscar for best actor. Then O'Donnell played an idealistic young lawyer in *The Chamber*, adapted from the bestselling novel by John Grisham; Cruise played an idealistic young lawyer in *The Firm*, adapted from the bestselling novel by John Grisham.

Not surprisingly, O'Donnell is aware of the connection – such as his identification as 'a mini-Tom Cruise': 'Well, even a mini-Tom Cruise bank account wouldn't be bad,' he counters, 'I think Cruise is great. I'm a huge fan.'

O'Donnell is also the first to acknowledge that he couldn't compete with Pacino or Hoffman. 'The ideal world is to do films that Tom Cruise and Tom Hanks and Harrison Ford have done – huge films. But they're still respected as actors. That's the best of both worlds. I think Harrison Ford is great. I look more towards his career than anybody else's. I know I'm not going to be a Pacino or a De Niro. That's just not who I am.' Yet O'Donnell is not above admitting: 'I do think I have quite a range as an actor – but I don't think I could play a black person.'

Certainly, the actor's handful of films exhibit some scope: the small-town Southern drama *Fried Green Tomatoes*, the prep school drama *School Ties*, the character-driven *Scent of a Woman*, the swashbuckling *The Three Musketeers*, the period Irish drama *Circle of Friends*, the sci-fi extravaganza *Batman Forever* and the legal thriller

*As college jock Jack Foley in the surprise hit **Circle of Friends***

The Chamber. Indeed, O'Donnell chooses his projects for their versatility. That much he's sure of. As for the media's constant solicitation for his views on politics, religion and the theory of relativity, he has the maturity to grant: 'I'm 26, what the hell do I know? It's ridiculous. And it bothers me when I read articles about young actors and athletes who have these opinions about various things. They say things that are so stupid. As far as politics and stuff go, I've got thoughts, but they're just things I think. I don't have what I consider to be well-formed ideas.'

Christopher O'Donnell was born on 26 June 1970 in the comfortable suburb of Winnetka, Illinois, on Chicago's North Shore, the youngest of

seven kids. His father, Bill O'Donnell, operated a number of radio stations, but Chris was more into TV, glued to *The Brady Bunch*, *Happy Days* and *The Six Million Dollar Man*. Hell, he even became a lifetime member of the Lee Majors fan club.

For pocket money he set up a lemonade stand, then, at 13, he got really serious and started modelling on the side. Later, he moved on to the all-boys Loyalo Academy and TV commercials, winning a stint opposite baseball legend Michael Jordan in a 1987 McDonald's spot. With an agent in his pocket, the movies were just an audition away, or so you'd think. 'My agent called and told me about some auditions for a movie, but I didn't go,' he relates. 'That was the night of the

With Drew Barrymore in Mad Love

Bruce Springsteen concert. The second time I had crew practice. Finally I went and they called me back. Then they sent me to New York to read with Jessica Lange. I had heard of Jessica Lange, but I couldn't fit the face with the name.'

After another reading in Chicago, O'Donnell was flown to Los Angeles for a screen test and got his first movie role – as Jessica Lange's mutinous son, Chris, in *Men Don't Leave*. While the film won warm praise from American critics, it didn't travel far and, on its international release, it was virtually thrown away by its distributor, Warner Brothers.

In the interim, O'Donnell attended Boston College to pursue a marketing degree, but returned to work with Jessica Lange in Tony Richardson's *Blue Sky* – this time as the boyfriend of Lange's daughter, played by Amy Locane. Produced by the ill-fated Orion Pictures, *Blue Sky* slid onto ice for three years until its belated release in 1994 won Lange an Oscar.

Meanwhile, O'Donnell landed a small but pivotal role (as Buddy, the doomed brother of Mary Stuart Masterson) in *Fried Green Tomatoes*, the actor's first hit. Then, in a spooky twist of fate, he was re-teamed with Amy Locane in *School Ties*, an extremely well-made, powerful and absorbing tale about a skilled football quarterback (Brendan Fraser) who is persecuted at an elite prep school for being Jewish.

O'Donnell played Fraser's privileged, gentile roommate and turned out to be in the right place at the right time.

Along with several other members of the cast of *School Ties*, he auditioned for the role of Charlie Simms in *Scent of a Woman*, 'but I was the only one who got called back,' he notes with some contented discomfort. 'I kept that quiet from the guys because, although I get real competitive, they had become my friends. It was weird because I'd been kind of like the ringleader of goofing off and playing jokes, and when *Scent of a Woman* came along I stopped that cold and got more serious. I just wanted to get real focused and ready for the auditions.'

In *Scent of a Woman* he played another member of the Ivy League, although this time he was the outsider. On a scholarship and in need of extra pocket money, Simms agrees to babysit a blind old warhorse, the fearsome Lieutenant-Colonel Frank Slade, played by Al Pacino. Just as Simms sticks to the rules set by society and academia, so Slade shatters them in his wake, taking Simms on a ride through New York that will change him forever.

To settle O'Donnell into his part as the timid fawn to his bull elephant, Pacino let the young actor have it in true method style. 'Al really tore into him,' the director Martin Brest recalls. 'The whole crew started to sweat, but Chris stayed right on his mark. It produced wonderful stuff.'

'We were doing this real dramatic close-up and Al was shouting and slobbering all over me,' O'Donnell adds. 'But all I could think was, "This is so neat! This is going to be one of Al's greatest moments and I'm closer than the audience!"'

Pacino repaid the compliment. In front of one billion TV viewers, the star clasped his Oscar to his chest and said: 'I thank Chris O'Donnell, my co-star. He made every day a pleasure for me.' Some moment. Ironically, O'Donnell just comments: 'I don't remember if he mentioned my name at the Oscars,' but, 'at the Golden Globes I was afraid he was going to forget my name.'

Still, while Pacino marched off with the lion's share of the glory, O'Donnell contented himself with a Golden Globe nomination and a trophy from the Chicago Film Critics' Association for most promising actor. He also landed a salary of $500,000 to play D'Artagnan – in a fright wig – in Disney's *The Three Musketeers*, opposite Charlie Sheen as Aramis and Kiefer Sutherland as Athos. A bland, albeit energetic bastardization of the Alexander Dumas classic, *The Three Musketeers* went on to gross well over $100 million worldwide, further sowing the seeds for O'Donnell's celebrity.

He then changed gear dramatically to play Jack Foley, handsome star of the Dublin University rugby team, in Pat O'Connor's *Circle of Friends*, a delicate, moving tale (adapted from Maeve Binchy's acclaimed novel) that, thankfully, refused to teeter into mawkish blarney or overly tasteful period romance. 'It was a great story and a great adaptation,' O'Donnell noted, 'and from an actor's viewpoint it offered me the challenge of working with an accent for the first time. It was strange arriving in Ireland, looking around and not seeing the big star,' he admitted, obviously bewildered, then tactfully adding: 'Instead, I was surrounded by a bunch of great actors.'

Indeed, without a Pacino or Lange in sight, O'Donnell found his name above the title for the first time, with the prospect of the film's success sitting on his own shoulders. As it happens, *Circle of Friends* was a surprise box-office success, both in the USA and abroad.

He was another clean-cut, but-

As Robin in **Batman Forever**

toned-up soul (and amateur astrologer) in *Mad Love*, an earnest romance cluttered by touristy shots of the Pacific Northwest, and there was a pushy opportunity to slip in yet another trendy rock song. Drew Barrymore, as the wayward girl he falls for, did all the acting, while O'Donnell slipped easily into the sort of role that was becoming his hallmark: the boy next door.

Then, in marked contrast (well, not that much), he climbed into a heavy-duty rubber suit to play Robin (alias Dick Grayson, alias The Boy Wonder) to Val Kilmer's Caped Crusader in *Batman Forever*. Having beaten the likes of Michael J. Fox, Leonardo DiCaprio and Marlon Wayans to the role, O'Donnell was suddenly in the merchandising spotlight – and added much to an increasingly mindless formula. The film (budgeted at $100 million) went on to become the top-grossing feature of 1995 in the USA, and virtually doubled O'Donnell's price overnight.

Indeed, he got $4 million to play Adam Hall, the rookie lawyer in *The Chamber* who fights to keep his grandfather (Gene Hackman) out of the gas chamber. It was Hackman's film, to be sure, but O'Donnell got top-billing and that's what counts in an industry run by agents and money-men.

'Fame can be really uncomfortable, but it's a part of what you're asking for if you get into this business,' O'Donnell mused. 'Some people seek out the attention, but I'm happy to go out and publicize the films I'm in – but my personal life is private.' However, O'Donnell has talked publicly about his girlfriend, Caroline, who works for a non-profitmaking organization in Washington. But is he in love? 'Yeah,' he hesitates. 'I definitely trust her.'

Next, he played a 19-year-old Ernest Hemingway in Richard Attenborough's big-budget romance *In Love and War*, in which the legendary writer is wounded in World War I and falls for a nurse seven years his senior, played by Sandra Bullock. Bullock, herself pegged as the ultimate girl next door, confessed: 'Everything I ever read about Chris was "He's a really nice guy and there's sort of a playful, odd preppiness to him." I thought, "This guy sounds *disgusting*".' But she went on: 'He might wear the little button-down and he might do a little golfing and he might wear a little plaid every once in a while when he shouldn't. But with Chris, what you see is not what you get. He's got a nice dark little place. You just have to watch him when he doesn't know he's being watched.'

Unfortunately, he failed to mine the dark sexuality that his character so desperately needed in *In Love and War*, and it was up to Bullock to carry the emotional resonance in what was otherwise a fine romance.

Then it was time for the old rubber suit again, in *Batman and Robin*, with George Clooney taking the cape from Val Kilmer. O'Donnell doesn't pretend he's in the *Batman* films for art, admitting: 'It's hard to talk about my part in *Batman*. Half the time I am hiding behind a mask and then a whole day will be spent learning how to get in and out of the Batmobile. For an actor it's not as satisfying as working on a film like *Circle of Friends*. I do like to speak real dialogue and deal with real emotions.'

Talking of emotions, in April '97 O'Donnell married kindergarten teacher Caroline Fentress, 23, the sister of his old college roommate, Andrew.

FILMOGRAPHY
1990: *Men Don't Leave*. 1991: *Blue Sky* (released 1994); *Fried Green Tomatoes* (UK: *Fried Green Tomatoes at the Whistlestop Cafe*). 1992: *School Ties; Scent of a Woman*. 1993: *The Three Musketeers*. 1995: *Circle of Friends; Mad Love; Batman Forever*. 1996: *The Chamber; In Love and War*. 1997: *Batman and Robin*. 1998: *The Flight Before Christmas*.

As Ernest Hemingway in Richard Attenborough's ambitious **In Love and War**

P

Gwyneth Paltrow confides in Elizabeth Perkins in the touching, insightful *Moonlight and Valentino*

If Brad Pitt gives off the aura of a terrier that had crawled out of the wrong side of the kennel, Gwyneth Paltrow is a swan that has just had an Estee Lauder makeover. Yet (at the time of going to press) the pit bull and its royal mate – an Audrey Hepburn for the 1990s – seemed set for life. Of course, Pitt had previously been inseparable from Juliette Lewis, but somehow his new standing in the international spotlight – not to mention that string of box-office hits – gave him and Gwyneth a new lasting credibility. Like Tom Cruise and Nicole Kidman with character.

In the autumn of 1996 it would have been easy for tabloid editors to believe that Ms Paltrow was beginning to eclipse her boyfriend in popularity. But, with the release of *Twelve Monkeys* and *Sleepers*, the Brad cult was as concrete in the cinema as ever – if not as visible in the glossy magazines.

Gwyneth Paltrow had been stirring the scribes of film journals as far back as 1993 with her attention-grabbing performance in *Flesh and Bone*. As the down-and-dirty Texan girlfriend of James Caan, she looked set for a career in the mould of Barbara Stanwyck or, in *Johnny Guitar*, Joan Crawford.

When the writer-director Douglas McGrath heard her Texan accent he was knocked out. McGrath – who was nominated for an Oscar for his screenplay to Woody Allen's *Bullets Over Broadway* – is himself Texan. He said it was the most authentic Texas accent he had ever heard on screen. Yet Paltrow was born in Los Angeles.

'Once I knew she had that ear,' McGrath notes, 'I knew she could handle *Emma*.' But the role of the aristocratic Emma Woodhouse in Jane Austen's quintessentially English comedy of manners was a real stretch. At least, it would have been for any mortal actress. 'Her English accent came so easily and was done so proficiently that even English people thought she was British,' McGrath, the director, insists. 'One of our sound supervisors wanted to know why he didn't know this lovely British actress. When I told him she was from that little English village of New York, he almost hit the floor. Frankly,' McGrath continues, 'I don't think there's any kind of acting she *can't* do.'

Such praise is not just the preserve of those who have directed her. Julia Roberts, who played Tinkerbell to Gwyneth's Wendy in *Hook*, volunteered: 'Gwyneth has an incredibly interesting look, which I think transcends time. She can look very today, she can look very Sixties, she can look very period. And also she can go from being incredibly, exquisitely beautiful to being just plain interesting-looking. She's got a face you want to look at for a very long time; you want to absorb it.'

Gwyneth Paltrow was born on 28 September 1973 in Los Angeles, the older sister of Jake and Laura, and the daughter of TV producer Bruce Paltrow (*St Elsewhere*) and the Tony-winning actress Blythe Danner. Obviously, acting was in her blood. 'I remember in eighth or ninth grade going into the bathroom after a movie and kind of looking in the mirror and pretending that I was an actress,' she reminisces. 'I knew that I would do it someday. I just couldn't wait until I got the chance.'

After attending school at St Augustine by the Sea, she moved with her family to New York, aged 11, and completed her education at the exclusive all-girls Spence School on Manhattan's East Side. Graduating in 1990, she enrolled as an art major at the University of California, Santa Barbara, but shortly afterwards jettisoned further education in favour of a career as an actress. Her father disapproved, until he saw her on stage in a production of William Inge's *Picnic* – at the prestigious Williamstown Theater – playing opposite her mother.

Her very first movie audition landed her a role in the John Travolta musical *Shout* (a dud), then she was swiftly signed up to play the young Wendy in *Hook*, cast by Spielberg after the director bumped into her while queuing for a movie. She was re-teamed with her mother in the TV mini-series *Cruel Doubt*, then returned to the Williamstown Theater to appear in *The*

Gwyneth as Tracy Mills, wife of Brad Pitt, in the colossal hit **Seven**

Sweet By and By. It was while she was rehearsing this production that she was asked to audition for *Flesh and Bone.*

A grim, atmospheric drama from Steve Kloves, director of *The Fabulous Baker Boys, Flesh and Bone* was not a commercial success, but critics were struck by Paltrow's turn as Ginnie, a hard-as-nails kleptomaniac who announces (in a perfect Texan drawl), 'I'm not a nice girl,' and tells Dennis Quaid, 'You don't have the balls to shoot a fly off a steak.'

She had a bit part as Paula Bell in Harold Becker's enjoyable thriller *Malice,* and then played Paula Hunt in Alan Rudolph's dreary, star-laden *Mrs Parker and the Vicious Circle.* She had a bigger part in James Ivory's *Jefferson in Paris,* playing Patsy, the eldest daughter of Thomas Jefferson (Nick Nolte). Yet while the film showed audiences she could look just as good in a corset as cowboy boots, the end product was spectacularly boring.

Much, much better was the under-rated *Moonlight and Valentino,* in which she played the timorous younger sister of Elizabeth Perkins. Indeed, both actresses were at the top of their form as women coming to terms with grief in their own way. The scene in which Perkins tries to explain to her sister (a virgin) how to get the best out of sex is a master class in the fusion of great writing and acting. Had the film been a hit, Paltrow would have secured her first Oscar nomination for sure.

However, her next film was *huge.* Yet another grim-faced thriller chronicling the exploits of a sadistic serial killer, *Seven* brought class and excitement to a jaded genre. Morgan Freeman and Brad Pitt were cops on the trail of a scholastic psychopath who got his kicks fashioning murders after the Seven Deadly Sins. While resigned to what was essentially a supporting role, Paltrow turned out to be a key player in the film's most overpowering moment. And, as the wife of detective Brad Pitt, she was an essential human ingredient, teetering in the divide between the exigencies of her husband's work and her own needs for a domestic environment. Yet, in a thriller of powerful and outstanding qualities, Paltrow's subtle emotional shading went almost unnoticed.

Despite this, the film's sensational

$300 million gross couldn't help but improve the actress's public profile – and it also opened up her private life. Still only 22, Paltrow found herself battling the impossible demands of fame when she moved in with Brad Pitt, the couple becoming the hottest tabloid item since Bruce and Demi. The crunch came when paparazzi photographers snapped the couple's nude antics on holiday in the Caribbean, the pic-

Gwyneth Paltrow as the meddlesome Emma Woodhouse

tures – showing Brad and Gwyneth starkers, kissing – circulated around the world. Brad Pitt went ballistic, while Gwyneth simply asserted: 'Of course, we learn things. We'll obviously never go sunbathing naked again.' She does, however, avow: 'I don't want to be rich and I don't want to be famous. I want to live in Spain and have children.'

Her next film, the offbeat comedy-drama *The Pallbearer,* with David Schwimmer, more or less kept her name out of the headlines, but the future was just around the corner ...

In the low-budget thriller *Sydney,* she played a cocktail waitress-cum-hooker and called the film 'the best movie I've ever been in'. She then took on the title role of *Emma.*

Arriving in the wake of *Sense and Sensibility* and *Persuasion,* this umpteenth Jane Austen adaptation looked a day late and a dollar short. Yet the film's exquisite wit, emotional power and glorious production values knocked the stockings off the competition. Besides being unfashionably thin (Jane Austen would have been very

worried about her health), Paltrow perfectly captured the frail beauty and obsessive altruism of the socially meddlesome Emma. Furthermore, her upper-class English accent was flawless. And considering the magnificent supporting cast – Toni Collette, Jeremy Northam and Juliet Stevenson were particularly impressive – Paltrow's achievement was extraordinary. Moreover, the film was an enormous hit with critics and audiences alike. Above all, *Emma* was the sort of actor-driven vehicle that made stars of great talent. Gwyneth Paltrow had arrived.

Next, she played Jessica Lange's daughter-in-law in the psychological drama *Hush,* and was then Estella in a new screen version of Dickens' *Great Expectations,* with Ethan Hawke as Pip and Robert De Niro as Magwitch. She was also due to star in the film version of Jim Cartwright's award-winning play *The Rise and Fall of Little Voice,* which the author had written expressly for the English actress Jane Horrocks. Much debate ensued, with Paltrow eventually bowing out to make way for Horrocks. But then filming was postponed when Horrocks committed to another picture, *Bring Me the Head of Mavis Davis.*

Meanwhile, Paltrow signed on to star opposite Brad Pitt in *Duets,* to be directed by her father, and committed to the low-budget English comedy-drama *Sliding Doors,* and was rumoured to be joining Demi Moore and Nicole Kidman in a big-screen spin-off of *Charlie's Angels.* She and Pitt then split in June of '97.

FILMOGRAPHY

1991: *Shout; Hook.* 1993: *Flesh and Bone; Malice.* 1994: *Mrs Parker and Vicious Circle.* 1995: *Jefferson in Paris; Moonlight and Valentino; Seven.* 1996: *The Pallbearer; Sydney* (UK: *Hard Eight*); *Emma.* 1997: *Hush; Great Expectations; Sliding Doors.*

MARY-LOUISE PARKER

Thanks to a handful of astutely-realized performances in some very good pictures, Mary-Louise Parker was suddenly a force to reckon with. It was hard to miss her in Norman Rene's critically acclaimed *Longtime Companion,* as she was virtually the only woman in it. In Lawrence Kasdan's intelligent, contem-

Mary-Louise Parker (left) and Mary Stuart Masterson enjoy each other's company in Jon Avnet's winning **Fried Green Tomatoes**

plative *Grand Canyon*, she was equally hard to overlook, as she was the only 'non-star' alongside the likes of Danny Glover, Kevin Kline and Steve Martin, while in *Fried Green Tomatoes*, she was one of four women who held the story strands together.

In the space of two years Mary-Louise Parker appeared in five films, and found herself upgraded from respected stage actress to respected film actress – although in 1991 she revealed: 'I've never had much of a fascination for film. I respect it, but people in Hollywood can have cash registers where their hearts are.'

Born in Fort Jackson, South Carolina, on 2 August 1964, Mary-Louise gave up thoughts of medicine to pursue acting, and enrolled at the North Carolina School of Arts. Outside New York, she appeared in such plays as *The Importance of Being Earnest*, *Hay Fever*, *Night of the Iguana* and, in Texas, *The Little Foxes*. On TV, she appeared with Ricky Schroder in the so-so war movie *Too Young the Hero*, based on a true story, and had a recurring role in the daytime soap *Ryan's Hope*. In 1989, she made her film debut in the warmly-received American Playhouse drama *Signs of Life*, in which she played Charlotte, the waitress girlfriend of Kevin J. O'Connor (punching him on the head when he announced his plan to leave her for Miami). In a cast that

included Arthur Kennedy, Beau Bridges and Kathy Bates, Parker was sensational – particularly in light of her under-written role.

But she was most comfortable on stage, explaining: 'Theatre is ephemeral, and that, to me, is romantic – those moments between people that come and then disappear.'

She was nominated for a Tony for originating the part of Rita Boyle in Craig Lucas's *Prelude to a Kiss*, opposite Alec Baldwin, and became involved with Timothy Hutton when he took over the male lead. Later, she and Hutton appeared together again in the play *Babylon Gardens*, at New York's Circle Rep.

It was Norman Rene, who had directed *Prelude*, who cast her as Lisa in *Longtime Companion*, Craig Lucas's beautifully-written and perceptive look at a group of gay men coming to terms with AIDS. Of her performance, Peter Travers wrote in *Rolling Stone*: 'Parker, in the only major woman's role, is a radiant actress of rare spirit and sensitivity.'

In *Fried Green Tomatoes* she played Ruth, the demure, God-fearing innocent who is befriended by Mary Stuart Masterson's hard-drinking, hard-talking Idgie Threadgoode. Set in the 1940s, the story is related in flashback by a garrulous 82-year-old Jessica Tandy, who embroils a spellbound Kathy Bates

in her tale of rural Alabama in the good ol', bad ol' days. Considered a risk by Hollywood investors, the comedy-drama – superbly played by its female cast – went on to gross over $81 million in the USA, something of a small miracle.

In a total turnaround, the actress played Dee, secretary and part-time lover of Kevin Kline, in Lawrence Kasdan's biting adult drama *Grand Canyon*. Single, desirable and confused, Dee is a woman of intelligence and vulnerability, driven to distraction by her affair with Kline (who is married to Mary McDonnell). The actress explained: 'Dee is feeling very lonely and alienated, and I think *Grand Canyon* is about how people's problems are so relative to themselves. I loved the fact that the movie cannot be easily pigeon-holed. In some ways it seems as though nothing really happens, yet a million things happen. And there is such wonderful humour. But it's not fabricated and it's not elitist. It's "human humour".'

Next, Parker joined Matt Dillon and William Hurt (as the former's girl-friend) in the bitter-sweet *Mr Wonderful*, an exploration of the ironies and complexities of human relationships, directed by the British writer Anthony Minghella (*The English Patient*). An engaging, touching romantic comedy, *Mr Wonderful* veered just far enough away from Hollywood formula to make it interesting, and was distinguished by some peerless performances. Yet in spite of first-rate turns from

Mary-Louise as Dee in Lawrence Kasdan's thoughtful, intelligent drama **Grand Canyon**

Mary-Louise Parker with Eric Stoltz in the little-seen **Naked in New York**

Dillon and Annabella Sciorra, it was Parker's multi-layered performance as the canny, defenceless Rita that informed the human integrity of the piece.

After that, she starred in the Martin Scorsese-produced *Naked in New York*, as Joanne, a young Bostonian whose ambition to become a photographer polarizes her loyalties between her boyfriend (Eric Stoltz) and a prosperous gallery owner (Timothy Dalton). Unfortunately, the film's determination to be a total original resulted in some bizarre flights of fantasy that knocked it sideways.

She was better served as the white-trash mother of Brad Renfro in Joel Schumacher's gripping, credible adaptation of John Grisham's bestseller *The Client*, a hit that spawned a TV series, but she was largely wasted in Woody Allen's star-laden *Bullets Over Broadway* (as John Cusack's unfaithful girlfriend).

In the TV movie *A Place For Annie* she played a drug addict with AIDS who fights to get her HIV-infected daughter back from the paediatric nurse (Sissy Spacek) who adopted her. Both intelligent and perceptive, the film – which was inspired by a true story – was a wonderful platform for

three outstanding actresses, all at the peak of their mettle (Joan Plowright completing the Holy Trinity). In another spectacular shift, Parker played a frail, anally-retentive woman (who thinks the world of The Carpenters) in Herbert Ross's *Boys on the Side*, a female road movie that crossed *Thelma & Louise* with *Terms of Endearment*. With Whoopi Goldberg and Drew Barrymore in on the ride, the film proved enormously entertaining while refusing to lose sight of its emotional centre.

The actress was then coerced to play a fraudulent mute called Pooty in the fatally misconceived *Reckless*. What was obviously intended as a dark, off-beat fairy tale (adapted from the play by Craig Lucas) actually emerged as a tiresome and unpleasant shambles. No doubt Parker felt indebted to the film's director, Norman Rene, and the writer (both of whom created *Longtime Companion*), but why were Mia Farrow, Scott Glenn and Stephen Dorff also involved?

She had no more luck with the wildly anticipated *The Portrait of a Lady*, Jane Campion's sexless, humourless adaptation of the Henry James novel. Reduced to fourth-billing as the condescending Henrietta Stackpole, she was all but lost in the top-heavy cast. She then played real-life singer Phyllis

McGuire to John Turturro's gangster, Sam Giancana, in the well-received HBO movie *Sugartime*, and joined Nigel Hawthorne and Jimmy Smits for *Murder in Mind*. Next, she starred in *The Maker* for director Tim Hunter, with Matthew Modine and Michael Madsen also in the cast. She was due to join Turturro again in the comedy-drama *OK Garage*, but dropped out to join Patricia Arquette, Dermot Mulroney and Don Johnson in Roland Joffe's thriller *Goodbye Lover*.

Romantically, she has been linked with Adam Duritz, lead singer of the rock group Counting Crows, and the fitness guru Pat Manocchia (who later went on to date Julia Roberts). She then took up with the rising actor Billy Crudup (*Sleepers*, *Inventing the Abbotts*, *Pre*), whom she met during the Broadway run of *Bus Stop*.

FILMOGRAPHY

1988: *Too Young the Hero* (TV). 1989: *Signs of Life*. 1990: *Longtime Companion*. 1991: *Fried Green Tomatoes* (UK: *Fried Green Tomatoes at the Whistlestop Cafe*); *Grand Canyon*. 1993: *Mr Wonderful*; *Naked in New York*. 1994: *The Client*; *A Place for Annie* (TV); *Bullets Over Broadway*; *Boys On the Side*. 1995: *Reckless*; *Sugartime* (TV); *Nightwood Bar* (TV). 1996: *The Portrait of a Lady*. 1997: *Murder in Mind*; *The Maker*.

With Whoopi Goldberg and Drew Barrymore in **Boys on the Side**

JASON PATRIC

Jason as Lord Byron in Roger Corman's
Frankenstein Unbound

Nobody could accuse Jason Patric of being prolific. And yet, in a remarkably short time, he became a household name. Not, mind you, because of his meagre handful of films, but because of an all too brief fling with the then highest-paid actress in Hollywood. And there was irony to spare.

When Patric made his first celluloid breakthrough – in Joel Schumacher's slick MTV vampire comedy, *The Lost Boys* – he played a handsome hunk who steals the girl from Kiefer Sutherland. In real life, in June 1991, when Julia Roberts cancelled her wedding to Sutherland, Patric escorted her on an impromptu holiday to Ireland. A month later, in a blaze of media coverage, she moved in with him, finished work on Steven Spielberg's *Hook*, and then the couple went on another holiday. By November, rumours of the stars' engagement were plastered all over the tabloids, followed by talk of pregnancy. Of course, all this was nothing but the product of the fertile imagination of story editors and a year later Julia was dating a 'scruffy' (tabloid quote) unknown actor called Russell Blake. However, in private, she and Patric were still holding hands. At least, for a while.

This explosion of unwanted publicity could not have happened to a shyer man. Although blessed with the kind of looks models die for (note those perfectly-formed lips, those Mel Gibson-

blue eyes), Patric didn't even like to be photographed. In interviews he is at pains to point out: 'I'd rather not talk about my personal life, if that's OK' – and that was *before* the Kiefer kerfuffle. Patric won't even thank you for mentioning his formidable lineage. But, for the record, it has to be said that he is the grandson of comedy legend Jackie Gleason, and son of the playwright and actor Jason Miller.

Jason Patric was born in New York City on 17 June 1966, and was raised in the neighbourhood of Queens. At 16, he moved to Los Angeles, where he performed in a number of stage productions at Santa Monica High, before spending a summer with Vermont's Champlain Shakespeare Festival. There, he stretched himself in such classics as *The Tempest* and *Love's Labours Lost*, before making his film debut in the TV movie *Toughlove*, playing Bruce Dern's son.

Earlier, Patric had come across Dern when he acted as a trainee on the film *That Championship Season*, the film version of his father's Pulitzer Prize-winning play. According to Dern, 'Jason was a 16-year-old high school kid who was very sports orientated. He was there to learn and he learned. But he did not leave the movie with any desire to be an actor that I could see.'

Patric inspired no more confidence when he landed the young male lead in the awful sci-fi nonsense *Solarbabies*, opposite Jami Gertz. Gertz was not impressed: 'Jason would mumble and wouldn't look me in the face when he talked,' she revealed. 'Finally I told him I wasn't going to talk to him anymore unless he looked at me. I couldn't believe he was so shy.'

Nevertheless, Ms Gertz later teamed up with him in the two-handed play *Outta Gas on Lover's Leap* – at the Coast Playhouse in Los Angeles – and played his romantic interest in *The Lost Boys*. This presented Patric with his breakthrough cheesecake role in a film with a decidedly high profile. As Michael Emerson, a recent arrival in California's Santa Carla – the murder capital of the world – Patric is seduced into the dangerous company of a gang of supernatural bikers (led by Kiefer Sutherland). Gertz is the attraction, but to win her love Michael must first become a 'creature of the night' – at

great personal cost. *The Lost Boys* proved to be hugely entertaining hokum, which thankfully never took itself seriously and boasted a cast of fine young actors at the peak of their performance.

Less could be said for *Denial*, a really confusing mess about a woman (Robin Wright) still obsessed by her old, brooding swain (Patric). Filmed under the eye-catching title of *Loon*, the film went straight to video three years later. In more serious mode, Patric played the brave, compassionate driver of a Russian tank, nicknamed *The Beast*. The film, although a tad predictable, was an intelligent look at the strife in Afghanistan, and a welcome antidote to the jingoistic excesses of *Rambo III*. He took a supporting role – as a brooding Lord Byron – in *Roger Corman's Frankenstein Unbound*, a schlocky, time-travelling slant on the old Mary Shelley shindig which produced a certain famous novel. Still, Patric looked stunning in tight trousers and lace.

Next, he was offered the leading role in *Flatliners* by Joel Schumacher, who had discovered him in *The Lost*

As the disenchanted ex-boxer Kevin 'Kid' Collins in James Foley's brooding ***After Dark, My Sweet***

*As US Cavalry lieutenant Charles Gatewood in Walter Hill's picturesque **Geronimo: An American Legend***

Boys. But Patric thought he was now beyond such things, and his old friend Kiefer Sutherland took the part. Instead, Patric accepted the lead in *After Dark, My Sweet* – for a seventh of the price. 'With everything I do,' the actor explained, 'I have to move forward. I'm not willing to put myself in things that are not worthy of the emotional investment and the time commitment.' Of course, this would not explain his obligation to *Frankenstein Unbound*, but *After Dark* did provide him with his best role yet. Based on the novel by Jim Thompson, the film starred Patric as a scruffy, dislocated ex-boxer who stumbles into bed with Rachel Ward and ends up in the middle of a kidnapping scam engineered by her friend, 'Uncle Bud', played by Bruce Dern. For all its knowing close-ups and stifling atmosphere, *After Dark* – directed by James Foley – was very dull film noir, superbly acted by Dern and Patric.

This time, Bruce Dern was more impressed with his co-star. 'In all my career, I had never seen anybody as prepared to play a role,' he vouchsafed. 'When I saw the movie, I said to myself, "This kid has a chance to be the acting movie star of his generation." I actually thought that I watched a star being born.'

After Dark was not the most visible

film of 1990. In fact, producer Richard Zanuck and his wife, Lili Fini, were intending to see another movie when they found it was sold out. 'Somebody was coming out of another cinema,' Mr Zanuck relayed, 'and said, "You ought to see this picture *After Dark, My Sweet* – there's an incredible actor in it."'

The Zanucks were currently casting *Rush*, the movie adaptation of the semi-autobiographical bestseller by Kim Wozencraft. The story of an undercover narcotics cop who becomes a drug addict in the line of duty, the film was earmarked for Tom Cruise, but he became unavailable. Jason Patric was duly signed.

Like *After Dark*, the film was a raw, unrelenting look at the underbelly of American life, and Patric turned in another mesmerizing performance as a man at war with his inner demons. Again, *Rush* was an atmospheric if depressing tale, redeemed by outstanding performances from its two leads – Patric and Jennifer Jason Leigh (who played his committed partner).

Two years later he landed top-billing in Walter Hill's noble and picturesque *Geronimo: An American Legend*, as a young officer who takes the Chiricahua Apache leader into custody. However, in spite of his billing on the poster, he was eclipsed by the performances of co-stars Robert Duvall and Gene Hackman, while the Cherokee actor Wes Studi dominated every scene he was in as the eponymous warrior subjugated by the US government.

Furthermore, it was Matt Damon (*The Rainmaker*) who got to narrate the shameful events, which rather left Patric out in the cold.

However, after playing a farmer who befriends a slave in the little-seen *The Journey of August King*, Patric made sure he got to narrate the proceedings himself in the high-profile *Sleepers*. Although essentially an ensemble picture, *Sleepers* unfolded its dreadful story through the eyes of 'Shakes', played by Patric. Loosely based on true events as chronicled in Lorenzo Carcaterra's semi-autobiographical bestseller, the film followed the lives of four childhood friends who grow up in the Hell's Kitchen quarter of 1960s New York. When a more or less innocent prank backfires, the boys are locked away in a correctional facility where they are subjected to routine mental abuse, rape and torture. Emerging years later in the guise of Patric, Brad Pitt, Billy Crudup and Ron Eldard, the victimized friends embark on a tortuous path of revenge and redemption. Directed with enormous style by Barry Levinson, the film also starred Robert De Niro, Dustin Hoffman and Kevin Bacon, and was a box-office hit, finally establishing Patric as a household name.

He then made *Incognito* for director John Badham, and took his first seriously mainstream role (since *The Lost Boys*), replacing Keanu Reeves as the heroic male lead of *Speed 2: Cruise Control*. He also returned to the glare

*With Minnie Driver in Barry Levinson's **Sleepers***

of the tabloid spotlight when he dated Christy Turlington and insisted that she drop her frivolous lifestyle. In a startling manifestation of her love, the supermodel ducked out of a million-dollar promotion for the cosmetic eatery Fashion Cafe and announced that she was enrolling at New York University.

FILMOGRAPHY

1985: *Toughlove* (TV). 1986: *Solarbabies*. 1987: *The Lost Boys*. 1988: *The Beast*. 1990: *Roger Corman's Frankenstein Unbound*; *Teach 109*; *After Dark, My Sweet*. 1991: *Denial* (a.k.a. *Loon*; filmed in 1988); *Rush*. 1993: *Geronimo: An American Legend*. 1995: *The Journey of August King*. 1996: *Sleepers*. 1997: *Incognito*; *Speed 2: Cruise Control*.

SEAN PENN

Sean Penn with his ex, Madonna, in the catastrophic **Shanghai Surprise**

Sean Penn was the genuine angry young man. Pugnacious in appearance, he became better known for punching out photographers than for his films. Blisteringly outspoken in his views on the press, Penn was an intensely serious actor who, ironically, became a star in a comedy. He then married a rock singer more famous than himself, which, according to many, caused more bitterness, ending in a Waterloo of press coverage. Finally, the actor ended up behind bars, serving 32 days in Los Angeles County Jail for assaulting a photographer and violating probation.

For his critics, it was just deserts. But not according to Sean's friend and colleague, Dennis Hopper. 'I tell you,' Hopper declared, 'if that incident had happened to anybody but Sean Penn – *anybody* but Sean Penn – he would never have gone to jail. I mean, if somebody says, "Don't step on my blue suede shoes," and somebody comes over and steps on his blue suede shoes, what does that guy think is gonna happen to him?'

Gary Oldman, who starred opposite Penn in *State of Grace*, joined the fray: 'We were shooting in Times Square and all these newspaper photographers showed up, and they wouldn't stop. They took flash photographs while we were doing takes. I said, "I don't mind you taking photographs, but don't do it while I'm working! 'Cause it ruins the film." And they just wouldn't stop. There was this one particular guy, and I said to Sean, "I'm gonna go whack this guy out!" And Sean was just … he waved it all aside. What a life!'

Yet Sean Penn was an unlikely candidate for screen celebrity. He wasn't pretty like Tom Cruise or Rob Lowe, he wasn't funny like Matthew Broderick, and he didn't emerge from a hit TV series like Michael J. Fox. He got to the top through sheer good acting and devotion to his craft. And when the exposure became too much for him, he became a filmmaker of some accomplishment.

According to James Foley, who directed the actor in *At Close Range*: 'Sean is one of the greats. And it's a shame he's become a director, because there are already too many directors out there, but not enough actors of his calibre.' Hopper says: 'Sean is a much more disciplined actor than I was at his age. I'm not gonna say he's more talented than I was, but my fight was a different fight. I wasn't punching out photographers – I was punching out directors.' And the director Rick Rosenthal offers: 'The only reason that people compare Sean to Robert De Niro is that Sean is the only actor of his generation who can really become a different person for each acting job.'

As it happens, Sean Penn was born on Robert De Niro's birthday, on 17 August 1960, in Burbank, California, the second of three sons. His father was the TV and film director Leo Penn, his mother the actress Eileen Ryan, who retired when he was born. His younger brother, Christopher, has become an actor of some repute (*Short Cuts*, *Reservoir Dogs*, *Mulholland Falls*), while his older sibling, Michael, is a successful singer-songwriter ('No Myth').

For the first ten years of his life, Sean lived in different parts of LA's San Fernando Valley, from North Hollywood to Woodland Hills. When he was ten, the family moved to Malibu, where Sean became obsessed with surfing. His friends included neighbourhood boys Emilio Estevez, Charlie Sheen and Rob Lowe, and they would often dabble in a bit of Super-8 filmmaking, although this was nothing more than a hobby. The surf was still Sean's first love.

After graduating from Santa Monica High School, he skipped college and spent two years with the Los Angeles Group Repertory Theater, where he worked backstage and directed a one-act play, *Terrible Jim Fitch*. He then studied with the legendary drama coach Peggy Feury and, at 19, made his professional acting debut with one line in an episode of TV's *Barnaby Jones*. He had a supporting role in the acclaimed TV movie *The Killing of Randy Webster*, with Hal Holbrook, and appeared in *Hellinger's Law*, an unsuccessful pilot for a TV series starring Telly Savalas.

Dissatisfied with TV, he bought a one-way ticket to New York and tried his luck on stage. His first audition was for the Broadway play *Heartland*, and it went badly. 'He was nervous, tight and nearly inaudible,' the director Art Wolff remembers. Nevertheless, a second reading won him the role and decent reviews which, in turn, led to his first film, *Taps*.

Set in a military academy, the movie starred Timothy Hutton as a rebellious cadet, with newcomers Penn and Tom Cruise as his partners-in-defiance. Penn simply acted his co-stars off the screen and was immediately the talk of Hollywood as the Next Big Thing. He landed top-billing in the riotous high school comedy *Fast Times at Ridgemont High*, playing the spaced-out surfer Jeff Spicoli who famously orders pizza in the middle of class. Penn was very, very funny, the film was a hit, and a whole school of new stars graduated with honours.

Penn turned to drama with Rick Rosenthal's hard-hitting *Bad Boys*, the story of a 16-year-old Chicago kid (Penn) who accidentally kills the younger brother of a drug dealer. Incarcerated in a juvenile correction facility, Penn finds himself face-to-face with his victim's brother – leading, inevitably, to some pretty violent confrontations. Again, Penn was magnificent in a part he studied for rigorously, accompanying Chicago's police gang-crimes unit on duty and, reportedly, applying real tattoos to his arms. Generally, the film was extremely well-acted by a cast of young unknowns, but Penn towered over them all, displaying the steely bile of a latter-day James Cagney.

In *Crackers* he returned to comedy, third-billed behind Donald Sutherland and Jack Warden as a dopey misfit forced into crime. Surprisingly, this limp comedy was directed by none other than Louise Malle, which is presumably why Penn took it. He had the lead in Richard Benjamin's wartime romance *Racing With the Moon*, a turgid, period-bound piece that failed to arouse any sympathies for its protagonists. As a romantic leading man, Penn was lacking in charisma, although he did exhibit a raw, touching ingenuousness that might have worked under more auspicious circumstances. He played Henry 'Hopper' Nash, the son of a gravedigger who falls for the local Gatsby girl, Elizabeth McGovern. Rumours of an off-set romance were reported, but worse, word got out that Penn persuaded McGovern not to publicize the picture. 'Totally bogus,' the actor scoffed. 'I was busy in Mexico shooting another movie. There wasn't time to allow me to participate in the publicity for the film. But the people involved in that movie didn't respect my answer when I said no, and then they did something I don't believe has been done any other time: they spoke in public against the actor who was in their movie! They also insinuated that I had influenced the other actors. I wouldn't play the game. I'd had no problems at all with the press up to that time. I was doing what I wanted to do – I was acting. I was trying to do the best job that I could.'

The 'Mexican' film was John Schlesinger's *The Falcon and the Snowman*, the true story of two young men (Penn, Timothy Hutton) who decide to sell government secrets to the Russians. Again, Penn stole the notices as the unpredictable, out-of-his-mind drug pusher, Daulton Lee. Schlesinger admitted that he found Penn 'quite difficult', but also volunteered that he 'really gets into the skin of the character he's playing. And as Daulton Lee resists all authority, so Sean naturally hated me. I must say that the feeling was reciprocated, although I thought he was marvellous in the film.'

The actor had a better time on his next movie, *At Close Range*, another true-life drama, about a teenage boy (Penn) who comes to blows with his criminal father (Christopher Walken). James Foley directed, and the filmmaker and actor worked well together. However, there was one incident (much admired in the media) in which Penn reportedly slugged a crew member for flirting with co-star Mary Stuart Masterson. Penn denies it.

It was at this time that the actor entered into a whirlwind romance with – and married – the singer-songwriter Madonna Louise Ciccone, whose song 'Live To Tell' was featured on the soundtrack of *At Close Range*. If the paparazzi were finding Penn a pain, they unleashed a monster when they zeroed in on his wife. Unlike her husband, Madonna was not adverse to publicity, but even she found the mounting battery of flashbulbs an unwelcome intrusion.

'You have to understand,' Penn explains, 'when Madonna and I got together, she was an up-and-coming star. She was not a superstar; she was not an icon. Soon she became public property and her husband-to-be was treated likewise.'

The couple's wedding turned into the ultimate media circus, with press helicopters hovering above the outdoor ceremony. The groom became so incensed by the intrusion that he reputedly started firing a gun into the air. And Penn *doesn't* deny that.

Career-wise, he and Madonna teamed up for the abysmal *Shanghai Surprise*, a movie he did for the money and, no doubt, to be with his wife. Ironically, it was the only film he made

during his marriage. After the divorce and tabloid stories of the actor beating Madonna with a baseball bat, Penn simply conceded: 'I can just say it ended. It just didn't work out.' It is charitable of him not to put more blame on the media.

He returned to the cinema with something of a splash, playing a rookie LA cop who believes the only way to fight violence is with more violence. The film was *Colors*, and Penn took the screenplay to Orion Pictures himself, suggesting that Dennis Hopper direct. Orion agreed, and Hopper had the script re-written to accommodate Penn and co-star Robert Duvall (the original story centred on a black cop and a white cop in Chicago). *Colors* was both timely and ahead of its time, examining the escalating gang warfare in Los Angeles, and the limited police resources to combat it. When the movie opened in April 1988, it caused such an uproar that many cinemas refused to show it. In New York, protests were staged in an attempt to deter cinemagoers, while two days later, in LA, a teenager was shot dead

*Penn as the quick-tempered LA cop Danny 'Pacman' McGavin in Dennis Hopper's hard-hitting **Colors***

Penn directing Dennis Hopper in a scene from his atmospheric drama **The Indian Runner**

Penn, back from retirement, threatens Al Pacino in **Carlito's Way**

while queuing to see it. Arguably, *Colors* was Sean Penn's best film to date, and a frightening piece of contemporary *cinéma vérité*.

He had a small part, but was very good, in his father's *Judgement in Berlin*, playing a German defector (with a convincing accent), and then portrayed the brutish Sergeant Meserve in Brian De Palma's *Casualties of War*. Based on a true incident, this was a rather obvious drama in which the bad guys – American soldiers who rape a Vietnamese girl – were really, really bad, and the good guy (Michael J. Fox) too squeaky clean to be true.

Worse still was the misguided comedy *We're No Angels*, a remake of the 1955 Humphrey Bogart caper, which wasn't very good to start with. Robert De Niro and Sean Penn played a couple of goofy escaped convicts disguised as priests, and De Niro mugged shamefully. Penn was not much better. His next film, the gritty, violent *State of Grace*, was about a gang of Irish-American criminals in New York, and the acting honours went to Ed Harris, Gary Oldman and Robin Wright. Still, the movie introduced Penn to Robin Wright, who later bore the actor's child, Dylan Frances. Of his new girlfriend, Penn said: 'She's the first young actress of her generation to come along, I think, who has intelligence and elegance. She's been extremely choosy in everything she's done. She's got a really big career ahead of her.'

However, Sean Penn's acting career was about to stop in its tracks. 'I hooked into acting real strong,' he illu-

minated, 'and it grew into an obsession. It got to be such an obsession that I didn't realize how much I *wasn't* enjoying it. I got to the place where if I wasn't doing it, it was like withdrawing from an addiction, so that I'd start barfing on the floor or something like that.' In short, 'I realized acting was no longer making me happy.'

Instead, he turned to directing and writing, and made the thought-provoking drama *The Indian Runner*, about two brothers – one a heroic cop (David Morse), the other a self-destructive ex-con (Viggo Mortensen). Beautifully-crafted and well-acted, the film verged on the self-indulgent at times, but was none the less a powerful directing debut, evincing much promise.

For three years after announcing his retirement from appearing in front of the camera, Penn kept to his word, turning down all offers – including a proposition from Mickey Rourke, an actor he much admires. However, he said that if the price was right, he would act again. This he did when he accepted a co-starring role in Brian De Palma's *Carlito's Way*, playing a lawyer and mercurial friend to Al Pacino's former gangster.

After that, he embarked on his second film as director, *The Crossing Guard*, starring Jack Nicholson, David Morse, Robin Wright and Anjelica Huston. Like *The Indian Runner*, this was the story of two men (Nicholson, Morse) coming to terms with each other, this time over the death of a little girl. Again, Penn exhibited an enor-

mous maturity in his work, coaxing the best performance out of Nicholson in aeons. Marlon Brando wrote to Penn saying that *The Crossing Guard* 'wiped me out. I was in tears.'

Against his better judgement, Penn returned to acting once more, playing an amalgamation of two real-life Death Row convicts (Patrick Sonnier and Robert Willy) in *Dead Man Walking*, directed by Tim Robbins. Acting opposite Robbins' domestic partner, Susan Sarandon, Penn gave the best performance of his career. As the white-trash no-hoper accused of the death of two teenagers, he displayed an astonishing understanding of his character, revealing glints of the danger and compassion of the man inside. Caricature would have been an easy option, but Penn presented a frighteningly real figure torn between swaggering braggadocio and incomprehensible fear. His performance won him his first Oscar nomination and citations as best actor at the 1996 Berlin Film Festival and the 11th Independent Spirit Awards. Susan Sarandon won the Oscar.

Meanwhile, Penn's relationship with Robin Wright puttered to a close – after what he described as a 'four-year headache' of separation and reconciliation. 'I would never end a relationship where there were kids,' he grumbled. 'She just doesn't love me. She thinks I've got horns on my head.' Shortly afterwards, in April 1996, they were married.

Then, in a burst of uncharacteristic activity, he joined Robert Downey Jr, Cathy Moriarty, Alan Arkin, Richard

With Susan Sarandon in Tim Robbins's *Dead Man Walking*, the film that won Penn his first Oscar nomination as best actor

Lewis and Malcolm McDowell in the romantic comedy *Hugo Pool*, directed by Robert Downey Snr, starred alongside Robin Wright and John Travolta in Nick Cassavetes' drama *She's So Lovely*, and played the brother of Michael Douglas in the David Fincher-directed thriller *The Game*, in the role vacated by Jodie Foster (!). He then starred in Oliver Stone's *U-Turn* (replacing Bill Paxton a week before production), portraying a drifter in what is described as a 'dark comedy of errors and choices'. He was also announced to star alongside Holly Hunter, Kevin Spacey and Robin Wright in the screen adaptation of the award-winning David Rabe play *Hurlyburly*.

A happy ending: Sean Penn not only got to marry the woman he loved, but rediscovered his love for acting and won the best actor award at Cannes for *She's So Lovely*.

FILMOGRAPHY
1980: *The Killing of Randy Webster* (TV). 1981: *Hellinger's Law* (TV); *Taps*. 1982: *Fast Times at Ridgemont High* (UK: *Fast Times*); *Bad Boys*. 1983: *Crackers*. 1984: *Racing With the Moon*. 1985: *The Falcon and the Snowman*; *At Close Range*. 1986: *Shanghai Surprise*. 1988: *Dear America* (voice only); *Colors*; *Judgement in Berlin*. 1989: *Casualties of War*; *We're No Angels*. 1990: *State of Grace*. 1991: *The Indian Runner* (directed only). 1993: *Carlito's Way*. 1995: *The Crossing Guard* (directed, script and co-produced only); *Dead Man Walking*. 1997: *Hugo Pool*; *She's So Lovely*; *The Game*; *Loved*; *U-Turn*; *Hurlyburly*. 1998: *The Thin Red Line*.

ELIZABETH PERKINS

Elizabeth Perkins is a rebel. As a girl she hung out with motorcycle gangs and smooched in graveyards. When she became engaged to a local boy, her parents sent her off to boarding school. There, she smoked marijuana in the washroom, but was suspended for stealing muffins. Later, she was expelled for telling the dean that he stank. She enjoys regaling journalists with the practices of serial killers ('Ed Gein skinned people alive and his furniture was made from human skin ...') and is obsessed by the perverse photography of Diane Arbus ('She's a master of dichotomy.').

After accepting a role in David Mamet's prestigious production of *Speed-the-Plow* on Broadway, she bowed out, complaining, 'I'm not a raving fan of David Mamet. He doesn't write roles for women' – and was replaced by Madonna. In fact, after making a name for herself in the hit comedy *Big*, she turned down a lot of major Hollywood films. She says: 'I could have taken some serious blockbuster movies. It's not like the offers weren't there. But nothing came along that I wanted to do or that I thought was going to do anything for me as an actress. I'm not attracted to anything that's not off the beaten path. I get very bored playing comfortable people, people that just kind of come in and out of the room. I'd much prefer to stumble over the ottoman.'

Indeed, she was stealing the best notices in her very first film appearance – as Demi Moore's catty roommate in *'About Last Night ...'*. Penny Marshall, who directed the actress in *Big*, believes: 'Her work is never boring. When we were shaping the film, my editor and I kept saying, "Let's cut to Elizabeth."' Alan Rudolph, who was behind the camera on *Love at Large*, reckons: 'She can steal a scene or she can be invisible, but if you watch Elizabeth when she's part of a large group of people, you'll see that she's always doing something. She's sexy in unspectacular ways, but ways that last. To me, she's like a good standard song. Elizabeth is the actor's equivalent of "Star Dust".'

Elizabeth Pisperikos was born on 18 November 1960, in Forest Hills,

New York, the youngest daughter (of three) of a writer-businessman and first-generation Greek immigrant. After her parents divorced when she was still little, she grew up with her mother on her stepfather's secluded 600 acre farm in Vermont, broken by occasional stays with her father in New York City. When he moved to Chicago, she followed him there, completed high school and contemplated becoming a veterinarian. 'But,' she recalls, 'all I was thinking about during biology class was getting back to the community theatre because we were doing a production of *Guys and Dolls*.'

She had started acting in school, and had already honed her interest in offbeat roles when, in seventh grade, she appeared in a production of *Hansel and Gretel* – as Hansel! She studied for three years at Chicago's Goodman School of Drama, moved back to New York in 1984 and, within two weeks, won the role of Nora in a touring production of Neil Simon's *Brighton Beach Memoirs*. Six months later she was playing the character on Broadway.

In 1985 she married the actor-director Terry Kinney, co-founder of Chicago's Steppenwolf Theater Company, and was given the chance to audition for Debbie, the lead part in the Chicago-set movie *'About Last Night ...'* She declined the offer (the part went to Demi Moore) and won the far meatier role of Joan, Debbie's sassy, wise-cracking sidekick. 'There are so many times that I read scripts and I love the supporting character more than I love the lead,' she says, 'because usually they're the ones that have a dark side, something that is not quite right.' The critics jumped on the picture with knives bared, but spared praise for Perkins, who, with James Belushi, hijacked the film from Moore and Rob Lowe. Lowe, who is still a friend, noted: 'She reminds me of what Katharine Hepburn must have been like at 27 – strong, stubborn and sexy. But she's very vulnerable.' In spite of the film's mixed reception, Perkins was suddenly in demand and was a close contender for the Holly Hunter part in *Broadcast News*, opposite William Hurt. But everybody was offering her comic roles. 'You do one movie like *"About Last Night ..."* and that's all anyone in this industry thinks you *can* do,' she

*Elizabeth Perkins as she appeared in Penny Marshall's **Big** in 1988*

complained.

She did do another comedy, the legal farce *From the Hip*, and as Judd Nelson's down-to-earth girlfriend, she was about the only credible character in the film. However, most of her contribution ended up on the cutting room floor. Meanwhile, Penny Marshall was casting the female lead in *Big*, the part of the toy executive Susan Lawrence. Marshall had envisaged Debra Winger in the role, but as Winger was pregnant, she sought her advice instead. 'I asked Debra, "Who's closest to you as an actress?", and she mentioned Elizabeth. Physically they're very different, but they have a similar appeal. There's always something going on behind their eyes.' Perkins was simply a knockout as the assertive but vulnerable Lawrence, who realizes that her new boyfriend (Tom Hanks) is actually a 12-year-old trapped in the body of a 35-year-old man. *Big* was a colossal hit, and Perkins was suddenly in a position to turn down every film offered her.

She took a supporting role in the silly, terminally saccharine *Sweet Hearts Dance*, as a plucky Vermont schoolteacher who falls in love with her principal (Jeff Daniels) – and she managed to make the dialogue sound witty. In a cast that included Daniels, Don

Johnson and Susan Sarandon, Perkins was the only character worth spending time with, a mischievous spirit refusing to conform to small-town cliche. If there was any reason to see the film, it was to see her.

In Alan Rudolph's quirky, intermittently amusing *Love at Large*, she played a private detective, Stella Wynkowski, who falls in love with a private detective (Tom Berenger) she is asked to tail. In real life, following her divorce from Terry Kinney in 1990, she fell in love with the British writer-director Maurice Phillips, who steered her through the bizarre antics of the jet-black farce *Enid is Sleeping*. Enid was Perkins' sister, whom Perkins accidentally kills when she is caught in bed with her sister's husband, who happens to be a policeman (Judge Reinhold). Much to-ing and fro-ing follows, as Perkins attempts to dispose of the body, exhuming memories of similar corpse-dumping comedies such as Hitchcock's *The Trouble With Harry*, *Weekend at Bernie's*, *Out Cold* and *Cold Dog Soup*. Sadly, the film was a stiff and a waste of Perkins' comedic talents, with her reduced to a bleating dumb blonde. Still, some critics thought Perkins had never been better.

She turned to drama, and very successfully, in *Avalon*, Barry Levinson's superb evocation of the life of an immigrant family in Baltimore, playing a character based on Barry Levinson's own mother. She lifted weights to prepare for her role, because, she says, 'A mother has strength in her arms and strength in her hips.' Then it was back to screwball romantic comedy with *He Said, She Said*, co-starring Kevin Bacon. The film, made by real-life couple Ken Kwapis and Marisa Silver, showed the same tempestuous relationship from two viewpoints, the male objective directed by Kwapis, the female by Silver. Again, Perkins was the best thing in an uneven project, a film dismissed by critics for being gimmicky.

She was forced to drop out of the British comedy of manners *The Object of Beauty* due to illness (and was replaced by Lolita Davidovich), but got her chance to act opposite William Hurt in Randa Haines' harrowing, funny and moving *The Doctor*. Discarding make-up and hair, she

played a patient dying of cancer and gave both Hurt and Christine Lahti, as his wife, a run for their money. During production she discovered she was pregnant. 'To deal with the issue of death for three months is very draining,' she revealed. 'And yet, knowing you've got life growing inside you made it twice as poignant. Yes, my character was dying, but she was so filled with life, experiencing so much for the last time, that my baby served as an impetus.'

For the next two years she devoted her life to motherhood ('I think the baby is enough of a production.'), then stepped into the nostalgic ensemble comedy-drama *Indian Summer* – as a woman desperate for love (and was the best thing in it).

When the powers that be were looking for the perfect Fred in the $45 million *The Flintstones* (everybody from Robin Williams to James Belushi was discussed), nobody disputed Elizabeth Perkins' candidacy to play Fred's wife, Wilma. And, apparently, she won the part at her audition after uttering just one line of dialogue. Based on the beloved 1960–66 cartoon TV series, the film promised to be 'a comedy on

*Elizabeth Perkins as the quirky private detective Stella Wynkowski in Alan Rudolph's **Love at Large***

*As Wilma (with John Goodman as Fred) in the hugely successful **The Flintstones***

steroids', complete with special effects by Industrial Light & Magic, dinosaurs courtesy of Jim Henson's Creature Shop and a $100 million marketing campaign (an offensive that tagged everything from pinball machines to McDonald's). Perkins herself described Fred and Wilma as: 'the first perfect American family. Look at Wilma: she's a perfect mother, a perfect wife, she adores her husband, she loves taking care of her child. She's Donna Reed!'

However, the end result was a witless mess, marked by feeble puns, murky photography, corny music, overblown sets and a glut of noisy visual gags. Still, the merchandising drive paid off and the film went on to gross $130.5 million in the USA, also becoming one of the ten biggest money-making films in Britain – of all

time.

Next, she played the hard-boiled mother in *Miracle On 34th Street*, the John Hughes-scripted remake of the classic 1947 tearjerker, a serviceable update that was saved by Richard Attenborough's magical, guileless performance as Kris Kringle. Then she starred in David Anspaugh's witty, moving and extremely well-observed *Moonlight and Valentino*, with no less than Whoopi Goldberg, Kathleen Turner, Gwyneth Paltrow and Jon Bon Jovi in support. As a teacher unable to reconcile her grief when her husband dies, she played every emotion like a virtuoso violinist. Whether repeatedly changing her answerphone message, instructing her students to write a poem 'without words', explaining the complexities of love-making to her younger sister (Paltrow) or finally surrendering to her anger, the actress hit every note perfectly. The film should have been a contender, but it was misplaced in an overcrowded marketplace that included such heavy-hitters as *Seven*, *Dangerous Minds* and *The Usual Suspects*.

FILMOGRAPHY

1986: *'About Last Night ...'*. 1987: *From the Hip*. 1988: *Big*; *Sweet Hearts Dance*. 1990: *Love at Large*; *Enid is Sleeping* (UK: *Over Her Dead Body*); *Teach 109* (short); *Avalon*. 1991: *He Said, She Said*; *The Doctor*. 1993: *Indian Summer*; *For Their Own Good* (TV). 1994: *The Flintstones*; *Miracle On 34th Street*. 1995: *Moonlight and Valentino*.

She says: 'I think I look like a duck. I mean, my face is completely crooked. And my lips are lopsided. The less I have to think or talk about my looks, the better.' In spite of these words, Michelle Pfeiffer has become a synonym for beauty in an industry stuffed to the gills with cosmetic precision. And yet Ms Pfeiffer has even something more. She possesses that rare component that ignites the flame of beauty and turns it into a roaring furnace. She radiates sex appeal and intelligence, has simmered seductively in such pictures as *Grease 2* and *Tequila Sunrise*, but has never lost sight of her function as a human being. In *The Fabulous Baker Boys*, she asks Jeff Bridges: 'Listen, you're not going soft on me are you? I mean, you're not going to start dreaming about me, waking up all sweaty and looking at me like I'm some kind of princess when I burp?'

Michelle Pfeiffer could also be very funny, thrilling to the chase in Jonathan Demme's wonderful *Married to the Mob* and sending herself up rotten as Catwoman in *Batman Returns*, in which, with a simple 'Miaow', she brought the house down.

Women admired her down-to-earth honesty and self-deprecation, and men – well, they just adored her. There were reports of an affair with Alec Baldwin during the making of *Married to the Mob*. Michael Keaton fell for her years before he was menacingly cat-licked by her in *Batman Returns*. 'The truth of the matter,' Keaton reveals, 'is that we just dated for a while. It probably enriched things [in the movie]. I think it was just enough history to help us and not enough of a history to get in our way. She's good to work with. I'm such a fan. In a way, I think she has more range than anybody.'

And then there was the furore over her fling with John Malkovich, on the set of *Dangerous Liaisons* – an affair which terminally damaged the actor's marriage to Glenne Headley. For three years she was involved with the character actor Fisher Stevens, seven years her junior, but broke off the relationship when she caught him in the arms of a 17-year-old stand-in. At the time, she told friends: 'It's over. I deserve better

*Perkins sharing an intimate moment with Jon Bon Jovi in the glowing **Moonlight and Valentino***

*Michelle as the mysterious Diana in John Landis's supremely enjoyable **Into the Night***

than that.' Then, at the end of 1992, she was linked with the legendary guitarist Eric Clapton, and shortly after that was romantically involved with the producer-writer David Kelley. For years she had told journalists that she wanted children, and when Kelley supported her dream to adopt, he seemed a likely candidate for longevity. In November 1993, Michelle and David were married.

And then there were the critics. For her role as the sexy, hard-edged chanteuse in *The Fabulous Baker Boys*, she won the Golden Globe award and was voted best actress by the Los Angeles Film Critics' Circle, the New York Film Critics' Circle, the National Board of Review and the US National Society of Film Critics. The Oscar that year went to Jessica Tandy for *Driving Miss Daisy*, but then the Oscars aren't chosen by critics. Still, she won a nomination and, furthermore, was a front-runner for her roles in *Dangerous Liaisons* and *Love Field*. She was also a star player in innumerable lists of 'the ten most beautiful women in the world'.

Michelle Pfeiffer was born on 29 April 1957 in Santa Ana, California, the second of four children of a heating and air-conditioning contractor, and grew up in Orange County. At school she attended drama classes, but a teacher remembers her as 'this sunshine surfer beach girl, more out of the class than in'. After school, she worked as a check-out girl in a local supermarket, and in 1977 she won the Miss Orange County beauty title. This led to an agent, and small roles in TV. On *Fantasy*

Island she got to say, 'Who is he, Naomi?', and was then levered into hot pants and a padded bra in the sitcom *Delta House*, a small-screen rip-off of *National Lampoon's Animal House*. This led to a regular role on the car chase series *B.A.D. Cats*, as Officer Samantha Jensen, but the show was dropped after five episodes. She also appeared in the TV movie *The Solitary Man*, about the break-up of a marriage, made her theatrical film debut as a car hop in *The Hollywood Knights* (a weak imitation of *American Graffiti*), and played 'Susannah York' in the flashback sequences of *Falling In Love Again*.

At 22, she married the actor Peter Horton, who later became a star as Gary Shepherd in TV's *thirtysomething*, and the marriage lasted seven years. 'I had a great marriage with a great man,' she says in retrospect, 'but as we grew older our views changed and we went in different directions.'

There were three more TV movies and *Charlie Chan and the Curse of the Dragon Queen*, a dire attempt to resurrect the Oriental detective with Peter Ustinov, in which Pfeiffer played a wealthy airhead called Cordelia Farrington III. Then, following a nationwide search, she won the role of Stephanie Zinone, the sizzling leader of 'the Pink Ladies' in *Grease 2*. Although the musical died at the box-office, some critics thought it superior to the original, and Pfeiffer was outstanding as the most beautiful catch at Rydell High (and probably in all of California).

A year later she starred opposite Al Pacino in Brian De Palma's adrenalin-pumping *Scarface*, as Elvira, the cocaine-snorting gangster's moll with ice running through her veins. She was even better in John Landis's terrific, offbeat comedy-thriller *Into the Night*, as the dream girl who leads Jeff Goldblum into no end of trouble, and did her only nude scene (which lasted for – what? – two seconds). She was miscast in Richard Donner's lush period fantasy *Ladyhawke*, as a woman transformed into a hawk by day, but successfully competed with the beauty of the Italian scenery. She then had two roles in Alan Alda's likeable satire on the movie business, *Sweet Liberty*, as a no-nonsense movie actress and the virginal maiden she plays in a costume drama

set during the American War of Independence.

With George Miller's jet-black comedy *The Witches of Eastwick* she had her first major hit, as Sukie Ridgemont, a small-town reporter and recently-widowed mother (of six little girls) who falls for the devil (Jack Nicholson). Ironically, she says: 'The first time I saw it, I hated it. It was so different than the way I had envisioned it. The original script was more of a dark comedy, as opposed to ... there were no special effects; there wasn't all that flying in the air.'

Nevertheless, the film upped Pfeiffer's ante in Hollywood, and

*Michelle in her award-laden performance as Susie Diamond in **The Fabulous Baker Boys***

besides a cameo in the slipshod *Amazon Women on the Moon*, she headed for greater things. She was hilarious in Jonathan Demme's *Married to the Mob*, as the dizzy, red-headed Italian-American widow of a gangster (Alec Baldwin) who tries to escape the clutches of the Mafia by moving into a grotty apartment on Manhattan's Lower East Side. It was Pfeiffer's first instance of top-billing, and the film was a hit. She was second-billed to Mel Gibson, but billed above Kurt Russell, in the slick, moody romantic crime thriller *Tequila Sunrise*, but she couldn't generate any sexual chemistry with

Purr-fect: Michelle as everybody's ideal Catwoman in **Batman Returns**

Gibson, in spite of a steamy sequence in a hot tub. With Gibson and Pfeiffer stripping down for a bit of slap-and-tickle, the film should have been a monster hit. It wasn't.

Dangerous Liaisons was even less successful at the box-office (in the USA, at least), but was far sexier, and enjoyed an avalanche of rave reviews. Pfeiffer was the virtuous, convent-bred Madame de Tourvel, who is ruthlessly courted by the unscrupulous womanizer Vicomte de Valmont (John Malkovich, on chilling form). Based on the scorchingly well-written play by Christopher Hampton, and set in pre-Revolution France, the film was a mesmerizing look at the politics of debauchery, and gathered a handful of Oscar nominations, including citations for best film, best actress (Glenn Close) and best supporting actress (Pfeiffer).

Hot on the heels of her first Academy Award nomination, Pfeiffer was flooded with laurels for her portrayal of Susie Diamond, the earthy nightclub singer in *The Fabulous Baker Boys*. The actress trained hard to perfect her voice for the role, and who could forget her turn in a red dress, atop Jeff Bridges' piano, crooning 'Making Whoopee'? It was the sensation of the season.

She won more good reviews for her part as a Russian book editor involved with Sean Connery in *The Russia House*, from John La Carré's novel, and then played a bored beautician from Dallas whose eyes are opened when she has an affair with a black man. Her swain was originally to have been played by Denzel Washington, but when he walked (Washington complained: 'It was Michelle's film, I was just a guy who helped the story move along.'), he was replaced by an unknown, Dennis Haysbert. The word on the film was outstanding, but then its distributor, Orion, ran into financial difficulties and the picture was jammed in pre-distribution limbo.

Next, she was announced to play the shy, frumpy and love-starved waitress in Garry Marshall's adaptation of the off-Broadway play *Frankie and Johnny in the Clair de Lune*, a part originated by Kathy Bates. Linda Winer, the theatre critic for *Newsday*, was astounded: 'Either this is the funniest casting since Dustin Hoffman was Sean Connery's son in *Family Business*, or director Garry Marshall has rethought the concept.' Bates herself 'laughed hysterically' when she heard Pfeiffer was playing the role. As it happens, Pfeiffer *was* miscast, but she gave such an outstanding performance of emotional insecurity that at times you believed in

her pathetic life. Al Pacino played Johnny, and he, too, looked misplaced.

She was the first choice for the role of Clarice Starling, the FBI trainee on the trail of a serial killer, in Jonathan Demme's *The Silence of the Lambs*, but declined on the grounds that she found the subject 'too chilling'. Jodie Foster replaced her, and won an Oscar. Pfeiffer was also mentioned for the role of Catwoman in *Batman Returns*, competing alongside Julia Roberts and her friend, Cher. However, Michael Keaton decided on Annette Bening, and only after Bening had to back out due to pregnancy (courtesy of Warren Beatty) was Pfeiffer handed the role (for a reported sum of $3 million). And thank God, for – frankly – she was the best thing in it. Strapped in skin-tight black leather, she oozed sexual menace and jumped into the spirit of the occasion, saying it was 'the most sophisticated and inspirational movie I have ever done'. It was certainly her most successful.

She then started research for her role in *Lorenzo's Oil*, as Michaela Odone, the mother of a boy stricken with a rare and supposedly fatal disease. Andy Garcia had already dropped out of the part of her husband (and was replaced by Nick Nolte), when Pfeiffer got cold feet. The film's director,

With Daniel Day-Lewis in Martin Scorsese's **The Age of Innocence**

George Miller, who previously worked with the actress on *The Witches of Eastwick*, explained: 'Michelle met Michaela and sort of got this sense that she wasn't up to the role. It's this terrible inferiority she's got about being uneducated. You know, she said, "I'm from Orange County, and I worked as a check-out girl." And I kept on saying, "*And* you're extremely intelligent."'

Susan Sarandon, who was also in *The Witches of Eastwick*, took over the role, and was duly nominated for an Oscar. But this time so was Pfeiffer, for *Love Field*, which was hurriedly dusted off to qualify for the 1992 Academy Awards.

Meanwhile, the actress landed the female lead in Martin Scorsese's 1870s romantic drama *The Age of Innocence* (based on the novel by Edith Wharton), as a Bohemian countess courted by Daniel Day-Lewis. A brave attempt by Scorsese to try something new, the film was an exquisite, eloquent labour of love which died on its feet. Scorsese became so caught up in the manners and silverware of the period that he seemed to overlook the characters. Still, Pfeiffer was soundly praised, although she failed to nail the fourth Oscar nomination that some predicted.

In March 1993, Michelle Pfeiffer caused a storm of media controversy when – through a lawyer – she privately adopted a baby girl, Claudia Rose, making her an instant unmarried mother. Then, following her subsequent marriage to David Kelley, she promptly got pregnant and gave birth to little John Henry in August 1994.

She was then re-teamed with Jack Nicholson in Mike Nichols' *Wolf*, in which Nicholson played a New York book editor who is bitten by a wolf and takes on the attributes of the beast. Nicholson was perfect, and Pfeiffer provided a splendid, feisty turn as the romantic interest, but the film degenerated into melodrama and was a mild disappointment at the box-office.

The actress continued her habit of abandoning choice projects (including *Sleepless in Seattle*, *Basic Instinct* and *Disclosure*), and then infuriated Oliver Stone when she decided to back out of the film version of *Evita* because she didn't want to leave the USA. She did, however, accept $6 million to play the part of LouAnne Johnson, a former marine who ends up teaching a class of ghetto kids. The film was *Dangerous Minds*, based on Johnson's autobiographical novel *My Posse Don't Do Homework*, and was a resounding success. It grossed some $83 million in the USA alone, and Pfeiffer was surprisingly good in a convincing and heartfelt performance. Billed solo above the title, the actress could finally take credit for a film's box-office achievement.

Up Close and Personal was another hit – skewering $51 million Stateside – but was an artistic travesty. Pfeiffer played a kookie, ambitious would-be TV reporter who reluctantly falls for the charms of Robert Redford's sardonic, weathered TV producer. However, by duplicating a number of the mannerisms that she had perfected in *Dangerous Minds*, Pfeiffer was an embarrassment (as was Redford). An attempt to resurrect the hard-boiled romantic comedy format of the 1930s,

As LouAnne Johnson in her biggest solo success, **Dangerous Minds**

Michelle in fine comic form in **One Fine Day**

the film itself was an implausible, sentimental glob of candy floss that missed most of its comic opportunities.

Next, Pfeiffer took a supporting role in the over-earnest, sickly-sweet weepy *To Gillian On Her 37th Birthday* – co-produced and scripted by her husband – and looked highly uncomfortable as the ghost of the title. She then turned executive producer on the romantic comedy *One Fine Day*, exercising the clout of her own production company, Via Rosa. In it she played a harassed New York architect who is forced to alternate babysitting duties with a smug columnist played by George Clooney. Although playing another variation of her scatty, accident-prone siren, Pfeiffer layered the character with some grit and was quite touching as the divorcée torn between her maternal and professional commitments. She then joined Jessica Lange and Jennifer Jason Leigh in *A Thousand Acres*, under the direction of Jocelyn Moorhouse.

FILMOGRAPHY

1979: *The Solitary Man* (TV). 1980: *The Hollywood Knights; Falling In Love Again.* 1981: *Charlie Chan and the Curse of the Dragon Queen; Splendor in the Grass* (TV); *The Children Nobody Wanted* (TV); *Callie & Son* (TV). 1982: *Grease 2.* 1983: *Scarface.* 1985: *Into the Night; Ladyhawke.* 1986: *Sweet Liberty.* 1987: *The Witches of Eastwick; Amazon Women on the Moon.* 1988: *Married to the Mob; Tequila Sunrise; Dangerous Liaisons.* 1989: *The Fabulous Baker Boys.* 1990: *The Russia House.* 1991: *Love Field; Frankie and Johnny.* 1992: *Batman Returns.* 1993: *The Age of Innocence.* 1994: *Wolf.* 1995: *Dangerous Minds.* 1996: *Up Close and Personal; To Gillian On Her 37th Birthday; One Fine Day.* 1997: *A Thousand Acres; The Prince of Egypt* (voice only).

BRAD PITT

Brad Pitt as the quintessential dumb jock in Tom DiCillo's **Johnny Suede**

As a sex symbol, Brad Pitt is unbearably cute. Puckish, boyish, athletic and as cool as a chilled glass of Evian, he has also proved himself to be a versatile actor. Whether playing the brain-dead, sexually naive *Johnny Suede*, or the wily, carnally confident J.D. in *Thelma & Louise*, he was totally the part – and had women swooning.

Brad Pitt snatched his 15 minutes of fame in *Thelma & Louise* and kept on running. The part of J.D., the hitch-hiker who gives Geena Davis her first orgasm and takes her last penny, was pencilled in for William Baldwin, but he bowed out when he won the lead in *Backdraft*. Auditions were called, and nearly 400 hopefuls showed up (including George Clooney). Casting director Lou Di Giaimo jumped on Brad Pitt. 'There are stars that aren't great actors,' Di Giaimo reckons, 'but when I met Brad, I thought, "He's going to be a star *and* he can act. His career is going to be a capital B-I-G."'

Thelma & Louise was a hit, and Pitt's brief but telling contribution rocked the movie community in its seats. And yet the 5'11" actor was already coming up fast on the outside – before *Thelma*

& Louise had even opened. He had been having discussions with Robert Redford about starring in *A River Runs Through It*, he had landed the title role in *Johnny Suede*, and movie publicists were falling over themselves to represent him. He was already a star of the gossip columns in 1989, thanks to a liaison with Robin Givens, while tabloid queen Liz Smith agitated things further when she reported that Pitt and Geena Davis were rumoured to be having an affair on the set of *Thelma & Louise*. The gunpowder was there; *Thelma & Louise* just lit the fuse.

Born William Bradley Pitt on 18 December 1963, in Oklahoma, Brad was raised in Springfield, Missouri. His father, Bill Pitt, owned a trucking company in the city, where his son was educated. After taking small parts in school musicals, Brad enrolled at the University of Missouri and studied journalism – with an eye for the advertising industry. However, he continued acting in fraternity 'Spring Fling' shows, and dropped out of college two weeks before graduation.

In 1986 he left for Los Angeles to attend art school, when he decided he wanted to be in movies instead. While studying to act, he took on a variety of jobs, including a stint as a giant chicken plugging a fast-food chain, and chauffeuring strip-o-gram artistes in a limousine. He got an agent, and shortly afterwards secured a part on *Dallas* as 'an idiot boyfriend who gets caught in the hay'. He had another regular turn on the daytime soap *Another World*, popped up in the family sitcom *Growing Pains*, and snatched a small role in the critically acclaimed TV movie *A Stoning in Fulham County*, starring Ken Olin and Jill Eikenberry.

He moved on to the big screen in the romantic comedy *Happy Together*, and then landed a starring role in the slasher spoof *Cutting Class*. A dire attempt to lampoon such horror entries as *Friday the 13th* and *Prom Night*, *Cutting Class* featured Pitt as a high school sadist and bully who romances Jill Schoelen (of *The Stepfather* fame) while tormenting his old friend, Donovan Leitch, who has been released from a mental home for supposedly murdering his father.

Pitt played another low-life, Billy King, in the mercilessly manipulative

Brad Pitt as Paul Maclean in Robert Redford's excessively tasteful **A River Runs Through It**

TV movie *Too Young To Die?*. The story of a 14-year-old girl (Juliette Lewis) dumped on by society, the film featured Pitt as a hirsute dope addict who pushes Lewis into prostitution and, eventually, murder. Neither Pitt nor Lewis thought much of the movie, although it was the beginning of a long-term romance.

'Yeah, it was quite romantic,' Pitt jokes, 'shooting her full of drugs and stuff.' He had another recurring role – as Walker Lovejoy, a college dropout – in the Fox series *Glory Days*, but the

*The ugly side of Pitt: the actor as he appeared as serial killer Early Grayce in Dominic Sena's hard-kicking **Kalifornia***

show was cancelled after six episodes; and then he took a small bit part in the so-so TV movie *The Image*, starring Albert Finney.

He was the competitive athletic brother of Rick Schroder in *Across the Tracks*, a tenable teen drama that failed to find its audience, and then came Ridley Scott's *Thelma & Louise*.

His next big breakthrough was the title role in Tom DiCillo's delightfully idiosyncratic *Johnny Suede*, the story of a dumb jock obsessed by his hair and Ricky Nelson. 'At the time I cast the movie,' explains DiCillo, 'Brad was a complete unknown. He read for the part, and there was no doubt that he was the one for the role. He was the only one to get that Johnny was this guy who has no idea what he's doing. And there was a beautiful transparency to his work – whatever's going on inside Brad, you can see it.' *Johnny Suede* was a real departure for Pitt, who played DiCillo's offbeat comedy completely straight – which, believe it or not, was no small feat. Although a decidedly low-budget independent feature (price tag: $1 million), the film attracted a respectable following in urban circles.

After that he was in *Cool World*, Ralph Bakshi's witless adult take on *Who Framed Roger Rabbit*, in which he played a young detective trapped in a bizarre cartoon universe. And then there was Robert Redford's meticulous recreation of Norman Maclean's celebrated autobiographical novel *A River Runs Through It*. Pitt was Maclean's troubled younger brother, Paul, and with his sandy hair blowing in the Montana wind, he looked uncannily like a young Redford. The film was beautifully composed and acted, but was *so* tastefully done that it nudged the boredom factor once too often – in spite of Philippe Rousselot's Oscar-winning cinematography.

In Dominic Sena's numbing, poetic and visceral road movie *Kalifornia*, the actor was back in trailer park territory with Juliette Lewis and a vengeance. He and Lewis had officially broken up, but he had lost none of his admiration for his co-star: 'Juliette is the best,' he asserted. 'She's probably the best actor I've ever seen. She has this ability to just pick up a script, see it and then do it.' Veering from horror to black come-

With Julia Ormond in **Legends of the Fall**

This time Pitt is on the trail of a serial killer, in the whopping hit **Seven**

dy with frightening ease, *Kalifornia* was distinguished by a sensational turn from Pitt as a hunk of white trash who won't let his girlfriend (Lewis) curse or drink, yet thinks nothing of cutting up an invalid for petrol money. A bearded, bulked-up psycho, Pitt's Early Grayce was the most powerful, unflattering performance of his career.

In Tony Scott's black thriller *True Romance*, he was a hoot as a spaced-out junkie, and then he turned down the role of D'Artagnan in Disney's *The Three Musketeers* (replaced by Chris O'Donnell). Instead, he took the part of Tristan Ludlow in *Legends of the Fall*, the hot-headed, gorgeous son of Anthony Hopkins' anti-war rancher. Conjuring up the spirit of epics like *Gone With The Wind* and *Giant*, the film was an earnest, sweeping saga that ultimately suffered from one too many leaps across an ambitious timetable. Still, Pitt smouldered magnificently as the romantic hero, with his luxurious, sun-kissed hair blowing energetically in the Montana breeze, beautifully lit by John Toll's Oscar-winning cinematography. While Pitt's performance may have appeared narcissistic, it was at least his first starring role in a major Hollywood film (he was top-billed above Hopkins and Aidan Quinn) – and the public loved it. *Legends of the Fall* grossed a handsome $66.2 million in the USA and was nominated for best film and best actor (Pitt) at the 1994 Golden Globes. There was also an alleged romance with his leading lady, Julia Ormond.

He then had the lead in an even bigger hit, although Tom Cruise had the better billing. Pitt played the bloodsucker of the title in Neil Jordan's meandering *Interview with the Vampire*, but the actor appeared to be sleepwalking for most of the time (through two centuries, at that). Still, the movie's till-ringing gross of $105.3 million (in the USA) upped Pitt's salary to $4 million for *Seven*, a searingly intelligent thriller about the hunt for a serial killer. This time Pitt was on the right side of the law, as a brash young detective teamed with Morgan Freeman. While Freeman won the lion's share of the glowing notices, Pitt secured the affections of his leading lady, Gwyneth Paltrow (who played his wife). Furthermore, the movie went on to gross a sensational

$326.2 million worldwide.

He took a supporting role in Terry Gilliam's epic, complex and gripping sci-fi masterpiece *Twelve Monkeys* – as the insane, seditious son of a prominent scientist – and strolled off with the Golden Globe as best supporting actor. Insiders declared his Oscar a *fait accompli*, but he had to suffice with a nomination (Kevin Spacey won that year). However, with *Twelve Monkeys* grossing $163.6 million globally, Brad Pitt was hotter than ever.

He turned down the lead in the John Grisham thriller *The Chamber* (which Chris O'Donnell, again, snapped up) and opted to join the ensemble cast of *Sleepers* instead. A wise move, as it turned out, as *The Chamber* flopped and *Sleepers* didn't. However, the actor had little to do in the latter, playing an assistant DA bent on revenge, sorely overshadowed by co-stars Dustin Hoffman, Robert De Niro, Jason Patric and Kevin Bacon.

He then got $10 million to star opposite Harrison Ford in Alan J. Pakula's action-thriller *The Devil's Own* (as an insane terrorist), a venture he publicly dismissed as 'ridiculous; the most irresponsible bit of filmmaking that I've ever seen'. He received another $10 million for *Seven Days in Tibet*, and then $17.5 million for *Meet Joe Black*, a remake of the 1934 Fredric March vehicle *Death Takes a Holiday* (with Pitt as a love-struck Grim Reaper). In two years, Pitt's salary had increased by a whopping 338 per cent. Then, in December 1996, Gwyneth Paltrow accepted his offer of marriage (after three proposals), but they split up seven months later.

FILMOGRAPHY

1987: *Less Than Zero* (crowd scene). 1988: *A Stoning in Fulham County* (TV). 1989: *Happy Together; Cutting Class*. 1990: *Too Young To Die?* (TV); *The Image* (TV). 1991: *Across the Tracks* (a.k.a. *Nowhere To Run*); *Thelma & Louise; Dark Side of the Sun; The Favor*. 1992: *Johnny Suede; Cool World; A River Runs Through It*. 1993: *Kalifornia; True Romance*. 1994: *Legends of the Fall; Interview with the Vampire*. 1995: *Seven; Twelve Monkeys*. 1996: *Sleepers*. 1997: *The Devil's Own; Seven Years in Tibet*. 1998: *Meet Joe Black*.

With Jason Patric in Barry Levinson's **Sleepers**

R

Although Keanu Reeves has made a career out of playing gormless young men (brain-dead or otherwise), he has also, uncharacteristically, appeared in his share of costume dramas. And, until *Speed*, he was perhaps best known as Theodore Logan, the time-travelling high school moron in *Bill & Ted's Excellent Adventure* and *Bill & Ted's Bogus Journey*. These were a pair of wildly popular adolescent comedies that overcame the spectre of their self-conscious trendiness through an irresistible energy and enthusiasm. They even spawned a Saturday morning cartoon series. Keanu, who previously was best known as the sullen Matt in *River's Edge*, was a revelation as Ted, the bone-headed student who couldn't keep still for a moment. Whether playing air-guitar with co-star Alex Winter (as Bill) or romancing some 'medieval babes' from Olde England, his frenzied, infantile bonhomie was infectious.

In fact, Ted Logan was far more in keeping with the real Keanu, whose concentration and syntax are all over the place. He positively exudes a boyish excitement and speaks in a street lingo as fresh as his name (Keanu is Hawaiian for 'a cool breeze over the mountains'). And yet he was commandeered for a

number of serious period pieces in direct contrast to his personality. But whether he's playing a straight-F student or a far-from-straight street hustler, he invariably conveys a sense of upstanding propriety. On stage he was Trinculo in *The Tempest*, he played the righteous, profoundly Victorian Jonathan Harker in *Bram Stoker's Dracula*, was Prince Siddhartha in Bernardo Bertolucci's Himalayan epic *Little Buddha* and played Don John in Kenneth Branagh's *Much Ado About Nothing*. Even Scott Favor, the male prostitute in *My Own Private Idaho*, had his genesis in Shakespeare – or, as Keanu eloquently put it: 'Yeah, Scottie's based on ... Hal? Prince Hal? From, um, Shakespeare.'

Like his syntax, Keanu Reeves is from all over the place. Born in Beirut, Lebanon, on 2 September 1964, to a Hawaiian-Chinese father and English mother, he lived for a while in Australia and New York and was raised in Canada. Confessing to 'a safe and sheltered upbringing', he dropped out of high school at 15 to study acting. A year later he made his professional debut in the Canadian TV series *Hanging In* and earned himself a handsome income from a Coca-Cola commercial. He then attended Toronto's High School for the Performing Arts. 'It was a fun year,' he says, 'but I got kicked out and failed. I was rude and stuff – talking too much.'

He then spent a summer at the

Hedgerow Theater in Pennsylvania and studied with Jaspar Deeter. His favourite role at that time was Mercutio – in, um, *Romeo and Juliet*. On TV, he played a psychotic assassin in the HBO movie *Act of Vengeance*, with Charles Bronson, and he had a good part in the highly-acclaimed TV movie *Under the Influence*, with Andy Griffith.

He made his theatrical film debut in *Youngblood*, an ice hockey melodrama with Rob Lowe and Patrick Swayze, in which he drew on his reputation as most valuable player on his school's hockey team (here he played the goalie). He then had the lead in the slick TV movie *The Brotherhood of Justice*, as Derick, a hunky, privileged kid who not only drives a flash red sports car but is captain of the school football team. Derick is also nominated captain of a vigilante gang that gets out of control. Kiefer Sutherland played the good guy.

Next, Keanu joined Drew Barrymore for an overlong TV version of the Victor Herbert operetta *Babes in Toyland*, with a new score by Leslie Bricusse, and was in the CBS Disney 'Family Movie' *I Wish I Were Eighteen Again*. Then came *River's Edge*.

Both a critical success and something of a cult, *River's Edge* was a disturbing, honest drama inspired by a true murder case in 1981. Not since Francis Coppola's *The Outsiders* had a cast of unknowns exhibited such an ensemble force. Reeves was simply superb as Matt, the story's conscientious anchor, who reluctantly comes to terms with his moral duty. Although both Crispin Glover and Dennis Hopper enjoyed showier roles, it was Keanu who had the toughest part to play.

Marisa Silver's *Permanent Record* covered parallel ground, but failed to find an audience, and a similar fate befell the teen comedy *The Night Before*, in which Keanu played a high school nerd suffering from alcohol-induced amnesia. He had a supporting role in *Dangerous Liaisons*, cast against type as the French nobleman Chevalier Danceny, and he then landed the part of a rebellious teenager in *The Prince of Pennsylvania*, a genuine oddity. Still, it allowed Keanu to have a rare crack at comedy, although with lines like 'I don't want to be a tadpole, I want to

A young Keanu with Ione Skye in River's Edge

be a dolphin,' it was hard to distinguish between what was *meant* to be funny and what wasn't. The director, Ron Nyswaner, certainly took a risk with his casting.

*Keanu Reeves (right) with Alex Winter, in the totally bodacious **Bill & Ted's Excellent Adventure***

'I loved Keanu in *River's Edge*,' Nyswaner ventured, 'but it was a very serious drama, and I had no idea whether or not he could be funny. So I had him up to the hotel in LA to talk about the part, and he made us laugh for a solid 45 minutes. After that, I knew he had to be ideal.' Although the film was not a hit, it mustered a small following and even prompted a dance called the Keanu Stomp, enthusiastically enacted by Toronto punks.

Keanu Reeves had found his own feet and, leaving teen angst behind him, started on a new career in comedy. First there was the phenomenally successful *Bill & Ted's Excellent Adventure*, and then the even bigger hit, *Parenthood*, with Steve Martin, in which Keanu played Martha Plimpton's compassionate boyfriend and a prospective parent, and delivered the film's most poignant line: 'You have to have a licence to have a dog, even to catch a fish, but you don't need a licence to be a father.'

He had another supporting role in the starry, sporadically hilarious *I Love You To Death* (as a reluctant hitman, partnered with William Hurt), and then played the idealistic young writer Martin Loader in *Tune in Tomorrow* (based on the novel *Aunt Julia and the Scriptwriter* by Mario Vargas Llosa). The director was the London-born Jon Amiel. 'When I first met Keanu, his hair was shaved bald on one side and long on the other,' the filmmaker remembers. 'The hair had time to grow before rehearsals, but on the first day he turned up swathed in bandages and was limping after yet another tumble off his motorbike.'

Reeves is a self-confessed speed freak, and dotes on his various sets of wheels – his rented Harley, his 850 Norton Commando, his Moto Guzzi ... And, as a confirmation of his first love, he has a prominent scar running from his navel to his chest and another on his calf. Cheerfully, he admits: 'My body's a wreck, man.'

He indulged in more dangerous sport when he took on the role of tough rookie cop Johnny Utah in *Point Break*, a part originally earmarked for Matthew Broderick. The part demanded that he not only learn to surf and fire a gun, but also jump out of an aeroplane. Till now, Keanu had steered clear of the action genre, but made an imposing, fast-talking cop in what turned out to be a popular, muscular get-up-and-go thriller. Patrick Swayze co-starred (as the villain), and Kathryn Bigelow signed on to direct.

'I've been an enormous fan of Keanu since *River's Edge*,' Bigelow explained. 'When this film came up, I thought Keanu's innate physicality, intelligence and charm would make him perfect to play Utah. He holds the screen, and he's got a magical ability to put the audience in his back pocket. In addition, the role was a departure from the work he'd done in the past. We all felt it would be a fresh approach for the picture.'

He returned to familiar ground with *Bill & Ted's Bogus Journey*, and then starred opposite River Phoenix in Gus Van Sant Jr's dark, pretentious *My Own Private Idaho*. While the gimmick of mingling Shakespearian text with contemporary slang was a fatal mistake, the film did have its moments, not least the affectionate fireside confession between the two stars. Next, he was all but swallowed by the grisly special effects in *Bram Stoker's Dracula* (but who could refuse a Coppola movie?), and he then did an unbilled cameo in *Freaked*, which his friend Alex Winter co-wrote and co-directed. Next came *Much Ado About Nothing*, Kenneth Branagh's exquisite, hugely successful adaptation of Shakespeare's play, although Keanu looked far from comfortable as a sulky Don John, bastard brother of Denzel Washington's Don Pedro (the actor later confessed that he was 'out of my

*Keanu in action mode in Kathryn Bigelow's adrenaline-pumping **Point Break***

Keanu as Jack Traven in Speed

depth'). Indeed, when Don John announced, 'I am not of many words,' there was an audible sigh of relief at the critics' screening. Nevertheless, in January 1995 he went on to play the bard's melancholy Dane in a Winnipeg production of *Hamlet*. While the *Toronto Star* noted that Reeves 'said all the words in the right order', and Britain's *Guardian* observed, 'for most of the first act he was the lead actor in a school play. He gabbled his lines, oblivious to metre, like a learner driver falling on the accelerator,' *The Sunday Times* took a different tack: 'He was wonderful,' wrote Roger Lewis. 'He quite embodied the innocence, the splendid fury, the animal grace of the leaps and bounds, the emotional violence, that form the Prince of Denmark. He is one of the top three Hamlets I have seen, for a simple reason: he *is* Hamlet.'

He took a cameo in Gus Van Sant's awful *Even Cowgirls Get the Blues* (as an asthmatic artist), and was then seriously miscast as Prince Siddhartha in Bernardo Bertolucci's *Little Buddha*, a visually seductive, powerfully sincere celebration of cinema and Buddhism.

Meanwhile (as if his stream of movies weren't enough to keep boredom at bay), the actor started up his own folk-rock band, Dogstar, for whom he played bass guitar. His manager, Jay Davis, described the act as 'Nirvana mixed with The Sex Pistols'.

He also appeared in a Paula Abdul video and acted in a couple of student movies.

In his spare moments – ha! – he confessed to an insatiable appetite for reading, favouring Dostoevsky, Philip K. Dick, T.S. Eliot and Greek mythology. Such workaholism and devotion to post-college education, not to mention his dedication to researching his roles, left little time for Hollywood parties and the inevitable inclusion in the gossip pages. But, he insists, 'I dig going out, but I don't get many invitations. It's just kind of whatever happens. I'll go see art, buy a drink, dance, play. Have *fun*. I dig the blues, man.' And then, with a mischievous twinkle, he brushes off his apparent lack of famous girlfriends with, 'No, I'm not gay – but you never know.' However, just to set the record straight, in 1993 he was dating Sofia Coppola, actress daughter of the Brat Pack guru. A year later, his father, Samuel Reeves, was sentenced to ten years in prison on a drug charge. 'The last time I saw my father was when I was 13,' he notes. 'And I remember him speaking about the stars. Something about how the world is a box. And I looked up, and I had no clue what he was talking about.'

Then came *Speed*. Reeves played Jack Traven, a young, gung-ho cop with testosterone to spare, who finds himself on board a bus that has been wired to

blow if it slows down to 50 miles an hour. Combining a slick screenplay by Graham Yost, taut editing and enough stunts and explosions to guarantee heart failure for anybody over 50, the film was an action junkie's wet dream. Keanu was paid $1.25 million for his services ($650,000 more than co-star Sandra Bullock), and the film went on to gross more than $320 million worldwide.

Suddenly, the dude was a major player – and his salary reflected the fact. He was paid $2 million for *Johnny Mnemonic*, but the movie (adapted from William Gibson's short story) was a travesty, starring Reeves as a courier of the future who uses his brain to transport top-secret coded information. However, besides its dishevelled clash of half-baked ideas, the film featured one of the great moments of cod cinema when, stranded in a dystopian no-man's-land, Johnny/Keanu screams: 'I want room service! I want the club sandwich! I want the cold Mexican beer! I want a $10,000-a-night hooker!' Priceless.

He was offered $7 million for Savoy Pictures' *Without Remorse*, but opted instead to star in Alfonso Arau's gushingly romantic *A Walk in the Clouds* for a fraction of the price. Set to a sweeping score by Maurice Jarre, complimented by mouth-watering shots of California's Napa Valley (not to mention close-ups of fruit and sunshine), the film was forty years behind its time and was savaged by the critics. None the less, it did go on to gross over $50 million in the US, which said something for the dedication of Keanu's fans.

He did accept the $7 million offered him for *Chain Reaction*, a thrill-a-minute conspiracy romance that flopped with critics and public alike (undeservedly), then he took $200,000 to play a disaffected nomad (who steals his brother's wife) in the fatally misconceived *Feeling Minnesota* (a major dud). Having turned down *Heat* (a major hit), he then spurned the sequel to *Speed* (for which he was reportedly offered $11 million) in order to tour Europe with Dogstar.

He then played a lawyer who suspects his boss (Al Pacino) of being Lucifer himself in Taylor Hackford's *The Devil's Advocate*.

Keanu, back in heroic vein, in **Chain Reaction**

FILMOGRAPHY

1984: *Act of Vengeance* (TV). 1986: *Under the Influence* (TV); *Youngblood; The Brotherhood of Justice* (TV); *Babes in Toyland* (TV). 1987: *I Wish I Were Eighteen Again* (TV); *River's Edge*. 1988: *Permanent Record; The Night Before; Dangerous Liaisons; The Prince of Pennsylvania*. 1989: *Bill & Ted's Excellent Adventure; Parenthood*. 1990: *I Love You To Death; Tune in Tomorrow* (UK: *Aunt Julia and the Scriptwriter*). 1991: *Point Break; Bill & Ted's Bogus Journey; My Own Private Idaho*. 1992: *Bram Stoker's Dracula*. 1993: *Freaked* (unbilled); *Much Ado About Nothing; Little Buddha*. 1994: *Even Cowgirls Get the Blues; Speed*. 1995: *Johnny Mnemonic; A Walk in the Clouds*. 1996: *Chain Reaction; Feeling Minnesota. The Last Time I Committed Suicide*. 1997: *The Devil's Advocate*.

MOLLY RINGWALD

Teen princess Molly Ringwald

Pauline Kael praised her 'charismatic normality', Warren Beatty plagued her with phone calls, John Hughes wrote *Sixteen Candles* with her photograph pinned above his word processor. At the height of the Brat Pack phenomenon, the media labelled her 'Princess of the Brat Pack' and 'The Teen Queen'. In 1986 *Time* magazine put her on their cover, describing her as 'our model modern teen'. Molly wannabes ('Ringlets') materialized in their droves, emulating her thrift shop fashion sense while dying their hair orange.

At the age of three, Molly Ringwald was performing at the California State Fair, at six she recorded her first album ('Molly Sings'), and at 11 she was a regular in the TV sitcom *The Facts of Life*. Her film debut at 14 prompted Beatty's interest (a subsequent romance was reported), and her three back-to-back films for John Hughes were all hits ('the Molly trilogy'). Hughes, who was largely responsible for the engineering of the Brat Pack, marvelled: 'Molly is in a class of her own.'

And then the actress grew up. Her career descended as fast as it had risen. Later, the actress explained: 'I'm always looking for different things to do in my work' – but her fans were no longer behind her. She grew up, she says, when she opted to play Cordelia in Jean-Luc Godard's bizarre screen version of *King Lear* (also starring Woody Allen and Norman Mailer), but it was an ill-advised career move.

In an attempt to revive her popularity she teamed up with her *Pretty in Pink* co-star Andrew McCarthy for *Fresh Horses*, but it turned out to be a grim, unconvincing drama. Nevertheless, she stretched herself as an actress (playing a frumpish, abused wife) and won the admiration of her director, David Anspaugh. 'Once we began shooting I found myself mesmerized,' he allowed. 'It was fascinating to watch Molly work. She could do take after take and each would be different, yet each was as honest as the last. She was wonderful to work with and is one of the most talented performers of her generation.' The producer of the abortive *Betsy's Wedding* was equally impressed: 'She's a fine actress. There's a sense of joy about her. She's a contemporary young woman with a lot of energy and a mature quality.'

It was after that that her production company, Kelbeth Productions (named after her older brother and sister, Kelly and Beth), folded. At least now she could lead a less stressful life. Philosophically, she mused: 'I'd like people to see my movies, obviously. But I never wanted to get to the point of being some crazy superstar. I just don't think I could deal with it.'

Molly at the height of her fame in the John Hughes scripted/produced **Pretty in Pink**

Molly Ringwald was the most unlikely of 'crazy superstars'. She was pretty, to be sure, but not in the drop-dead good-looking sense of such contemporaries as Demi Moore or Diane Lane. She was blessed with the most generous set of lips, soulful doe eyes and a shock of astounding red hair (which she dyed constantly, hiding her natural dark reddish-brown). She was, unquestionably, photogenic and unequivocally distinctive. But she was this side enough of normal for her legion of young female fans to identify with her. Her problems on screen were those of every attendant 'Ringlet', whether it be parental, academic, romantic or physical. She was not so

*Molly as Betsy Hopper with Alan Alda in the latter's **Betsy's Wedding***

much the Princess that the tabloids painted her as the perfect 'everyteen'.

Born on 18 February 1968, in Roseville, California, Molly was the youngest daughter of the blind jazz pianist Bob Ringwald. At the age of four she was singing in her father's Great Pacific Jazz Band and, at five, she played the Dormouse in a production of *Alice in Wonderland*. At eight, she landed a guest appearance on TV's *The New Mickey Mouse Club*, and aged nine, played Kate in a 15-month tour of *Annie*. This, in turn, led to her recurring role as Molly Parker on NBC's *The Facts of Life*, set in an exclusive girls' boarding academy. She was axed from the show after a year, and for a further twelve months was out of work.

In 1982, following an unorthodox audition with the director Paul Mazursky, Molly won her film debut in his *Tempest*. Loosely based on Shakespeare's play, the film starred John Cassavetes as a New York architect (Prospero) who escapes to a Greek island with his daughter, Miranda (Ringwald). It was not a box-office success, but enough of the right people saw it (Beatty, Hughes) for Molly to find herself in demand.

After two inconsequential movies and a mediocre TV film, she speared the starring role in Hughes' *Sixteen Candles*. Hughes explained: 'I was sent this picture of Molly in which she looked like a female version of Huck Finn. She was kind of boyish and interesting – not a beauty – but she had a real honest, innocent look. I stuck her

picture up in my office and as I was writing I couldn't stop staring at her.' In *Sixteen Candles*, she played Samantha, a teenager gauchely in search of Mr Right. She was both charming and natural, and the film went on to capture a huge following in the USA (although, strangely, it was never shown in British cinemas).

The Hughes-Ringwald success was repeated with *The Breakfast Club*, an ensemble comedy-drama that also starred Emilio Estevez, Anthony Michael Hall, Judd Nelson and Molly's future friend, Ally Sheedy. At a time when *Porky's* and *Friday the 13th* offered the only opportunity for teenage actors to air their acting skills, *The Breakfast Club* was a godsend. Hughes, then aged 36, had an uncanny knack for capturing the content and cadence of teenage dialogue, while eliciting performances of adult complexity from his young cast. And, as simple as the film's dramatic structure was (five kids on detention in a classroom), the film made even more money than *Sixteen Candles*.

Molly won further good notices as a potential suicide in the superior TV movie *Surviving*, and then segued into her last film for Hughes, *Pretty in Pink*. This time the filmmaker handed the directing chores to Howard Deutch, but his sparkling script, comic invention and adolescent know-how were all over the screen. Molly played the poor girl romanced by a wealthy, good-looking Andrew McCarthy, whose proposition (well, an invitation to the prom) sends her into a tizzy. Again, the acting

was of the highest order (Molly was enchanting, but almost had the movie stolen from her by co-stars Jon Cryer and Annie Potts), and the film was another formidable hit.

Not so *The Pick-Up Artist*, a romantic comedy developed by Warren Beatty and then disposed of when he took his name off the credits. This one had Molly top-billed, but she was secondary in spirit to the wild and wonderful Robert Downey Jr in the title role. In fact, whenever the former Teen Queen appeared on screen the movie stopped dead in its tracks. After that it was *King Lear* and then the enormously engaging *For Keeps*, which should have been a hit. The story of two teenage lovers (Ringwald, Randall Batnikoff) who have a baby, the film managed to make one care for its protagonists while retaining its sense of humour. Unfortunately, the sight of Hollywood's favourite virgin coping with motherhood was too much for audiences, and it was downhill from there.

Fresh Horses was a flop, *Strike it Rich* (in which she replaced Emily Lloyd) was worse, and then there was a supporting role in Alan Alda's bland nuptial comedy *Betsy's Wedding* (she was Betsy), with Ally Sheedy playing her sister. Two TV roles followed (she was an unconvincing flapper in Ken Russell's *Dusk Before Fireworks*, and a real-life AIDS victim in *Something To Live For*) and then *Face the Music* in Paris, a romantic comedy in which she and Patrick Dempsey played a songwriting team who hated each other's guts.

Paris, as it turned out, became Ringwald's new residence. 'I went to France on a work holiday,' the actress explained. 'I was only supposed to be there for a month and a half, but I fell in love with Paris, and then I fell in love with my boyfriend [the novelist Valery Lameignere]. But I missed my friends and I missed the energy of New York.'

So, after almost four years, Ringwald returned to the USA and instantly began making herself known, gracing first nights, fashion events and high-profile showbusiness parties. Furthermore, after her appearance in a number of forgettable movies (such as the mediocre video thriller *Baja*, with Lance Henriksen), she popped up in her own TV sitcom, *Townies*. The latter, which the star describes as '*Friends* for the *Roseanne* set', received glowing reviews and featured Ringwald as Carrie, a pragmatic twentysomething stuck in a provincial Massachusetts fishing village. Loaded with atmosphere and affectionate, raunchy humour, the show promised to reinstate Ringwald with her fans.

FILMOGRAPHY

1982: *Tempest*; *P.K. and the Kid.* 1983: *Packin' It In* (TV); *Spacehunter: Adventures in the Forbidden Zone.* 1984: *Sixteen Candles.* 1985: *The Breakfast Club*; *Surviving* (TV). 1986: *Pretty in Pink.* 1987: *The Pick-Up Artist*; *King Lear*; *For Keeps* (UK: *Maybe Baby*). 1988: *Fresh Horses.* 1989: *Strike It Rich.* 1990: *Betsy's Wedding*; *Women & Men: Stories of Seduction* (episode: 'Dusk Before Fireworks') (TV). 1992: *Something To Live For: The Alison Gertz Story* (UK: *Fatal Love*) (TV); *Face the Music.* 1993: *Seven Sundays*; *The Stand* (TV). 1996: *Malicious*; *Enfants de Salaud* (a.k.a. *Bastard Brood*); *Baja.* 1997: *Office Killer*.

TIM ROBBINS

Tim Robbins came into his own in 1992. Not only did he star in Robert Altman's critically worshipped *The Player*, but he walked away with the best actor prize at that year's Cannes

Film Festival. If that was not enough to keep one ego buzzing, Robbins had another film at the festival, *Bob Roberts*, which met with equal applause. The difference here, though, was that the picture was written and directed by him. He also starred in it, wrote the music and sang the songs. That same month, in May, the renaissance actor became a proud parent, fathering Susan Sarandon's second son, Miles Guthrie.

Six feet five, loose-limbed and baby-faced, Tim Robbins' physical appearance belies his fierce intellectual beliefs and his standing as a theatrical guru. Acclaimed as both a director and playwright, the actor frequently ploughed his movie salary into a theatre collective, The Actor's Gang, which he set up with friends from his university days.

As a movie star, Robbins has shied away from making mainstream Hollywood pictures and has fought to work with directors of calibre. And although a deft performer, he has always put the film before his performance.

In *The New York Times*, Pauline Kael wrote: 'He has the gift of looking just right for each of his roles, and has a puckish, commanding presence ... He makes you feel that behind his sneaky, demon eyes he's thinking thoughts no character in a movie ever thought before.'

Nightmares are made of this: Tim Robbins strapped down again - in Adrian Lyne's terrifying *Jacob's Ladder*

Mary Steenburgen, who played Robbins' sister in *Miss Firecracker*, called him 'the ultimate brother. He is amazingly mature and insightful one minute and a nine-year-old brat the next. The second we met, his odd sense of humour made me laugh – and that carried into our scenes together.'

Tim Robbins was born on 16 October 1958, in New York City, the son of a magazine distributor (his mother) and Gil Robbins, a Greenwich Village folk singer. At one time his father was a member of The Highwaymen, who produced the No. 1 hit *Michael, Row the Boat Ashore*. Both Tim's parents were staunchly Democratic, dragging him and his siblings along to various Vietnam rallies and teaching them the advantages of recycling before it became fashionable.

At the age of 12, he was already acting in experimental theatre and attended New York State University before transferring to the theatre course at the University of California, Los Angeles. Although he intended to move back to New York, he won an agent in Tinseltown and decided to make the most of it. He landed a string of cameos in some good TV shows, like *Hill Street Blues* and the first three episodes of *St Elsewhere*, and cornered the market playing psychos. 'I got to kill a lot of people,' the actor winced.

In 1981, he and a group of fellow UCLA students founded The Actor's Gang, for whom Robbins served as artistic director. 'We got together to buck the UCLA establishment,' he explained. 'We wanted to do Surrealism, German Expressionism, a

Tim Robbins bonding with real-life love Susan Sarandon in Ron Shelton's *Bull Durham*

lot of strange shit. Anyway, not musicals or classical re-hashes. We combined the discipline of Shakespeare with the vitality of rock 'n' roll.'

In 1984, Robbins was cast in the part of 'Ace' in *Toy Soldiers*, a reasonably well-tuned potboiler set in Latin America, starring Jason Miller and Cleavon Little. In the same year he found himself in Jerry Schatzberg's *No Small Affair*, way down the cast list below Jon Cryer and Demi Moore.

Robbins as the ruthless Hollywood executive Griffin Mill (with Greta Scacchi) in Robert Altman's acclaimed **The Player**

A year later he was 'one of the boys' in the execrable teen outing *Fraternity Vacation* (alongside, among others, Britt Ekland), and then he had a good part – as Gary Cooper – in Rob Reiner's celebrated teenage romance *The Sure Thing*. The starring role went to John Cusack, he was not above fraternizing with Robbins and the duo have remained good friends ever since.

Robbins was another team member in *Top Gun* (as Merlin, Tom Cruise's co-pilot in the climactic dogfight), the biggest hit of 1986, and he then landed the human male lead in the same year's biggest flop, *Howard the Duck*. Robbins, looking absurdly young, was the geeky, bespectacled Phil Blumburtt (such a funny name), a would-be scientist who befriends the bird from outer space. Still, it was experience.

It took two years and a number of

worthy theatrical productions before Robbins would show his face on screen again. He reappeared, to good effect, opposite Jodie Foster and John Turturro in Tony Bill's excellent *Five Corners*, a gritty, atmospheric dramatic comedy. He was Harry, an earnest Bronx native caught up in the 1964 civil rights movement. For Robbins, it was the most important role of his film career to date.

Next, he teamed up with John Cusack in *Tapeheads*, in which they played a couple of security guards trying to make it in the LA music scene. The comedy was a little too hip for its own good, and although it attracted a small cult following, most dismissed it as too silly for words. Then came *Bull Durham*.

At the time, in 1988, the game of baseball was considered anathema in the hallowed halls of Hollywood. Nevertheless, Ron Shelton's wry, smartly-calibrated *Bull Durham* gave the game a new sexual edge – and the movie became the sleeper hit of the US summer. Set in the dingy world of the minor league, the comedy submitted a trio of outstanding performances from three very hot actors. Kevin Costner was the world-weary catcher down on his luck, a spicy Susan Sarandon the fan who collected the sexual favours of players like trophies, and Robbins the bull-headed pitcher with 'a megaton throw'. Of course, Costner and Sarandon were already well known outside the film community, but it was Robbins' naive, boastful Ebby Calvin 'Nuke' LaLoosh that captured the imagination of filmgoers. Who can forget the scene in which the rookie pitcher is tied to Sarandon's bed as she purrs Walt Whitman to him? Or the dream sequence in which he imagines himself on the field in nothing but a jock strap and garter belt?

Sarandon, although 12 years his senior, subsequently became the woman in Robbins' life, and mothered his two sons, Jack Henry and Miles Guthrie.

In 1989 Robbins joined Holly Hunter, Mary Steenburgen and Scott Glenn in the film version of Beth Henley's play *Miss Firecracker*, and continued his flirtation with comedy, playing Delmont 'Jughead' Williams, a loony who scrapes dogs off the high-

way for a living. He won the title role in another starry affair, Terry Jones' *Erik the Viking*, a very silly, Pythonesque romp that went sour. Explaining why he was attracted to the part, the actor asserted: 'Basically, I feel I've been a Viking all my life. I have an affinity for the adventure. I like to take chances with my life and that takes a certain Viking spirit.'

Following a cameo in the would-be cult comedy *Twister*, Robbins ill-advis-

Tim Robbins as political candidate **Bob Roberts**, in the cult film he also wrote and directed and for which he sang his own songs

edly teamed up with Robin Williams in the manic *Cadillac Man*. A Feydeau farce crossed with a siege thriller, the melodrama featured Robbins as a demonically jealous husband who holds Williams hostage. Not a good move.

Adrian Lyne's psychological thriller *Jacob's Ladder* was considerably better, although it was a disturbing trip for the actor. At one point he wrote in his diary: 'The past two weeks have been nothing but horror. I find myself fraternizing less with the crew, taking refuge in my dressing room as much as I can ...' Five weeks later he confessed: 'I am getting lost in my role. My days are full of gut-wrenching emotional pain.' Robbins starred as Jacob Singer, a Vietnam vet haunted by demons in New York who imagines a terrible conspiracy. The film was not to everybody's taste, but overall it was a stylish, frightening and intellectually challenging addition to the horror genre.

Earlier, Robbins had had discussions with director Robert Altman about appearing in a film called *Short Cuts*. When that project fell through, Altman turned to *The Player* and hired the actor to play the leading role of movie executive Griffin Mill. Until now, Robbins had played awkward, goofy, ingenuous men, at the mercy of those around him. Even when he was portraying arrogance (*Bull Durham*) or aggression (*Cadillac Man*), he was still one sandwich short of a picnic. With *The Player*, Altman was offering Robbins the chance to play a clever man, a knowingly callous manipulator to whom winning the game was everything. Yet, ruthless as Robbins' homicidal studio executive is, the actor still allows us to feel pity for him. Even as he beds his victim's girlfriend (Greta Scacchi), we feel for him. Yes, Tim Robbins had achieved the impossible: he had made a villain if not likeable, at least sympathetic.

The Player proved to be both a critical success and a star-making platform for Robbins. He was now not only the lead of a hit movie, but his supporting cast was the stuff of legend. No fewer than 75 Hollywood names agreed to play themselves in the film, including Cher, Peter Gallagher, Jack Lemmon, Nick Nolte, Burt Reynolds, Julia Roberts, Susan Sarandon, Fred Ward, Bruce Willis and, of course, Tim's old pal John Cusack.

Cusack reappeared in *Bob Roberts*, Robbins' brilliant political satire about a clean-cut but decidedly corrupt candidate running for the US Senate (Robbins on icy good form). This, too, boasted its share of star cameos (Sarandon, Gallagher, Ward, Alan Rickman, James Spader) – which just shows the sort of respect Tim Robbins commands in his profession. Even as *The Player* attacked the very gut of Hollywood, so every segment of its community wanted a piece of its action. And Tim Robbins, with a best actor prize on his mantleshelf (and a Golden Globe nomination), was at the very centre of the frenzy.

In Altman's next film, the sublime, all-star *Short Cuts*, the actor was deliciously brutal and manipulative as a two-timing cop, and he was then per-

fectly ingenuous as the Preston Sturges-esque hero of the Coen brothers' *The Hudsucker Proxy*. He played Norville Barnes, a mailboy working for the grandiose Hudsucker Industries who is promoted to president in order to send the company's stock crashing – thereby making it affordable to buy back off the market. However, Norville's little invention – 'you know, a circle, for kids' – turns into an unintentional money-spinner, a household sensation that came to be known as the hula-hoop. The film was both stylish and hilarious, but its abstruse title hardly helped the box-office.

Robbins' next venture was also lumbered with an unwieldy title: *The Shawshank Redemption*. This time, however, the ecstatic reviews gave the movie a fair shot of the spotlight, not to mention a generous fistful of prizes. Robbins played Andy Dufresne, a lost innocent who may or may not be guilty of the murder of his wife. Committed to two life sentences at Shawshank State Prison, he embarks on a new endeavour that transforms all those around him, including fellow convict Morgan Freeman.

In *Pret-a-Porter*, Altman's frolicsome satire of the Paris fashion industry, Robbins had fun as a sports journalist stuck in the same hotel room as Julia Roberts, but he was wasted in *I.Q.*, playing an amiable garage mechanic who's set up with Meg Ryan by her uncle, Albert Einstein (Walter Matthau). Then he took up megaphone duty again on the Death Row polemic *Dead Man Walking*, which he adapted himself from the autobiographical novel by Sister Helen Prejean. The story of the friendship between a New Orleans nun (Susan Sarandon) and a convicted killer (Sean Penn), the film steadfastly refused to succumb to melodrama, instead uncovering the shortcomings of the whole debate surrounding capital punishment, both for and against.

'I'm not big on prison reform,' the director mooted. 'I think that if they're in for a violent crime, then they should stay there. They can understand incarceration. They can respect that. They can't respect that society has the right to take away their life. But then again, on a personal level I can definitely understand immediate retribution,

when my safety and the safety of my children is concerned.' As for his film, Robbins admitted: 'I don't think we can convert anyone who's anti-death penalty to pro, but I don't think this is a movie about conversion. It's a movie about showing things that are not talked about, on both sides.'

A driving human drama that simultaneously assaulted the intellect and Adam's apple, *Dead Man Walking* deservedly won a long-overdue Oscar for Sarandon and also skewered a nomination for Robbins as best director. He then returned to acting duty in *Nothing to Lose*, playing an advertising executive on the verge of a nervous breakdown who kidnaps a car-jacker (Martin Lawrence).

In meditative mood in *The Shawshank Redemption*

FILMOGRAPHY

1984: *Toy Soldiers; No Small Affair*. 1985: *Fraternity Vacation; The Sure Thing*. 1986: *Top Gun; Howard the Duck*. 1988: *Five Corners; Tapeheads; Bull Durham*. 1989: *Miss Firecracker; Erik the Viking; Twister* (cameo). 1990: *Cadillac Man; Jacob's Ladder*. 1991: *Jungle Fever*. 1992: *The Player; Bob Roberts* (also wrote and directed). 1993: *Short Cuts*. 1994: *The Hudsucker Proxy; The Shawshank Redemption; Ready to Wear* (UK: *Pret-a-Porter*); *I.Q.* 1995: *Dead Man Walking* (directed only). 1997: *Nothing To Lose*.

ERIC ROBERTS

Eric Roberts, as Paul Snyder, confronts Carroll Baker in Bob Fosse's glossy recreation of the facts leading to Playmate Dorothy Stratten's murder - in Star 80

Like a weed, Eric Anthony Roberts could spring up anywhere. He could be starring on Broadway in the highly-acclaimed *Burn This*, and then do an Italian TV mini-series, and then, on film, turn up opposite Cheech Marin in the hippy farce *Rude Awakening*. He is, in the vernacular of the business, 'a useful leading man', a committed actor who gives his all to his work and is willing to try anything. With his sensuous, classical features, athletic grace and intense acting style, he has coloured many a monochromatic enterprise. And yet his career has so far failed to fulfil expectations.

He is at his best playing men on the edge. He turned in notable villains in *Star 80* and *Final Analysis*, and won an Oscar nomination for his role as an escaped convict in *Runaway Train*. He *is* a very good actor, but has been accused of over-doing the psychotic bit, while one viewer questioned in *Movieline* magazine opined: 'The creepiest thing about Eric Roberts is the way he talks. I mean, it sounds like maybe he's on a low dose of some anti-psychotic drug and he has a spoonful of peanut butter stuck on the roof of his mouth.' He is also famous as the brother of Julia Roberts, an actress who made her film debut as his little sister in the costume melodrama *Blood Red*.

It was on 18 April 1956 when, he says, 'My mother was about to have me, and the airplane landed in Biloxi, Mississippi, and so I was born there.' The son of Walter Roberts, the black-listed scriptwriter and founder of the Atlanta Actors and Writers Workshop, Eric was raised in Georgia and encouraged to act to cure his persistent stammer. 'My dad always found ways of making acting magical to me,' he recalls. 'He would wake me up in the middle of the night to see something special on TV. And I learned in grade school that if I memorized something, I wouldn't stutter, which made acting a cure.'

At seven, he was already appearing in such stage productions as *Charlie's Aunt*, *The Taming of the Shrew* and *A Member of the Wedding*, and at 15 he won a place at RADA in London. That year he was also named America's national cross-country running champion. On his return from England, he enrolled at the American Academy of Dramatic Art in New York.

In 1977 he played Ted Bancroft in the long-running daytime soap *Another World*, and won the lead in his first film, *King of the Gypsies*, co-starring Sterling Hayden, Susan Sarandon and Brooke Shields, in which he played the title role, as the leader of a tribe of New York gypsies, and was nominated for a Golden Globe for his performance. The film's producer, Dino De Laurentiis, subsequently offered him a three-film contract, but the actor turned it down to concentrate on theatre. He also passed up a good part in Peter Yates' sleeper hit *Breaking Away*, afraid of being typecast as a juvenile lead. Instead, he waited three years until his next film, *Raggedy Man*, in which he starred opposite Sissy Spacek as Teddy, an enigmatic sailor who befriends her two kids and moves into her bed. When Teddy is banished from Spacek's life, the movie immediately loses its potency. *Raggedy Man* was not a commercial success, but critics noted Roberts' presence and versatility, although he almost lost the role. Shortly before he was due to make the film, he was involved in a car accident that put him in a coma for three days.

Again, he turned down a hit movie, *An Officer and a Gentleman*, waiting a further two years to play the thoroughly unstable Paul Snyder in Bob Fosse's gripping *Star 80*. Snyder was the real-life hustler who used Playmate of the Year Dorothy Stratten as his ticket to success, and who eventually murdered

Roberts in an unlikely role as ageing hippy - with Cheech Marin - in Aaron Russo's Rude Awakening

*With Teri Hatcher in **Heaven's Prisoners***

her. Roberts' disturbing performance was the best in the film, and the actor won his second Golden Globe nomination.

A year later he was top-billed in Stuart Rosenberg's gritty drama *The Pope of Greenwich Village*, with Mickey Rourke and Daryl Hannah, as a loser who turns to crime, and he then travelled to Australia to star in Dusan Makavejev's *The Coca Cola Kid*. The latter was a deliciously idiosyncratic comedy, in which Roberts played a narcissistic sales executive who tries to boost Coke sales in Australia. Greta Scacchi co-starred, but their relationship on set was strained (to say the least). 'The impression he gave me,' Scacchi confided, 'was that he didn't know I existed. He even ordered me off the set at one juncture.'

For *Runaway Train*, he put on 30 pounds and trained with weights to prepare for the character he described as: 'white trash, a man with no education, not very bright, but basically nice'. The film was a cuticle-chewing thriller and earned Roberts and co-star Jon Voight Oscar nominations. He also became engaged at the time – to actress Dana Wheeler-Nicholson – although the liaison was short-lived.

And then his career nose-dived. *Slow Burn*, for TV, and the romantic comedy *Nobody's Fool*, with Rosanna Arquette, were both stillborn, even though the actor did win good reviews

for the TV movie *To Heal a Nation* (as real-life Vietnam vet Jan Scruggs). He had more luck on stage. When he took over from John Malkovich in Lanford Wilson's *Burn This*, he received the Theater World Award.

Meanwhile, his films seemed to be a mixed bag of exploitation and TV movies, with few bright spots. Of the better entries there was the surprisingly amusing and pertinent *Rude Awakening*, with Cheech Marin and Julie Hagerty. Roberts was on good form as a 1960s hippy who, after an absence of twenty years, returns to New York to find the world troubled by AIDS, acid rain and a depleted ozone layer. In the taut corkscrew thriller *Final Analysis*, he played a sleazy businessman married to Kim Basinger, and gave the movie a nice edge of menace. Richard Gere, the film's star and executive producer, offered: 'Although Eric is probably a little younger than the character was conceived, he brought something unexpected to the role. Eric is able to play the tough guy without making him a cliche. He is a very persuasive actor.' And then there was the exceptionally credible and gripping TV movie *Fugitive Among Us*, with Roberts as a sinister murder suspect hunted down by a Texan cop (Peter Strauss).

The actor then went into overdrive, turning out an impossible number of movies that, for the most part, went straight to video. Only a good-natured cameo (as himself) in *The Cable Guy* and his chilling turn as real-life killer Perry Smith in the TV mini-series *In Cold Blood* revealed a more interesting talent.

FILMOGRAPHY

1978: *King of the Gypsies*. 1980: *Paul's Case* (TV). 1981: *Raggedy Man*. 1983: *Star 80*; *Miss Lonelyhearts* (TV). 1984: *The Pope of Greenwich Village*; *The Coca Cola Kid*. 1985: *Runaway Train*. 1986: *Slow Burn* (TV); *Nobody's Fool*. 1987: *Dear America* (voice only). 1988: *To Heal a Nation* (TV); *Blood Red*. 1989: *Into Thin Air*; *Grandmother's House*; *Rude Awakening*; *Best of the Best*. 1990: *Fire Princess*; *The Lost Capone* (TV); *The Ambulance*; *Descending Angel* (TV). 1991: *By the Sword*; *Lonely Hearts*. 1992: *Final Analysis*; *Vendetta*; *Fugitive Among Us* (TV). 1993: *Mistress Cottage*; *Best of the Best II*; *Love, Cheat and Steal*; *Freefall*; *The Last Mafia Marriage*; *Voyage*; *Love is a Gun*.

1994: *The Specialist*; *Babyfever*; *Sensation*; *The Hard Truth*. 1995: *Heaven's Prisoners*. 1996: *Public Enemies*; *Hatchet Man*; *It's My Party*; *Power 98*; *The Cable Guy* (as himself); *American Strays*; *The Grave*; *Dark Angel* (TV); *The Glass Cage*; *In Cold Blood* (TV). 1997: *Past Perfect*; *Prophecy II*; *The Odyssey* (TV). 1998: *Adam and Smoke*.

JULIA ROBERTS

In 1988 Julia Roberts was paid $50,000 to play one of the leading roles in *Mystic Pizza*. Four years later she was touted as the highest-paid actress of all time, reportedly commanding $7 million a picture (one source quoted her price to be as high as $12 million). In four years she had accumulated six hits to her name, and audiences just couldn't get enough of her.

It was easy to see why. She had a smile that could run a nuclear power station, legs that went all the way to China and a naturalness that was just plain irresistible. She also possessed a sunny, dynamic beauty that gave entire streets of men neck ache. And yet she was the first to knock her own looks. Described as 'the lips of the 1990s', she owned up: 'There was a time in high school when I felt a little grief because I had an unusual mouth, unlike the other girls who had perfect mouths with little heart-top lips. My mouth is crooked and I have a couple of little scars.' Equally, she has dismissed her luxuriant, spectacular hair as 'total straw'. She then caps her autobiographical assault with: 'I'm too tall to be a girl. I never had enough dresses to be a lady, and I wouldn't call myself a woman. I'd say I'm somewhere between a chick and a broad.'

As an actress, she has elicited nothing but praise from her colleagues. Joel Schumacher, who directed her in *Flatliners* and *Dying Young*, feels: 'There's this wonderful dichotomy with Julia. There's this woman, this little girl, this shit-kicker, this very innocent lady. There's a *My Fair Lady* thing in there, and I think the reason she can pull it off is that all those people are in her.' Patrick Bergin, who played her brutal husband in *Sleeping With the Enemy*, believes: 'Julia just gives everything to what she's doing. She doesn't know any way of blocking that. In a sense, she's got no technique. If it's not happening,

The Face That Launched a Thousand Stories: Julia Roberts

it's not happening.'

Of course, her leading men are famous for falling in love with her. For a while, she shared her life with Liam Neeson (who played her lover in *Satisfaction*), was briefly engaged to Dylan McDermott (her husband in *Steel Magnolias*), was linked to Richard Gere (*Pretty Woman*) and engaged to Kiefer Sutherland (*Flatliners*).

She was also in much demand from the studios who seemed to be endlessly publicizing new JR movies that never materialized. She was due to appear opposite Kiefer Sutherland in *Renegades*; was set to star with Tom Cruise in *The Princess of Mars* (for director John McTiernan) and was even announced to play the Amish wife of a 12-year-old Macaulay Culkin in the comedy *Holy Matrimony*. And then there was the *Shakespeare in Love* debacle.

In 1992, she was signed up to star in Universal's period romantic drama to be directed by Ed Zwick in England, from a screenplay by Tom Stoppard. She was to play a woman who disguises herself as an 'actor', triggering a hormonal rush from Shakespeare himself at a time when actresses were deemed unseemly. Daniel Day-Lewis was plugged as everybody's favourite Bard, but when he turned the project down, Roberts surveyed Universal's four replacements – Sean Bean, Ralph

Fiennes, Colin Firth and Paul McGann – and passed on the project. The film was then abandoned, putting an estimated 200 English technicians out of work. The native tabloids accused Roberts of single-handedly destroying the British film industry, while others applauded her guts and business sense.

She was also a leading contender for the role of Catwoman in *Batman Returns*. However, when the Chosen One – Annette Bening – became pregnant, the part went to Michelle Pfeiffer. This in itself is ironic, as Pfeiffer had earlier been put on hold to play Tinkerbell in Steven Spielberg's *Hook* following Roberts' hospitalization for nervous exhaustion. But Ms Roberts recovered and played the mischievous elf in what turned out to be her sixth box-office hit. It seemed to be the story of her life. Everything was a battle, but the results paid dividends.

She was born Julie Roberts on 28 October 1967 in Smyrna, Georgia, the daughter of Walter Roberts, the black-listed screenwriter who, with his wife, ran a local drama school. Her older brother is Eric Roberts, the actor who made his name in such pictures as *King of the Gypsies*, *Star 80* and *Runaway Train* – but, Julia declares: 'We're really different. He went to the Royal Academy of Dramatic Arts in London and I'm a kamikaze actress.' Their parents divorced when she was four, and their father died when she was nine. At first, she owns up, 'I said I wanted to be a veterinarian, but I was just afraid to admit that I wanted to be an actor.' As

high school graduation approached, she gave herself three options: 'I could go to the University of Georgia, get married or move to New York. Nobody was asking me to get married, and I wasn't fond of higher education, so I moved to New York and began studying acting. I didn't know what else I could do.'

In the Big Apple she worked at a women's clothing store, did some brief modelling for the Click agency and changed her name after joining the Screen Actors Guild (to avoid confusion with another Julie Roberts). In 1986 Eric got her an acting job in the historical melodrama *Blood Red*, playing his younger sister. However, the film was deemed so bad that it failed to secure a release until the end of 1990, and even then it evaporated. She then had a bit part on the TV cop series *Crime Story*, and had a decent role – as a man-devouring bass player – in the awful rock 'n' roll caper *Satisfaction*. Next came the engaging HBO movie *Baja Oklahoma*, in which she played the plucky daughter of barmaid-songwriter Lesley Ann Warren, and then the role of Daisy Araju in *Mystic Pizza*. This was a vibrant, low-budget saga about three animated waitresses who work at Leona's Mystic Pizzeria in Connecticut, following their various adventures with the opposite sex. Superbly played by the three actresses – Roberts, Annabeth Gish and Lili Taylor – the film was a piquantly honest and touching tale that became the sleeper American hit of 1988.

Julia Roberts (left) in her first screen success, Donald Petrie's captivating low-budget **Mystic Pizza** *(with Lili Taylor)*

*Julia as the **Pretty Woman** who steals the heart of Richard Gere*

When Daryl Hannah turned down the role of Shelby Eatenton Latcherie to play the less glamorous part of Annelle in *Steel Magnolias*, Julia Roberts was cast in her place and found herself up against the most impressive line-up of star actresses in recent history. Besides Hannah, there was Olympia Dukakis, Shirley MacLaine, Dolly Parton and Sally Field, and every one an Oscar contender. The film, based on the stage play by Robert Harling, gave everybody a chance to chew the Southern scenery, and they all did it sublimely – but it was Roberts' delicate, heart-breaking performance as Sally Field's tragic daughter that won the only Oscar nomination from the film. She also landed the Golden Globe, while the picture itself steamed off with $81 million at the US box-office, an extraordinary amount of money for a 'woman's film'.

Next, she was offered the role of Willem Dafoe's fiancée in the harrowing *Triumph of the Spirit*, based on a true story set in Auschwitz. She was required to shave her head for the part, and turned the offer down. As it happens, it was a prudent decision.

Disney were making a romantic comedy about a working-class hooker, and needed a very special actress to pull off the central role. According to one producer: 'There was no one else who could've played this part. What we

needed was a *woman*. And few actresses today seem like women. There are a lot of beautiful *girls*, but Julia Roberts is a beautiful *woman*. You don't know how rare that is.'

Although a low-budget movie by Hollywood standards (costing less than $20 million), *Three Thousand* (as it was then known) was still a major picture, and Roberts had the leading role. Ecstatic, she rang her mother. 'My mom works for the Catholic archdiocese of Atlanta,' the actress revealed. 'I mean, my mom's boss *baptised* me! So I called her at work, and it was like, "Hi, Mom. I got a job." She said, "You did? What'd you get?" And I said, "Oh, it's a Disney movie! I gotta go, Mom, I'll talk to you later."'

Eventually, *Three Thousand* had its name changed to *Pretty Woman*, Richard Gere was brought in as the male lead, and the film grossed $170 million in the USA, making it the second biggest hit of 1990 (after *Ghost*), beating such box-office certainties as *Die Hard 2* and *Total Recall*.

We first see the eponymous prostitute, Vivian Ward, half-naked in bed. The rump belonged to stand-in Shelley Michelle, but the fabulous 5'9" body striding down the sidewalk shortly afterwards was all Julia's: complete with blonde wig, thigh-high boots and an eight-inch blue leather skirt. She is the hooker from heaven, fresh on the streets with a heart ready to be broken. When Prince Charming (Gere) turns up in his flash Lotus, takes her to his flash hotel and offers her a business proposition to be his escort for a week – for $3,000 – the film revved up into an MTV *Pygmalion*. Of course, this was strictly Mills & Boon stuff, but thanks to the to-die-for magnetism of the stars, particularly Julia's seductive, vulnerable and incredulous Vivian, the film was eight-piston entertainment, polished kitsch for audiences baying for unerring escapism. And, not only was Roberts' Vivian the model little-girl-lost, but the actress's comic timing was perfect. Who can forget the scene when at the races she is told, 'Edward's the most eligible bachelor. Everybody is trying to land him,' to which she breezily replies: 'Well, I'm not trying to land him. I'm just using him for sex.' For her performance she was nominated for her second Oscar (this time as

best actress), and won her second Golden Globe. She was also voted NATO/ShoWest's Female Star of the Year, an accolade chosen by America's cinema owners.

Next, she was in another hit – Joel Schumacher's MTV thriller *Flatliners* – in which she played Rachel Mannus, a private and intensely focused medical student severely into the concept of life after death. Thus, she volunteers for a clandestine experiment in which her heart is stopped under scientific supervision (courtesy of fellow students Kiefer Sutherland, Kevin Bacon and William Baldwin), and then revived moments later. 'Rachel is obsessed with the idea of death and making sure that, when you die, you're going to a good place,' the actress explained. The film grossed a flashy $10 million in its opening week, and provoked reams of praise from the critics. *Rolling Stone* raved that Ms Roberts: 'combines beauty with a no-bull delivery that commands attention. Her private moments ... have an emotional intensity that is more compelling than all the hokum in the lab,' while *Variety* volunteered: 'The remarkably gifted Roberts is the film's true grace note.' This time she received the Movie Award for 'best actress in a drama'.

In Joseph Ruben's romantic thriller *Sleeping With the Enemy*, she played Laura Burney, who fakes her own death to escape her husband's brutality. The project had been kicking around for a while, and had been earmarked for Kim Basinger for more than a year. However, when Twentieth Century Fox couldn't come up with a leading man to fit Ms Basinger's taste, she left the project. Basinger wanted Kevin Costner or Harrison Ford, but Julia was happy with Patrick Bergin, an Irish actor with enough menacing presence to scare the lips off her. Indeed, the wife-battering sequences were harrowing in the extreme, causing the crew and director some alarm. It was, Roberts admits, 'physically the biggest part I've had, and the most exhausting'. One scene involved her being beaten to the floor, and the actress's fall was so authentic that Ruben admitted: 'I almost stopped the take. I thought she had hurt herself. Instead, what it did was open up this outpouring of tears and fears and emotion. She went all the way – to the point where everybody who was there was horrified. But she was willing to do that to get to that place where she really needed to be.' Again, her combination of effervescence and frailty went straight to the heart, but the film was too one-dimensional and slick to fully engage the emotions. Nevertheless, it grossed over $100 million in the USA alone, and was still drawing sizeable audiences when *Dying Young* opened.

Insiders blamed the title. And, to be honest, *Dying Young* was hardly a name to attract swarms of cinemagoers looking for a good time. But the film was not much good either. Ms Roberts played another working class girl with great legs (yes, she wore a mini-skirt), who answers an ad to look after a wealthy, good-looking guy (Campbell Scott) who is dying of leukaemia. Inevitably, they fall in love, spout platitudes to beautiful music ('I have only one thing to give you – my heart.') and discover that life is worth fighting for. It was all very lush and staged, and the film died young at the box-office with a disappointing $32 million in the US bank.

Meanwhile, Julia had hooked up romantically with Kiefer Sutherland (who had left his wife and child for her), and the publicity machine had started grinding out news of The Wedding. The big day was set for 14 June 1991, but things looked dicey when Julia found out about Kiefer's fling with the stripper Amanda Rice. In May, Julia started work on Steven Spielberg's epic fantasy *Hook*, playing Tinkerbell to Robin Williams' Peter Pan and Dustin Hoffman's Captain Hook. The budget was said to be in the $70 million range, and executives became nervous when Roberts was hospitalized. She was looking decidedly pale, took to wearing sunglasses and complained of severe headaches. In June, a week before the wedding, the actress cancelled the ceremony (estimated to cost $500,000) and, on the very hour she was due to voice her wedding vows, she left for a week's holiday in Ireland – with the actor Jason Patric on her arm. The rumour machine went into overdrive, and the *Hook* producers bit their nails. At least one newspaper suggested she had gone to Ireland to rekindle her affair with

Liam Neeson, but the *National Enquirer* assured us: 'RUNS AWAY WITH GROOM'S BEST FRIEND' – Patric (the two actors had worked together on Joel Schumacher's *The Lost Boys*). In July, Julia had moved in with Patric and finished her chores on *Hook*, much to the relief of certain executives. She then went on another holiday with her new boyfriend, while the rumour mill suggested that she was engaged and/or pregnant. In December 1991, *Hook* was savaged by the critics, most of whom seemed to miss the entire point of the film. Still, audiences loved its fresh approach to the J.M. Barrie classic, gobbled up the magical special effects and revelled in the guest cameos (Glenn Close, Phil Collins, rock star David Crosby). Julia was simply irresistible as the mutinous, ethereal Tinkerbell, and the picture went on to gross $250 worldwide.

She then took a well-earned rest, reassessed her career, and poked fun at herself (for free) in Robert Altman's *The Player*, one of the most highly acclaimed films of 1992, in which she

played herself, appearing alongside Bruce Willis (as himself) in a fictitious film in which Willis bravely rescues her character from the electric chair. Meanwhile, she and Jason Patric had broken up, and she was seen in the company of various men, including her fitness trainer and an actor friend of her ex-lover. She finally put the lid on all the tabloid rumours when, in June 1993, she married singer-actor Lyle Lovett, who played the cop-cum-suspect in *The Player*.

She then turned down the female lead in *Sleepless in Seattle* (judiciously replaced by Meg Ryan), explaining: 'Um ... I *loved* it [the screenplay]. But after having waited for such a long time ... to have that be the first movie that I made didn't quite sit right with me. Part of it was the romantic comedy elements of it, and really wanting to do something different.'

Instead, she starred in Alan J. Pakula's highly-efficient film version of John Grisham's bestselling legal thriller *The Pelican Brief* (a huge hit), and joined Nick Nolte in the romantic

As the battered wife of Patrick Bergin in Joseph Ruben's box-office triumph, **Sleeping With The Enemy**

comedy *I Love Trouble* (a dud), as a newspaper reporter. Then, for the phenomenal sum of $10 million (a record for an actress at the time), she was signed up to play the title role in Stephen Frears' *Mary Reilly*.

It was an indication of her standing as a contemporary icon that the press seemed to turn on her so vehemently. Tabloid headlines that had once screamed 'Pretty Woman', 'Pretty Woman Indeed' and 'More Than Just a Pretty Woman' were suddenly turning sour with such catchy banners as 'Fall of the Pretty Woman', 'Frump in a Slump' and the pugnacious 'I Won't Let Sandra Steal My Crown.'

Meanwhile, Roberts defended her marriage to Lyle Lovett, saying: 'It's wonderful being married. It's nice to have such a perfectly correct, grounding home environment. It makes your work much easier because you have this great home base to fall back on. People are always telling me I look healthy and happy. Why should it be a surprise? Am I supposed to look sorrowful and sick?' Not long afterwards she was dating Ethan Hawke.

As *Mary Reilly* languished in pre-production purgatory, Roberts exhibited her knack for romantic comedy in Robert Altman's *Pret-a-Porter*, a stellar, daring and spot-on satire of the fashion industry. However, the critics, who had only recently salivated over the director's *The Player* and *Short Cuts*, dismissed Altman's latest exercise as pointless. Nevertheless, a few reviewers reserved some praise for Roberts, who played a reporter from the *Houston Chronicle* who inadvertently ends up sharing a hotel room with a sports writer (Tim Robbins).

She then received a whopping $12 million to star in *Something To Talk About* as a mother and heiress who discovers that her husband (Dennis Quaid) has been cheating on her. The film was not bad, but Kyra Sedgwick, who played her wise-cracking sister, abducted the acting laurels. To be fair, Roberts seemed a little out of her depth and was maybe too young for the role. Yet, in spite of reports in the press that the film was a stiff, it did reap a respectable $50.8 million in the USA.

Meanwhile, her marriage to Lyle Lovett officially ended in March 1995, and following a guest appearance on

TV's *Friends* (in which she played a mischievous high school chum of Chandler), she paired up with Matthew Perry.

Mary Reilly, straining under a runaway budget (as much as $70 million by some reports), finally opened to devastating box-office results and damning reviews. The American critic Michael Medved opined: '*Mary Reilly* is a front runner for worst picture of the year' – and he wasn't far off. Roberts was wildly miscast as the housemaid of Dr Jekyll (John Malkovich), and her Irish accent was arguably the most awful ever committed to celluloid.

Sticking to her career strategy of choosing the film and not the part, the actress opted to play another Irishwoman, a supporting role, in Neil Jordan's handsome, accomplished biography of the Irish revolutionary *Michael Collins*. Of course, the fact that former lover Liam Neeson was playing Collins may have played a part in her acceptance of the role (as the whole cast worked for scale, money certainly wasn't a factor).

Roberts volunteered: 'You get a much better idea of the humanity behind the political struggle because Michael has this woman in his life.' However, her character, Kitty Kiernan – wistfully torn between Collins and his best friend, Harry Boland (Aidan Quinn) – only detracted from the dramatic momentum of the film. She was better in Woody Allen's musical comedy *Everyone Says I Love You*, in which she played Woody's fantasy woman, 'Von', an art historian with a passion for Tintoretto, Bora Bora and Mahler's Fourth. Woody pursues her to Venice, where the actress got to sing her first number on film, 'All My Life'. After the initial recording was done – 'which was nerve-wracking,' she says, 'it was fun to do something that I was almost entirely unqualified for. It was nice to venture into different territory.'

Meanwhile, she was (allegedly) dumped by Matthew Perry and entered into a serious relationship with the fitness guru Pat Manocchia, previously the boyfriend of Mary-Louise Parker. A wedding day (14 February 1997) was then set – and cancelled. Then, professionally, she returned to what she does best – romantic comedy. In *My Best Friend's Wedding* she played a food critic

As Kitty Kiernan in Neil Jordan's ***Michael Collins***

who realizes that she's in love with her best friend – just as he's about to get married. The male lead was due to be played by Perry, but he passed on the project when the couple split up, and was replaced by Dermot Mulroney.

She then took the $12 million offered her to star in the Richard Donner thriller *Conspiracy Theory*, opposite Mel Gibson.

FILMOGRAPHY

1988: *Blood Red*; *Satisfaction* (a.k.a. *Girls of Summer*); *Baja Oklahoma* (TV); *Mystic Pizza*. 1989: *Steel Magnolias*. 1990: *Pretty Woman*; *Flatliners*. 1991: *Sleeping With the Enemy*; *Dying Young*; *Hook*. 1992: *The Player*. 1993: *The Pelican Brief*. 1994: *I Love Trouble*; *Ready to Wear* (UK: *Pret-a-Porter*). 1995: *Something To Talk About*. 1996: *Mary Reilly*; *Michael Collins*; *Everyone Says I Love You*. 1997: *My Best Friend's Wedding*; *Conspiracy Theory*.

MEG RYAN

Meg Ryan

Meg Ryan was one of the most irresistible new stars of the late 1980s. She was cute, bubbly, bright as a button and very, very funny. She was also sexy, although she retaliates with: 'I never thought I was real sexy. I'm sexy sometimes, but I'm never going to be a glamour puss.'

In a relatively short period she stole a scene from Tom Cruise in *Top Gun* (her third film), partnered the likes of John Candy, Dennis Quaid and Sean Connery, and then became a household name in *When Harry Met Sally ...* – all because of one sequence. You know the scene:

Harry Burns (Billy Crystal) and Sally Albright (Ryan) are enjoying a meal in a New York delicatessen. It's Manhattan, the clientele are predominantly Jewish, and winter is in the air. Harry and Sally are just good friends, chatting about the great divide

between the sexes. But Sally is getting a trifle annoyed by Harry's attitude. Harry, on the other hand, is attempting to be as casual as his masculinity will allow.

Taking a large bite of her stacked sandwich, Sally announces: 'You are a human affront to all women – and I am a woman.'

Taking the defence, Harry counters: 'Hey, I don't feel great about this, but I don't hear anybody complain.'

'Of course not. You're out of the door too fast.'

'I think they have an OK time.'

'How do you know?'

'Whadya mean "how do I know?" I know.'

'Because they ...' Sally gesticulates with her left hand in a circular motion.

'Yes, because they ...' Harry copies her, irritated.

Sally, repeating the motion, continues, 'How do you know that they're really ...?'

Harry, clearly annoyed by now, speaks as if to a deaf child: 'What – are – you – saying? That – they – fake – orgasm?'

'It's possible.'

'Get out of here.'

'Why? Most women at one time or another have faked it.'

'Well, they haven't faked it with me.'

'How do you know?'

'Because, I ...'

'Oh. Right. That's right,' Sally declares firmly, screwing up her napkin. 'I forgot. You're a man.'

'What is that supposed to mean?'

'Nothing. It's just that all men are sure it never happens to them and most women at one time or another have done it. So you figure it out.'

Harry, amazed: 'You don't think that I could tell the difference?'

Sally, quietly: 'No.'

'Get out of here.'

Sally quietly surveys her partner. Her eyes burn with defiance. Her stare, unnoticed, declares war. Its message is clear: YOU – HAVE – GONE – TOO – FAR. It's the sort of chin-clenching expression of determination that can shrivel the apparatus of a Greek statue. Then it is gone.

Sally Albright lowers her eyes. For a split second a smile plays at the corners of her gorgeous mouth. And then she slips out the first groan.

It was that scene in *When Harry Met Sally ...* that made Meg Ryan a star. It was a scene that became almost as famous as the movie itself. The Scene in Which Meg Ryan Fakes an Orgasm in a Crowded Delicatessen.

Considering the actress's shyness, it's amazing that Meg suggested the idea for the sequence in the first place: 'There are very few times in the movie where Sally one-ups Harry, so I thought it might as well be good,' the actress explains. 'The night before the scene I sat in my hotel room writing down every ooooh and aaaah so that I had a diagram of what I was going to do in my head. But when it came to the first take it was really hard. There I was in front of 150 New York extras, all listening. The worst thing was that nobody else was doing it with me.'

Meg with the man of her dreams, Dennis Quaid, in the 1988 thriller D.O.A.

Billy Crystal meets Meg Ryan in Rob Reiner's magical **When Harry Met Sally**

Usually you do a love scene and everybody fakes it, and it's on a closed set. Not in a restaurant. As we went on I was oooohing and aaaaahing off-camera as well as on. I did so many takes.'

But it was worth every grunt. The sequence became the most memorable in the movie. The film was a surprise hit, grossing $92.8 million at the US box-office alone, and for her performance Meg Ryan was nominated for a Golden Globe award as best actress and actually won the American Comedy Award.

She was born on 19 November 1961, in the Norman Rockwell town of Bethel, Fairfield County, in Connecticut. She had a comfortable upbringing, her parents were both teachers and Meg strived to be an exemplary daughter. At school, she was voted homecoming queen ('The girl they chose first was suspended.'), and endeavoured to be 'a do-gooder type'. Her parents divorced when she was 15, and her mother, who was active in amateur dramatics, dabbled in casting, sending Meg to audition for the role of Debby, Candice Bergen's daughter in *Rich and Famous*. She got it. She had ten lines, but because of an actors' strike, it took her five months to complete her role. She found the experience, she says, 'too overwhelming. I didn't understand actors.' Still, acting seemed a profitable way to pay for night classes in journalism at New York University, and so Meg persevered. She won the role of Betsy Stewart Montgomery Andropoulos in the daytime soap *As The World Turns*, working 14-hour days for two years. 'I was kidnapped. I was pregnant. I was married

to a psychotic paraplegic. But I learned how to act,' she recalls.

In 1984 she quit school and TV (Betsy was severely injured in a car accident), travelled to Europe, tried school again and then decided on a full-time acting career. She played Callie Oaks, the owner of a newspaper, in Disney's western TV series *Wildside* (it lasted a month), and she then took a small role (Lisa) in *Amityville 3-D*, popped up in the TV movie *One of the Boys*, with Mickey Rooney, and then played Anthony Edwards' wife, Carole, in *Top Gun*, in which she had three scenes, filmed over three days, and stole each one of them. But the sequence everyone remembers is the one in which Edwards improvises 'Great Balls of Fire' on the piano and Ryan screams to him, 'Hey, Goose, you big stud. Take me to bed or lose me forever!'

The film was a huge success (the biggest that year) and Meg was in demand. She had a good part in the derisory *Armed and Dangerous*, and stole the comedy from John Candy, and she was then given the female lead in the vastly entertaining fantasy *Innerspace*, executive-produced by Steven Spielberg. She played Lydia Maxwell, a feisty journalist in search of ex-boyfriend Dennis Quaid, a micro-sized astronaut injected into the rear end of Martin Short. Short glowed at the time: 'Meg's a phenomenal actress and she has just enough self-doubt to make her even better. She takes a role that could be something we've seen before and turns it into something we've never seen.' Quaid, too, was struck by his co-star: 'Meg has such great range,' he marvelled, 'she's really a female

chameleon.'

Next, she seized her most dramatic character to date, a pink-haired drifter with sexuality to burn, in Michael Hoffman's *Promised Land*, produced by Robert Redford and co-starring Kiefer Sutherland. She was re-teamed with Quaid in the film noir thriller *D.O.A.* (a remake of the 1950 classic), playing an 18-year-old student infatuated by her dying professor (Quaid). This time the sparks really flew, and Quaid and Ryan quietly became 'an item' (although she kept on her small apartment with the actress Daphne Zuniga).

In Peter Hyams' testosterone-packed *The Presidio*, she played Lieutenant-Colonel Sean Connery's spirited daughter (who falls for her father's old protagonist, Mark Harmon), a character she described as 'a hot vixen'. She was good, but frankly, her role slowed down the action. She then lost the part of Tom Cruise's girlfriend in *Rain Man*. However, her next picture more than made up.

This was Rob Reiner's *When Harry Met Sally ...*, an effervescent, bittersweet New York comedy about a man and a woman who meet, hate each other, become friends and do everything in their power not to become lovers. A stylish and engaging look at the battle of the sexes, the film highlighted Ryan's best performance to date, a plucky demonstration of a woman confused by love.

In the plodding, structurally sabotaged *Joe vs the Volcano*, she played three roles, but failed to really shine in any of them. The film didn't seem to know what it wanted to be, and co-star Tom Hanks didn't seem to know what he was doing. Nevertheless, *Joe* clocked up $40 million in the USA, so it wasn't a total failure. Neither was Ryan's personal life, which saw her and Dennis Quaid finally tie the knot on St Valentine's Day, 1991.

Again, she was wasted in Oliver Stone's ambitious *The Doors*, playing rock legend Jim Morrison's flower-child wife, Pamela Courson. Still, who could turn down an opportunity to work with Stone? She did, however, turn down the lead in *The Butcher's Wife*, which, although a box-office flop, was an enchanting romantic fantasy which might have been even better had Ryan played the role of the naive clair-

*Meg Ryan in **Sleepless in Seattle***

voyant (in place of Demi Moore, who was miscast).

Still, Meg had an even more important production in the works – Jack Henry, who was born by caesarean section on 24 April 1992. Three months later, the actress popped up in the romantic fantasy *Prelude to a Kiss*, playing the character originated by Mary-Louise Parker in the Broadway original. Alec Baldwin co-starred (recreating his stage performance), and the film received favourable reviews, although audiences failed to embrace the story of a love-struck beauty who ends up in the body of an old man.

She was re-teamed with Tom Hanks and director Nora Ephron (who had scripted *When Harry Met Sally ...*) in the ten-Kleenex weepy *Sleeping in Seattle*, inspired by the 1957 tear-jerker *An Affair To Remember* (with Cary Grant and Deborah Kerr). Ryan played Annie Reed, a journalist working for *The Baltimore Sun* who's about to commit to a boring Bill Pullman. However, when she hears mourning widower Tom Hanks on the radio – talking all the way from Seattle – she's spun into a romantic maelstrom. Manipulative, sentimental and irresistible, *Sleepless in Seattle* was a staggering success, collecting a monumental $126.7 million in the USA and a second Golden Globe nomination for Ryan.

She then joined Quaid for the third time, in Steve Kloves' atmospheric drama *Flesh and Bone*, playing an attractive, outgoing woman who finds herself

inexplicably linked with a shy vending machine salesman (Quaid). Then, in Luis Mandoki's *When a Man Loves a Woman* – a horrifying, startlingly truthful examination of a marriage sliding into hell – she gave arguably the best performance of her career. As an alcoholic clinging to what's left of her marriage (to Andy Garcia), Ryan exposed the most intimate nuances of her soul. She should have won an Oscar. She says: 'I just loved making that movie. There's something about being able to go in there and think about stuff in a slightly detached way, because you're acting it.' However, the actress also allowed: 'You can look at an actor's body of work and you can see an autobiography.'

She failed to strike any sparks off Tim Robbins in the dim romantic comedy *I.Q.* (in which she played the niece of Albert Einstein), and was then miscast – in a supporting role – as an Irish inmate of a Quaker asylum in *Restoration* (for director Michael Hoffman).

She returned to her Goldie Hawn act in *French Kiss*, a charming, engaging concoction (which she co-produced), playing a neurotic who runs off to Paris to catch up with errant fiancé Timothy Hutton – only to fall into the lap of a lecherous, devious, chain-smoking Kevin Kline. She was also in the flashback sequences of *Courage Under Fire*, a meditative, intelligent

Rashomon-style drama, in which she played a Gulf War pilot nominated to become the first female recipient of the Medal of Honor (albeit posthumously).

She was due to receive $8 million for a film called *Easy Women*, but dropped out of the project due to 'creative differences'. She was also announced to produce and star opposite Julia Roberts in a contemporary remake of the 1939 Joan Crawford/Norma Shearer vehicle *The Women* (previously remade as *The Opposite Sex* with June Allyson and Joan Collins). However, the actress first segued into *Addicted to Love*, in which she and Matthew Broderick take revenge on their ex-partners, and she then joined Nicolas Cage in *City of Angels*, about a woman who finds that her guardian angel has fallen in love with her.

FILMOGRAPHY

1981: *Rich and Famous*. 1983: *Amityville 3-D*. 1985: *One of the Boys* (TV). 1986: *Top Gun; Armed and Dangerous*. 1987: *Innerspace; Promised Land*. 1988: *D.O.A.* (UK: *Dead On Arrival*); *The Presidio*. 1989: *When Harry Met Sally ...* 1990: *Joe vs the Volcano*. 1991: *The Doors*. 1992: *Prelude to a Kiss*. 1993: *Sleepless in Seattle; Flesh and Bone*. 1994: *When a Man Loves a Woman; I.Q.* 1995: *Restoration; French Kiss* (also co-produced). 1996: *Courage Under Fire; Anastasia* (voice only). 1997: *Addicted to Love*. 1998: *City of Angels*.

*Pretty in uniform: Meg Ryan in **Courage Under Fire***

WINONA RYDER

Winona with Christian Slater in Michael Lehmann's revolutionary teen comedy Heathers

The whole world was in love with Winona Ryder. At least, those who had seen her movies. Saddled with a very pretty face and an enviable body, Winona Ryder was also bright, well-read, outspoken and very funny. Oh yeah, and she could act the socks off her contemporaries.

Britain's *Telegraph Magazine* accused her of being 'the most exciting young actress in America'; *You* magazine echoed the phrase verbatim, and *Rolling Stone* called her 'the single most exciting actress of her generation'. Well, everybody was saying it, really. Tim Burton, who directed the actress in *Beetlejuice* and *Edward Scissorhands*, went one further: 'She's the best. She has something you can't even talk about. She's a throwback to movie stars throughout film history. There's something about her skin and her eyes and her ability and her gravity that you can't verbalize. Magical.'

Jim McBride, director of *Great Balls of Fire!*, is also a fan: 'It's amazing that Winona can be so sophisticated yet so unaffected. She's very sexy without seeming to be somebody who has a lot of sexual experience. She's just so charming and seductive, she's impossible to resist.'

Winona herself finds it hard to understand what all the fuss is about: 'My friend and her boyfriend had just seen *Mermaids*, and they were, like, saying, "You were *really* sexy in that." I was like "*What?*" That was, like, the most unsexy thing I've ever done.'

By the time she was 19, Winona Ryder had clocked up nine movies and had invariably received shining reviews. There were, however, a *few* dissenters. 'I did this press junket for *Mermaids*,' she recalls, 'and everyone there was saying, "Why are you always playing teenagers?" And, like, I'm *19*, what am I supposed to do – play a *judge?*'

Besides her startling performances in some rather good films, she was also receiving publicity for her engagement to Johnny Depp. Depp, who made his name in the TV series *21 Jump Street*, had already been married to the musician Lori Anne Allison, five years his senior, and had subsequently been engaged to Sherilyn Fenn and Jennifer Grey. This was not a good track record. Depp and Winona first spotted each other at the premiere of *Great Balls of Fire!* ('It was a classic glance,' he says; she adding: 'It wasn't a long moment, but it was suspended.'). They finally dated months later, discovered a mutual obsession for J.D. Salinger, and to prove his undying love for her he had 'WINONA FOREVER' tattooed on his arm. For a while, they were the hottest couple in Hollywood. Later, tabloid rumours paired her with Daniel Day-Lewis and other men, but whatever the invented stories, her engagement to Depp was off. In retrospect, she revealed about the break-up: 'I was just really young. I don't know what his excuse is, but that's mine.'

Born Winona Laura Horowitz on 29 October 1971, in Winona, Minnesota, the actress was the third of four children. Her father, Michael, was a bohemian intellectual and established a well-known book shop, Flashback Books, in Petaluma, California, specializing in the beat generation of the 1960s. Her mother, Cindy Palmer, headed her own video production company. Her godfather was the psychologist and LSD authority Timothy Leary.

As a child, she attended Black Flag and Agent Orange protests and spent a year travelling round South America. She admits, 'I was a really weird kid',

*Winona in a dramatic shift of image for Jim Jarmusch's sublime **Night On Earth***

*Winona with Gary Oldman in the box-office smash **Bram Stoker's Dracula***

and she enjoyed dressing up in boys' clothes while sporting a very short haircut. Once, she was mistaken for a 'faggot' and was beaten up, but she brushes off the experience with a casual, 'It was sort of great. I felt like a real gangster or something.'

Recognizing the eccentricity of their child, Michael and Cindy Horowitz enrolled her at the American Conservatory Theater in San Francisco. There, she was spotted in a school play by talent scout Deborah Lucchesi and put forward for a screen test. The film was *Desert Bloom*, starring Jon Voight, but the role of Rose finally went to Annabeth Gish. Instead, Winona (or Noni, to her friends) won a good part (as a love-sick schoolgirl ignored by Corey Haim) in *Lucas*, opposite fellow unknown Charlie Sheen. She had also stumbled across a screenplay by Alan Hines, *Square Dance*, but, she says, 'thought the movie had already been made'. As it happens, the director Daniel Petrie had been scouring the countryside for a suitable female lead and was coming to the end of his tether. Winona auditioned, and a week later she was starring in the movie.

Square Dance was the story of Gemma, a naive 13-year-old living with her grandfather (Jason Robards) on a Texas egg farm. Out of the blue, her mother (Jane Alexander) turns up to re-claim her, sending Gemma into shock. The girl refuses to accompany Mom back to Fort Worth, but after much soul-searching boards a bus to find her. Once in the big city, she falls for a retarded 21-year-old boy (Rob Lowe). If nothing else, the picture was a platform for some exceptional acting. Rob Lowe was nominated for a Golden Globe for his turn, and Robards and Alexander were showered with praise. However, it was Winona who truly stole the movie – but she was so good that nobody noticed she was acting.

It wasn't until her next picture, Tim Burton's colossal box-office hit *Beetlejuice*, that Hollywood sat up with a jolt. As the morgue-friendly Lydia Deetz, a pocket version of Morticia, she was an absolute scream. Veiled in black, she befriends ghosts Alec Baldwin and Geena Davis in favour of her own family and delivers her lines with the deadpan subtlety of an actress twice her age.

She took a step back with the meditative teen drama *1969*, which she admits she did, 'because I was 16 years old, I was really bored, and I wanted to work. It was a big mistake.' Robert Downey Jr and Kiefer Sutherland shared the error.

However, she relished the role of Myra Gale, the 13-year-old child bride of Jerry Lee Lewis (Dennis Quaid) in *Great Balls of Fire!* Until now, this was the best dramatic work she had handled, and while Quaid played with his

As May Welland in Martin Scorsese's ***The Age of Innocence****, for which she received her first Oscar nomination*

piano tops she quietly stole his thunder. It was an energetic, knockabout screen biography – and well-hyped – but it was a disappointment at the box-office.

Much, much better was *Heathers*, a cunning black comedy that put *Blue Velvet* through high school. Winona played Veronica, a reluctant member of a bitch-riddled peer-pressure group, who mutinies when she teams up with a gun-toting Christian Slater. The actress enthuses: 'It turned out one of the best movies I've ever seen in my life.'

There was another treat in store with *Welcome Home, Roxy Carmichael*, a witty, off-beat comedy-drama about a 15-year-old misfit, Dinky Bossetti

(Ryder), who imagines herself the daughter of the town's returning celebrity. Nicknamed 'Rosemary's Baby' by her legal mother, Dinky is a quirky cross between Joan of Arc, Saint Clare and James Dean, and was winningly played by Winona at the top of her form. Unfortunately, the film was swallowed up in distribution hell, and few were lucky enough to find it.

More successful was Richard Benjamin's *Mermaids* – thanks, no doubt, to the stellar presence of Cher, Bob Hoskins and a top-selling soundtrack. Winona (who replaced Emily Lloyd) portrayed another 15-year-old, Charlotte, who dreams of being a nun and parades under the sobriquet of 'Joan Arc'. While Cher appeared ill at ease as Charlotte's man-devouring mother, and Bob Hoskins did his cheery American routine for the umpteenth time, Winona proved to be the only thing worth watching. Deservedly, she was voted best supporting actress by the National Board of Review.

She was then signed up to play Mary Corleone – Al Pacino's daughter – in Francis Ford Coppola's long-awaited final instalment of *The Godfather* trilogy. Arriving in Rome on the back of three movies, Winona collapsed from a debilitating upper respiratory tract infection and retired from the picture. Coppola replaced her at the eleventh hour with his own daughter, Sofia.

Shortly after recovering, she starred in Tim Burton's exquisite modern fairy tale *Edward Scissorhands*. An updating of *The Beauty and the Beast*, the film featured Winona as a suburban teenager who falls for the misfit of the title (Johnny Depp), a gentle soul whose hands are replaced with metallic shears. Both a magical love story and a witty satire on modern Americana, *Edward Scissorhands* should have been a much bigger hit than it was (although, to be fair, it was mildly successful).

The actress then appeared in Jim Jarmusch's inventive five-part omnibus film, *Night On Earth*. Winona had asked her agent to arrange a meeting with Jarmusch, as she was an enormous fan of his work (*Stranger Than Paradise*, *Down by Law*, *Mystery Train*). It was a mutual admiration society. He says: 'When I met her I really liked her

energy and enthusiasm, her interest in certain kinds of music, books and films; a lot of things. We just got along really well.' He suggested writing a part for her in his next celluloid journey, and she was over the moon.

Jarmusch makes a habit of creating parts for people he likes, and he gave Winona a plum on a plate. She played a chain-smoking, down-to-earth LA taxi driver who is offered the chance to become a movie star (by casting director Gena Rowlands). But, in true Jarmusch fashion, she turns the offer down to pursue her dream of becoming a mechanic.

Meanwhile, Francis Coppola had been considering a script Winona had given him: James V. Hart's *Dracula – The Untold Story*. Based on Bram Stoker's original 1897 novel (as yet not translated faithfully to the screen), the property fired Coppola's enthusiasm, both for its historical context and for its human allegory. 'I never thought he would even read it,' the actress recalls. 'I thought he would be too busy, or not interested.' On the contrary, Coppola had been a fan of the novel since reading it to a group of eight- and nine-year-old boys at summer camp.

Later, Winona discovered that she and Coppola 'liked the same things about the script, which was very romantic and sensual and epic, a real love story that was very passionate. It's not really a vampire movie. To me, it's more about the man Dracula, the warrior, the prince.' Winona was cast both as the fiancée of Vlad the Impaler – in 15th-century Transylvania – and as the 19th-century English innocent, Mina Murray. Although her accent wasn't entirely consistent, her performance demonstrated a new dramatic range – and sexuality. The film, retitled *Bram Stoker's Dracula*, went on to become the most commercially successful the actress had appeared in.

During shooting, she was sitting in her trailer when the phone rang. It was Martin Scorsese. 'I was just, like, "Oh. Yes. Mr Scorsese. Hello." I was so caught off-guard.' He was offering her the role of May Welland in his adaptation of Edith Wharton's romantic drama *The Age of Innocence*. It just happened that Winona wrote about the novel in her final high school English report and won an 'A' for it. 'And he

Winona as Lelaina Pierce in Reality Bites

Even more successful was *Little Women*, the fourth screen incarnation of the popular 1868 novel by Louisa May Alcott. Ryder had been a fan of the book since the age of 12, and now had enough clout in Hollywood to greenlight an update. She insists that the story is still very relevant: 'It's about issues and themes that are important today. It has something to say about developing character, developing your mind, helping others. It's not just about how to be hip or how to be cool.'

She was also instrumental in hiring the film's director, the Australian Gillian Armstrong – in spite of the latter's initial reluctance. 'I bombarded her with compliments, she couldn't even speak,' recalls the actress. 'I just talked her into it, thank God.' In spite of the film's romantic excesses and episodic nature, it turned a healthy profit at the box-office and earned Ryder a second Oscar nomination.

She teamed up with another female Australian director, Jocelyn Moorhouse, for the equally episodic and romantic *How To Make An American Quilt* – a sort of white *Joy Luck Club* – that failed to register with audiences, in spite of a prestigious cast (Anne Bancroft, Ellen Burstyn, Alfre Woodard, Jean Simmons, Samantha Mathis, etc.). She then starred in the fatally lugubrious *Boys*, a static tale of illicit romance, because, she says: 'I had a bizarre reaction to it. It was a terrific story that seemed to happen in real time, not movie time.' And in no time at all it vanished.

She was then back in period costume for Nicholas Hytner's adaptation of Arthur Miller's *The Crucible*, playing a devious young woman who accuses neighbours of witchcraft in order to save her own skin. Her co-star was old flame Daniel Day-Lewis, although, at the time, she was dating David Pirner, lead singer of the Minnesota rock group Soul Asylum. She was then a female android (teamed opposite Sigourney Weaver's re-cloned Lieutenant Ripley) for the fourth instalment of the *Alien* series, *Alien Resurrection*, a most surprising – if commercial – career move. Rumours that she was dating David Duchovny, star of TV's cult phenomenon *The X-Files*, were unsubstantiated at the time of going to press (besides, he then married Téa Leoni).

FILMOGRAPHY

1986: *Lucas*. 1987: *Square Dance*. 1988: *Beetlejuice*; *1969*. 1989: *Great Balls of Fire!*; *Heathers*. 1990: *Welcome Home, Roxy Carmichael*; *Mermaids*; *Edward Scissorhands*. 1991: *Night on Earth*. 1992: *Bram Stoker's Dracula*. 1993: *The Age of Innocence*; *The House of the Spirits*. 1994: *Reality Bites*; *Little Women*. 1995: *How To Make An American Quilt*. 1996: *Boys*; *The Crucible*; *Looking For Richard*. 1997: *Alien Resurrection*.

Close, but no Oscar: Winona as Abigail Williams in Nicholas Hytner's powerful The Crucible

was going, "So we're going to do this, and it will be fun. Yeah. Looking forward to it." And I was, like, "OK." And then I kind of just flipped out in my trailer. Inside, I was, like, "Oh my God, I can't wait for three months from now."' Her co-stars turned out to be Daniel Day-Lewis and Michelle Pfeiffer, but it was Winona who eventually walked off with both a Golden Globe and an Oscar nomination for her performance.

After that, she joined another stellar cast – Meryl Streep, Glenn Close, Jeremy Irons, Antonio Banderas – for Bille August's *The House of the Spirits*. Based on the bestselling novel by Isabel Allende, the film followed the escapades of a family in Chile. Winona replaced the director's wife, Pernilla August, playing Meryl Streep's daughter, Blanca. Winona was not bad, but the film tripped up badly over its ambition, and resembled a melodramatic TV mini-series squashed into a movie.

Returning to more contemporary fare, she was better served by Ben Stiller's romantic comedy *Reality Bites*, in which she played the affluent product of a broken home who fails to spirit her ideals into practice. The film was a canny, honest examination of the X generation, and a worthy feather in her cap.

ANNABELLA SCIORRA

Sciorra as the bride that wouldn't in
True Love

One extraordinary thing about Annabella Sciorra is that she has been starring in progressively more successful movies, yet has remained relatively unheard-of to the cinemagoing public. She was top-billed in her first film, a critical triumph, and subsequently went on to play opposite Tim Robbins, Richard Gere, James Woods, Michael J. Fox, Wesley Snipes, Matt Dillon, Gary Oldman and Matthew Broderick – in a space of three years.

Another extraordinary thing about Annabella Sciorra is that she is only one-quarter Italian. However, she seems to have cornered the market in playing hot-headed, olive-skinned beauties from the Bronx. 'In role after role, I find myself doing these parts,' she complains, 'but I don't even talk that way.' Indeed, her mother, a fashion stylist, is native French, while Annabella's father, a veterinarian, is half-Cuban, half-Italian.

In fact, Annabella was born, not in the Bronx, but on Manhattan's Upper East Side, on 24 March 1964 (although, she says, she's fiercely secretive about her age: 'When I walk into an audition and they ask how old I am, I like to say, "How old do you want me to be?" I'm an *actress*.'). She was 13 when she enrolled at the prestigious HB Studio, later extending her studies at the American Academy of Dramatic Arts. She says, 'I grew up thinking acting was what I was supposed to do,' but first she had to endure the obligatory support group – you know, that group of jobs that encompass waitressing, secretarial work, bartending ...

At 20, Sciorra founded her own theatre outfit, The Brass Ring Theater Co., and produced several plays. Four years later she badgered every agent she could find to play the role of Sophia Loren's daughter in the mini-series *Mario Puzo's 'The Fortunate Pilgrim'*, and was offered the part. She then won the lead in *True Love* by answering an ad in *Backstage* magazine. A low-budget comedy about the angst-ridden preparations for a Bronx wedding, *True Love* was a distinctive debut for director Nancy Savoca, boasting recognizable characters and plenty of memorable moments. Perhaps most unforgettable of all was the scene in which Donna (Sciorra) cannot face her new husband

(newcomer Ron Eldard, coincidentally a good friend of the actress's, now a regular on TV's *ER*) and, in full nuptial regalia, locks herself in a stall in the ladies' washroom. The film attracted ecstatic reviews and walked off with the Grand Prize at the 1989 United States Film Festival in Park City, Utah. The actress recalls: 'It was, like, overnight – Boom! All of a sudden, here were all these people calling me who wouldn't take my phone calls before.'

In Roger Donaldson's frantic comedy *Cadillac Man*, the actress played Tim Robbins' wayward wife, provoking her husband to lay siege to the car salesroom at which she works. Donaldson, who had previously directed the hits *No Way Out* and *Cocktail*, thought: 'Annabella was perfect. She has real range, real instincts, a real sort of fiery quality.' In Mike Figgis's *Internal Affairs*, she was the trusting wife of rogue cop Richard Gere, but she almost turned the role down. She told the director that she thought the script was 'horrible', explaining: 'All I could do was be honest. I couldn't really hide that.' Figgis was impressed, shared her views, cast her and re-wrote the script. The film was a hit.

Next came the part of a young lawyer who becomes romantically involved with defence attorney Alan

With Wesley Snipes in Spike Lee's tough romantic drama ***Jungle Fever***

A mother scorned: Anabella Sciorra (with Madeline Zima) in the nail-biting **The Hand That Rocks The Cradle**

Dershowitz (Ron Silver) in *Reversal of Fortune*. Again, it was a supporting role in a film that cornered more than its fair share of attention (for starters, Jeremy Irons won the Oscar for it). Although third-billed, Silver actually had the biggest part in the movie – and was magnanimous enough to shower praise on his leading lady. 'There's an honesty about Annabella,' he revealed. 'She can't make a false move. She doesn't know how.' She was stuck in another 'girlfriend role' (belonging to James Woods, but admired by Michael J. Fox)

Sciorra with Matt Dillon in Anthony Minghella's **Mr Wonderful**

in *The Hard Way*, a slam-bang comic-thriller. Fox agrees: '*The Hard Way* was a real guys' movie and there was no easy niche for her to fit in. But Annabella held up well; she created a terrific energy of her own.' Sciorra herself was more dismissive: 'I'm [just] the girl in the buddy movie. I think I giggle in very scene.'

She then landed her first lead in a major production, as Angela Tucci, a working-class Italian-American woman coping with the stigma attached to her affair with a black middle-class architect (Wesley Snipes). The film was Spike Lee's *Jungle Fever*, which attracted acres of newsprint and landed on the cover of *Newsweek*, a sure sign of making it as 'an event movie'. It was also a box-office success, yet was nothing compared to Annabella's next outing, *The Hand that Rocks the Cradle*. Originally, the actress was offered the role of the nanny from hell (who takes over a middle-class Seattle family), but ended up playing the persecuted wife and mother instead. Still, she had top-billing, although Rebecca De Mornay, as the babysitter, had the flashier part. 'We screen-tested both ways,' Sciorra discloses. 'I don't know if Rebecca had real strong feelings either way – I know I didn't. I think Rebecca was great.' The film touched a universal cord and had audiences reacting out loud. 'People were screaming all through the movie,' Sciorra recalls. 'The weird thing was, it was like they had already seen it. They knew a lot of the lines: "*Don't go in the cellar, Claire!*".'

The Hand that Rocks the Cradle knew which buttons to push and was arguably the year's most exciting thriller – but it wouldn't have been half as convincing had Sciorra not produced a character to root for. There was another thriller, *Whispers in the Dark*, in which the actress played a psychiatrist who falls in love with a man whom she discovers was involved with a murdered patient. Again, Sciorra was top-billed, with Alan Alda and Jill Clayburgh in support, but the film barely caused a whisper at the box-office.

She then played Matt Dillon's staunch ex-wife in *Mr Wonderful*, who is set up with a series of men (with a view to marrying one of them) so that Dillon doesn't have to fork out his

Sciorra with John Hannah in the British-made **The Innocent Sleep**

alimony payments. A bitter-sweet, well-observed romantic comedy from the British writer-director Anthony Minghella (*The English Patient*), the film was one of those priceless gems that you wish had stayed around long enough for your friends to have caught, too. And Sciorra, juggling the contradictory strands of her character, was sensational. She then played the wife of a corrupt New York cop (Gary Oldman) in Peter Medak's sexy black comedy *Romeo is Bleeding*, and joined the ensemble cast of *The Night We Never Met*, the delightful, funny story of a romantic mix-up in a New York apartment.

In Abel Ferrara's *The Addiction* she played a predatory vampiress (who attacks Lili Taylor in the first five minutes of the film), then, conversely, she played the mother of a boy with AIDS (Joseph Mazzello) in the touching, sensitive drama *The Cure*, the story of two boys whose tenuous friendship finds them sailing down the Mississippi in search of a panacea. Sciorra was particularly fine as the caring, defensive mother in a film that deserved far greater exposure than it received. In the low-budget British thriller *The Innocent Sleep* she was a feisty reporter sheltering a down-and-out (Rupert Graves) from a corrupt cop, and she then returned to work with Ferrara in *The Funeral*. This time she doubled as associate producer, although her role as the frustrated wife of gangland mobster Christopher Walken is a secondary – and largely thankless – one.

Next, she teamed up with Denis Leary and Joe Mantegna in the comedy-thriller *Underworld* – in another thankless part, that of the latter's estranged wife – and then joined the heady ranks of Sylvester Stallone, Robert De Niro, Ray Liotta and Harvey Keitel in James Mangold's *CopLand*, a tale of police corruption. After that, she starred alongside Jon Bon Jovi, Penelope Ann Miller and Josh Charles in the comedy-drama *Little City*, the story of the romantic exploits of six friends in San Francisco, and appeared opposite Eric Stoltz in the romantic comedy *Mr Jealousy*.

FILMOGRAPHY

1988: *Mario Puzo's 'The Fortunate Pilgrim'* (TV). 1989: *True Love*. 1990: *Cadillac Man; Internal Affairs; Reversal of Fortune*. 1991: *The Hard Way; Jungle Fever; Prison Stories: Women on the Inside* (TV). 1992: *The Hand that Rocks the Cradle; Whispers in the Dark*. 1993: *Mr Wonderful; Romeo is Bleeding; The Night We Never Met*. 1995: *The Addiction; The Cure; The Innocent Sleep*. 1996: *The Funeral; Underworld*. 1997: *Asteroid* (TV); *CopLand; Little City; Mr Jealousy*. 1998: *Highball; How to Visit New York; Lesser Prophets; What Dreams May Come*.

CHARLIE SHEEN

In a nutshell, Charlie Sheen was helped into the classroom by his father, made head prefect by Oliver Stone and saved from expulsion by his family.

The son of the actor Martin Sheen, Charlie notes: 'A lot of people believe that, because of him, I was able to get a foot in the door. And that may be true on some level. But it's what you do once you get *behind* that door that really counts.' And yet an equally strong influence on Charlie's professional life was his older brother, Emilio Estevez: 'Watching Emilio work, seeing the life he had, made me think maybe I should try films, too.' In fact, after Emilio turned down the lead in Oliver Stone's *Platoon* (due to a prior commitment), Stone opted for Charlie to replace him. The movie was a box-office sensation,

Back then: Charlie Sheen (right) aged 19 in Penelope Spheeris's atmospheric, uncompromising **The Boys Next Door**, with Maxwell Caulfield

Charlie Sheen as Yuppie trader Bud Fox in Oliver Stones's giddy drama **Wall Street** - with Michael Douglas

Charlie with Kristy Swanson in **The Chase**

won four Oscars (including a statuette for best picture) and made Charlie Sheen a star.

The following year, Stone cast him as the yuppie hero of *Wall Street*, another success, and Sheen was made. But – like his childhood friends, Rob Lowe and Sean Penn – Sheen pushed his life to the brink and became a target of the press. He complained: 'I was angry when certain things were written about me, but I did all those things.' After the success of *Platoon*, 'I started assuming this role of the young movie star who's into money, wine, cars, women and partying all night,' he allows. Indeed, his womanizing became legend. He later admitted that he kept a list of all his dates numbered in order of preference, with star ratings beside their names. For a while he was devoted to the actress Charlotte Lewis (who had previously been linked with Eddie Murphy), and was engaged to Kelly Preston (who later married John Travolta).

'It got so I couldn't tell where the film world stopped and the real world started,' he confessed. And, worst of all, 'I realized I was an alcoholic.' But in 1990, after a 32-day stint at a rehabilitation clinic, he cleaned up his act and faced the music. In 1991 he announced: 'I've cut out the booze. I've cut out the drugs. And I've settled down considerably. And it feels good.' Interestingly, his personal redemption coincided with the surprising success of *Hot Shots!*, an exhausted spoof of hit movies which grossed over $68 million in the USA alone. Sheen – clean, keen and wiser – was back.

He was born Carlos Irwin Estevez on 3 September 1965, in New York City, the third of four children – all of whom went on to film careers with varying degrees of success. Emilio Estevez (born 1962) is an actor, writer and director; Ramon Estevez (born 1963) is an actor with such films as *Beverly Hills Brats* and *Common Ground* to his credit, and Renee Estevez (born 1966) is an actress who has appeared in *For Keeps*, *Heathers*, *Paper Hearts* and starred in *Marked For Murder*. Meanwhile, Janet Sheen, wife of Martin and mother of all of them, turned associate producer on the domestic satire *Beverly Hills Brats*, while even Uncle Joe Estevez jumped on the bandwagon, starring in *Soultaker*, *One Shot Sam* and *Double Blast*.

When Charlie was three, his father moved the family to Santa Monica, California, to pursue his film career, and made a point of taking his children on location with him. Soon Charlie was making movies of his own, directing Super-8 features with all-star casts (at least, stars of the future): brother Emilio, Sean and Christopher Penn, Rob and Chad Lowe ...

At nine, he made his professional acting debut in the TV movie *The Execution of Private Slovik*, starring his father, and a year later was an extra in *Apocalypse Now*. But when Sheen Snr suffered a heart attack during the making of this film, Charlie swore off acting. Instead, he channelled his energies into baseball – and was good enough to win a college scholarship. But then Emilio started getting all the attention, making money, going places, influencing people (Charlie admitted: 'There was a lot of friction between us.'). And while Emilio was making movies, his younger brother was making trouble. 'At 16,' Charlie owns up, 'I was arrested for possession of marijuana. Then I was arrested again – a year later – for this five-day crime spree. I went to the Beverly Hills Hotel and told people that I'd been a guest and had lost my term paper. They'd let me look through the trash, and I found all these credit card receipts and used the numbers to make phone orders.'

Thanks to his father's influence, Charlie was spared a term in jail, but ran into more trouble when he was caught buying exam answers and, later, for assaulting a teacher. Such behaviour, and an intolerable attendance level, punctured Sheen's academic future and, consequently, his career as a baseball star.

Inevitably, he turned to acting. His father's manager circulated some publicity stills, and Sheen ended up in a B-movie called *Grizzly II – The Predator* (with Laura Dern and George Clooney), which was never released. He was 19 when he starred in his first major film, *Red Dawn*, which united him with Patrick Swayze and C. Thomas Howell, his brother's co-stars from *The Outsiders*. The film, in which Sheen played a student on the run from a Russian invasion of the USA, was a box-office success and something of a controversy. The same year, he courted some controversy of his own when he fathered a daughter, Cassandra, and broke up with the child's mother before she was born.

He played Chad Lowe's best friend in the TV movie *Silence of the Heart*, and a killer in Penelope Spheeris's compelling drama *The Boys Next Door* (with Maxwell Caulfield), and then he received top-billing for the first time in the sluggish *Three for the Road*, as a junior aide escorting his senator's daughter to a psychiatric clinic. However, it was a supporting role in the hit comedy *Ferris Bueller's Day Off* that made Sheen feel he had made it. 'The first time I really felt like people really knew who I was when I picked up *MAD* magazine and they were doing a parody of *Ferris Bueller* and there I was in the artwork. Some artist interpreted the character I played in the film. I thought, "This is kind of cool." *MAD* magazine, a magazine I grew up worshipping, and they've got my ugly ass in there gracing the pages. Forget the Oscars, forget all the hoopla, that really stood out for me.'

Then came *Platoon*, Oliver Stone's outstanding, Oscar-winning Vietnam epic, with Sheen as Chris, the film's reluctant hero and narrator (much as his father was in *Apocalypse Now*, which, coincidentally, was filmed not a hundred miles away from the same Philippines location). However, Sheen Jr brushed off the new acclaim, saying: 'It may be oversimplifying, but what was my role in *Platoon*, really? It was one every boy acts out as a kid, playing war.'

He found his part in Stone's *Wall Street* altogether more demanding, but he was left standing by Michael Douglas in his Oscar-winning role as the corrupt financial wizard, Gordon Gekko. Sheen was Bud Fox, Gekko's callow fall guy and, quite frankly, wasn't up to the demands of the part. He was better as a slick car thief in the stylish thriller *No Man's Land*, and then agreed to a supporting role – as Oscar 'Hap' Felsch – in the arty, baseball-themed *Eight Men Out*, which he took in order to play in a World Series on film and to work with the director, John Sayles. However, the picture was a commercial flop (it *was* very boring), and due to a serious injury while making it, Sheen was forced to lose the lead in Ridley Scott's action-thriller *Johnny Utah*, a part the actor had been counting on (it was made three years later as *Point Break*, starring Keanu Reeves). With his career bumping downstairs, Sheen rang Emilio in desperation.

'I called Emilio and said, "This is really bad, I feel like shit." So he said, "Call Chris Cain [the director of *Young Guns*]. Dick Brewer has not been cast ...We can play bitter rivals on film."' So, at the eleventh hour, Charlie was cast as Young Gun Brewer, although he had to suffer the indignity of fourth-billing, behind Emilio, Kiefer Sutherland and Lou Diamond Phillips. Nevertheless, the film was a hit. He then took a cameo in *Never on a Tuesday*, which he called 'my most extreme character role to date', in which he sported a menacing scar and a Southern accent. After that he had another hit, as Ricky Vaughn, the wild boy of the ill-fated Cleveland Indians baseball team, in David S. Ward's riotous *Major League*. This time his baseball fanaticism paid off – in spades.

Then his career nose-dived. He was miscast as a pipe-smoking goatherd in a *Heidi* update, *Courage Mountain*; had a cameo as Jodie Foster's boyfriend in *Backtrack*; was a gung-ho commando in the awful *Navy SEALS*; was simply embarrassing as a garbage collector in the intolerable *Men at Work* (written, directed by and co-starring Emilio), and was unmemorable as Clint Eastwood's preppie, clean-cut partner in the routine cop thriller *The Rookie* (a dud). He was then directed by his father in the undistinguished *Cadence*, as a rebellious AWOL soldier incarcerated in a German stockade (with Sheen Snr as his warden).

His career in tatters, he was invited to his father's birthday party in Malibu, only to find his family had rallied around for a confrontation. 'They said, "Sit down. We're gonna talk." And we had it out.' It was Emilio's charitable words that turned Charlie's head, and at his brother's behest he checked himself into rehab. Charlie recalls: 'Emilio said, "If you kill yourself with drugs and alcohol, you're robbing the rest of the world of a very valuable talent."'

Then came *Hot Shots!*, Charlie's most successful film to date (that is, in which he had top-billing). He played Sean 'Topper' Harley, a renegade pilot who's turned his back on the navy, preferring to spend time with the Indians and a wolf called Two Socks. But when an urgent mission brings him out of retirement, Topper proves himself as charismatic, dashing and horny as ever. A blatant spoof of *Top Gun*, with sidelong swipes at everything from *Gone With the Wind* to *The Fabulous Baker Boys*, Jim Abrahams' *Hot Shots!* was truly, in the words of the publicity, 'the Mother of all Movies'. Such was its success that two years later a sequel appeared – *Hot Shots Part Deux* – taking on the legend of *Rambo*. Sheen then took a cameo (as a valet parking attendant) in *National Lampoon's Loaded Weapon 1*, starring Emilio; had the lead in the crime adventure *Beyond the Law* (unrecognizable as a long-haired, heavily-bearded cop on the run from his past), and joined a starry cast in the atrocious *Deadfall*, a story of murder and deceit.

He was due to star in the Alcatraz drama *Murder in the First*, but when he was replaced by Christian Slater he teamed up with Chris O'Donnell and

Kiefer Sutherland for Disney's *The Three Musketeers*, which was was an insult to the memory of Alexandre Dumas, albeit an energetic, periodically witty and blandly handsome production, complete with American accents. It also struck a chord with audiences, galloping off with well over $100 million at the worldwide box-office.

Sheen was now earning between $3.5 million and $5 million a movie, although his choice of projects was suspect (he turned down the Woody Harrelson roles in *White Men Can't Jump* and *Indecent Proposal*). His private life was also coming under some media scrutiny. Besides his string of girlfriends (including, briefly, the supermodel Stephanie Seymour), there was the much-publicized case of the actor racking up a $53,000 bill at the illegal residence of Heidi Fleiss, the Hollywood madam (who, in January 1997, was sentenced to 37 months in prison for laundering profits from her call girl activities). However, in September 1995, he finally popped the question to the model Donna Peele, and showed every sign of settling down to a life of domestic tranquillity.

Meanwhile, he cashed in on his career upswing, starring in the predictable, lightweight *The Chase* (playing – rather unconvincingly – an escaped convict who kidnaps Kristy Swanson in order to elude the police), reprised his role as Rick 'Wild Thing' Vaughn (now transformed into a respectable bore) in the predictable, lightweight *Major League II*, and played a wise-cracking skydiving instructor (opposite Nastassja Kinski) in the escapist, breakneck romantic comedy-thriller *Terminal Velocity*.

Although these films failed to make a significant impact at the box-office, Sheen still pocketed $4 million for the spy thriller *Shadow Conspiracy* (playing a worried employee of the US president) and a handsome $5.25 million for *The Arrival*, a low-grade monster flick that *Variety* predicted 'should infiltrate vid stores quicker than aliens take over NASA'. And as his career plunged into video hell, Sheen's personal life went straight with it.

His marriage only lasted a matter of months and, on 21 December 1996, he was arrested and charged for assault. His victim, an unnamed 24-year-old woman, claimed that the actor knocked her down and then kicked her unconscious. Armed police raided Sheen's home in Agoura, Los Angeles, and drove him away in handcuffs.

FILMOGRAPHY

1974: *The Execution of Private Slovik* (unbilled; TV). 1979: *Apocalypse Now* (as an extra). 1983: *Grizzly II – The Predator* (unreleased). 1984: *Red Dawn*; *Silence of the Heart* (TV). 1985: *The Boys Next Door*; *Three for the Road* (released 1987). 1986: *Lucas*; *The Wraith*; *Ferris Bueller's Day Off*; *Platoon*; *Wisdom*. 1987: *Wall Street*; *No Man's Land*. 1988: *Eight Men Out*; *Young Guns*; *Never on a Tuesday* (cameo). 1989: *Beverly Hills Brats* (cameo); *Major League*; *Courage Mountain*; *Backtrack* (UK: *Catchfire*). 1990: *Navy SEALS*; *Men at Work*; *The Rookie*. 1991: *Cadence* (UK: *Stockade*); *Hot Shots!*. 1993: *National Lampoon's Loaded Weapon 1* (cameo); *Hot Shots Part Deux*; *Beyond the Law* (a.k.a. *Fixing the Shadow*); *The Three Musketeers*; *Deadfall*; *Frame by Frame*. 1994: *The Chase*; *Major League II*; *Terminal Velocity*. 1996: *All Dogs Go To Heaven 2* (voice only); *The Arrival*; *Loose Women*; *Shadow Conspiracy*. 1997: *Money Talks*; *Bad Day on the Block*. 1998: *Martin Eden*.

The jury is still out on whether Alicia Silverstone is a good actress. But of the fact that she is a highly seductive mouthpiece for the mall rat generation there is no doubt. She is also the youngest actress-producer in Hollywood history, and is largely responsible for implementing a wholly fresh vernacular for the late 1990s. 'As if!' became as immediately associated with the pouting lips of Ms Silverstone as 'bodacious' and 'excellent' with Keanu Reeves. But the idioms didn't stop there. Such expressions as 'hymenally challenged' (for 'virginal') and 'surfing the crimson wave' (for 'having one's period') were promptly embraced by the cooler alumni of the new teenage generation.

Of course, this is not to say that Alicia Silverstone used these expressions herself, but the character she played in *Clueless*, Amy Heckerling's hip, witty update of Jane Austen's *Emma*. Silverstone was busy making waves elsewhere. With the help of her best friend and manager, Carolyn Kessler, she nailed a $7 million two-movie contract with Columbia Pictures that gave her script approval and veto control over who she worked with.

Barry Josephson, President of Production at Columbia and boyfriend

ALICIA SILVERSTONE

Alicia phoning her agent for a pay rise

Alicia with Cary Elwes in The Crush

of Sharon Stone, vouchsafed: 'She is very smart about story and movies. She does the homework. She does the research.' Of her new power, Alicia herself confides: 'It's nice, because they [Columbia] know that I have proved myself to be a good actress, so that's very useful to them. And how they're useful to me is that I want to be able to create really brilliant projects that are going to mean something to people and mean something to me.'

Of course, Silverstone's new-found power has nothing to do with her being a good actress, just that she was the right pretty face in the right project at the right time. And her fans are willing to pay good popcorn money to see more of her. Wisely, she turned down a role in TV's fading *Beverly Hills 90210*; wisely, she accepted the role of Batgirl in *Batman and Robin* – for a reported $1.5 million. But there's more to her than good business sense and a provocative smile. She has that indefinable 'something' that distinguishes a movie star from a prom queen.

Raquel Welch, who played Alicia's mother in the TV movie *Torch Song*, notes: 'She's sophisticated and unsophisticated at the same time. You want to be nurturing and protective of her. But I don't think she's anybody's fool. She's a real smart girl.'

Marty Callner, who directed the young actress in a trio of Aerosmith videos, adds: 'I knew the second I met her. Certain people have a presence; there is a sort of aura around them. She walked into my office and I knew ... there was something in her eyes.'

Amy Heckerling, director of *Clueless*, said: 'I was blown away by Alicia's sexuality and naturalness. She has a kind of inherent intelligence you have to have to pull off the flighty and seemingly clueless character she plays in the movie.'

Alicia Silverstone was born on 4 October 1976 in San Francisco, the daughter of English parents Monty, a real estate financier and inverstment adviser, and Didi, a former Pan Am flight attendant. Growing up with her older brother, David, in Hillsborough, an affluent neighbourhood south of San Francisco, Alicia enjoyed frequent trips to England, where she was exposed to the theatre. 'I was fascinated,' she says. 'I knew I wanted to be an actress – although I didn't know what that meant.'

She began acting classes at the age of 12 and, at the insistence of her father, toyed with modelling, promoting the merchandise of Yves Saint Laurent and Levi's. However, she hated being a mannequin and decided to leave home at 14, moving to LA to live with the acting coach Jodi O'Neil. A year later she landed the lead in her first film, *The Crush* (after Fairuza Balk

turned the project down), and was legally emancipated from the custody of her parents.

In *The Crush*, she played Darian Forrester, a prodigiously intelligent 14-year-old vixen who homes in on dashing journalist Cary Elwes, feigning stupidity as a screen for her obsessive, deadly deeds. She was dreadful, and so was the movie (an unconvincing mix of *Lolita* and *Fatal Attraction*), and it deservedly withered at the box-office. Still, the film's director, Alan Shapiro, raved: 'I consider Alicia a character actor, like Dustin Hoffman' – and it didn't do badly on video. Meanwhile, MTV bestowed their Best Breakthrough Performance award on her.

The Crush also attracted the attention of the hard-rock group Aerosmith, who cast her in three of their videos – *Cryin'*, *Amazing* and *Crazy* – the first of which was voted Best Video of All Time by MTV. Suddenly she was blossoming into a minor pop icon, and started appearing in a string of movies.

She was better in the TV feature *Torch Song*, playing the alienated, frumpy daughter of an alcoholic Hollywood star played by Raquel Welch. The film itself teetered between the risible and the insightful, but Leonora Thuna and Janet Brownell's half-way decent screenplay and a few moments of unexpected humour were undermined by Welch's profoundly artificial performance.

Next, Alicia was in two more TV movies, supporting Tyne Daly in *Shattered Dreams*, and playing a sexually-driven vamp in Ralph Bakshi's abysmal *Cool and the Crazy*. Then, in the thriller *True Crime*, she played a geeky schoolgirl with an instinct for detective work (who gets it off with rookie cop Kevin Dillon in the back of a car). She had the title role in *The Babysitter*, in which she was the focus of much male lusting (and although the film went straight to video, it was resurrected for theatrical release after the success of *Clueless*).

She was in another dud with *Hideaway*, an unbelievably bad film version of Dean R. Koontz's bestseller about a psychic psycho (she was the 'hymenally challenged' daughter of Jeff Goldblum), and then she journeyed to France to play the frisky attraction of a

Alicia (left) with Brittany Murphy and Stacey Dash in Clueless

local boy (Nicolas Chatel) in *Le Nouveau Monde*, Alain Corneau's nostalgic, soapy hymn to all things American.

Then, on the strength of her wordless role in Aerosmith's *Cryin'* (in which she bungee-jumps off a motorway bridge), she won the lead in *Clueless*, a fresh, funny and breezy take on the Californian Valley Girl syndrome. Alicia was Cher, a spoilt brat who takes delight in engineering romances between her classmates (and teachers) and improving the sartorial standing of her friends. Recognizing that "'Tis a far, far better thing like when you do stuff for other people,' Cher sticks her nose in other people's business while worshipping Luke Perry, shopping and Mel Gibson (in that order) and dismissing The Cranberries and foreign politics. Yet, while she claims to know what's important, Cher still thinks Bosnia is in the Middle East, Billie Holiday is a man, and that Kirk Douglas starred in an epic called *Sporadicus*.

Under the direction of Heckerling (who previously made stars of Sean Penn and Jennifer Jason Leigh in *Fast Times at Ridgemont High*), Silverstone exhibited some wicked comic timing.

Nevertheless, without Raquel Welch around to make her look good, she had to work hard to hold her own. In fact, if anything, her female cohorts – Stacey Dash and Brittany Murphy – came close to acting her off the screen. Indeed, it is Dash who nails the film's funniest line, responding to Cher's enquiry, 'Would you call me selfish?', with a sharp, 'No. Not to your face.'

But Alicia was the star, and the film ambled off with almost $100 million at the box-office. And, as already noted, Silverstone became responsible for introducing a whole new vocabulary to the English/American language. The somewhat derisive, dismissive response, 'Whatever,' reached its apex in *Clueless*, although scholars of the actress's career will know that she actually used it first in *Torch Song*. Whatever. Such expressions as 'not even', 'do-able' and 'majorly' were duly absorbed into the language.

Suddenly Alicia was the hottest babe in Hollywood – and the media moved in. Her private life was no longer private, and her involvement at 15 with a French hairdresser, Moize Chabbhou, 13 years her senior, became public knowledge. 'I was a very good

girl,' she insisted, 'we didn't even kiss until six months after we met.' She was also reported to have been involved with the zany comic Adam Sandler (*Happy Gilmore*, *Bulletproof*) and Leonardo DiCaprio – although of DiCaprio, she asserts: 'I will not say anything about him.'

And while she was passed over for the role of Juliet in *William Shakespeare's Romeo + Juliet*, she was busy setting up her own projects under the umbrella of her production outfit First Kiss Productions. She chose to kick off her career as producer with an action-comedy called *Excess Baggage*, in which she played an heiress who organizes her own kidnapping, and signed up Christopher Walken and Benicio Del Toro to co-star, and Marco Brambilla (*Demolition Man*) to direct. She admits that her agent could have squeezed a bigger payday out of Columbia, but creative leverage was the price she paid for a smaller sum (even though this amount was extensively misquoted as $10 million). 'What was important to me was creative control,' she confirms, 'to be a producer, to have a deal where I made real, educated decisions and choices.'

Still, it must have been a relief to take a supporting (albeit lucrative) role in *Batman and Robin*, with the likes of George Clooney, Arnold Schwarzenegger, Uma Thurman and Chris O'Donnell shouldering the main responsibility. However (according to reports in the tabloids), Silverstone put on so much weight during the shoot that she had to be greased down in order to be squeezed into her costume.

While her fluctuating weight may be a sore point, the actress asserts: 'I do my best. But it's much more important to me that my brain is working in the morning than getting up early and doing exercise. But unfortunately, it's the perception that women in film should look a certain way.'

Way true, as Cher would have said.

FILMOGRAPHY

1993: *The Crush*; *Judith Krantz's Torch Song* (TV). 1994: *Shattered Dreams* (TV); *Cool and the Crazy* (TV); *True Crime*. 1995: *The Babysitter*; *Hideaway*; *Le Nouveau Monde* (*The New World*); *Clueless*. 1997: *Excess Baggage*; *Batman and Robin*. 1998: *The Breakers*.

CHRISTIAN SLATER

Christian Slater as JD, the ultimate rebel without a cause - in Michael Lehmann's **Heathers**

Christian Slater was the embodiment of teenage cool. He wasn't particularly handsome like, say, Luke Perry. He wasn't wildly athletic like Patrick Swayze. He didn't mumble in the tradition of Matt Dillon. And he wasn't as notorious as Rob Lowe. And, let's be honest, he wasn't as good an actor as Sean Penn or Eric Stoltz. But he had attitude. And that, in the 1990s, counted for a hell of a lot. As the selling line for *Kuffs* proclaimed: 'When you have attitude – who needs experience?'

Had Christian Slater been born under another star sign, he could have been the film industry's pet nerd. But a combination of street savvy and a wacky charm kept him at the head of the class. There was also an arrogance, an attitude that even the timid, bookish Mark Hunter in *Pump up the Volume* couldn't entirely camouflage. In addition, there was an honesty, a 'gee whiz' sensibility that endeared Slater to filmgoers. Thankfully, Christian Slater is still awe-struck by it all.

Allan Moyle, who directed the quintessentially hip *Pump up the Volume*, noted: 'Christian has an ineffable blend of innocence and power that makes him thrilling to watch. He brings both wit and charisma to his role.'

Winona Ryder, who got to know the actor even better, volunteered: 'He's one of the funniest people I know. He has a style that's really his own. Forty years from now someone's going to write a book: *Slater – The Legend.*'

The son of stage actor Michael Hawkins and casting director Mary Jo Slater, Christian was born on 18 August 1969, in New York City. He confessed that his father was 'a little offbeat and strange', while his mother was far from run-of-the-mill. As an example, she staged a rather unusual 20th birthday party for him. 'Yeah, she hired a stripper,' Slater confirms. 'I was sitting there in a chair, with all my friends watching, while a woman danced naked in front of me. That's a position I *never* want to be in again. This woman went on for, like, four or five songs. She did the entire soundtrack to *Last Tango in Paris.*' Slater also notes: 'When I was baby, my mother took me up on stage – I mean, it was like, *Roots*. She held me up above her head and said: "This is your life, my son." This is what she tells me. Of course, it could be a lie.'

He was seven when Mary Jo cast him in a small part in the daytime TV serial *One Life To Live.* 'Everybody

applauded, and that was it,' he said. 'I was sold.' Two years later he was spotted on TV by the theatre director Michael Kidd and was signed up to play the cute, all-American Winthrop in a nine-month tour of *The Music Man,* starring Dick Van Dyke. 'In the beginning,' Slater recalls, 'I'd be onstage

Christian Slater as DJ, the ultimate rebel with a cause -in Allan Moyle's **Pump Up The Volume**

*As crusading lawyer James Stamphill, with Kevin Bacon, in **Murder in the First***

and start waving to my mother in the audience. I was just a young, excited kid. Then as the show went on I began to understand what it was all about.'

With typical candour he says, 'I'm all for nepotism,' and indeed, he made the most of both his parents (who divorced when he was six). He played D.J. LaSalle in the daytime soap *Ryan's Hope*, in which his father was the original Frank Ryan, and, aged 14, he had a small role in the well-received TV movie *Living Proof: The Hank Williams Jr Story* – starring Richard Thomas as the country singer. He had a big role – Binx – in *The Legend of Billy Jean*, opposite Keith Gordon and Helen Slater (no relation), but the film played to small audiences.

His breakthrough arrived with the young lead in *The Name of the Rose*, which, especially in retrospect, seemed a bizarre casting choice. Slater says: 'When I first read the script, I thought, "There's no way I can play a medieval monk; there's just no chance." It was such an intense role, with this wild love scene, and I was just 16. I was surprised when the director, Jean-Jacques Annaud, cast me. I played Sean Connery's apprentice in the film, and our relationship on screen reflected real life. He was teaching me, and I was trying to take it all in.'

Of course, Jean-Jacques Annaud is a Frenchman, and was little concerned that Connery, Slater and Michel Lonsdale all had competing accents, as long as they spoke English. The film's moody, Rembrandtian look was the order of the day, while Slater's deflowerment at the hands of the voluptuous Valentina Vargas was one of the most

unexpectedly erotic moments of 1980s cinema. As it happens, Slater and Vargas became an item off-screen as well (he was 16, she 22).

He had the lead as a sadistic killer in the rather nasty *Twisted*, but the film wasn't released until 1992, when he was a name. He was then star-struck again in the company of Francis Ford Coppola and Jeff Bridges – as Bridges' son – in the distinguished *Tucker: The Man and His Dream*, the stirring story of the persecuted auto genius Preston Tucker.

Slater then secured top-billed for the first time in the skateboarding thriller *Gleaming the Cube*, in which he played a bad seed from Orange County – complete with spiked hair and earrings. 'I dyed my hair, let it grow long, pierced my ears, and practised on a skateboard for three months,' the actor recalls. 'Then a camera guy came over to me and said, "Jeez, you really sound like Jack Nicholson." At that point I hadn't seen any of his films; not really. Anyway, it was thrilling to hear that – especially as I had no idea I was doing it. Now I can't escape it. It's cool, but I gotta be me.'

He intentionally injected a dash of Nicholson – combined with a dollop of his father – in *Heathers*, the film that established him as the coolest dude on the Hollywood block. Ironically, he was advised against the project, but he couldn't resist the temptation of playing J.D., the high school outsider who dishes out a terrible fate to three snotty princesses all called Heather. Slater's high school girlfriend, Kim Walker, played Heather Chandler, while his future (albeit brief) companion, Winona Ryder, co-starred as Veronica – an honorary Heather, and Bonnie Parker to his Clyde Barrow. The film was as hip as tomorrows's catch phrase, and turned the teen comedy on its head with a satanic flourish. *Newsweek* hailed the picture as 'a work of genuine audacity', and *GQ* called it 'the ultimate send-up of high school angst movies'. Slater was 20 years old.

By rights, he should have been an instant star, but his career failed to gather momentum. He had the lead in an unexceptional TV movie, *Desperate For Love*, loosely based on a real-life tragedy; took a supporting role in *Personal Choice*, a talky dud with Martin

Sheen; was wasted as Fred Savage's older brother in the little-seen *The Wizard*; was insignificant in the omnibus horror film *Tales from the Darkside – The Movie*, as a college student menaced by a 3,000-year-old mummy, and was in another miss, *On the Prowl*, with Corey Haim.

If Slater's film career was going nowhere, his private life was even worse. He admits was 'hitting an emotional and physical bottom', and in December 1989 he was sentenced to ten days in jail after pleading no contest to his second driving while intoxicated charge within a year. His driving licence was withdrawn for 18 months, he was fined $1,400 and put on five years' probation. The 'incident' occurred when the actor, under the influence of illegal substances, exceeded the speed limit in LA and resisted arrest. With the police in hot pursuit, he slammed his Saab 900 into a telephone pole and then, as he scaled a chain-link fence, he hurled a cowboy boot at a highway patrolman. 'I did what a lot of people do at a certain age,' he explained ruefully. 'I went through a wild period, although I think I took it to an extreme. I know I could have been smarter. But I don't regret my past. I actually learned from the negative experiences.'

He ignored advice to turn down the lead in *Pump up the Volume*, and returned with a professional bang as the shy high school student (Mark Hunter) who doubles as an underground DJ called 'Happy Harry Hard-On'. This was his best performance yet, a tour-de-force in which his bespectacled recluse comes out at night to transform a sleepy Arizona suburb into a state of frenzy. Preaching rebellion and sexual honesty from the makeshift studio of his bedroom, Slater was nothing short of mesmerizing. Ironically, Allan Moyle's ultra-hip screenplay had been sitting around for years due to the fact that the filmmaker couldn't think of anybody who could carry off the dual demands of the role. Moyle marvelled: 'When I met Christian Slater, I finally saw the character come alive.'

With his career back on track, the actor segued into the Hollywood mainstream. He was an outlaw with an inferiority complex in *Young Guns II – Blaze of Glory*, played Will Scarlett in the phenomenally successful *Robin Hood: Prince of Thieves* and, when Matt Dillon turned the role down, he starred as the young Charles 'Lucky' Luciano in *Mobsters*. He said he took those roles, 'to protect myself in case I had to back things up. On the other hand, they were attractive projects because of the people involved.'

Because his mother was a *Star Trek* groupie, he found himself cast in a cameo in *Star Trek VI: The Undiscovered Country* (for which he was paid $750), and then starred in the lightweight caper *Kuffs*, as a drop-out who inherits a police precinct when his brother is murdered. He supplied the voice of the hip wood nymph Pips in the animated feature *FernGully The Last Rainforest*, took a cameo as a social worker in *Where the Day Takes You*, and then gave one of his very best performances in the sweet, touching romantic drama *Untamed Heart*, in which he played Adam, a withdrawn orphan boy who believes he has the heart of a baboon, and who falls in love with an attractive, spirited waitress (Marisa Tomei). To her surprise, the waitress finds herself reciprocating his love, leading to a most unconventional and tender romance. The film had every right to drown in sentimentality, but artfully sidestepped mawkishness to become one of the year's most touching and surprisingly memorable films.

He then got his biggest break yet, top-billed in Tony Scott's hard-hitting romantic comedy-thriller, *True Romance*, in which he and Patricia Arquette attempt to find true happiness with a suitcase of Mafioso contraband. Based on a hot screenplay by Quentin Tarantino, the film co-starred Dennis Hopper, Gary Oldman, Brad Pitt, Val Kilmer and Christopher Walken, and should have launched Slater into the front rack of Hollywood beefcake. It didn't – maybe the film was *too* violent for multiplex consumption.

Still, it performed better than *Jimmy Hollywood*, Barry Levinson's tiresome satire on Tinseltown, with Slater playing second banana to Joe Pesci's irritating loser. And then there was a biggie: *Interview with the Vampire*. River Phoenix was due to play the interviewer of the title, but when he died from a drug overdose (in October 1993), Slater was asked to step in. 'I felt really

*Testing the testosterone: Christian gets tough in John Woo's **Broken Arrow***

uncomfortable about it,' the actor confessed. 'I had met [director] Neil Jordan six months before they started shooting because I was interested in another role, that of Armand [eventually taken on by Antonio Banderas]. I really hated Jordan, to be honest with you, because he spent most of the interview on the phone. I was offended by that. I've since found out that he's very shy and has a difficult time communicating. When I heard that they wanted me for River Phoenix's role, I wanted no part of it. Then my agent suggested I donate the money to his charities and ones that I'm involved with.'

It was a supporting role (Slater only worked on it for one week), but it was a visible one, with the film going on to gross $105.3 million in the USA. Then, in Marc Rocco's *Murder in the First*, he took over from Charlie Sheen as the lawyer James Stamphill, a composite of several real-life attorneys. A 24-year-old greenhorn, Stamphill defends a convict who has murdered a fellow inmate (in front of 200 witnesses), in the process turning the whole Alcatraz foundation on its head. As the convict, Kevin Bacon had the showier part, while Gary Oldman, as a depraved warden, stole every scene he was in. However, the director reserved praise for Slater: 'Audiences are going to see a Christian Slater they haven't seen before,' Rocco pledged. 'He is a very good actor and he brought so much to this role that I ended up being able to do much more with the story than I had envisioned.'

He returned to romantic gear for the gentle, sweet love story *Bed of Roses* (spouting lines like 'Every now and then I think everybody is entitled to too much perfection.'), and then he attempted a Keanu Reeves (in *Speed* mode) by tackling the part of crack military pilot Riley Hale in John Woo's *Broken Arrow* (for which he passed on the Antonio Banderas role in *Assassins*). However, while Slater quit smoking and gained 15 pounds to lend muscular credence to his character, it was John Travolta, as a charismatic villain, who hijacked the film from Slater's lightweight heroics. And, let's be truthful, it was Travolta's name above the title that pushed the film to a worldwide box-office gross of $148.3 million.

He then teamed up with Morgan Freeman and Minnie Driver in the action-thriller *The Flood* (playing a crooked security guard on the lam), and starred in the New York comedy *The Tears of Julian Po*, with Robin Tunney. After that he went to England to star in *Basil*.

Romantically, he settled a palimony suit with ex-girlfriend Nina Huang, and went on to date supermodel Christy Turlington, followed by a liaison with the actress Courtney Cox.

FILMOGRAPHY

1983: *Living Proof: The Hank Williams Jr Story* (TV). 1985: *The Legend of Billy Jean*. 1986: *The Name of the Rose*; *Cry Wolf* (TV); *Twisted* (released 1992). 1988: *Tucker: The Man and His Dream*. 1989: *Gleaming the Cube*; *Heathers*; *Desperate For Love* (TV); *Personal Choice* (later *Beyond the Stars*); *The Wizard*. 1990: *Tales From the Darkside – The Movie*; *On the Prowl*; *Pump up the Volume*; *Young Guns II – Blaze of Glory*. 1991: *Robin Hood: Prince of Thieves*; *Mobsters* (UK: *Mobsters – The Evil Empire*); *Star Trek VI: The Undiscovered Country* (cameo). 1992: *Kuffs*; *FernGully The Last Rainforest* (voice only); *Where the Day Takes You* (cameo). 1993: *Untamed Heart*; *True Romance*. 1994: *Jimmy Hollywood*; *Interview with the Vampire*. 1995: *Murder in the First*; *Bed of Roses*. 1996: *Broken Arrow*. 1997: *The Flood*; *The Tears of Julian Po*; *Basil*.

WILL SMITH
Will Smith

Displaying the sex appeal of a young Harry Belafonte, the comic effortlessness of Eddie Murphy and the acting smarts of a budding Denzel Washington, Will Smith was pre-ordained for stardom. Yet his meteoric rise through the ranks of his peers flabbergasted even his staunchest disciples.

Bounding from hip-hop celebrity to sitcom stardom with apparent ease, Will Smith took on the cinema with a vengeance. His second film, with Whoopi Goldberg, was a hit (albeit an inexplicable one), and the next earned him unstinting praise. His fourth more than doubled the box-office gross of its nearest competitor and instantly activated a sequel. And his fifth became the first movie in history to gross over $100 million in under a week (besting the previous record holder, *Jurassic Park*, which had grossed the same figure in nine days).

Will Smith was a phenomenon. And he was the first black man to land top-billing in a film that grossed more than $350 million worldwide (let alone $780 million).

The son of Willard Smith, a refrigeration engineer, and Caroline, a school board administrator, Will Smith II was born on 25 September 1968, in West Philadelphia. By the time he was 14, he was already a seasoned rap singer and, in 1986, started up his own hip-hop group with Jeff Townes: D.J. Jazzy Jeff and The Fresh Prince. Smith was The Fresh Prince, a streetwise but more or less upstanding mouthpiece for disenchanted youth whose calls for justice proved to be a far cry from the cop-killing variety endorsed by Ice-T.

'I think the one thing that has always helped us is who we are,' he said back then. 'We like to have fun. That was the beauty of D.J. Jazzy Jeff and The Fresh Prince. Everyone was saying, "Oh, that's soft. That ain't black." But I don't think that anybody can dictate what's black or not black.'

The duo's first album, 'Rock the House', was released in 1987 and sold over a million copies, while their second, 'He's the DJ, I'm the Rapper', went platinum and spawned the hit single 'Parents Just Don't Understand', which went on to win the 1988 Grammy for best rap performance. Their fourth LP, 'Homebase', was also a

Will Smith (right) whips up a sophisticated storm in **Six Degrees of Separation**, with Donald Sutherland, Ian McKellen and Stockard Channing

platinum seller and produced the Grammy-winning single 'Summertime'. Then, a year later, Jeff and Will were selected as the year's outstanding rap artists at the NAACP Image Awards. All in all, they were the proud authors of *five* top-selling albums.

In fact, such was Smith's success that NBC TV – under the guidance of executive producer Quincy Jones – built a sitcom around his persona. This was *The Fresh Prince of Bel-Air*, in which Smith's princely alter ego is packed off to Bel-Air, California, to stay with wealthy relatives. The formula worked a treat, translating Smith's record appeal into sitcom gold – and four highly watchable seasons.

However, as the series evolved, Smith found himself increasingly at odds with The Prince. 'I had gotten married and had a baby,' he noted, referring to his son, Will Smith III. 'I was finding myself having to act more to play the Will character. I began to refer to him as "the Will character," when in the beginning I referred to him as me. He was 18; he couldn't grow up as quickly as I could.'

Smith met his wife, Sheree Zampino, at a taping session of *A Different World*, the successful spin-off of TV's *The Cosby Show*. He followed up their meeting with a string of phone calls, but Sheree was slow to commit. None the less, she did, eventually, agree to see him again. 'We went out to dinner,' Smith recalls, 'and she was impressed with my sense of humour and my outlook. People in my position tend to be more pompous. She thought I was down-to-earth and fun.'

Be that as it may, the actor was not above flexing his celebrity muscle. 'Once,' he admits, 'I flew from Philadelphia to Atlanta with ten of my friends and closed the Gucci shop down so I could shop in peace.'

While still enjoying his status as Bel-Air's Will Smith, the real McCoy debuted on celluloid in the streetlife ensemble drama *Where the Day Takes You*, tenth-billed as 'Manny'. However, audiences weren't ready for a glossy take on the homeless, and in spite of a happening young cast – Dermot Mulroney, Lara Flynn Boyle, Balthazar Getty, Kyle MacLachlan – the movie found no home to call its own.

A year later, Smith cut an engaging presence as the nerdy boyfriend of Whoopi Goldberg's daughter (Nia Long) in *Made in America*. An illogical, farcical and critical disaster, the film was the story of a black girl (Long)

What ya gonna do? Smith (right) with Martin Lawrence in **Bad Boys**

Saving the planet: Smith and Harry Connick Jr in Independence Day

who not only discovers that she is the product of artificial insemination, but that her father is Ted Danson. An excruciating waste of Hollywood talent, the film underlined its sense of humour with much screaming and wide-eyed bewilderment before dive-bombing into the depths of sentimental predictability. Seldom have Whoopi Goldberg or Ted Danson been caught over-acting so appallingly, so it was not entirely surprising that Smith won the only good reviews going. Still, the film was a hit at the box-office, presumably because audiences had taken the title to heart.

A number of Afro-American actors had been approached to play Paul, the central character in the film version of John Guare's award-winning play *Six Degrees of Separation*. The part was in fact based on real-life conman David Hampton, a black 19-year-old who convinced a pair of eminent New Yorkers that not only was he a friend of their own children, but the son of Sidney Poitier. Thus welcomed into his victims' luxurious Manhattan apartments, he set about divesting them of some of their more precious possessions. The play – which starred Stockard Channing in both its Broadway and London runs – was a superbly-written piece of social comment with a dream part for the charismatic intruder. The film's director, Fred Schepisi, admits that he auditioned 'all sorts of hot, young actors', but settled on Smith because: 'He had the desire. He came to convince me that he could really do it, and in doing that, he was kind of like Paul.'

It was a role to die for, but it was also unlike anything the former rapper had hitherto taken on. He acknowledges: 'My first impression was that this was going to be the most difficult thing I ever had to do in entertainment.' His second realization was that the character was homosexual. 'The biggest consideration for me was that if I pulled this off I would be a legitimate actor. Hollywood really doesn't respect TV actors; film is the medium to succeed in. I want to be considered by Spike Lee and Martin Scorsese. I want people to know there is something beyond what I do on *Fresh Prince*.'

Before starting work on the film, Smith called Denzel Washington for advice. 'Denzel said, "you're pretending to be a character. It's not you".' But, Smith continues, 'he also had an interesting perception: He says white people tend to accept their stars as actors, but because black people have so few heroes, they hold each hero responsible for the roles he chooses. That's very true.' As a compromise, Smith ducked out of the play's notorious homosexual kiss, noting: 'I wasn't mature enough to handle the homosexuality and forced the director to work around my hang-ups.'

Nevertheless, Smith not only stood up to his prestigious co-stars – Channing, Donald Sutherland, Ian McKellen, Bruce Davison – but cajoled, nudged and seduced the living daylights out of them. Slick, smooth and articulate, the actor sashayed off with the film (although, perhaps predictably, it was Channing who received the sole Oscar nomination).

Two years later, Will Smith starred in Michael Bay's *Bad Boys*, cast as the affluent, smooth-talkin' Mike Lowrey, a ladies' man and law-enforcer partnered with the hen-pecked husband-and-father Marcus Bennett (Martin Lawrence). The lads' mission was to uncover the identity of the mastermind behind the theft of $100 million in uncut heroin – stolen from under the nose of the Miami police force. A high-octane comedy-thriller cut from the cloth of the MTV school of filmmaking, *Bad Boys* was nasty, funny and hugely entertaining, stuffed with guns, gags and some criminally attractive girls. While in essence the formula seemed box-officeproof, the concept of two *black* guys painting Miami red was

a risky one. But Smith's flourishing star charisma and sex appeal married to the comic bickering of Lawrence was a match made in celluloid Heaven. And, sure enough, *Bad Boys* achieved the biggest opening gross of the first five months of 1995.

Biding his time, Will Smith next signed on to star in an ambitious tale of alien invasion from Roland Emmerich, the German director of *Stargate*. Flaunting a budget of $71 million, *Independence Day* was not in the same financial league as the *Batman* films, *True Lies* or even *CutThroat Island*. However, by the time the bets were on for the summer of 1996, the film had moved into fourth position as the season's dominant money-maker (behind *Twister, Mission: Impossible* and *The Hunchback of Notre Dame*). Top-billing Will Smith as a cocky fighter pilot who volunteers to save the planet – literally – the film found its budget predominantly ploughed into the astonishing special effects, notably the detonation of the capital's White House. But there were still plenty of recognizable names – Bill Pullman, Jeff Goldblum, Mary McDonnell, Randy Quaid – and Smith was at the top of the pile.

He modelled his character, Steve Hiller, on Harrison Ford's Han Solo in the *Star Wars* films, and spent time working out in the cockpit of a marine simulator, complete with proportionate G forces. He was attracted to the role, he says, because: 'These types of films haven't been made much recently, but I grew up watching them and it's fun to be in one.' Furthermore, 'Steve Hiller is interesting because he's serious, but he's also able to be funny. I've never experimented with that before; it's either been one or the other.'

While essentially an ensemble piece, *Independence Day* belonged to Smith's heroic pilot, who gets to punch an alien in the face, spout lines like 'Elvis has left the building' (as he exits the alien mother ship) and, in perhaps his most memorable scene of all, give the longest double-take in recent cinema history (as he slowly – ever-so-slowly – gazes from his panicking neighbours to the portentous sky above).

The film itself, drawing on key elements from *Close Encounters of the Third Kind, Top Gun, Star Wars, Alien* and *The War of the Worlds*, proved to be the ultimate popcorn movie, orchestrating special effects, thrills, laughs, romance and social commentary in a dynamic and thoroughly entertaining cocktail. Even so, when it evaporated box-office figures in July 1996, the collective jaw of Hollywood dropped in silent awe.

Then, later that year, Smith's marriage was over and he was sharing his life with the successful actress Jada Pinkett, the star of *Jason's Lyric*, *The Nutty Professor* and *Set It Off*. Next, he starred opposite Tommy Lee Jones and Linda Fiorentino in Barry Sonnenfeld's *Men in Black* – the tongue-in-cheek story of an elite government force trained to track down alien life on earth. '*Independence Day* was a great step,' the actor notes. 'I'm hoping *Men in Black* will be another huge leap – I think it's going to be great. Rick Baker has designed some of the most beautiful and disgusting alien creatures you'll ever see.' Then he signed on for *Bad Boys II*.

FILMOGRAPHY

1992: *Where the Day Takes You*. 1993: *Made in America*; *Six Degrees of Separation*. 1995: *Bad Boys*. 1996: *Independence Day*. 1997: *Men in Black*. 1998: *The Wild, Wild West*; *Bad Boys II*.

*Wesley as the ruthless drug lord Nino Brown in Mario Van Peebles's **New Jack City***

When black cinema became box-office gold in the 1990s, a new star system was born. Suddenly, stand-up comedians like Robert Townsend and Damon Wayans, and rap artists such as Ice-T and Ice Cube were being turned into movie stars. But the biggest name of all, who represented the new urban cool of Afro-American audiences, was a theatrically-trained actor. Looking for all the world like an accidental star,

*With Lonette McKee in Spike Lee's **Jungle Fever***

Wesley Snipes nevertheless excited critics and secured top-billing in extremely successful pictures. Maybe thanks to timing, or to good luck, or to sheer talent, Snipes became a box-office phenomenon.

Born on 31 July 1962, and raised in the tough neighbourhood of the South Bronx, New York, Snipes enrolled at the High School for Performing Arts, the setting of Alan Parker's *Fame*. Naturally athletic (Snipes is a trained martial artist and student of the Afro-Brazilian Capoeria, a form of unarmed combat), he initially saw himself as a dancer, and possibly a singer, before deciding on drama. 'It was,' he noted, 'so easy.'

However, when in 1977 his family upped sticks and moved to Orlando, Florida, Snipes was deeply upset. So, as soon as he had completed high school in the Sunshine State, he returned to New York to attend SUNY-Purchase, and graduated with a degree in theatre arts. A year later he married a college classmate. 'We married thinking we could change each other,' he says now, 'although we didn't know who we were ourselves. We were too young – I

had the ideal but not the insight. I was devastated when my marriage ended after six years. My dad left when I was two, and I was doing the same thing to my son [Jelani Snipes].'

In the mid-1980s he and a group of friends formed a puppet troupe called 'Struttin' Street Stuff' and toured for three years performing comedy, satire and drama at public parks and schools. 'We did everything from building sets to making the costumes,' he says. 'It was a lot of fun.' He also appeared on Broadway in a series of plays, including *Boys of Winter*, *Death and the King's Horsemen* and *Execution of Justice*. But he was still not ready to make it in films. In 1984 he auditioned for a role in the Harry Belafonte-produced musical *Beat Street*. 'Here's this piece about cats from the 'hood, and I'm enunciating my lines like a Shakespearean actor,' he recounts. 'Harry took one look and said, "That's enough, son. Go back to school".'

On television, he appeared in an episode of *Miami Vice*, then made his film debut in the Goldie Hawn comedy *Wildcats*, as a high school football player. In the same year he won third-billing in the routine *Streets of Gold*, playing an ambitious boxer trained by Klaus Maria Brandauer, and then he had a minute part in the abysmal Richard Pryor comedy *Critical Condition*. But his breakthrough role arrived not on film nor on TV nor on stage, but in the 1987 music video for Michael Jackson's 'Bad'. Martin Scorsese directed, and Snipes gave a performance of such aggressive power (as the gang leader who shoves Jacko up against a wall) that, in the words of Spike Lee: 'He was so real, Michael Jackson must've been scared to death.'

Of course, *Bad* was no ordinary video, and its subsequent exposure got Snipes noticed. He turned down a part in Spike Lee's *Do the Right Thing* in

Enjoying the mayhem: Snipes mocking the machismo of Sylvester Stallone in Demolition Man

order to play the showier role of Willie Mays Hayes in the hit baseball comedy *Major League*. It was a wise move. His high-octane comic performance deftly overshadowed his co-stars (Tom Berenger, Charlie Sheen and Corbin Bernsen) and when, five years later, the

cast was reassembled for the sequel, Snipes was out of the producers' price range.

On TV, he played police officer Lou Barton in the pilot movie *H.E.L.P.* and appeared in the subsequent, short-lived series. Next, he starred in another series, HBO's *Vietnam War Stories*, and won the 1989 ACE Award as best actor for his performance. He then accepted Spike Lee's offer to play the ambitious, quick-tempered saxophonist Shadow Henderson in *Mo' Better Blues*, rival to Denzel Washington. He also appeared in the hard-hitting, stylish thriller *King of New York*, as a New York cop trying to bust a nefarious crime ring.

He switched sides in *New Jack City*, winning top-billing as the gold-medal-lioned, super-smooth and ultra-vicious crime lord Nino Brown, a part special-ly written for him. His exercise in unremitting evil was nothing short of mesmerizing, epitomized by his heart-less order to a henchman when his girlfriend wimps out on him: 'Cancel that bitch – I'll buy another.'

In a disastrous 1991 spring season, *New Jack City* was the only film in the USA to turn a profit – but it attracted more than just eager cinemagoers. The movie was criticized for glamourizing crime and, indeed, much violence and looting erupted around its release, leaving one murdered teenager in its wake. Snipes argues that young audiences 'can delineate between facts, fiction and naked reality', adding: 'The violence in the movie don't compare in no way, form or fashion to the violence that happens here in the streets. I've seen people get killed right in front of me.'

His next role, in Spike Lee's contro-versial *Jungle Fever*, was also written specifically for him. He played the mid-dle-class architect Flipper Purify, who conducts an affair with a white Italian woman (Annabella Sciorra) against the wishes of his community. The actor admits: 'I was petrified. You couldn't find a person more unlike me. Everything I do is aggressive, sponta-neous and emotional. Whereas Flipper Purify is an analytical, nonconfronta-tional character belonging to a yuppie business world I rarely spend time in. Basically, Flipper's a straight line. I'm a jagged edge.'

Nevertheless, Snipes was excellent in a powerful, engrossing drama that

addressed some very pertinent issues with enormous style. The film was a huge critical triumph at Cannes and became an enormous talking point, landing the cover of *Newsweek*. Needless to say, it was another box-office success.

The actor took a supporting role in the affecting drama *The Waterdance*, playing a fast-talking, optimistic para-plegic in the process of losing his wife. The film was written and co-directed by Neil Jimenez, himself a paraplegic, whose insight provided *The Waterdance* with a conviction and dignity missing from most wheelchair dramas. It may now be a cliche to state that Snipes was the best thing in the movie, but his character was by far and away the most complex and interesting – although, to be fair, Eric Stoltz, William Forsythe and Helen Hunt were all superb.

He had another major hit on his hands with *White Men Can't Jump*, a richly entertaining, sharply-written comedy (scripted and directed by Ron Shelton) set in the world of pick-up basketball. Snipes played Sidney Deane, an unscrupulous conman who meets his match when he's cheated by would-be nerd Woody Harrelson. They subse-quently team up to make a formidable duo, betting sports-proud black men that they can't beat Harrelson. Again, Snipes proved to be compulsive view-ing, and his athletic grace was a huge asset to the basketball sequences. The film itself was a surprise success, knock-ing *Basic Instinct* off the top of the charts after only one week, grossing $70 million in less than three months.

Snipes was back at the number one slot half a year later in the action-packed, muscular thriller *Passenger 57*, playing a security expert who happens to be on board a jumbo jet when it is hijacked by an international terrorist (Bruce Payne). It was good to see a thriller of this size with a black man as hero (rather than sidekick), and Snipes gave *Passenger 57* his customary credi-bility and charisma, while showing off his martial arts skills into the bargain.

Next, he played a Treasury agent in the flaccid *Boiling Point*, tracking down conman Dennis Hopper for killing his partner, and then he teamed up with Sean Connery for Philip Kaufman's thriller *Rising Sun*, a politically mild-mannered adaptation of the Michael

*Pretty in pink: Snipes puts his best foot forward - with John Leguizamo and Patrick Swayze - in **To Wong Foo, Thanks For Everything! Julie Newmar***

Crichton bestseller (Snipes was Connery's hot-headed partner, another cop). It was an indication of Snipes' new standing in the film community that he was now starring in pictures not specifically aimed at black audiences, and that he could hold his own against a cinematic giant like Connery. Indeed, Spike Lee complained that he could no longer afford Snipes, who received a polite $200,000 for his role in *Jungle Fever*. For *Sugar Hill*, the story of two brothers who build a drug empire in New York, the actor was paid $2.25 million regardless of whether the film got made or not. It did, but to poor reviews and box-office.

He received $4 million for *Demolition Man*, in which he starred opposite Sylvester Stallone as a ruthless, cackling, psychopathic killer with a peroxide hair-do. A wonderful opportunity for Snipes to show off, the film was better than most Stallone vehicles, and went on to gross over $150 million worldwide.

His fee rose to $5.5 million for *Money Train*, in which he was re-teamed with Woody Harrelson, playing the selfless, responsible foster brother to Harrelson's carefree, irresponsible one. This time they were bickering transit cops for the New York subway who are united in their mutual hatred of their

boss (Robert Blake). The ultimate in buddy-buddy comedy-thrillers, *Money Train* was shamelessly guilty of stealing gags from other movies, but thanks to the irresistible chemistry cooked up by Wesley and Woody (as they were billed), the film worked a treat. However, its violent content, in particular a scene in which a pyromaniac pours gasoline through the window of a ticket booth, caused an uproar when two real-life hoodlums re-enacted the

crime, incinerating the occupant. The British release was subsequently delayed by over two months, tarring the film with a notoriety it really didn't deserve.

For *Drop Zone*, in which he played a disgraced US marshall who pursues a crack team of stunt skydivers, Snipes received $7 million (against 10 per cent of the first-gross dollar), but the movie failed to make much of an impression against the commercial power of *Disclosure* and *The Santa Clause*

*Snipes with Robert De Niro in **The Fan***

(released simultaneously in the USA), dropping off to just $27.7 million after 12 weeks.

Swapping his habitual badge for stockings and mink in *To Wong Foo, Thanks For Everything! Julie Newmar*, Snipes landed one of the most coveted roles of the year, joining Patrick Swayze and John Leguizamo as a trio of urban drag queens stranded in a Midwestern backwater. As in *Demolition Man*, Snipes seemed to be enjoying himself enormously, but the comedy was not a patch on the similarly-themed *The Adventures of Priscilla, Queen of the Desert*. And, in spite of some gorgeous frocks, Wesley was no RuPaul.

He took an unbilled cameo (as James Wheeler, Angela Bassett's mystery man) in *Waiting to Exhale*, a surprise hit, and starred in one segment ('The Boy Who Painted Christ Black') of the three-part HBO movie *America's Dream*, co-produced by Danny Glover, in which he played the ambitious principal of a 'coloured-only' Georgia school who has to wrestle with his conscience over a theologically 'incorrect' depiction of Christ. He then teamed up with Robert De Niro in *The Fan*, playing a baseball superstar who hits a bad patch and then has to contend with a manic admirer. The critics hated it, the public walked, but it was efficient enough, with Snipes returning to the milieu that first got him noticed (baseball, *Major League*).

He was now enjoying a salary of $10 million and was reported to be dating *Sports Illustrated* swimsuit model Roshumba.

FILMOGRAPHY

1986: *Wildcats; Streets of Gold*. 1987: *Critical Condition*. 1989: *Major League*. 1990: *H.E.L.P.* (TV); *Mo' Better Blues; King of New York*. 1991: *New Jack City; Jungle Fever*. 1992: *The Waterdance; White Men Can't Jump; Passenger 57*. 1993: *Boiling Point; Rising Sun; Demolition Man*. 1994: *Sugar Hill; Drop Zone*. 1995: *Money Train; To Wong Foo, Thanks For Everything! Julie Newmar; Waiting to Exhale* (unbilled cameo). 1996: *The Fan; John Henrik Clarke: A Great and Mighty Walk* (executive produced/narrated only); *America's Dream* (TV). 1997: *One Night Stand; Murder at 1600*. 1998: *Blade* (also produced); *US Marshals*.

MIRA SORVINO

Discussing shaving: with Chris Eigeman in Whit Stillman's priceless **Barcelona**

Having graduated from Harvard with an honours degree and produced a documentary on Russian anti-Semitism, Mira Sorvino entered that rarefied arena governed by Geena Davis and Sharon Stone: brains who play bimbos. Geena Davis, who won an Oscar for playing the scatty, batty dog trainer in *The Accidental Tourist*, is a member of Mensa and speaks fluent Swedish. Sharon Stone, who claims she has an IQ of 154, has brought some choice airheads squealing to life – before, that is, playing the calculating Catherine Tramell in *Basic Instinct*.

In Woody Allen's *Mighty Aphrodite*, Mira Sorvino (who also speaks fluent Mandarin) gave birth to the ultimate halfwit, a prostitute and porn star who cannot function beyond her own world of commercial sex. And, on the night of 25 March 1996, Sorvino walked up to the podium at the Dorothy Chandler Pavilion to collect the Oscar for best supporting actress. Exchanging full-frontal kisses with her escort, one Quentin Tarantino, she proceeded to reduce her father to tears by announcing to one billion viewers: 'When you give me this award you honour my father, Paul Sorvino, who has taught me everything I know about acting. I love you very much, dad.'

Yet Paul Sorvino, himself a much-respected actor (in such films as *Cruising, Reds, GoodFellas* and *Nixon*), had gone on record to admit: 'I was very upset when Mira told me she wanted to be an actress. My problem

was not that she wouldn't make it, but that she would.'

Born in 1970 in Tenafly, New Jersey, Mira initially toyed with ballet, appearing in a professional production of *The Nutcracker* at the age of 12. Then, four years later, she attempted to follow in her father's more vocal footsteps. 'I started trying to act professionally when I was 16,' she says. 'I went to acting classes during the school holidays, came in second for a lot of movie roles in my teens, but never got them.'

Instead, she enrolled at Harvard and studied East Asian languages and civilizations, going on to spend eight months teaching English in Beijing, later moving on to Hunan Province and Shanghai. 'I might be in China now, working as a journalist,' she reveals, 'but shortly after I left, Tiananmen Square happened. So that was that.'

As it happens, she kept her hand in with showbusiness, singing in a jazz band in China while she put together a thesis on racial conflict between African students and the local Chinese. She then warmed to her theme of discrimination, producing the anti-Semitism documentary *Freedom to Hate*.

Back in New York, she modelled, waited tables and served as a script reader for Robert De Niro's Tribeca Studios. She also returned to the soul-destroying routine of auditions – with absolutely no luck. 'I was doing so much that I didn't have any focus at all,' she said later. 'And I didn't get a

*As Judy Cum in **Mighty Aphrodite**, the role that won her an Oscar*

single booking the whole year. Nothing. I had become way too intellectual about everything. And also, maybe as a reaction to the divorce [of her parents], I had cut off my own emotional reactability. I made myself very strong and self-sufficient. I was shut off, and I think that was hurting my acting.'

She took drama lessons and accepted a job as third assistant director on the grim, exceedingly low-budget camaraderie shoot-up *Amongst Friends*, calling the actors to set and fetching their doughnuts. She was also involved in the casting process, and suggested to the director, Rob Weiss, that she play the female lead. He had envisioned a diminutive blonde for the part of Laura, a girl emotionally torn between two friends, and Sorvino was not only brunette but six feet tall. Weiss told her definitely not. So, dutifully, she looked elsewhere – but when the movie ran three months over schedule, she had had enough and announced her departure to pursue an acting career. Weiss then offered her the part on the spot, but only on the condition that she stay on as third assistant director. 'My duty was to both jobs,' she insisted. 'But later I thought, "God, what if my performance is terrible because I'm exhausted?"'

She pulled through, revealing a strong, quiet presence (and great legs), and before the film attracted some interest at the Sundance Film Festival she was already cast as a Spanish siren in Whit Stillman's *Barcelona*. 'We were lucky there,' Stillman admits, impressed by the actress's Castilian accent. Instantly adapting to the director's deadpan style of humour, Sorvino acted as a perfect foil to the film's star, Chris Eigeman, as she attempts to comprehend his bedbound lecture on the art of shaving.

Then there was the female lead in the questionable *NY Cop*, with Chad McQueen and Andreas Katsulas, and the role of Rob Morrow's long-suffering Jewish wife in Robert Redford's superb *Quiz Show*, Oscar nominee for best picture of the year. She joined her father in the all-star TV movie *Parallel Lives* (also featuring Liza Minnelli, Dudley Moore and Gena Rowlands), and then enlisted in the nineteenth-century frolics of the BBC's ambitious

costume drama *The Buccaneers*. The notices were not too kind, but Mira, who played the earthy, half-Brazilian Conchita, notes: 'I had a lot of fun; being in a British costume drama was such a contrast from some grim drug movie set in New York.'

While in England, Sorvino auditioned for Woody Allen, who was holed up at the Dorchester Hotel in London preparing for *Mighty Aphrodite*. He was looking for an actress to play the role of Linda Ash, a friendly hooker and part-time porn star (who, as Judy Cum, featured in such underground classics as *Snatch Happy* and *The Enchanted Pussy*). Sorvino failed the audition, but after Woody caught a screening of *Barcelona*, he called her back for a second reading. 'This time I developed a character,' she recalls, 'and came dressed for the part in a very clinging little black-and-fluorescent-yellow striped dress, with fishnets and plastic shoes with flowers growing out of the toes. There were some raised eyebrows when I asked for Mr Allen's room, I can tell you.'

Once cast, Sorvino was encouraged to improvise by her director, who played a sportswriter who's convinced that the biological mother of his adopted son must be some sort of genius. She isn't: she's Linda Ash. 'I worked on the voice particularly, because Woody had told me she was not only cheap, but stupid. So the voice had to reflect that stupidity. Then I would walk around my neighbourhood in character.'

Endowed with a blonde wig, kitted out in an outrageously kitsch wardrobe and armed with a vocal impression of Mickey Mouse on helium, Sorvino stole the film from her famous co-stars and stormed off with an armful of prizes – including the Oscar, a Golden Globe and trophies from the National Board of Review and the New York Film Critics' Circle.

She had a cameo in Wayne Wang and Paul Auster's priceless, improvised *Blue in the Face* (as a pedestrian who lectures Harvey Keitel on clemency, prompting him to pass over her handbag to a young thief), played the materialistic wife of crack addict Michael Imperioli in the observant, true-life *Sweet Nothing*, received top-billing (for the first time) as a young photographer

As Sharon Cassidy in Ted Demme's Beautiful Girls

who rediscovers her roots in the heart-felt *Tarantella*, was a highlight in the highly personal TV movie *Neil Simon's 'Jake's Women'* (as Alan Alda's first wife), and was largely wasted as Matt Dillon's girlfriend in the trendy ensemble drama *Beautiful Girls*.

She received terrific reviews in the TV movie *Norma Jean & Marilyn* (in which she played Marilyn Monroe), and continued to make the most of her new-found celebrity, starring in the comedy *Romy and Michele's High School Reunion* (with Lisa Kudrow), headlining the sci-fi thriller *Mimic* (with England's Jeremy Northam), joining Hong Kong action star Chow Yun-Fat in *The Replacement Killers*, and re-teaming with Harvey Keitel for the Puerto Rico-set drama *Dreaming of Julia*.

FILMOGRAPHY

1993: *Amongst Friends*; *NY Cop* (UK: *New York Cop*). 1994: *Quiz Show*; *Barcelona*; *Parallel Lives* (TV). 1995: *Mighty Aphrodite*; *Blue in the Face*; *Sweet Nothing*; *Tarantella*. 1996: *Neil Simon's 'Jake's Women'* (TV); *Beautiful Girls*; *Norma Jean & Marilyn* (TV). 1997: *Romy and Michele's High School Reunion*; *The Replacement Killers*; *Mimic*; *Dreaming of Julia*.

JAMES SPADER

James Spader was the king bee at playing hot WASPs. If a white, Anglo-Saxon, Protestant snob was needed, Spader was there. He sneered his way through *Pretty In Pink*, slunk through *Mannequin* and positively leered a hole through *Less Than Zero*. And yet the actor seemed hurt when journalists suggested that he was typecast. 'I never clumped any of those roles together,' he accounted. 'They all seemed to be very different people to me. I thought I was telling different stories and doing different films. But maybe I wasn't.'

He was reluctant to accept the role of the impotent yuppie voyeur in *sex, lies, and videotape* because: 'The humour was very hard to gauge. If it didn't work, I thought the film would be extremely self-indulgent and a huge bore.' As it happens, *sex, lies, and videotape* was one of the most original and daring films of the year, not because of the sex revealed, but because of the psychology it exposed. Spader was outstanding as the self-possessed stranger who ambles into the lives of a dysfunctional couple in Baton Rouge, opening the eyes of the sexually repressed Andie MacDowell. Neither Spader nor MacDowell were known as great actors, which made their triumph all the more sweet. MacDowell was voted best actress by the Los Angeles Film Critics' Circle, and Spader was honoured as best actor at the 1989 Cannes Film Festival, while the film itself walked off with the coveted Palme d'Or.

Luis Mandoki, who directed Spader in *White Palace*, noted that he 'has the ability that great actors have that makes you feel there's a character living inside, that they're not just saying the lines and feeling the feelings of the moment, but there's a whole background, the way we all have'.

The son of an English teacher, James Spader was born on 7 February 1960 in Boston, and grew up on campus at Brooks School in Massachusetts. His mother was also a teacher, and his two older sisters became teachers later. But Jimmy Spader had his sights set on the theatre. Even at the prestigious Phillips Academy in Andover, Spader jettisoned academia in favour of drama and made his stage debut (as a

James Spader

The breakthrough role: James Spader with Andie MacDowell in Steven Soderbergh's mesmerising **sex, lies and videotape**

Chinaman) in a school production of Cole Porter's *Anything Goes*. At 17, he dropped out of school and moved to New York, where he studied acting at the Michael Chekhov Studio and gained practical experience appearing in summer stock. To support himself, he endured a string of menial jobs, including the obligatory waiting on tables and the less routine shovelling of manure. On one occasion, he persuaded a health club to take him on as a yoga instructor, although his sole qualification was the handbook he had picked up at a supermarket. It was there that he met a fellow instructor, Victoria Kheel, whom he befriended, moved in with and married eight years later (they now have two sons).

Another of Spader's humble positions was as janitor at a rehearsal studio in Times Square. One day his employer bent the rules and left the actor's photo on a casting agent's desk. Spader was duly called up to audition for a new film, and in his excitement he brought along his mother. He recalls: 'I was the only one to bring my mom.' But, the next day, 'I flew to Chicago and started shooting. And the day after that I met Tom Cruise.' The movie was Franco Zeffirelli's *Endless Love*, and Spader had nailed the part of Brooke Shields'

brother. Likewise, Tom Cruise was making his movie debut and found himself billed eleven places beneath 'Jimmy' Spader, as he was known in those days. (Actually, Spader had previously appeared as a drunk in a soft porn venture called *Team-Mates*, but we won't talk about that.)

It was then time for TV movies and some high living. Spader was well known for his crazy antics, for drinking too much, frequenting strip venues, breaking the speed limit and driving cross-country for weeks on end in his vintage Porsche. His friend Eric Stoltz recalls: 'We'd take road trips to the [Florida] Keys or up the coast, and he'd insist on having weapons in the trunk. He'd drive like a maniac – fast, with the music blaring – and I was always in fear that we'd be pulled over and some officer would find his crossbows, his lance, his 12-inch knife, his whip ...' But Stoltz is quick to point out that Spader is, 'a very peaceful man. He's the sweetest, nicest man in the world. He's just a tad eccentric.'

Work-wise, Spader and Stoltz had good roles in the TV movie *A Killer in the Family*, as the sons of Robert Mitchum, and were then re-teamed in Sean S. Cunningham's tepid thriller *The New Kids*, with Spader as head

slimeball. He had the lead as a preppie Romeo in *Tuff Turf*, but the film was dated and unconvincing, and he had even less luck in the TV outing *Starcrossed*, as a guy in love with a beautiful alien. He was reduced to fifth billing in his next film, but at least it was a hit. The movie was John Hughes' *Pretty in Pink*, and Spader marvelled at the writer-producer's 'incredible memory – visual, audio, emotional – of his own high school years'. Spader was at his smarmy best as the snobbish friend of Andrew McCarthy (who looks down on McCarthy's liaison with poor girl Molly Ringwald), and the offers started flowing.

Next, he was in *Mannequin*, in which he portrayed the sleazy vice-president of a department store, and volunteered: 'It was like some medieval torture sitting through that film.' In *Baby Boom*, he played Diane Keaton's assistant, a yuppie who is 'hungry, young and fresh out of some training programme. I move in for the kill and take over her job.' Then he was in the critically lambasted film version of Bret Easton Ellis's cult novel *Less Than Zero*, in which he played 'someone who's into selling drugs and pimping and who handles it like a businessman'. As it happened, he was perfect in the role.

*Spader as Egyptologist Dr Daniel Jackson (with the late Viveca Lindfors) in the smash hit **Stargate***

*The Iceman killeth: Spader in **2 days in the Valley***

He took a cut in billing in Oliver Stone's *Wall Street*, as a workaholic yuppie who takes to insider trading, but Spader says: 'I would have played a coffee filter in that movie. I really have got such respect for Oliver Stone.' Then, in *Jack's Back*, he was a dedicated doctor suspected of serial murder, and was sorely miscast.

Salvation arrived with the role of Graham in *sex, lies, and videotape*, and Spader was in demand. Meanwhile, he had portrayed a yuppie bore in the London-set *The Rachel Papers* (as Ione Skye's stuffy boyfriend), and played the yuppie, drippy victim of Rob Lowe in Curtis Hanson's stylish thriller *Bad Influence*, in which he is videoed *in flagrante delicto* by Lowe. During production, his wife gave birth to their first child, Sebastian.

He was another yuppie in *White Palace*, who falls for Susan Sarandon's working-class waitress, but it was hard to believe in their mutual attraction. He then played an upper-class employee of the Justice Department at odds with social climber John Cusack – but the outcome was predictable.

In *True Colors*, Cusack was campaigning for Congress, and in the melodramatic *Storyville*, Spader took over the task, although his political chances are marred when he is videotaped (*in flagrante delicto* again) in the jacuzzi with Charlotte Lewis. Students of Spader's career would be forgiven for suspecting a recurring pattern. He was then back in the world of politics in the canny satire *Bob Roberts*, in which he was a newsreader covering the campaign of Tim Robbins' two-faced senator (with Susan Sarandon as co-presenter).

Next, he changed tack dramatically, playing a low-life drifter caught in a scam engineered by Charles Durning and Joel Grey, in the static caper *The Music of Chance*, adapted from the novel by Paul Auster. Unfortunately, Spader got an attack of the gestures and just seemed unable to control himself in his most mannered performance to date. He then played a young hunk looking for Ms Right in the dark, steamy romance *Dream Lover*, and joined Jack Nicholson and Michelle Pfeiffer in Mike Nichols' lycanthropic *Wolf*, a stylish hit. After that, he starred opposite Kurt Russell in the $50 million sci-fi fantasy *Stargate* – as a maverick Egyptologist who is molecularly transported to another world. It was an enjoyable enough lark, with some remarkable special effects and terrific action sequences, although Spader is level-headed enough to dismiss it as 'dumb fun. I mean, let's be honest,' he reasons, 'no one's going to burn too many brain cells over this movie – except for trying to figure out the damn plot.'

Stargate was an unexpected success at the box-office, pushing Spader up the Hollywood ladder several rungs. His new celebrity enabled him to land top-billing in David Cronenberg's *Crash* – supported by Holly Hunter and Rosanna Arquette – a film exploring the sexual thrill of car accidents. But when it was presented with a 'special award' at the 1996 Cannes Film Festival (for its 'originality, audacity and daring'), it did so under a hail of verbal disapproval.

Spader then joined the ensemble cast of John Herzfeld's witty, compelling black comedy *2 days in the Valley*, and proved extremely effective as Lee Woods, a cold-blooded assassin. As it happens, Herzfeld allowed the actor to choose any character he wanted from the script. 'Every character was an important piece of the puzzle,' Spader noted, 'but Lee was the only role that I felt was appropriate for me. Lee is in the business of finality – he's fascinated by the expiration of time as it relates to life.' He then starred in Sidney Lumet's medical drama *Critical Care*, with Kyra Sedgwick, Helen Mirren, Anne Bancroft and Albert Brooks in support.

FILMOGRAPHY

1978: *Team-Mates*. 1981: *Endless Love*. 1983: *Cocaine: One Man's Seduction* (TV); *A Killer in the Family* (TV). 1984: *Family Secrets* (TV). 1985: *The New Kids; Tuff Turf; Starcrossed* (TV). 1986: *Pretty in Pink*. 1987: *Mannequin; Baby Boom; Less Than Zero; Wall Street*. 1988: *Jack's Back*. 1989: *sex, lies, and videotape; The Rachel Papers*. 1990: *Bad Influence; White Palace*. 1991: *True Colors*. 1992: *Storyville; Bob Roberts*. 1993: *The Music of Chance; Dream Lover*. 1994: *Wolf; Stargate*. 1995: *Keys to Tulsa; Driftwood*. 1996: *Crash; 2 days in the Valley; Keys to Tulsa*. 1997: *Critical Care*. 1998: *Curtain Call*.

ERIC STOLTZ

*Eric Stoltz as radio operator Danny Daly in **Memphis Belle**, directed by Michael Caton-Jones*

Eric Stoltz defies categorization – you don't quite know where he'll pop up next.

Take 1989. As the year started, Stoltz was on Broadway playing George Webb in Thornton Wilder's *Our Town*, for which he was nominated for a Tony award. Then, over the next four months he appeared in three films released in the USA. In January he was seen in a supporting role in *Manifesto*, a Yugoslav sex romp directed by Dusan Makavejev. Looking positively out of place, he played a love-struck postal clerk opposite such British faces as Alfred Molina, Simon Callow and Lindsay Duncan. In February he starred as the semi-human, half-insect son of Jeff Goldblum in *The Fly II*, a grisly, slick horror film. By way of explanation, the actor illuminated: 'These parts are very hard to find. I was attracted to the fact that my character gradually becomes an insect. I prepared for the role by watching a lot of TV specials, like *Life on Earth* and *National Geographic*.' Two months after that he appeared in a very small role (19th-billed) – as Vahlere, 'the Key Master' – in Cameron Crowe's *Say Anything*. This declaration of modesty was no doubt a favour to Crowe, who scripted the actor's very first screen character, 'Stoner Bud' in *Fast Times at Ridgemont High*.

An ambidextrous, vegetarian, piano-playing Episcopalian, Stoltz admits that he 'thrives on insecurity', which may account for his unusual career choices. Born in American Samoa (in the South Pacific) on 30 September 1961, the son of music teachers, Stoltz's upbringing was as unorthodox as everything else in his life. After Samoa the family moved to Paris, then London, then New York, before finally settling in Santa Barbara when Eric was eight.

Today, Stoltz is probably best known for anything but his face. Bearing a slight resemblance to Michael J. Fox, the actor spent five weeks playing Marty McFly in the first *Back to the Future* film – before director Robert Zemeckis fired him. Rumour has it that Steven Spielberg, the film's executive producer, thought Stoltz 'too intense' while, for the record, Zemeckis charitably declared: 'I found myself with a very good actor playing the wrong part.'

Stoltz, who explained that he wanted to act because it was 'a chance to reinvent myself', made his name under a ton of make-up as Rocky Dennis in *Mask*, Peter Bogdanovich's moving, true-life drama made the same year as *Back to the Future*. Starring Cher as a tough and tender biker who lavished love on her disfigured son, the film featured an unrecognizable Stoltz, who – like John Hurt in *The Elephant Man* – managed to convey a humanity and warmth under several layers of latex (which took four hours a day to apply). *Mask* was well-received, and won Cher the best actress prize at the 1985 Cannes Film Festival.

Then there was *The Fly II*, which recruited its own following. *Film Review* magazine described it as 'a damn fine sequel ... Stoltz and ... Daphne Zuniga ... exude an affecting innocence that underscores the cutting edge of this *Beauty and the Beast* remake.' Stoltz himself saw it as the story of a 'character's quest for humanity. It's the heightened version of what everyone is on earth for: looking for a reason to justify our existence.' The film also subjected the actor to another bout of make-up hell. As his character changed, so the latex increased, eventu-

Stoltz as the paraplegic writer Joel
Garcia in **The Waterdance**

Is it safe? Stoltz as safecracker Zed in
Killing Zoe

operator. And – in a departure daring
even by Stoltz' standards – he played
the romantic English poet Percy
Shelley in Ivan Passer's artificial
Haunted Summer.

Perhaps more significantly, Stoltz
starred in one of the better teen
romances around in the mid-1980s,
Some Kind of Wonderful, produced and
scripted by John Hughes. As Keith
Nelson, the all-American high school
student besotted with Lea Thompson
and loved by Mary Stuart Masterson,
Stoltz made a surprisingly agreeable
leading man in the Michael J. Fox
mould. On the surface, this may not
seem too hard a task to accomplish, but
as Nelson was actually a morally repre-
hensible snob, it took some acting skill
on Stoltz's part to keep him even
vaguely likeable and interesting.

The actor's other primary – and far
more dramatic – role was the paraplegic writer Joel Garcia in *The
Waterdance*. Written and co-directed by
Neal Jimenez, himself a paraplegic, the
film was a cliche-free drama that genuinely got under the skin of what it
must be like to be sexually impotent
and dependent on others. Playing his
role with a resigned, intellectual
detachment, Stoltz wasn't so much
aiming for the tear ducts as asking for a
little understanding.

Beside his eclectic film work, the
actor has done his share of television
(*St Elsewhere* and various TV movies),
theatre (including a stint at the
Edinburgh Festival), and is a talented
musician, having studied both the
trumpet and piano from an early age.
He also doubled as a production assistant on *Say Anything*, a job which
entailed cuing extras and fetching the
coffee. 'I figure if I do it at least once a
year, it will keep me humble,' he
explained. He didn't, and three years
later he was producing his own movie,
Bodies, Rest and Motion, starring his girlfriend Bridget Fonda. Described by the
film's director, Michael Steinberg, as 'an
existential romantic comedy', it starred
Fonda as the sensitive type who has an
affair with a dope-smoking house-
painter (Stoltz on excellent form) after
her boyfriend (Tim Roth) has ditched
her.

The actor then took a cameo (as an
aggressive mime artist) in *Singles*, also
with Ms Fonda, and starred in the TV

ally leading to a daily five-hour cosmetic ordeal.

In spite of his intellectual reasoning,
The Fly II would seem to have been a
strange choice for an actor who takes
his craft so seriously (less generous critics denounced the film as production-
line schlock). But then it's hard to predict what Stoltz will do next.
Thumbing through his credits, you
don't so much find a career as what
looks like a pot-pourri of dramatic
accidents.

In Amy Heckerling's seminal teen
comedy *Fast Times at Ridgemont High*
(scripted by Cameron Crowe from his
own book), the actor played Sean
Penn's surfer crony; in Franklin J.
Schaffner's ill-fated Crusades epic,
Lionheart, he played a 12th-century
knight; and in David Puttnam's gung-
ho *Memphis Belle*, he was Danny Daly,
the idealistic, Irish-American radio

movie *The Heart of Justice*, playing an
entirely unlikeable, cocksure reporter
covering the murder of a pulp novelist
(Dennis Hopper). The latter was a slick,
deftly-written 'Hitchcockian' thriller
with a good cast (Vincent Price,
Jennifer Connelly, Dermot Mulroney),
but it failed to live up to the promise
of its first half. He was also well-sup-
ported in *Naked in New York*, the story
of an aspiring young playwright
(Stoltz) who has to sacrifice love (to
Mary-Louise Parker) for career. This
time his co-stars included Timothy
Dalton, Tony Curtis, Ralph Macchio,
Kathleen Turner and, briefly, Whoopi
Goldberg.

He continued to churn out an
unreasonable number of credits, regardless of the size of his part. Notably, he
played an American safe cracker in
Paris in the Quentin Tarantino-pro-
duced *Killing Zoe*, a gripping, violent

*Stoltz with Illeana Douglas in Allison Anders's **Grace of My Heart***

heist thriller; he was caught between fiancée Meg Tilly and best friend Craig Sheffer in the observant, frequently very funny *Sleep With Me* (which he produced); he was Lance, the drug supplier in *Pulp Fiction*; the repressed John Brooke, tutor and suitor of Trini Alvarado, in *Little Women*; the Scottish Alan McDonald, the ill-fated best friend of Liam Neeson's *Rob Roy*; and the idealistic songwriter Howard Caszatt in *Grace Of My Heart*. He was his familiar, cheery self as Wes Taylor, a vice cop longing for more exciting work, in John Herzfeld's quirky black comedy *2 days in the Valley*; and then he played a documentary filmmaker at the mercy of a 1,000 pound snake in the all-Hollywood action-thriller *Anaconda*. Refusing to be button-holed as a conventional leading man, Stoltz described *Anaconda* as 'a phallic adventure story'.

Of course, it's impossible to button-hole Eric Stoltz. But isn't that the way he likes it? His answer is disappointing: 'I have absolutely no agenda. I have no career plan. I take what comes my way and what I think is interesting.'

FILMOGRAPHY

1981: *The Violation of Sara McDavid* (TV). 1982: *Paper Dolls* (TV); *Fast Times at Ridgemont High* (UK: *Fast Times*). 1983: *Thursday's Child* (TV); *A Killer In the Family* (TV). 1984: *Running Hot*; *Surf II*; *The Wild Life*. 1985: *Code Name: Emerald*; *Mask*; *The New Kids*. 1987: *Lionheart*; *Sister, Sister*; *Some Kind of Wonderful*. 1988: *Haunted Summer*; *Manifesto*. 1989: *The Fly II*; *Say Anything*. 1990: *Memphis Belle*. 1991: *The Widow Clare*; *A Woman at War* (TV). 1992: *The Waterdance*; *Singles*. 1993: *Bodies, Rest and Motion*; *The Heart of Justice* (TV); *Foreign Affairs* (TV); *Money*. 1994: *Naked in New York*; *Killing Zoe*; *Sleep With Me*; *Pulp Fiction*; *Roommates* (TV); *God's Army*; *Little Women*. 1995: *Fluke*; *Rob Roy*; *Kicking and Screaming*; *Keys to Tulsa*. 1996: *Inside*; *Grace Of My Heart*; *2 days in the Valley*; *Don't Look Back*; *Jerry Maguire* (cameo); *Perfect Crimes* (TV). 1997: *Anaconda*; *Inside* (TV); *Mr Jealousy*. 1998: *Highball*.

SHARON STONE

Not since Bo Derek emerged from the ocean in *10* had an actress so steamed up the pages of the tabloid press. Hers was not overnight stardom, but the velocity with which Sharon Stone hurtled from unknown to superstar was so potent that the effect was as giddying. The fuss was all about *Basic Instinct*.

The most controversial movie of 1992, *Basic Instinct* starred Michael Douglas as a San Francisco cop obsessed by a wealthy, bisexual novelist who may or may not be a serial killer. The story was nothing new (the device had been employed to some success in *Sea of Love*), but the film's patent homophobia had provided priceless publicity while the film was still in production. After its scriptwriter Joe Eszterhas toned down the lesbian content, the film's notoriety dramatically changed direction. Audiences were now talking about *that* sequence in the police station. You know, the scene in which Sharon Stone is called in for questioning after the horrific murder of her lover.

Douglas: 'Did you ever engage in sadomasochistic activity?'

Stone: 'Exactly what did you have in mind, Mr Correli?'

Douglas: 'Did you ever tie him up?'

Stone: 'No. Johnny liked to use his hands too much. I like hands and fingers.'

She then uncrosses her legs to reveal an obvious lack of underwear, the first official female flash in Hollywood history.

Much has been written about how this came about. Michael Douglas has been quoted as saying that the film's director, Paul Verhoeven, tricked her, promising that her privacy would be concealed in shadow. In direct contrast, it was later revealed that Sharon removed her own 'crotch pad', saying: 'Let's stop pretending. I'm nude, we all know. Let's get on with it.' Later still, she refused to talk about it, terminating the subject with a cool, 'I don't want to talk about it. It's all resolved now –

*As Stone looked in 1990, in Paul Verhoeven's **Total Recall***

*Romance with an ice-pick: Sharon Stone in Verhoeven's **Basic Instinct***

'Of the things I've done that have been made, no performance knocked me out more than what she did in *Basic Instinct*.' He subsequently fashioned his screenplay of *Sliver* especially for her.

Sharon Stone was born 10 March 1958, in the small town of Meadville, Pennsylvania, the daughter of a dye-maker (her father) and a bookkeeper. One of four children, she was a diabet-ic, bright kid and moved through school at the rate of knots before tak-ing college courses at the precocious age of 15. Winning a writing scholar-ship to Edinboro State College, she excelled at science but took acting classes instead. After graduation, and encouraged by her track record of win-ning local beauty contests, she turned to modelling and was signed up by the prestigious Eileen Ford agency in New York. She also studied with an acting coach and appeared on TV endorsing the virtues of Charlie perfume, Clairol hair products and Diet Coke. At an extras' casting call for Woody Allen's *Stardust Memories*, she so impressed the director that he cast her in a small role

water under the bridge.'

Whatever *really* happened, the scene was the talk of Hollywood and helped launch Sharon Stone into the forefront of Tinseltown's most visible ladies. British tabloids announced that she was to be paid $30 million for the sequel – a 'fact' which was discussed with some gravity in more serious newspapers. It was also disclosed that she was to get $7 million for her next film, *Sliver*, which was to make her the highest-paid actress in the world. And this in the same year that Whoopi Goldberg, Julia Roberts and Sigourney Weaver were bestowed with the same distinc-tion. A more realistic figure is that Ms Stone will receive $2.5 million for *Sliver*, plus a hefty chunk of the gross profits. That's still an impressive pay cheque. And she may well get $7 mil-lion for *Basic Instinct 2* (although nobody's talking about a sequel at the moment).

In a remarkably short period of time, Sharon Stone had become the

embodiment of men's primal fantasies. *Basic Instinct* became a talking point in newspaper articles, at dinner parties, at the bus stop ... Such was the power of the actress's performance as the hot-cold-hot siren Catherine Tramell that many seemed to forget she had actually *acted* the part. It must be said that the star was equally adept at playing giggly damsels-in-distress as well as predatory man-eaters. And let it not be forgotten that she had already made 17 movies and boasted an IQ of 154.

Still, Paul Verhoeven did find her 'very seducing. She does a lot of flirt-ing. One of the most threatening things about her is that she can change in a split second. I have hated her with all my heart, and I have loved her, too. She can be very clever with words and hit you with them right in front of the whole crew. And if you're not careful, she can be the victor.'

Joe Eszterhas, whose characters have been acted out by Glenn Close, Debra Winger and Jessica Lange, volunteered:

*Sharon in **The Quick and the Dead**, which she also produced*

in the film's opening scene – as the goddess who launches him a kiss from a passing train.

She had a good part in Wes Craven's Amish-esque thriller *Deadly Blessing*, starring Ernest Borgnine, and was a regular on the short-lived TV series *Bay City Blues*, about a minor-

*With Robert De Niro in **Casino**, the role that won her a Golden Globe and an Oscar nomination*

league baseball team (she played Patrick Cassidy's patient wife, Cathy St Marie). Next, she won the only good reviews going for her comic performance as a talentless starlet in *Irreconcilable Differences* with Ryan O'Neal, joined Tom Skerritt and Robert Culp in the TV movie *Calendar Girl Murders* (a thriller set in the porn industry), and she had the leading female role in the awful *The Vegas Strip Wars*, also for TV. However, the latter was vaguely notable for being Rock Hudson's last TV movie and, more importantly, for introducing Sharon to her future husband, the producer Michael Greenburg.

She followed this with the TV mini-series *War and Remembrance*, from Herman Wouk's novel, and *King Solomon's Mines*, the first of two movies exploiting H. Rider Haggard stories to cash in (unsuccessfully) on the *Indiana Jones* phenomenon. Still, the actress made a feisty heroine and seemed to have more fun than co-star Richard Chamberlain. The sequel, *Allan Quatermain and the Lost City of Gold*, was filmed simultaneously but wasn't released until 1987, the worst year of Sharon Stone's life. Never mind the film's failure – and the lack of artistic

merit evinced by *Police Academy 4* and the crime drama *Cold Steel* – 1987 was a devastating year for personal reasons. For a start, Sharon's marriage came apart at the seams.

'Michael was a real straight guy and we had a sort of a squeaky-clean little relationship,' she confided. 'I wanted us to be the perfect couple. I wanted to be the perfect wife. Maybe I thought being perfect, being better, was being different from whom I actually was. It has taken me a long time to understand that who I am is enough.'

In December of that year, her school boyfriend Richard Baker Jr, a successful pilot, was found dead at the wheel of his car. He had shot himself in the head.

Career-wise, there was little to offer Sharon Stone solace. She continued steaming up a series of mediocre films that invariably passed by in the night. She was the bad guy's innocent wife in *Action Jackson*; a love-struck American in the British home counties in the TV movie *Tears in the Rain*; Steven Seagal's wife in *Above the Law* (one of her worst performances); the Spanish *Blood and Sand* (which, Ms Stone declares, 'was more like *Drunken Spanish Keystone Cops Make a Bad C Movie*'), and the preachy, talky, virtually unheard of *Personal Choice*, in which she played the girlfriend of Robert Foxworth. *Personal Choice* was bad even by Sharon Stone standards, but then Martin Sheen, Christian Slater and F. Murray Abraham were also in it, so who's to

blame?

Salvation arrived with Paul Verhoeven's thrilling sci-fi extravaganza, *Total Recall*, with Stone slyly cast as Arnold Schwarzenegger's treacherous wife. The scene in which she and Arnie fight to the finish was a classic, capped by the muscleman blowing her away with the words: 'Consider that a divorce.' Ironically, Ms Stone almost turned the part down, saying: 'I've done every stupid action movie I'm gonna do. No thank you.' However, when she found out Verhoeven was directing, she changed her mind. The film was a colossal hit.

Unfortunately, more dross followed, namely the thriller *Scissors*, with Steve Railsback, and the romantic comedy *He Said, She Said*, starring Kevin Bacon. She was better in John Frankenheimer's *Year of the Gun*, as a tough frontline photographer, but the film was arguably Frankenheimer's worst.

When Ellen Barkin, Geena Davis, Michelle Pfeiffer and Julia Roberts turned down the central role of the temptress in *Basic Instinct*, Stone got a crack at the whip. She knew the part was big news, but she never dreamed they would give it to her, and refused to read the script at first. When she relented, she was stunned by the meatiness of the part and was determined to make it hers. She dressed up in the sexiest gear she could find and gave Verhoeven a run for his money. After five nights of screen tests, his defences were crumbling. Carolco Pictures wanted a name actress for the role, but they also knew it would be difficult to find a star who was willing to meet the sexual demands of the script. 'Some very successful actors make very safe choices,' Stone conceded. 'That's not my way. To those actresses who didn't think that was their way, I'm incredibly indebted.'

Before *Basic Instinct* transformed Sharon Stone into a household name, she appeared in two more films: the low-budget thriller *Where Sleeping Dogs Lie*, in which she played an agent who encourages her client to write a novel about a serial killer (sound familiar?), and *Diary of a Hitman*, as the offensive sister of Sherilyn Fenn.

Once *Basic Instinct* opened, the scripts came pouring in. She was reportedly offered the female lead in *In the Line of Fire*, opposite Clint Eastwood, but turned it down because she considered Eastwood a has-been. Of course, this was before Eastwood's *Unforgiven* bagged four Oscars, including a couple for best film and director. Anyway, the part went to Rene Russo. Instead, Sharon took the starring role in *Sliver*, the story of a literary editor who, through an obsessive love affair, becomes involved in the murky world of voyeurism and murder. Tom Berenger and William Baldwin co-starred.

According to the film's producer,

*The new look: Sharon Stone in her bravest performance to date, as death row inmate Cindy Liggett in Bruce Beresford's **Last Dance***

Robert Evans: 'It's the first time that the subject matter, the taboo fantasy of voyeurism, has been explored without being exploitative. It's everyone's fantasy, but it's dealt with [here] in an intellectual way.' Not that anybody noticed.

She then took a cameo in *The Last Action Hero* and starred opposite Richard Gere in Mark Rydell's *Intersection*, an American remake of the

Michel Piccoli/Romy Schneider French film *The Things of Life*. Playing against type, Stone portrayed the spurned wife of architect Gere, the latter falling for the more glamorous Lolita Davidovich. However, while the picture tried hard to capture the nuance of the original, it was so suffocated in lush production design and Hollywood gloss that the characters had a hard time gaining a credible foothold.

Meanwhile, Sharon Stone's private life picked up considerably. For a while she dated the popular country singer Dwight Yoakim (but, according to press reports, he ditched her after the 'shock' of *Basic Instinct*), and she was then seen escorting Chris Peters, son of movie mogul Jon Peters and actress Lesley Ann Warren. Later, she confessed, 'I'm too old for him,' and she announced her engagement to *Sliver* producer William J. McDonald on national TV. Unfortunately, the liaison was short-lived. Then, following her brief dalliance with second assistant director Bob Wagner – guess? – millionaire Michel Benasra reportedly lavished a spectacular engagement ring on her. However, the actress felt that Benasra was in love with the star and not the real Sharon Stone, so she moved on to Barry Josephson, president of production for Columbia Pictures.

Then, after playing an enigmatic mannequin to Sylvester Stallone's explosives expert in the over-produced romantic thriller *The Specialist* (for which she was paid $5 million), she turned producer on *The Quick and the Dead*, Sam Raimi's rip-roaring, spectacular and raunchy spoof of the spaghetti western. Again, she was paid $5 million, cutting a natty figure as a mysterious gunslinger who rides into Redemption, Arizona, to settle a few debts, particularly with Gene Hackman.

When Jodie Foster dropped out of Ridley Scott's real-life thriller *Crisis in the Hot Zone*, Stone was offered the role, but she passed to play the good-time girl Ginger McKenna in Martin Scorsese's *Casino*. A return to the stylistic, Mob-themed epics that made Scorsese so beloved by his fans, *Casino* was a laborious, gratuitously violent re-hash of *GoodFellas*. Still, a lot of critics seemed to love it, in particular embrac-

ing Stone's naked, shrill performance as the screaming, coke-snorting gold-digger. Indeed, her portrayal snagged her an Oscar nomination and a Golden Globe for best actress in a drama.

She demanded another $5 million to play the predatory schoolteacher Nicole Horner in the thriller *Diabolique* (another Hollywood remake of a French original), but walked when Warner Brothers refused to pay her fee (they offered her $4 million). But *Casino* was already creating ripples of excitement, and when Morgan Creek took over the producing chores on *Diabolique*, they wooed Stone back with $6 million (which says a lot for inflation). More fools they. The film was a spectacular dud, although Stone was always fun to watch – in a campy sort of way. When co-star Isabelle Adjani wakes up on the bathroom floor from a faint and croaks, 'I'm alive,' Stone snaps back, 'No, you're dead, this is Heaven and I'm the Virgin Mary,' with all the brio of Bette Davis in her heyday.

She also received $6 million for *Last Dance*, in which she played a piece of white trash on Death Row, convicted for the murder of a teenager schoolmate and her boyfriend when she was just 19. The film suffered badly from comparisons to *Dead Man Walking*, but Stone actually gave a better, braver performance here than in *Casino*.

She was then announced as the star of another remake, playing the title role of the gun-toting *Gloria*, previously portrayed by Gena Rowlands in 1980. She was also due to star in Peter Chelsom's *Freak The Mighty*, the story of a single working mother whose disabled son forms an extraordinary relationship with a boy who has a rare accelerated growth disorder.

FILMOGRAPHY

1980: *Stardust Memories*. 1981: *Deadly Blessing; Les uns et les autres* (a.k.a. *Bolero*). 1984: *Irreconcilable Differences; Calendar Girl Murders* (released on video in 1993 as *Victimised*); *The Vegas Strip Wars* (TV). 1985: *King Solomon's Mines*. 1987: *Allan Quatermain and the Lost City of Gold* (filmed in '85); *Police Academy 4: Citizens On Patrol*. 1988: *Cold Steel; Action Jackson; Tears in the Rain* (TV); *Above the Law* (UK: *Nico*). 1989: *Blood and Sand; Personal Choice* (later *Beyond the Stars*). 1990: *Total*

Recall. 1991: *Scissors; Year of the Gun; He Said, She Said.* 1992: *Basic Instinct; Where Sleeping Dogs Lie; Diary of a Hitman.* 1993: *Sliver; Last Action Hero* (cameo); *Intersection.* 1994: *The Specialist.* 1995: *The Quick and the Dead; Casino; Last Dance.* 1996: *Diabolique.* 1997: *Freak The Mighty.* 1998: *Sphere; Gloria.*

KIEFER SUTHERLAND

movies. He was 22.

Having established himself as a film star, Sutherland made the headlines via his stormy romance and engagement to Julia Roberts, which ended abruptly when she found out about his five-month affair with a stripper, Amanda Rice. Although their wedding was set for 14 June, the invitations mailed and the whole thing due to cost a bank-breaking $500,000, the actress cancelled

Kiefer William Frederick Dempsey George Rufus Sutherland, in London, England, on 18 December 1966, the twin brother of Rachel. His first name was taken from the writer Warren David Kiefer, who scripted Donald's debut movie, *Castle of the Living Dead*. At four, Kiefer was transported to California, where his father's film career was flourishing, and where his mother was exercising her 1960s radicalism.

Satanic Sutherland: Kiefer and his canines in Joel Schumacher's **The Lost Boys**

When Kiefer Sutherland was good, he was a wimp. But when he was bad, he was great. It was almost as if he were two actors. When he was projecting a gentleness and vulnerability, his features would discernibly soften, but the end product was frequently bland. However, when Sutherland sank his teeth into a villainous role, his lizard-like eyes would shine, his jaw would slip at a threatening angle, and his 5'10" frame would seem to stretch over six foot. He was mesmerizing.

After a mundane start as the gauche young lead in Daniel Petrie's prosaic *The Bay Boy*, the actor made a sizeable impression playing demonic bad guys in two hit movies: *Stand By Me* and *The Lost Boys*. In the former, he was the bully who antagonized River Phoenix, and in the latter was a sadistic biker and part-time vampire. Then came the starring role in the Robert Redford-produced *Promised Land* and a giddy attack of workaholism. In five-and-a-half years he clocked up 16

the event with four days' notice. She ran off to Ireland with Jason Patric (Kiefer's co-star from *The Lost Boys*); he was (reportedly) left in tears. Since then the actor's career has slowed down to a walking pace, stymied by the cancellation of *Renegades* (working title), a big-budget action adventure in which he was to have starred with Ms Roberts.

But if Kiefer Sutherland was not a model fiancé, he was a good actor. Michael J. Fox opined: 'He has a bizarre kind of energy all his own. He can get inside a role and mesh it with his own strange character.' While Meg Ryan reflected: 'Two seconds before the camera rolls, the guy just clicks in faster than anyone I've ever seen. And he's one of the best-listening actors I've worked with.'

Kiefer Sutherland was born with greasepaint in his veins. The son of Donald Sutherland, the film star, and Shirley Douglas, a successful stage actress, Kiefer wanted to act for as long as he could remember. He was born

She was blacklisted by the US government, Donald protested against the Vietnam War with Jane Fonda, and they separated – for ever.

Kiefer says: 'I remember it all very well. I remember marching with my mother in Watts at the time of the Watts riots – I was five years old. I remember we had everybody at our house – Black Panthers, a rehab group for people coming out of San Quentin, bikers from all over ...' He remembers his father less clearly, who was busy starring in such movies as *M*A*S*H*, *Klute* and *Don't Look Now*.

In 1974, Kiefer moved again, to Canada, his parents' country of birth, and there sampled a number of private boarding schools. At 16, three years away from graduation, he dropped out and took the train from Ottawa to Toronto. There, he shacked up with a musician friend for eight months, until he won the title role in *The Bay Boy* and could afford to live on his own (previously, he had a walk-on in *Max*

*Kiefer as Jeff Harriman in George Sluizer's **The Vanishing***

Dugan Returns, starring his father, Marsha Mason and Matthew Broderick). By international standards, *The Bay Boy* was nothing to write home about, but Kiefer won a Canadian Genie award nomination for his role as a teenager growing up in Nova Scotia in 1937.

In New York, he attended a number of auditions, but kept on returning to Canada to get work. Finally, he landed a lucrative jeans advertisement ('it paid $3,500') which enabled him to buy a car and drive to California. He was 17. In Los Angeles, he slept in his vehicle for six weeks to save money, before getting a role in the TV series *Amazing Stories*. His episode, *The Mission*, was directed by Steven Spielberg and was part of an omnibus released theatrically overseas (which also included segments starring Kevin Costner and Mary Stuart Masterson). He had a small role in *At Close Range*, with Sean Penn and Ms Masterson, and he almost won the young lead in John Boorman's jungle

epic *The Emerald Forest* – but the director found him too 'strange and quirky'. Then came his scene-stealing turn in Rob Reiner's *Stand By Me*, and the starring role – as an 'elective mute' – in an OK TV movie, *Trapped in Silence*, with Marsha Mason. He was also in an exploitative TV film called *The Brotherhood of Justice*, playing the good guy opposite Keanu Reeve's teenage vigilante.

He returned to Canada to star in *Crazy Moon*, as an alienated boyfriend of a deaf salesgirl, and then portrayed a psychotic murderer in *The Killing Time*, a low-budget thriller which co-starred and was produced by a Puerto Rican-born beauty, Camelia Kath, 12 years Kiefer's senior. This age gap, and the fact that she had an 11-year-old daughter from a previous marriage (her husband had killed himself in a game of Russian roulette), failed to deter Kiefer's interest, and the couple ended up living together before tying the knot.

In the mean time, Kiefer made a glamorous villain in Joel Schumacher's *The Lost Boys*, starred opposite Meg Ryan in the slow-moving but well-intentioned romantic drama *Promised Land* and had another flashy supporting role – as a cocaine-sniffing yuppie – in *Bright Lights, Big City*, starring Michael J. Fox. In *1969* he was dropping out and dropping acid with Robert Downey Jr, and then buckled on his guns to join Emilio Estevez, Lou Diamond Phillips and Charlie Sheen in *Young Guns*, a stylish, ultra-violent western. He was then re-teamed with Phillips in Jack Sholder's slick thriller *Renegades*, playing an undercover cop in search of a mysterious Indian lance. Frankly, he looked entirely too young to play an officer of the law, moustache or no moustache, but he was none the less surprisingly charismatic.

He was another cop in *Flashback*, escorting a 1960s fugitive (Dennis Hopper), and then he travelled to England to play a homicidal GI in *Chicago Joe and the Showgirl* (Emily Lloyd was the chirpy showgirl). The less said about *Chicago Joe* the better, except that it marked the break-up of Kiefer's short-lived marriage (which had produced one child, Sarah Jude – named after Kiefer's friend, Sarah Jessica Parker). Romance flourished again when he starred opposite Julia Roberts in Joel Schumacher's *Flatliners*, an MTV look at death, in which he, she and Kevin Bacon played medical students experimenting with mortality. Kiefer's father himself had 'died', briefly, of acute meningitis, which lent a chilling air of authenticity to Kiefer's performance. The film was a hit, and with Kiefer top-billed, it should have been an enormous career stepping stone. It wasn't.

There was a sequel, *Young Guns II*, followed by an all-star flop, *Article 99* (with Sutherland playing a materialistic medic), and then a walk-on in David Lynch's abysmal *Twin Peaks: Fire Walk With Me* (although, as an FBI agent, Kiefer managed to convey exactly the right deadpan tone).

For his next film, Rob Reiner's *A Few Good Men*, he was reduced to fifth-billing, cast as a villainous marine. With his hair shaved, his ears protuberant and his mouth fixed into a permanent sneer, he had never looked more like

White trash department: Kiefer threatens Sally Field in John Schlesinger's disappointing Eye For an Eye

his father. And, like his father, he was beginning to excel in evil cameos.

However, he did have the lead in *The Vanishing*, an American remake of the Dutch movie of the same name. Kiefer played Jeff, a man who becomes obsessed with his girlfriend (Sandra Bullock) after she suddenly and mysteriously disappears. 'To create an obsession on this level, you have to go through parts of your life,' Kiefer reasoned. 'You really have to figure out what you've ever been obsessed about, though I don't think I've ever been as obsessed as this character.' Jeff Bridges co-starred, and the film was a flop.

After that, he returned to Brat Pack mode (joining Charlie Sheen and Chris O'Donnell), playing Athos in Disney's shamelessly irreverent but quite enjoyable *The Three Musketeers*, a sizeable hit. However, this brief success was spoiled by a drink-drive conviction that earned the actor 36 months' probation, a $1,000 fine and 10 days' community service.

Then his career took another direction. 'There comes a point where actors have a really specific idea of what we think is interesting,' he explained. 'And after 30 films, I think that many actors want to put more of a stamp on their work and have a little more control over what is used of their work.' That control manifested itself in the actor taking over the directorial reins on *Last Light*, a cable movie in which he played a convict on Death

Row who strikes up a remarkable friendship with a prison guard played by Forest Whitaker, who had just made his own directing debut on the cable movie *Strapped*. Both films received unanimous praise from the critics, opening new doors for both performers.

In the interim, Sutherland continued as actor-for-hire, lending some weight to the brainless action-comedy *The Cowboy Way* (in which he and Woody Harrelson played cowpokes in New York City), a film that happened to pave the way for a new obsession: competing on the Southwest rodeo circuit.

More recently, he played a snarling, homicidal rapist who torments the mother (Sally Field) of his last victim in John Schlesinger's glossy, superficial thriller *Eye For an Eye*; took a supporting role (as a snarling champion of the Ku Klux Klan) in Joel Schumacher's *A Time to Kill*, which also starred his father, and then returned to directing with *Truth or Consequences N.M.*.

FILMOGRAPHY

1983: *Max Dugan Returns*. 1984: *The Bay Boy*. 1985: *Amazing Stories* (episode: 'The Mission') (TV; 1987 UK release); *At Close Range*. 1986: *Stand By Me*; *Trapped in Silence* (TV); *The Brotherhood of Justice* (TV); *Crazy Moon*. 1987: *The Killing Time*; *The Lost Boys*; *Promised Land*. 1988: *Bright Lights, Big City*; *1969*; *Young Guns*. 1989: *Renegades*. 1990: *Flashback*; *The*

Nutcracker Prince (voice only); *Chicago Joe and the Showgirl*; *Flatliners*; *Young Guns II – Blaze of Glory*. 1992: *Article 99*; *Twin Peaks: Fire Walk With Me*; *A Few Good Men*. 1993: *The Vanishing*; *The Three Musketeers*; *Last Light* (also directed). 1994: *The Cowboy Way*; *Teresa's Tattoo* (uncredited cameo). 1995: *Freeway*. 1996: *Eye For an Eye*; *A Time to Kill*; *Frankie the Fly*; *Truth or Consequences N.M.* (also directed). 1997: *Dark City*; *The Royal Way*.

PATRICK SWAYZE

Patrick Swayze is the oldest star in this book, but his role as C. Thomas Howell and Rob Lowe's brother in *The Outsiders* sanctions his position as the patriarch of the Brat Pack. And he continued to appear in Brat Pack movies – *Grandview, USA*, again with Howell; *Red Dawn*, with Howell, Lea Thompson, Charlie Sheen and Jennifer Grey, and *Youngblood*, with Rob Lowe.

Today, Swayze is a star with a faithful following of female fans (and a few male ones) who is struggling hard to shed his image as hunk of the month. In an attempt verging on desperation, he begged director Roland Joffe for the role of the tormented doctor working the slums of Calcutta in *City of Joy*.

Joffe, who had previously worked with such heavy-hitters as Paul Newman, Robert De Niro, John Malkovich and Jeremy Irons, was won over by Swayze's enthusiasm for the part: 'What I heard in his voice was not a man saying, "I want a leading role," or "I want to work with this calibre of director or this calibre of film." I heard a man saying, "I want to feel what this man feels – *I* feel it. I don't know if I'm a good actor, but I can feel it." In my meeting with Roland, my emotions went all the way across the board,' Swayze admits. 'Because this man stimulated so many things in me. I cried, things came out of me ... I came as close to begging for a role as I ever have in my life.'

Patrick Swayze's appeal – besides his sculptured good looks and athletic grace – is his straight-from-the-heart sincerity. He is unafraid to expose his emotions or to make a fool of himself. And that combination of sensitivity and catlike machismo is one hell of a cocktail. Swayze is the sort of dream lover who can feed your fantasies, whisper

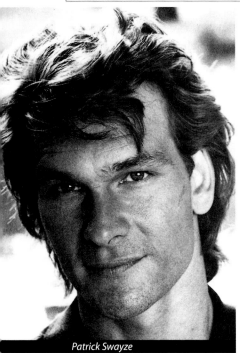

Patrick Swayze

sweet nothings *and* protect your home from outsize thugs. Some have accused the star of being unable to act, but even if that's the case, *boy* can he move.

'He's definitely got that *macho* edge,' volunteers his wife, actress Lisa Niemi. 'And he's good-looking, with that nice body. He fills that department very fine, thank you. But within all that masculinity, he's sensitive, caring, adores children. There's communication and understanding ... all the attributes you associate with females. That's a pretty nifty combination. Aren't many men who have that.'

Swayze, who was branded the local sissy at school, is perfectly honest about his trigger-alarm sensitivity. 'I'm a sap for kittens and puppies,' he admits, 'and there's nothing – *nothing* – that beats a new-born foal. Just picking up that little thing in your arms ... it brings tears to your eyes.'

Swayze's tears are now the stuff of legend. On an American chat show (hosted by Barbara Walters) he broke down while reminiscing about his late father – but he has the guts to be unashamed. He certainly boasts the credentials of a man with limitless self-confidence. Glancing quickly at his achievements, it would be understandable to assume that whatever Swayze turned his hand to came easily to him.

But the man has worked hard for his life. Besides being a popular movie star, Swayze earned the nickname 'Troph' at school for the number of sports trophies he won. He's also an accomplished carpenter and furniture maker, a successful singer (his single 'She's Like the Wind' made the American top ten and got to number 17 in the British charts), a proficient archer, businessman, martial artist, playwright, stuntman, music publisher and composer. In his spare time he rides his Harley Davidson, paints, tends his farm, raises Egyptian-Arabian thoroughbreds, skates and studies Zen Buddhism. He has also toyed with est, *I Ching*, transcendental medicine, t'ai chi and collects spiritual crystals. And, of course, he regularly trips the light fantastic.

If nothing else, Patrick Swayze was going to succeed as a dancer. Born on 18 August 1952, in Houston, Texas, the son of a chemical plant engineer, he was dancing at the age of four under the instruction of his mother, Patsy, a Houston dance instructor and later a movie choreographer (*Urban Cowboy*). From the first grade, Swayze was bullied for his love of ballet and eventually gave it up for gymnastics, diving, football, track and swimming, and became the school's star athlete. He won track and football scholarships to various universities, but attempted to make the national gymnastics squad instead. His short athletic career left its scars. To this

day he still has a slight limp, and at one time or another he has broken his ribs, ankle, foot and all of his fingers – his left knee alone has been shattered five times.

He made his showbusiness debut as Prince Charming in a year-long tour of 'Disney on Parade', returning to Houston for a brief stint as a professional ice skater. Finally, he moved to New York to pursue a career as a dancer. Then, as a member of the Feld Ballet, his ill-fated knee suffered a staph infection: amputation was a serious consideration. 'My life was screwed at that moment,' he remembers. 'I thought it was all over. That's when I started smoking.'

He also started acting, won a small role on Broadway in *Goodbye Charlie*, with Joel Grey, and then combined his acting, dancing and singing skills playing one of the lead roles in *Grease*. His performance was well received, and Hollywood took note.

He had a smallish part (eighth-billed, as Ace) in the forgettable *Skatetown USA*, starring Scott Baio, but won one unforgettable review. Kevin Thomas, writing in *The Los Angeles Times*, enthused: 'Not since Valentino did his tango in *The Four Horsemen of the Apocalypse* has there been such a confident display of male sexuality. Patrick Swayze sizzles.' It was a perspicacious premonition. Meanwhile, the nascent Valentino segued into a series

*Swayze as Sam Wheat, the sentimental spook, in **Ghost** - with Demi Moore*

*In the role of a lifetime: Swayze slums it in Calcutta in Roland Joffe's **City of Joy***

of The Drifters, The Shirelles, et al., *Dirty Dancing* transcended its cliches thanks to the chemistry discharged by Swayze (as a swaggering dance instructor) and Jennifer Grey as his up-market holiday love. Ever since the film was released there has been talk of a sequel but, as yet, none has materialized.

The success of *Dirty Dancing*, unlike such hits as, say, *ET* or *Star Wars*, could be directly attributed to its human ingredient. And nobody could deny that Swayze's hulking, muscular presence was the star attraction. Baring his (sensational) physique at the drop of a dance step, the actor strutted his stuff predominantly in tight jeans and a black cutaway T-shirt and became the most sought-after hunk in Hollywood. At least, for a while.

On one occasion, 300 fans discovered the whereabouts of his hotel and came looking for him. 'Just as they smashed down my door, I dived off the balcony from the third floor, into the shallow end of a swimming pool,' he recounts. 'I tell you, it was a narrow escape. Mass hysteria isn't a pretty sight, especially when it's your body they all want.'

However, the sex symbol's fidelity to his wife is well known. The couple met when Lisa, then 15, took dance lessons at Patsy Swayze's studio, when Patrick was 20. The story goes that he pinched her bottom, she protested, and they married three years later. In 1987, the year he made *Dirty Dancing*, they made their first movie together, *Steel Dawn*. A futuristic variation on the western classic, *Shane*, it was a box-office bomb, while Swayze's subsequent action films did little better.

The actor's main body of fans were women, and the violence displayed in *RoadHouse* and *Next of Kin* were definitely not for them. Swayze's attraction, whether he likes it or not, is as a romantic leading man. The hard-core action fans who queued up to watch Schwarzenegger, Eastwood, Stallone and Willis were just not interested.

If Patrick Swayze was to hold on to his stardom he had to act quick. When director Jerry Zucker was casting the male lead in *Ghost*, he famously announced: 'Over my dead body will Patrick Swayze get this role.'

In Hollywood, the word on *Ghost* was hot, and grown actors found them-

of TV movies before being signed up by Francis Coppola to play the oldest, and most heroic, of *The Outsiders*. As Darrel Curtis, the aggressive, volatile, but ultimately caring brother who fought for C. Thomas Howell's honour, Swayze gave a decent display of male sexuality. Besides flexing his (considerable) deltoids and throwing his fists, he also got to reveal his emotional side and – yes – he cried on screen.

The cult following that built around *The Outsiders* failed to launch Swayze's career immediately, and for a while he was the sole cast member who failed to land a subsequent hit vehicle. He *was* top-billed in the controversial *Red Dawn* (about the Russian and Cuban occupation of the USA), but this was an ensemble picture in which the cast were largely swamped by the hardware and rural scenery. Fame, to some degree, arrived when Swayze landed the part of Orry Main in the 1985 TV

mini-series *North and South*. A 12-part blockbuster about the American Civil War, the series starred Swayze as an officer and a gentleman on the side of the Confederates. It was followed by a sequel, *North and South Book II*, which co-starred, among others, James Stewart, Olivia De Havilland and Jean Simmons. 'That blew the lid of things,' the star recalls. 'It was the first time I ever experienced getting off a plane and being mauled by thousands of people.'

But that was just the beginning. In 1987 he speared the lead role in a modest independent film with the somewhat provocative title of *Dirty Dancing*. Laughed off the screen by the critics, the picture, with its simple blend of romance, 1960s music and good-looking bodies, hit all the right buttons and became one of the most visible hits of the year. Basically a *Romeo and Juliet* story set to the sound

selves begging for a piece of the action. Whoopi Goldberg fought for her role as the medium, Oda Mae Brown, and Swayze certainly pleaded for his part, the film's romantic title role. Swayze reports: 'I called Jerry and said, "Just give me a chance. I'll come in and I'll read for you. I'll do the whole script right in your office. The only thing I won't do is screen-test for it."' He got the part.

Only Demi Moore, it seemed – as Swayze's mourning wife – took the film in her stride. In fact, she almost turned it down. But, for her at least, Patrick Swayze was the perfect choice. 'I think Patrick did a good job,' she says. 'His haircut was bad news – he looks great when it's messy – but he's a sweet guy. He brought a tremendous sensitivity and a vulnerability to the role. Also, his physical attributes – and I don't mean his body – his talent to move served the film well. I don't know if there is anybody else who could have done it. It's difficult acting opposite special effects. He had to do the whole fight scene alone.'

In spite of Jerry Zucker's initial misgivings and some unkind reviews, Swayze won the role of Sam Wheat and made it his own. His heartfelt chant of 'ditto' became a national catch phrase, the film grossed $217.6 million in the USA (and $517.6 million globally) and was nominated for an Oscar as best picture. Swayze had won back his legion of fans.

He took a chance with his next film, *Point Break*, playing a supporting role to Keanu Reeves, and a villain at that. But then Swayze is not into career moves. For him, playing the gung-ho bank robber in *Point Break* allowed him to secure his licence as a skydiver and to surf some of the biggest waves in the world. Ironically, the film was a hit, and Swayze captured some of the best reviews of his career.

He then sought to extend his range even more and played the emotionally tormented doctor, Max Lowe, in *City of Joy*, Roland Joffe's harrowing look at a leper colony in Calcutta. However, the film failed to generate much box-office heat – but then, to be fair, even if Arnold Schwarzenegger had played an Indian slum medic, his fans would have thought twice about turning up. Still, Swayze was better than expected, and

his innate likeability was a welcome contrast to the horror of the ghetto. He says now: 'I would have done *City of Joy* for nothing. I would have paid *them* to do the movie.' It was a brave project for everybody concerned, and was incredibly arduous. Besides the inhumane filming conditions, the set was fire-bombed twice, and two assistant directors were accused of murder. Under the circumstances, the final product is a miracle and a masterpiece. And Patrick Swayze was right – *City of Joy* is the best film of his career.

But it was pretty much downhill from there. His next two films, *Father Hood* and *Tall Tale*, both plopped onto video in Britain, although the latter (in which Swayze enjoyed himself as Pecos Bill) found some critical defenders. He then fought hard for – and won – the role of Vida Boheme, a gay transvestite in the cross-dressing comedy, *To Wong Foo, Thanks For Everything! Julie Newmar.* 'As soon as this came up, I had to do this role,' he declared. 'But I couldn't get seen because they had this picture of me that I was seriously, terribly macho and heterosexual. But I could not have had a hope of pulling off Miss Vida if I had a problem with my masculinity or who I was as a person. But as soon as I read the script I realized she's a fantasy; she's the dream of a human being. However, I kept coming back to the realization that I had to make her real, I had to stop playing a man in a dress and see if I could create a woman.'

Unfortunately, in spite of Swayze's touching performance, the film suffered comparisons to the infinitely funnier, classier *The Adventures of Priscilla, Queen of the Desert*, which, as fate would have it, preceded it by a year. Then, with *Three Wishes*, he returned to the coziness of *Ghost*, playing a philanthropic hobo who dispenses such wisdom as 'Everything contains its opposite.' Regretfully, and in spite of the stubble, Swayze was unable to disguise his clean-cut persona, and the film's heavy dose of emotional molasses dragged it into the mire.

Philosophically, he says: 'I've now gotten to a place – having lived through the craziness of the career – where I'm not interested in the fame. I just want to see if I can be the best actor I can possibly be.'

FILMOGRAPHY

1979: *Skatetown USA*. 1980: *The Comeback Kid* (TV). 1981: *Return of the Rebels* (TV). 1982: *The Renegades* (TV). 1983: *The Outsiders; The New Season* (TV); *Uncommon Valor*. 1984: *Pigs vs Freaks/Off Sides* (TV); *Grandview USA; Red Dawn*. 1986: *Call to Action; Youngblood*. 1987: *In Love and War* (TV); *Dirty Dancing; Steel Dawn; Tiger Warsaw*. 1988: *RoadHouse*. 1989: *Next of Kin*. 1990: *Ghost*. 1991: *Point Break*. 1992: *The Player* (deleted from the final print); *City of Joy*. 1993: *Father Hood; Tall Tale*. 1995: *To Wong Foo, Thanks For Everything! Julie Newmar; Three Wishes*. 1997: *Letters From a Killer*.

Miracle worker: Patrick Swayze in the glutinous **Three Wishes**

UMA THURMAN

*Uma Thurman as the radiant Rose in Terry Gilliam's extraordinary **The Adventures of Baron Munchausen***

She has the face of a Renaissance beauty and the smouldering sex appeal of something out of a pre-war Berlin nightclub. She can convey a virginal innocence and yet exude a sexual mystery that promises forbidden fruit. Although she is American, there is nothing remotely apple pie about her – more a hint of oranges in Grand Marnier. Even her name – Uma Karuna Thurman – conjures up an exotic taste. And just to give her a further bohemian, rebellious edge, for a time she was married to that most anarchic of English actors, Gary Oldman.

John Malkovich, who played her seducer in *Dangerous Liaisons*, when she was just 18, offered: 'Normally, I can't talk to a girl under 30 for more than five minutes. They have nothing to say. But Uma's amazing for a girl her age. She's bright, instinctive, generous. She's a natural.'

Uma Thurman was born not in Stockholm or Copenhagen, but in Boston, Massachusetts – on 29 April 1970. Her father was a college professor, her mother a psychotherapist. But dig a little deeper, and the exotica

begins to surface. Her mother was born in Sweden, and her father taught comparative literature and Buddhism at Columbia University. To this day, Uma has a keen interest in the religion. When she was 12, her father moved the family to India, where they returned on several occasions. It was an appropriate change of locale for a girl named after a Hindu deity.

At 15, she moved to New York determined to make it as an actress. After attending the Professional Children's School, she spent time as a dishwasher and fashion model before landing her first film, *Kiss Daddy Good Night*. However, she is not overly proud of this movie, a nondescript, melodramatic thriller, but she did have the starring role – as a crazy vamp who lured men back to her New York apartment, drugged them and then robbed them.

Her second outing, *Johnny Be Good*, was no better. A scatological, obnoxious comedy about a high school quarterback unscrupulously courted by various colleges, the picture was an embarrassment for all concerned. Ms Thurman was the jock's steady girlfriend, with Anthony Michael Hall and Robert Downey Jr top-billed.

The good news arrived with Terry Gilliam's ambitious, epic fantasy, *The Adventures of Baron Munchausen*. Although a much-publicized financial

disaster (some reports put the film's budget as high as $52 million), it provided the actress with a scene-stealing turn. As Venus, the goddess of love, she emerged virtually naked from a giant clam (after Botticelli), and transfixed the eponymous Baron on the spot. 'She looks as though she floated down from the clouds,' Gilliam marvelled. 'When I learned that "Uma" was a goddess in Hindu mythology, I thought, "This is too good to be true." Because of this beautiful, long creature, I changed the concept of Venus and created a sense of someone who almost doesn't know her own power.'

In *Dangerous Liaisons* she played the virginal, angelic Cecile de Volanges, who is seduced by Malkovich's conniving Vicomte de Valmont. Cast for her fresh-faced innocence and European beauty, Uma clocked up another endorsement for scene-stealing. The director, Stephen Frears, was overawed: 'She's shocking in the scene where Valmont tricks her, deflowers her – she sobs and suffers. And ten minutes later she's jubilant. Shocking!' The production was a critical triumph, waltzing off with a trio of Oscars.

Bouncing from one English director to the next, Uma turned up in modern dress in John Boorman's sumptuous, bizarre comedy, *Where the Heart Is*. The story of a Capraesque family attempt-

*Uma as June and Fred Ward as Henry Miller in Phillip Kaufman's controversial **Henry & June***

ing to come to terms with the 1990s, the film was killed off by the critics, robbing the public of one of the year's more unusual, most charming cinematic treats.

More visible was Philip Kaufman's controversial screen adaptation of Anais Nin's diaries, *Henry & June*. Uma Thurman co-starred as June, the wife of the notorious novelist Henry Miller

pulse-accelerating, corkscrew thriller, with Thurman the wacko patient (who is 'ambivalent about her phallic fantasies') of psychiatrist Richard Gere. Nobody was who they seemed, and until the film ran into one U-turn too many, the audience was kept entirely out of breath.

In Bruce Robinson's intelligent, atmospheric thriller, *Jennifer Eight*, she

her cosmetic body shields and launching herself into the scene. McNaughton was understanding: 'You don't think of her as being so young,' he allowed, 'except once in a while she'll say something, and you go, "Ummaaa! Oh, yeah, that's right, you're 21."'

She then landed the biggest role of her career – playing Sissy, the central character in Gus Van Sant Jr's long-awaited *Even Cowgirls Get the Blues*. Based on Tom Robbins' cult novel, the film followed the exploits of Sissy and friends on a 'beauty ranch', where the cowgirls rebel and attempt to take the place over. Madonna was originally signed to star, but on a project-ditching binge vacated the part for Uma. The cast also included Keanu Reeves, Rain Phoenix (sister of River), Angie Dickinson and John Hurt – and it was a phenomenal embarrassment.

With Robert De Niro in John McNaughton's *Mad Dog and Glory*

(Fred Ward), and for the first time she played a character of depth, complexity and intelligence – and sexual awareness. The film itself leaned towards artistic pretension, but was beautifully acted and particularly well photographed. However, *Henry & June* will be best remembered for stirring up so much dust that the Motion Picture Association of America was forced to invent a new certificate – the NC-17 – so as to distinguish between 'art' and pornography.

She was back in costume – as a spirited, tomboyish Maid Marian – in John Irvin's lively TV movie *Robin Hood* (released theatrically outside the USA), and she then joined husband Gary Oldman in *Dylan*, a TV movie about the tragic Welsh bard, Dylan Thomas (she was Caitlin, the poet's wife). Next, she portrayed Kim Basinger's duplicitous sister in *Final Analysis*. This was a high-concept,

played a rather sweet, wise-beyond-her-years blind girl terrorized by an unseen attacker. Although treading on territory already explored in *Wait Until Dark* and *Blind Terror*, the film introduced a fresh reality to the condition of blindness, with Thurman bringing both acuity and vulnerability to her character.

In John McNaughton's seductive, edgy *Mad Dog and Glory* she played Glory, a gorgeous bartender who is presented to a shy forensic detective, Mad Dog (Robert De Niro), as a gift from loan shark Bill Murray. Reports from the set indicated that all was not well, as Thurman found the nude scenes particularly daunting. One source revealed that the crew was kept waiting six hours as she summoned up the courage to disrobe. This came as a surprise to some, as the actress had revealed her splendid form to the camera on several previous occasions. Eventually she came round, tearing off

Thank God, then, for *Pulp Fiction*. Cast as Mia Wallace, the junkie wife of a black gangster (Ving Rhames), Thurman stole a number of scenes from a picture that was visibly impinging itself on the pop culture of its time. Staring disdainfully from the film's poster (sporting a dark Cleopatra haircut), she became as synonymous with the movie as its male star, John Travolta. And, when Thurman and Travolta danced the Twist to Chuck Berry's 'You Never Can Tell', you could hear the chemistry bubble. 'I wondered about doing the movie at first because the script was so shocking,' Thurman owned up. 'I haven't made a habit of doing films with a lot of violence. But I let Quentin talk me into it, and I believe in him.' And, of course, there was Travolta. 'That dance scene was so camp, I couldn't pass it up. To dance with Travolta was like being able to do a western with John Wayne; you'd happily play some barroom slut just for the opportunity.'

Pulp Fiction not only trotted off with the Palme d'Or at Cannes and the best film award from the Los Angeles Film Critics' Association and the National Board of Review, it grossed $107.9 million in the USA – not bad for a feature that cost $8 million. And Thurman received her first Oscar nomination, becoming even more famous when the ceremony's host, David Letterman, made a running joke out of linking her name with Oprah

That famous **Pulp Fiction** look

Ethan Hawke in the sci-fi drama *Gattaca* and joined Liam Neeson and Geoffrey Rush in Bille August's adaptation of *Victor Hugo's Les Misérables*.

Romantically, she was linked with Robert De Niro and Mick Jagger, but was most consistently seen in the company of Timothy Hutton, her co-star from *Beautiful Girls*.

FILMOGRAPHY

1987: *Kiss Daddy Good Night*. 1988: *Johnny Be Good; The Adventures of Baron Munchausen; Dangerous Liaisons*. 1990: *Where the Heart Is; Henry & June*. 1991: *Robin Hood* (TV; UK: theatrical release); *Dylan* (TV). 1992: *Final Analysis; Jennifer Eight*. 1993: *Mad Dog and Glory*. 1994: *Even Cowgirls Get the Blues; Pulp Fiction*. 1995: *A Month By the Lake*. 1996: *Beautiful Girls; The Truth About Cats & Dogs*. 1997: *Gattaca; Batman and Robin*. 1998: *Victor Hugo's Les Misérables; The Avengers*.

Not smart enough for Ben Chaplin? Uma Thurman in the delightful **The Truth About Cats and Dogs**

Winfrey's – in front of a worldwide audience of one billion.

Next, she replaced Robin Wright in Ted Demme's male-bonding saga *Beautiful Girls*, as the exotic cat among the testosteronal pigeons, and was even more delightful in *The Truth About Cats & Dogs*, in which she played Noelle Slusarsky, a ditzy beauty who, as a favour to Janeane Garofalo's insecure talk show host, stands in for her on a date with English dreamboat Ben Chaplin. Fresh, charming and very, very funny, the film was a hit.

After frequent announcements in the press that she was due to play Marlene Dietrich in a film biography, Thurman did one better: she snatched the coveted role of Poison Ivy, the villainess in *Batman and Robin*, from such hot contenders as Demi Moore and Julia Roberts. She also teamed up with

V

JEAN-CLAUDE VAN DAMME

Whatever Jean-Claude Van Damme may tell you to the contrary, he is not a great actor. He has charm, he has grace and he has wonderful pectorals. But he is no actor. And, let's be honest, his innumerable fans don't check out his videos to watch Chekhov. What the name Van Damme promises is action, some spectacular martial arts and a great body. For some years insiders have been predicting that the Belgian karate champion was the next big thing, and to listen to him talk one might agree. 'I fight long,' he says in his makeshift English. 'I'm so flexible, smooth, a dancer, and I never get hurt. Look at my face – it's smooth, like a baby. Feel my arms. I don't believe in luck. By having a conviction, everything is possible if you train or push yourself.' He has, however (he swears), 'got a talent to act. No matter what any newspaper says about me, I am one of the most sensitive human beings on earth – and I know it.' Maybe his fans do, too. After

all, he has been known to receive 3,000 fan letters a month.

The second of two children, he was born Jean-Claude Van Varenberg on 18 October 1960 in Brussels, Belgium, where his accountant father and mother ran a florists shop. A weak and skinny child, hampered by poor sight and thick spectacles, he was taken to a karate class by his father and instantly fell in love with the art. 'I was nine years old,' he recalls. 'My father encouraged me to take karate because I was very small for my age and got picked on a lot. He is a very, very smart man. He knew that karate was not only physical – it also builds your mental attitude. But I also wanted to get bigger and stronger, so I started training with weights.' A few years later he added ballet class to his curriculum and was offered a position in a Paris company, but turned the offer down. His vision was to become a movie star – in Hollywood. 'It was a dream as a young child to do movies. I love movies. You can escape. Belgium is a beautiful but sad country. It is always raining and grey.'

After earning a black belt in *shotokan* (a Japanese style of karate), he

turned professional, and less than a year later won the European Professional Karate Association's middleweight championship. At 17, he quit school and established his own gymnasium – which he christened the California Gym – and which was soon bringing in $15,000 a month: 'I was making tons of money, but I was not happy.' He was still not a movie star.

He won the part of a villain in the French film *Rue Barbar*, but walked out after an argument with the director. Instead, he did some modelling in Hong Kong, sold his gym and, in 1981, headed for Hollywood. Behind him, he left his Venezuelan wife, Maria Rodriguez, seven years his senior. Unable to speak English, let alone American, Jean-Claude slept in a rented car for his first week in the USA, worked as a bouncer, carpet layer and limo driver, and eventually began teaching martial arts. Meanwhile, he distributed his photo all over the place, occasionally winning work as a film extra. The only problem was that he didn't have a work permit, nor permission to stay in the country for longer than six months (necessitating twice-yearly trips across the Mexican border). He also changed his name: 'It's better in America, Van Damme, than Van Varenberg: Van Dammage, Hot Damme, Damme Good, Wham Bamme Thank You Van Damme ...'

In 1985, he landed his first notable film part, playing the Russian villain Ivan in the unbelievably bad martial arts dud *No Retreat, No Surrender* – in which he gets beaten up by a kid (Kurt McKinney – *who?*). The same year he married his second wife, Cynthia Derderian, and left her after twelve months. 'I was very young,' he explains. 'I was full of passion and impatience. It was difficult to follow me – you have to be very strong physically to follow me. I can go day and night.' But he had already set his sights on his true love – the bodybuilder and fitness model Gladys Portugues. 'I was in love with her since I was 19,' he confessed. 'For many years I saw her picture in the magazines.' When he discovered that she was doing a photo shoot in Mexico for *Muscle and Fitness*, he telephoned the publisher and offered to pay his own way to appear alongside her. The publisher agreed, and the rest is legend.

*Jean-Claude in action in **Lionheart***

The Belgian relates: 'I see Gladys and I say, "I've come for you. I'm Van Damme, the karate champion." A month later, she moves from New York to LA to be with me.' Shortly after that they were married, and today have two children, Kristopher and Bianca ('I do everything fast. Life is so short.').

His stay on the Arnold Schwarzenegger blockbuster *Predator* was certainly short, as he was replaced mid-shoot by Kevin Peter Hall. Van Damme was cast in the title role, but felt constricted by his costume ('The director, John McTiernan, asked me to run and jump and make all these animalistic moves. Then they put me in a body cast. It was disgusting. They covered everything, even my face, with mud. It was very dangerous; I knew I was going to break something.'). Still, he got his SAG card, and Kevin Peter Hall was provided with a new outfit (incidentally, Hall is 7'2", compared to Van Damme's 5'10").

When he bumped into the movie mogul Menahem Golan in a Beverly Hills restaurant, the bulgin' Belgian threw a karate kick over Golan's head, and was invited to the tycoon's office the following day. There, he waited six hours before he was seen, and then performed a spectacular split while suspended between two chairs. According to Van Damme: 'Menahem stepped back. He said, "Bring me *Bloodsport*. You want to be a star? I'm gonna make you a star!"'

In *Bloodsport*, shot in five weeks for less than $2 million, he played the real-life American (!) commando Frank Dux, who was the first Westerner to win an illegal martial arts competition ('the *Kumite*') held every five years in Hong Kong. Van Damme finally got the chance to prove he couldn't act, but his admirable kickboxing skills helped the film to become a popular success, first in France and Asia, later in the USA.

His subsequent films gathered momentum at the box-office, their irresistible blend of bone-snapping violence, effortless plots and balletic karate appealing to a growing legion of fans. He was another Russian villain in *Black Eagle*, also starring Sho Kosugi; he was the hero in the post-apocalyptic *Cyborg*, and in *Kickboxer*, in which he sought to avenge the crippling of his

JC as the robot with a human memory in Roland Emmerich's thrilling **Universal Soldier**

brother, he illustrated his strength by kicking down a tree (Van Damme admits: 'I was really hurt, but I wanted to show something on the camera that was different.'). He was very different as a Royal Canadian Mountie with a strange accent in *Death Warrant*, but was more credible as a soldier of the French Foreign Legion who goes AWOL to avenge his brother's death (at the hands of drug dealers) in LA. He then tried very hard to act in *Double Impact*, playing twin brothers who reluctantly team up to avenge their father's death in Hong Kong (Chad Wagner smiled a lot, Alex Wagner snarled). Still, the Stanislavsky effort paid off, and the film

grossed $128 million worldwide.

For *Universal Soldier*, his best film, he was paid $1.35 million to play a Vietnam corpse resurrected as a robotic soldier-of-fortune. The problem is, the soldier starts remembering the good old days, not least his on-going feud with fellow stiff Dolph Lundgren. The film was actually a terrific action adventure, augmented by some spectacular set pieces, state-of-the-art technology and an agreeable self-mocking humour. Worldwide, it grossed over $100 million.

Next, he was paid $3.5 million to star in *Nowhere to Run*, furnished with a script by the estimable Joe Eszterhas

Van Damme as he appears in Van Damme's **The Quest**

(*Basic Instinct*, *Music Box*) and a leading lady of the calibre of Rosanna Arquette. Unfortunately, it was as dumb as his earlier movies, with the corn as high as an elephant's eye. For the record, Van Damme played a bank robber on the run, who shacks up with a farmer's widow (Arquette), and then fights for her property against an evil land developer (Joss Ackland). Not surprisingly, the film was a box-office disappointment.

Still, the Muscles from Brussels was booked up to the eyeballs with movies, and he next starred in *Hard Target*, under the direction of the controversial Hong Kong filmmaker John Woo. 'Lots of movie stars want Woo now,' the star explained. 'But he wants to do Van Damme. It will be a beautiful action film.' Well, it was stylish trash, but it was pretty gripping, too (Van Damme played a merchant sailor who is used as target practice by a gang of rich sadists).

Then, at the 1993 Cannes Film Festival, the Belgian announced his plans to direct a historical epic called *The Quest*. He pledged: 'I believe it's going to be the *Ben Hur* of martial arts. It has a great philosophical message.' He also announced his engagement to Darcy La Pier, a former Hawaiian beauty queen. She revealed: 'I believe

that our souls are married, that we were made for each other.' They did marry, but Van Damme missed his children so much that he returned to Gladys Portugues and announced divorce proceeding from Darcy. He then changed his mind, returned to Darcy and fathered a third child, Nicholas, by her.

However, his private life was not all wedding bells and divorce papers. He was ordered to pay out $487,500 in compensation to an actor who lost his sight in one eye during a fight scene in *Cyborg*, and he was then sued by a woman who claimed that he forced her to perform fellatio on him and join in a hanky-panky foursome. This lawsuit was settled out of court.

Meanwhile, his salary jumped to $3 million for *Timecop*, his first really big-budget, hand-tailored vehicle, an enjoyable, time-travelling saga with some impressive special effects. It was a good deal better than the moronic, illogical *Street Fighter*, an expensive hostage drama based on the video game, for which Van Damme pocketed $6 million. And in *Sudden Death* he played a washed-up French-Canadian fireman who has lost his will for heroism – until, that is, the Vice-President of the United States is kidnapped by a gang of ruthless terrorists. An enjoyable, fast-

paced yarn, peppered with humour and sadism, the film reunited Van Damme with Peter Hyams, director of *Timecop*.

It was a shame Hyams wasn't on hand for *The Quest*, the 'Ben Hur of martial arts' that Van Damme had promised us. It was more like a botched re-tread of *Bloodsport*, with Van Damme teaming up with Roger Moore for some shenanigans in the Far East. However, he hardly redeemed himself in *Maximum Risk*, a helter-skelter ride of spectacular stunts and explosions, orchestrated by the Hong Kong director Ringo Lam. Then he segued into the thriller *The Colony*, with Mickey Rourke, and in 1996, checked himself into rehab to dry out from a variety of naughty substances.

FILMOGRAPHY

1980: *Monaco Forever*. 1984: *Missing in Action* (extra). 1986: *No Retreat, No Surrender*. 1987: *Predator*; *Bloodsport*. 1988: *Black Eagle*. 1989: *Cyborg*; *Kickboxer*. 1990: *Death Warrant*. 1991: *Lionheart* (a.k.a. *AWOL – Absent Without Leave/Wrong Bet*); *Double Impact*. 1992: *Universal Soldier*. 1993: *Nowhere To Run*; *Hard Target*; *Last Action Hero* (cameo). 1994: *Timecop*; *Street Fighter*. 1995: *Sudden Death*. 1996: *The Quest* (also directed); *Maximum Risk*. 1997: *The Colony*. 1998: *Knock Off*.

W

ROBIN WRIGHT

Although Texan by birth, Robin Wright radiated a beauty of European grace and delicacy, topped by a sheaf of glowing, strawberry-blonde hair and a subtle smattering of freckles. She would be as perfect playing a Thomas Hardy heroine (Bathsheba Everdene, say) as any Dorset-bred graduate of RADA, and she had talent to spare.

After displaying her breath-catching loveliness in *The Princess Bride*, Ms Wright illustrated her acting mettle in the gritty realism of *State of Grace*, playing the strong-willed sister of Irish gangster Gary Oldman. And yet, in spite of her attention-seizing roles, the actress's films were decidedly few and far between. 'Good roles come along only once or twice a year, and if I can't get one of them, I'd rather not work,' she has said. 'It will probably hurt me, or so I hear, but I don't care. If you do a movie you don't really want to do and you sell yourself out, you get old, you burn out your facets.'

Indeed, Robin Wright was fast becoming more famous for the films she refused than for those she accepted. She turned down *Born on the Fourth of July*, *Jurassic Park*, *The Firm*, *Batman Forever*, *Sabrina*, *Beautiful Girls* and *Crisis in the Hot Zone*, the last ending up in a drawer at Twentieth Century Fox.

Robin Wright was born on 8 April 1966, in Dallas, Texas. She and her brother were raised by their mother, a cosmetics sales rep, and when Robin was four, 'We all got into the car and just kept driving till we hit the ocean.' The ocean was the Pacific, and Robin grew up in San Diego, California, becoming a model at the age of 14, working both in Paris and Japan. This, in turn, led to a series of commercials in California which paved the way for acting auditions.

In 1984 she landed a small part in the dramatic TV series *The Yellow Rose*, starring Cybill Shepherd and David Soul, and then made her name playing Kelly Capwell in the daytime soap *Santa Barbara*, for which she was twice nominated for an Emmy.

In 1987 she was just one of hun-

*Robin as the defiant Kathleen Flannery in Phil Joanou's **State of Grace***

dreds of hopefuls who auditioned for the title role in *The Princess Bride*, Rob Reiner's magical, comic romance. Reiner, who has an unerring nose for talent, cast Robin on the spot. 'She is stunningly beautiful,' he asserted. 'Two sentences out of her mouth, and I knew she was the girl I wanted.'

The film, a romping, playful parody of the traditional fairy tale, was one of the year's most enjoyable surprises. Robin Wright was perfect as the demure Buttercup, awaiting rescue from her Prince Charming (a dashing Cary Elwes) before being married to the dastardly Count Rugen (Christopher Guest, on excellent form). Part swashbuckling adventure and part spoof, the film was also a touching love story, appealing to audiences of all ages and persuasions.

At the time, the beauty was living with former *Santa Barbara* co-star Dane Witherspoon, and planned to marry him in April 1988, to be followed by a honeymoon in Africa. Instead, thanks to the success of *The Princess Bride*, she won the starring role in *Loon*, playing a young woman trapped in flashback hell as she moped after erstwhile love Jason Patric. The film was not good, and

resurfaced three years later on video under the title *Denial*.

A year later Robin skewered the female lead in the aggressively male *State of Grace*, the violent story of a gang of Irish-American thugs spreading fear across the streets of New York's Hell's Kitchen. Robin played Kathleen Flannery, childhood sweetheart of local boy Sean Penn, who was returning to the neighbourhood after an absence of some years. In amongst the bloodshed, Robin lent the film considerable nobility as the strong-willed Irishwoman who is not afraid to speak her mind. 'The female lead in these types of films is often a thankless role,' explained the movie's director Phil Joanou. 'It was one of the things on which we worked very hard. Kathleen is the character who ultimately stands up to the men, head to head, with self-respect and dignity.'

Although Robin Wright had met Sean Penn before, the couple warmed to each after during the shooting, and after the film's completion they started seeing a lot of each other. She was offered the role of Maid Marian in Hollywood's $50 million *Robin Hood: Prince of Thieves*, opposite Kevin

Costner, but had to back out when she became pregnant with Sean's baby. Mary Elizabeth Mastrantonio stepped into her part at the eleventh hour, and the film became the second highest-grossing sensation of 1991.

Following the birth of her daughter, Dylan Frances, the actress got her own back on Hollywood by winning the best role of her career. Annette Bening was signed to play the headstrong Tara Maguire in *The Playboys*, when she walked – followed by a lawsuit. Robin Wright stepped in and was promptly joined by Albert Finney and Aidan Quinn. Set in an isolated Irish village in 1957, *The Playboys* was a drama of considerable emotional strength and beauty, capped by a stirring performance from Ms Wright. As a single mother who refuses to name the father of her child, she was passionate, seductive and sympathetic in an exceptionally demanding role. She also obliterated all traces of her American

accent, opening up enormous avenues for her seemingly endless talent.

In Barry Levinson's long-awaited *Toys*, she played Gwen, Robin Williams' romantic interest, and revealed a hitherto unrealized sense of the wacky. In the memorable scene in which she and Williams fall for each other in a factory canteen, she displayed a delightful spontaneity – pulling faces, laughing and acting as both a romantic and comic foil to Williams. Although her role was a supporting one (she received fourth billing), it is obvious why she took it, as it let her shed her image as 'an intense beauty'. It also allowed her to use her own Texas accent on screen, which must have come as a shock to most of her fans. And even if the film was a critical and commercial bomb, Wright's zany, comic and delightful performance still left a sweet taste in the mouth.

Then came *Forrest Gump*. As the dream girl of America's favourite dun-

derhead (Tom Hanks), the actress was required to undergo a number of transformations as the film weaved its way across the years, via Vietnam and Watergate and on into the era of AIDS. She was Jenny, the beauty who grows up with Gump in the Deep South, strays and then returns to her No. 1 fan. The film, staggering off with six Oscars (including a statuette for best picture), was phenomenally successful, becoming the third highest-grossing movie in American history.

In August 1993 she gave birth to her second child, Hopper Jack, then in January 1994 she accepted a supporting role in *The Crossing Guard*, alongside Jack Nicholson and Anjelica Huston, with Sean behind the camera. Although she and Penn had just split up, she accepted the project because, she says, 'Sean is an astounding director.' Indeed, *The Crossing Guard* was a powerful, meditative drama with lashings of style. She then took the title role in an adaptation of Daniel Defoe's *Moll Flanders*, because, 'it's a great role for an actress,' she argued. 'It's very moving and very plausible, so you believe in the character and in the story.' *Variety*, the trade paper, was impressed, predicting that it 'should send Robin Wright to the upper echelon of actresses with the talent, charisma and unflagging watchability to carry a movie'.

The year was 1996, and she was still estranged from Sean. However, when she underwent minor surgery in late March, Penn missed the Oscar ceremony to be by her side (he was nominated as best actor for *Dead Man Walking*). A month later they married. 'We needed to become friends first,' Wright reasoned. 'We've got two kids, a whole life together ...'

Then, following her performance as an abused woman in *Loved* (with William Hurt), she joined Penn in two upcoming films, *She's So Lovely* and *Hurlyburly*.

FILMOGRAPHY

1986: *Hollywood Vice Squad*. 1987: *The Princess Bride*. 1990: *State of Grace*. 1991: *Denial* (a.k.a. *Loon*; filmed in 1988). 1992: *The Playboys*; *Toys*. 1994: *Forrest Gump*. 1995: *The Crossing Guard*. 1996: *Moll Flanders*; *Loved*. 1997: *She's So Lovely*; *Hurlyburly*.

As the stubborn Tara Maguire in Gilles Mackinnon's **The Playboys**

*Robin Wright with Tom Hanks in **Forrest Gump***

BILLY ZANE

The comparisons with Brando are inevitable and constant. There is the same etched bone structure, the fleshy mouth, the straight nose and that brooding, smouldering stare. At times, the similarity is uncanny. Billy Zane knows he has the physical presence to become a major star, but he downplays his looks by constantly referring to his Brandoesque features as 'the mug'. "The mug", he says, 'is a tool. To have looks is the bonus on top of what motivates me to be an actor. Not to realize they're an asset would be counterproductive to the cause – they serve the common good.' He does, however, concede: 'It was the image that led me to emotion, and emotion that led me to acting, and acting that led me back to emotion.' Billy Zane says things like that. Really. Maybe that's why his friends call him an armchair philosopher.

To prove he was not just a pretty face, Zane followed early roles as a deranged psychotic and as a serial killer with the part of a dashing bombardier, and then expanded his repertoire to include the complex portrayal of a government assassin wrestling with his conscience. He adds: 'A musical would be interesting. I'd love to be remembered for tap dancing and catching a pie in the face.'

The son of dedicated theatregoers and amateur actors, Billy Zane was born on 24 February 1966, and raised in Chicago, where he attended Lincoln Park's Francis Parker High School (at the same time as fellow students Darryl Hannah and Jennifer Beals). His parents' enthusiasm for the stage fired his professional interest, as it did his sister's, Lisa Zane going on to a successful screen career herself (she had leading parts in *Bad Influence* and *Freddie's Dead: The Final Nightmare*). During his high school summers, Billy cut his acting teeth on such musicals as *Oklahoma!* and *Guys and Dolls* and, in 1982, studied writing and acting at the American School in Switzerland.

In 1984 he moved to Hollywood, promising his father that if he didn't

Billy Zane as the menacing imposter in Phillip Noyce's gripping **Dead Calm**

make it as an actor within the year he would return to college. Three weeks later he landed the role of 'Match' – one of Biff's bullying sidekicks – in *Back to the Future*, shortly followed by a good role in the jokey horror film *Critters* (which spawned three sequels). He also flexed his thespian talents on stage, performing with the Second Theater Company (in *American Music*)

and with Tim Robbins' experimental group, the Actors' Gang (in *The Boys in the Backroom*). On TV, he was memorable in the movie *The Brotherhood of Justice*, as Les, a hip, gum-chewing and ultimately dangerous high school vigilante at odds with Keanu Reeves and Kiefer Sutherland – and then came his big break.

In April 1987, the Australian director Phillip Noyce called on Zane to audition for the role of Hughie Warriner, the psychotic survivor of a sinking ship, in *Dead Calm*. By Australian standards, the film was a big-budget production and Noyce had his pick of stars to choose from. But besides casting the reasonably well-known New Zealand actor Sam Neill in the film's third-biggest part, the director opted for two newcomers – Nicole Kidman and Billy Zane. 'We had our choice of any number of young, fairly well-known up-and-coming male actors, both from America and other countries,' Noyce noted. 'But we made a conscious decision to go with an unknown. This way, he comes into the audiences' lives as a real stranger.' After wading through a sea of publicity stills, the director zeroed in on 40 actors to audition for the part of Warriner. Zane was his man. 'He gave us something that was totally fascinating,' Noyce swears, 'without being neurotic or "strange". Billy's acting is always on the edge, always surprising in his choices of how to play a scene. He's entirely spontaneous; totally fresh.'

In the film, Hughie Warriner is rescued by a surgeon (Neill) and his beautiful young wife (Kidman), and is given hospitality aboard their luxury yacht. He explains that his companions have died of food poisoning, but while he sleeps the surgeon rows off to investigate the sinking schooner. There, he finds Warriner's shipmates brutally murdered and, as he frantically rows back to his yacht, Warriner wakes, sets sail and makes himself acquainted with Ms Kidman ...

Dead Calm was a nail-biting thriller in the traditional sense, beautiful to look at, superbly directed by Noyce, and backed by powerhouse performances from Kidman and Zane. It was both a commercial and critical success. Not only did it turn Billy Zane's career around, but it introduced him to his wife, the Australian actress Lisa Collins. Although she was only the model for a photograph in the film (as one of Warriner's shipmates spotted in a logbook), it was love at first sight. Later, she changed her name to Rachel to avoid confusion with Billy's sister.

After *Dead Calm*, Billy Zane dallied in more evil, playing a serial killer in the TV movie *The Case of the Hillside Strangler*, with Richard Crenna; he returned as 'Match' in *Back to the Future Part II*, and then won top-billing for the first time in the intriguing sci-fi

thriller *Megaville*, on good form as an idealistic cop in a futuristic fascist state. He was all swaggering charm and teeth – as bombardier Val Kozlowski – in the hit World War II flying adventure *Memphis Belle*, conjuring up favourable memories of Clark Gable.

On television, he joined the ensemble in David Lynch's cult *Twin Peaks*, as John Justice Wheeler, the environmentalist with the hots for Audrey Horn (Sherilyn Fenn), and then he returned to the big screen in the stylish comic-romantic thriller *Blood and Concrete*, with old schoolmate Jennifer Beals. He described *Blood and Concrete*, in which he played a car thief and reformed drug dealer, as 'a send-up of LA archetypes – from pseudo-beat poetry junkies to Santa Monica bad boys'. In Italy, he starred in Carlo Vanzina's *Miliardi*, as the ruthless heir to a family fortune (with supermodel Carol Alt) and then joined his sister (and Colin Firth) in the silly psychological drama *Femme Fatale*.

In the jungle-set thriller *Sniper*, he was a smarmy, irritating government agent assigned to oversee veteran assassin Tom Berenger, but the movie fell foul of its own pretensions. Both actors created some compelling, uneasy electricity, but the script's psychological

*Zane as the American adventurer Shelmerdine, with Tilda Swinton in Sally Potter's **Orlando***

*Billy Zane in a more familiar pose (with Kristy Swanson) in **The Phantom***

but super humane.'

So, when Zane was offered the title role in the $45 million film version, he couldn't resist. In fact, he took the venture so seriously that he started working out for the role 18 months before a single camera turned. His fitness trainer, Tom Muzila, 'introduced me to a lot of very interesting techniques', the actor divulged, 'including a Zen-like exercise with an eight pound ball'. Indeed. Anyway, considering the close-fitting, purple leotard he was required to wear, Zane was wise to come physically prepared. Any lesser actor would have looked a complete dork in such a costume.

While some reviewers embraced the film's irreverent, tongue-in-cheek approach to the material (how else could you have pulled it off?), this critic found the whole thing trite and hackneyed. Still, it was a major stepping stone in the actor's career – although the movie had its price. Zane acknowledges that the pressure of carrying such a big-budget production on his shoulders, combined with his turning 30, contributed to the end of his marriage: 'I was going through a very emotional time,' he disclosed. The divorce papers were signed in early 1996.

He then joined Harvey Keitel and Cameron Diaz in the engaging black comedy *Head Above Water* (as a naked corpse), played an incestuous conman in the stylish, sexy *This World, Then the Fireworks* and got that sinking feeling in James Cameron's $200 million-plus blockbuster *Titanic*.

FILMOGRAPHY

1985: *Back to the Future*. 1986: *Critters; The Brotherhood of Justice* (TV). 1988: *Dead Calm*. 1989: *The Case of the Hillside Stranglers* (a.k.a. *The Hillside Stranglers*) (TV); *Back to the Future Part II*. 1990: *Megaville; Memphis Belle*. 1991: *Blood and Concrete, A Love Story; Miliardi* (a.k.a. *Billions/Millions*); *Femme Fatale*. 1993: *Sniper; Orlando; Lake Consequence; Posse; Tombstone; Cyborg Agent; Poetic Justice* (cameo). 1994: *The Silence of the Hams; Tombstone; Reflections on a Crime; Only You; Flashfire; Betrayal of the Dove*. 1995: *Tales from the Crypt: Demon Knight; The Set-Up*. 1996: *The Phantom; Danger Zone; Head Above Water; This World, Then the Fireworks* (also co-ex. prod.). 1997: *Titanic*. 1998: *Noose*.

belly-aching tripped up a perfectly decent action-thriller. It was, however, a mild box-office success.

He then took a supporting role in the bizarre English film *Orlando*, as a hunky American, 'in the pursuit of liberty', who is first seen riding out of the mist following the caption '1850 – SEX'. Next, he starred opposite Joan Severance in *Lake Consequence*, a silly erotic drama from Zalman King (the producer of *9 1/2 Weeks*), and then played a colonel of the Spanish-American War who tracks down a gang of deserters in Mario Van Peebles' *Posse*.

Besides acting, Billy Zane spent his time making comedy shorts, directed a music video for Robbie Nevil ('Back on Holiday') and wrote a screenplay, *Gargoyle*. However, his subsequent film

parts were either flashy cameos in A-product or starring roles in video fodder. With one exception: *The Phantom*.

Created by Lee Falk in 1936 (thus pre-dating both Batman and Superman), The Phantom is a comic-strip hero still read by 60 million people, appearing daily in over 500 newspapers worldwide. Nevertheless, Zane hadn't come across the character until filming *Dead Calm* in Australia. 'I read my first Phantom comic in 1987,' he admits, 'and for me this guy was the end-all as far as role models and super-heroes. The books were everywhere. It was the only comic I ever collected. The Phantom was a national hero – and he was different. He had no super powers, no super bank accounts. He's just super decent. Not super human,

Billy Zane and Joan Severance in Lake Consequence.

*An unrecognisable Gary Oldman menaces Keanu Reeves in **Bram Stoker's Dracula***

*A period piece with vicious undertones: Glenn Close and Uma Thurman in **Dangerous Liaisons***

*Woody Harrelson with co-star Bridget Fonda in the romantic comedy **Doc Hollywood***

Dumb and Dumber: *a less than clever move for Jim Carrey and Lauren Holly*